contemporary college

PHYSICS

third edition
2001 update

Dr. Edwin R. Jones
University of South Carolina

Dr. Richard L. Childers
University of South Carolina

Physics 201

Special Edition for the
University of South Carolina

Volume 1

 **Learning Solutions**

Boston   Burr Ridge, IL   Dubuque, IA   New York   San Francisco   St. Louis
Bangkok   Bogotá   Caracas   Lisbon   London   Madrid
Mexico City   Milan   New Delhi   Seoul   Singapore   Sydney   Taipei   Toronto

Contemporary College Physics, Third Edition, 2001 Update
Special Edition for the University of South Carolina
Physics 201
Volume 1

This book is a McGraw-Hill Learning Solutions textbook and contains select material from *Contemporary College Physics*, Third Edition, 2001 Update by Edwin R. Jones and Richard L. Childers. Copyright © 2001, 1999, 1993 by The McGraw-Hill Companies, Inc. Reprinted with permission of the publisher. Many custom published texts are modified versions or adaptations of our best-selling textbooks. Some adaptations are printed in black and white to keep prices at a minimum, while others are in color.

8 9 0 QDB QDB 15 14 13 12

ISBN-13: 978-0-07-735899-0
ISBN-10: 0-07-735899-6

Learning Solutions Specialist: Jeff Schmitt
Production Editor: Lynn Nagel
Printer/Binder: Quad/Graphics, Dubuque

Conversion Factors

Length and Volume

1 inch = 2.54 cm (exact)
1 ft = 30.48 cm (exact)
1 m = 39.37 in.
1 mi = 1.609 344 0 km
1 liter = 10^3 cm^3 = 10^{-3} m^3

Time

1 year = $365\frac{1}{4}$ day = 3.1558×10^7 s
1 d = 86,400 s
1 h = 3600 s

Mass

1 kg = 1000 g
1 u = $1.660\ 540\ 2 \times 10^{-27}$ kg
1 kg has a weight of 2.205 lb

Force

1 lb = 4.448 N

Pressure

1 Pa = 1 N/m^2
1 atm = $1.013\ 25 \times 10^5$ Pa
1 mm Hg = 133.3 Pa
1 $lb/in.^2$ = 6895 Pa

Energy and Power

1 J = 0.239 cal
1 kWh = 3.60×10^6 J
1 eV = 1.602×10^{-19} J
1 u = 931.494 32 MeV
1 hp = 746 W

Speed

1 m/s = 3.60 km/h = 2.24 mi/h
1 km/h = 0.621 mi/h

Angle

1 rad = 57.3° = 0.159 revolution
1 revolution = 2π rad = 360°

Common Prefixes

10^{12}	tera	T
10^9	giga	G
10^6	mega	M
10^3	kilo	k
10^{-2}	centi	c
10^{-3}	milli	m
10^{-6}	micro	μ
10^{-9}	nano	n
10^{-12}	pico	p

Index of Tables

Atomic mass of light elements	920
Color scale of temperatures	858
Color temperature of light sources	964
Densities	310
Dielectric constants and breakdown strengths	545
Dose equivalent, estimated annual effective	933
Doses, recommended maximum permissible	932
Drag coefficients	332
Elastic moduli	279
Elementary particles, partial list	1010
Energy conversion table	356
Energy gap in semiconductors	986
Friction coefficients	124
Heat of transformation	361
Indices of refraction	690
Molecular mass of common gases	382
Moments of inertia	284
Planets, orbits, and periods	159
Pressure units	309
Quality factors for several types of radiation	932
Quarks, properties of the u, d, and s	1016
R values of building materials	365
Resistivity, electrical	565
SI base units	7
SI prefixes	10
Sound absorption coefficients	475
Sound velocities	471
Specific heats	357
Spectrum, colors of the visible	962
Surface tension	321
Thermal conductivities	365
Thermal expansion coefficients	353
Viscosities	328
Work functions	863

Reviews, Techniques, and Mathematical Assistance

Areas and volumes	A-1
Arithmetic with exponents	10
Binomial series	A-1
Circuit symbols	567
Conic sections	A-2
Exponential function	400
Field lines	168, 506
Free-body diagrams	116, 117
Kinematic equations	267
Logarithms	402
Problem solving	19, 119
Quadratic equations	62
Ray tracing	696–700
Scientific notation	9
Significant figures	12
Simultaneous equations	143
Trigonometry	94
Unit conversion	11
Vectors	64

Contents

1 Measurement, Models, and Analysis 1

1.1 Measurements and Models 2
Back to the Future: Echoes of the Big Bang 6
1.2 Units and Standards of Measurement 7
1.3 Unit Conversions 11
1.4 Measurements, Calculations, and Uncertainties 12
1.5 Estimates and Order-of-Magnitude Calculations 15
1.6 How to Study Physics 18
1.7 Problem Solving 19

2 Motion in One Dimension 25

2.1 Reference Frames, Coordinate Systems, and Displacement 26
2.2 Average Speed and Average Velocity 29
2.3 Graphical Interpretation of Velocity 33
2.4 Instantaneous Velocity 36
2.5 Acceleration 40
2.6 Motion with Constant Acceleration 44
2.7 Galileo and Free Fall 48
Back to the Future: Galileo and Experimental Science 53
Appendix: Solving Quadratic Equations 62

3 Motion in Two Dimensions 63

3.1 Vectors 64
3.2 Addition of Vectors 65
3.3 Resolution of Vectors 68
3.4 Relative Velocity in One Dimension 72
3.5 Relative Velocity in Two Dimensions 73
3.6 Kinematics in Two Dimensions 78
3.7 Projectile Motion 81
Appendix: Review of Trigonometry 94

4 Force and Motion 96

4.1 Events Leading to Newton's *Principia* 97
4.2 What Is a Force? 98
Back to the Future: The Writing of the Principia 99
4.3 Newton's First Law—Inertia 103
4.4 Newton's Second Law 105
4.5 Weight 109
4.6 Newton's Third Law 112
4.7 Some Applications of Newton's Laws 116
4.8 Friction 123
Physics in Practice: The Friction of Automobile Tires 127
4.9 Static Equilibrium 128
4.10 The Laws of Motion as a Whole 132
Appendix: Solving Simultaneous Equations 143

5 Uniform Circular Motion and Gravitation 145

5.1 Uniform Circular Motion 146
5.2 Force Needed for Circular Motion 152
5.3 Kepler's Laws of Planetary Motion 157
5.4 The Law of Universal Gravitation 160
Back to the Future: Johannes Kepler 161
5.5 The Universal Gravitational Constant G 164
*5.6 Gravitational Field Strength 166
Back to the Future: Henry Cavendish and the Density of the Earth 167

6 Work and Energy — 176

6.1 Work 177
6.2 Work Done by a Varying Force 179
6.3 Energy 181
6.4 Kinetic Energy 182
6.5 Potential Energy 185
6.6 Conservation of Mechanical Energy 189
***6.7** Energy Conservation with Nonconservative Forces 197
6.8 Power 199
Physics in Practice: Human Energy 202

7 Linear Momentum — 210

7.1 Linear Momentum 211
7.2 Impulse 211
7.3 Newton's Laws and the Conservation of Momentum 214
7.4 Conservation of Momentum in One-Dimensional Collisions 216
7.5 Conservation of Momentum in Two- and Three-Dimensional Collisions 221
***7.6** Changing Mass 225

8 Applying the Conservation Laws — 234

8.1 Definition of Elastic Collisions 235
8.2 Elastic Collisions in One Dimension 236
***8.3** Elastic Collisions in Two Dimensions 242
***8.4** General Form of Gravitational Potential Energy 245
Physics in Practice: Symmetry and Conservation Laws 246
***8.5** Motion in a Gravitational Potential 250
***8.6** Escape Speed 252

9 Rigid Bodies and Rotational Motion — 263

9.1 Angular Velocity and Angular Acceleration 264
9.2 Rotational Kinematics 267
9.3 Torque 269
9.4 Static Equilibrium 272
***9.5** Elasticity: Stress and Strain 278
Physics in Practice: Bridges 280
9.6 Torque and Moment of Inertia 282
9.7 Angular Momentum 286
9.8 Conservation of Angular Momentum 287
9.9 Rotational Kinetic Energy 291
9.10 Conservation of Energy: Translations and Rotations 293
Physics in Practice: The Earth, the Moon, and the Tides 296

10 Fluids — 307

10.1 Hydrostatic Pressure 308
10.2 Pascal's Principle 312
10.3 Archimedes' Principle 315
Physics in Practice: Measuring Blood Pressure 316
***10.4** Surface Tension 320
10.5 Fluid Flow: Streamlines and the Equation of Continuity 322
Physics in Practice: Surface Tension and the Lungs 323
10.6 Bernoulli's Equation 324
***10.7** Viscosity and Poiseuille's Law 327
***10.8** Stokes's Law and Terminal Speed 329
Physics in Practice: How Airplanes Fly 330
***10.9** Turbulent Flow 333

11 Thermal Physics — 344

11.1 Temperature and States of Matter 345
11.2 Thermometry 346
Back to the Future: Fahrenheit's Thermometer 349
11.3 Thermal Expansion 350
11.4 The Mechanical Equivalent of Heat 354
11.5 Calorimetry 356
11.6 Change of Phase 360
11.7 Heat Transfer 363

12 Gas Laws and Kinetic Theory — 373

12.1 The Pressure of Air 374
12.2 Boyle's Law 376

Back to the Future: Gas Laws and Balloons 378
12.3 The Law of Charles and Gay-Lussac 379
12.4 The Ideal Gas Law 381
12.5 The Kinetic Theory of Gases 384
12.6 The Kinetic-Theory Definition of Temperature 388
12.7 Internal Energy of an Ideal Gas 389
*12.8 The Barometric Formula and the Distribution of Molecular Speeds 390
Appendix: The Exponential Function 400

▼

13 Thermodynamics 403

13.1 Thermal Equilibrium 404
13.2 The First Law of Thermodynamics 405
13.3 The Carnot Cycle and the Efficiency of Engines 410
Physics in Practice: Gasoline Engines 416
13.4 Refrigerators and Heat Pumps 417
13.5 The Second Law of Thermodynamics 421
13.6 Entropy and the Second Law 422
*13.7 Energy and Thermal Pollution 426

▼

14 Periodic Motion 434

14.1 Hooke's Law 435
14.2 The Simple Harmonic Oscillator 438
14.3 Energy of a Harmonic Oscillator 442
14.4 Period of a Harmonic Oscillator 444
14.5 The Simple Pendulum 447
*14.6 Damped Harmonic Motion 449
Physics in Practice: Walking and Running 450
*14.7 Forced Harmonic Motion and Resonance 453

▼

15 Waves and Sound 463

15.1 Pulses on a Rope 464
15.2 Harmonic Waves 465
*15.3 Energy and Information Transfer by Waves 467
15.4 Sound Waves 468
*15.5 Measuring Sound Levels 472
15.6 The Doppler Effect 474
Physics in Practice: Room Acoustics 475
*15.7 Formation of a Shock Wave 478
15.8 Reflection of a Wave Pulse 479
15.9 Standing Waves on a String 480
15.10 Waves in a Vibrating Column of Air 486
*15.11 Beats 487
Physics in Practice: Hearing and the Ear 488

Appendices

A Formulas from Algebra, Geometry, and Trigonometry A-1
B The International System of Units A-4
C Alphabetical List of Elements A-5

Answers to Odd-Numbered Problems A-6

Photo Credits C-1

Index I-1

* Different teachers will emphasize different parts of the text. To make the choices easier, we have designated some material as optional. Sections marked with an asterisk may be safely omitted without fear that their content will be needed in subsequent sections or chapters.

Preface

We are pleased to present the third edition of *Contemporary College Physics.* By building on the strengths of the first two editions of our non-calculus general physics text, we feel this edition introduces students to the beauty and usefulness of physics while teaching problem-solving skills that can help them throughout their studies and careers. With considerable help from students and instructors from across the country, we have updated and improved a wide variety of elements and introduced new features to create the third edition.

New to the Third Edition

▪ Consistent color coding of line art elements helps students identify and differentiate between force vectors, velocity vectors, acceleration vectors, magnetic fields, and positive and negative charges.

▪ *Master the Concept* boxes walk students through the principles that apply to a given situation to clarify the application of concepts.

▪ Strategy boxes have been added throughout to guide students through problem-solving issues.

▪ An enhanced art program features more photographic illustrations of concepts and principles.

▪ The number of worked examples in the chapters has been significantly increased to help students understand how to approach problem solving.

▪ Expanded end-of-chapter exercises include conceptual questions as well as computational problems.

▪ New interior design makes this text easier to use than ever before.

2001 Update

This 2001 Update of *Contemporary College Physics,* third edition, differs from the 1999 third edition in two ways. First, we have further highlighted biomedical applications of physics and added coverage of some recent technologies. For example, we introduce hydrostatic weighing (to determine percentage of body fat) as an application of Archimedes' principle, and our new discussion of recent advances in laser eye surgery is accompanied by a detailed illustration (see page 957). This focus on the life and health sciences, achieved through new topic coverage as well as photographs and illustrations added to the Update, should help to motivate the many students who take this course in preparation for a career in health-related fields. For a list of relevant applications, see page xix following this preface.

The second change to the third edition is the expansion and improvement of the Interactive Student Tutorial, the CD-ROM that accompanies the book. The CD supports problems-solving practice with a wealth of new examples and exercises. For details, see the description of the CD under "Supplements" on page xvi.

The organization and exercise sets of the 1999 third edition remain unchanged in the Update, so the solutions manuals and other supplements have not changed, nor will users of the third edition need to change their lesson plans in any way.

Goals

Our main goals are to increase student understanding of natural laws and to develop the analytical skills critical for success in both educational undertakings and lifetime decision making. We approach these goals by emphasizing basic principles and the unity of physics.

We have the additional goal of providing students a thorough coverage of modern physics so that students will better comprehend the important public policy issues facing them as citizens. We want students to see that physics is a dynamic, exciting field. We are now preparing students for the twenty-first century, when the need for scientific understanding will be greater than ever. Classical physics is presented from a contemporary perspective. Modern physics is treated thoroughly, as an integral part of the course. The entire book speaks to today's students, using the latest pedagogical aids.

We introduce the concept of a model in Chapter 1 and then point out throughout the text how physicists use models as part of the scientific process. We emphasize that the first part of developing any theory is to make a model of the physical situation and state its assumptions. Then we show how later observations serve to refine the model and improve our overall understanding. Examples include such fundamental models as the kinetic theory of gases, the free electron model of metals, the wave model of particles, and the quark model of matter.

Problem Solving

Solving physics problems has long been regarded by physics instructors as a key to learning. We are aware of the difficulty students have in developing good problem-solving skills and habits. For this reason, we have put special emphasis on helping students with problems.

■ **Examples** There are over 340 worked examples in the body of the text, and in most cases the solutions are divided into three sections: strategy, solution, and discussion. The strategy section shows the students a conceptual way of analyzing the problem in order to decide what to do. The solution section presents the analysis and computation, and the discussion section points out to the student the significance of the answer and analysis. This approach helps direct students to a more productive way of solving problems than merely grasping for equations.

Example 4.2

Safety regulations require that all cars traveling at a given speed be able to stop within a given distance. What must be the relationship between the minimum braking forces allowed by law for two cars whose masses have the ratio of 3 to 2?

Strategy We can use Newton's second law to relate the force to mass and acceleration. From your knowledge of kinematics, you know that the requirement for stopping in equal distances from the same initial speed for both cars means they must both have the same acceleration.

Solution We can write the two accelerations in terms of the braking forces F_1 and F_2 and the masses m_1 and m_2 as

$$a_1 = \frac{F_1}{m_1} \quad \text{and} \quad a_2 = \frac{F_2}{m_2}$$

When we set the accelerations equal we find

$$\frac{F_1}{m_1} = \frac{F_2}{m_2}$$

so

$$\frac{F_1}{F_2} = \frac{m_1}{m_2} = \frac{3}{2}$$

Discussion This result tells us that a larger braking force is needed to stop a larger (more massive) car in the same distance that a smaller (less massive) car is stopped.

Pedagogical Use of Color

Displacement and position vectors		Torque (τ) and angular momentum (**L**) vectors		
Velocity vectors (**v**) Velocity component vectors		Linear or rotational motion directions	or	
Force vectors (**F**) Force component vectors		Springs		
Acceleration vectors (**a**) Acceleration component vectors		Pulleys		
Electric fields		Capacitors		
Magnetic fields		Inductors (coils)		
Positive charges	+	Voltmeters	V	
Negative charges	–	Ammeters	A	
Resistors		Galvanometers	G	
Batteries and other dc power supplies	– +	ac generators	~	
Switches		Ground symbol		

◼ **Problem-Solving Guidelines** A general step-by-step guide to problem solving is given in Section 1.7 (p. 19) and this approach is reinforced throughout the book: in the examples, in the **Hints for Solving Problems** distributed throughout the end-of-chapter problems, and in the **Problem-Solving Strategy** boxes included in the narrative.

◼ **Master the Concepts** A step-by-step solution of conceptual questions is presented utilizing the basic principles. This nonnumerical analysis will help students visualize the concepts involved.

Color Key

We have implemented a color key to help students identify elements in the illustrations. (Top of page.)

Master the Concept

Force and Circular Motion

Question: The Wave Swinger ride at the fair has two circular rows of chairs suspended by chains of equal lengths. The outer row is along the outer edge of the top of the ride and the inner row has a smaller radius. Do riders in both rows swing out at the same angle when the ride is rotating?

Answer: When the ride is in motion, the passengers in the chairs swing outward. At one particular angle the chain provides the necessary horizontal force for circular motion and the vertical force needed to balance the gravitational force. Riders in both rows move with the same angular velocity, but those in the outer row move in a larger radius and thus have a larger angular acceleration. Because of this larger angular acceleration, a larger centripetal force is needed. Thus, for riders in the outer row, the horizontal component of the chain force is larger relative to their gravitational force than it is for those on the inner row. The result is that riders in the outer row swing out to the larger angle from the vertical direction than do the riders in the inner row as you can see in Fig. 5.22 on p. 170.

Problems

The end-of-chapter problem sets have been significantly expanded. There are now over six hundred conceptual questions and more than 2,250 problems, many of them new or revised. The problems are divided into three levels of difficulty. Those marked with one or two bullets typically require the synthesis of two or more ideas for their solution and occasionally include material from previous chapters. About two-thirds of the problems are arranged according to the section of the chapter in which the topic is discussed. Answers to the odd-numbered problems appear at the end of the text.

Coverage

As with the previous two editions, the coverage of topics is comprehensive, but not encyclopedic. We introduce a new section on measurements and models. Model building is introduced with discussions of blackbody radiation and Planck's discovery. We have expanded our treatment of vectors and included more material on vector addition. There is more coverage of Maxwell's equations and electromagnetic waves. Care has been taken to include all topics covered on the MCAT.

We understand that different teachers will emphasize different parts of the text. To make the choices easier, we have designated some material as optional. **Sections marked with an asterisk may be safely omitted** without fear that their content will be needed in subsequent sections or chapters.

Emphasis on Basic Principles

"The student can't see the forest for the trees," say our colleagues. Having heard this over and over again, we have made the emphasis of basic principles one of our highest priorities. A good example is our treatment of conservation laws. The ability to explain and predict observations using conserved quantities is emphasized conceptually as well as mathematically.

Unity of Physics

Our treatment of conservation laws also illustrates another of our goals: to show that physics is not just a collection of independent ideas but is an interconnected whole. We believe this approach reflects the spirit of physics today, and we also believe that it helps students retain more of what they've learned after they leave the course.

If you read a mystery novel all the way through in one sitting, you immediately have at your fingertips all the clues necessary to solve the puzzle. However, students generally read a physics textbook in small sections and cover groups of chapters over a period of time. As a result, they inevitably forget some of the clues and are less prepared to solve the puzzle—or in this case, to see the big picture and appreciate the beauty of physics. For this reason, we give frequent reminders in the text and examples of previously covered topics and of topics to be covered later.

Level

The text assumes that students have no previous background in physics. The basic mathematical working tools are algebra, and trigonometry, and a high school course in these subjects is certainly a prerequisite. One of the challenges in teaching this course is that the students' math preparation is often weaker than the teacher would like. Most students need a math refresher beyond the typical review stuck in the back of texts. To that end, we have included chapter appendices on key math topics in those chapters where they are first needed: quadratic equations (Chapter 2), basic trigonometry (Chapter 3), simultaneous equations (Chapter 4), and the exponential function (Chapter 12).

The exponential function is first used in Chapter 12 in describing the barometric formula and the distribution of molecular speeds. Subsequently, it appears in analyses of electric circuits, radioactive decay, and other topics. The addition of the exponential function to the usual mix of algebra and trigonometry affords students a better comprehension of the individual topics.

Motivation

Teachers frequently hear the complaint that the subject matter has no relevance to the students' subsequent courses and careers. To overcome this misconception, we have made a special effort to show applications of fundamental principles in everyday life as well as in biology, medicine, architecture, and technology.

- ■ **Physics in Practice** Applications can be found in the text and examples and in special essays called **Physics in Practice,** which deal with topics ranging from automobile tires to liquid-crystal displays. Great care has been taken to provide a diversity of applications that will appeal to the broadest range of students. A list of these applications follows on page xix.

- ■ **Back to the Future** Physics is a science based on the efforts of real men and women struggling to understand how the world works. In essays called **Back to the Future,** we present physics as a human activity in which new ideas are constantly being tried and in which scientific truth is never absolute. We generally introduce a new topic by describing the efforts of the scientists who made the breakthrough discoveries and advances. For example, in Chapter 1 we present the work of Arno Penzias and Robert W. Wilson, and discuss the problems they encountered on their way to the discovery of cosmic background radiation. This type of real-world illustration of the topics of measurements, models, and analysis is meant to bring to life the world of physics. Throughout, we have emphasized physics as a way of thinking, investigating, and understanding rather than as a body of facts and theories.

Accuracy

We have made a strenuous effort to ensure accuracy.

- ■ Realistic Examples: We have made a point to make the text correspond to reality. By this we mean that if we use an example of an airliner accelerating to takeoff, the numerical values given for mass, takeoff speed, and so on, are those of a real airliner. We have tried to introduce reality by referring to real objects such as baseballs, golfballs, automobiles, and animals with realistic masses moving with realistic speeds.

■ Adherence to Nature: We have taken care to correctly describe what is actually observed in nature as, for example, in the description of the temperature dependence of electrical resistivity of metals (Section 18.3) and to give correct information on friction (Section 4.8).

■ Fidelity to History: We have read original papers and the current history-of-science research in order to ensure the accuracy of the presentation. Discussions of experiments correspond to what was actually done and discussions of theories correspond to what the authors actually wrote.

■ Answers: We were also determined to have correct answers to the end-of-chapter problems. Both of the authors have independently worked each of the problems. University of South Carolina student Jeremy Thomason also worked the problems and provided insight into wording them more clearly. We hope that this process not only has confirmed the right answers, but also has eliminated problems that students might find confusing.

Supplements

For the Student:

■ **Study Guide/Solutions Manual** This study guide provides a variety of exercises designed to help the student master the important concepts of each chapter. Solutions for the odd-numbered end-of-chapter problems from the text are in a separate section. The manual was written by the authors and Professor John Safko of the University of South Carolina.

■ **Interactive CD-ROM** This is included free with each textbook. It is a powerful study tool for the student—a browser-based CD with interactive simulations, animated sequences, quizzes, glossary, links to related web-based tutorial material, and more. The 2001 Update adds Practice Problems and Practice Quizzes that greatly expand the opportunities for solving problems like those in the book. Many of these new problems are taken from *Schaum's Outline of College Physics,* Ninth Edition, by Bueche and Hecht (the complete *Schaum's Outline* is available from McGraw-Hill).

For the Instructor:

■ **Instructor's Solutions Manual** This manual provides the answers and solutions to all the problems in the text. Expanded explanations will help with classroom discussions, as will the graphs and diagrams.

■ **Test Bank** This compilation has been updated and expanded for the third edition by Professor Nancy Woods of Des Moines Area Community College. It contains two thousand testing questions. It is available as a bound book or in computerized format for either Windows or Macintosh systems.

■ **Overhead Transparencies** A collection of 275 four-color illustrations from the text is provided on acetate for use with overhead projectors.

■ **Visual Resource Library** A group of 150 four-color illustrations is provided on a CD-ROM. This CD-ROM allows you to quickly browse through the images and captions from the text, arrange images in your own custom-designed slide show, and enlarge images for greater projection. You can also print full- and half-size images and export images for use in word-processing programs. Additional features include:

(1) find and sort thumbnail image records by name, type, location, and user-defined keywords; (2) search using keywords or terms; (3) view hundreds of images at the same time with the Small Gallery View; (4) flip through hundreds of images quickly using a mouse; (5) display all important file information for easy identification; (6) drag and place images into virtually any graphics, desktop publishing, presentation, or multimedia application.

Special Text/MEPI Package

WCB/McGraw-Hill is offering a package of Jones/Childers, *Contemporary College Physics* 3/e plus *MEPI; Multimedia Enhanced Physics Instruction,* a two-CD boxed set produced by Maha Ashour-Abdalla at the UCLA Space Plasma Simulation Group.

Using a hyperlink interface, *MEPI* gives students hands-on experience in exploring the world of physics through interactive demonstrations and experiments. Each topic in *MEPI* is comprised of five tutorial components:

■ *Concepts.* In-depth topical explanations

■ *Videos.* 28 short (3–6 minute) videos enable students to view a wide variety of actual experiments being performed

■ *Simulations.* Students change variables to set up different scenarios or experiments in simulated physical phenomena (see below for list of *MEPI* simulations)

■ *Quizzes.* Approximately 8–10 conceptual multiple-choice questions per chapter

■ *Problems.* 3–5 computational problems are first animated, then carefully outlined for step-by-step solving; students who enter wrong answers receive hints for guidance, and the system "keeps score."

Website

A *Contemporary College Physics* website is available with additional information, course-presentation material, practice problems (including MCAT-type questions), chapter-by-chapter web links, and more. The website address is www.mhhe.com/jones.

Acknowledgments

We have been blessed with the continued strong support of our wives, Betty Jones and Sigrid Childers. We thank them for all their encouragement and patience. We have had many profitable discussions with our colleagues at the University of South Carolina. We again thank Stuart Johnson, David Chelton, and Jennifer Albanese for their help with earlier editions. We are grateful to Jill Birschbach, for her photo-research efforts, and to the professional staff at McGraw-Hill Higher Education for its efforts in bringing this project to completion. A special note of thanks goes to Jean Fornango, Jill Peter, J. P. Lenney, Lisa Gottschalk, David Dietz, Dave Edwards, Lloyd Black, and Jim Smith.

Reviewers

We would like to thank the many physics teachers whose reviews, focus-group discussions, and personal communications helped to shape this third edition:

David B. Aaron, *South Dakota State University*
B. N. Narahari Achar, *University of Memphis*
Zaven Altounian, *McGill University*
Michael S. Berger, *Indiana University*
John Berryman, *Palm Beach Community College*
Shane C. Brower, *Youngstown State University*
Michael E. Browne, *University of Idaho*
James J. Carroll, *Youngstown State University*
Neal M. Cason, *University of Notre Dame*
K. Kelvin Cheng, *Texas Tech University*
Marek Cieplak, *Rutgers University*
R. Kent Clark, *University of South Alabama*
Lawrence B. Coleman, *University of California, Davis*
Lawrence Corrado, *University of Wisconsin, Manitowoc*
Mark Davenport, *San Antonio College*
Don DeYoung, *Grace College*
Chaden Djalai, *University of South Carolina*
Paul Draper, *University of Texas, Arlington*
Miles J. Dresser, *Washington State University*
Andrew Duffy, *Boston University*
John J. Dykla, *Loyola University, Chicago*
Angelo M. Ferrari, *Santa Fe Community College, Florida*
Leonard N. Feuerhelm, *Oklahoma Christian University*
Lewis Ford, *Texas A&M University*
Charles Gale, *McGill University*
J. David Gavenda, *University of Texas, Austin*
Simon George, *California State University*
Peter K. Glanz, *Rhode Island College*
John L. Hubisz, *North Carolina State University*
Fred W. Inman, *Mankato State University*
Larry D. Johnson, *Northeast Louisiana University*
Alain Karma, *Northeastern University*
Sanford Kern, *Colorado State University*
Diandra Leslie-Pelecky, *University of Nebraska*
Bo Lou, *Ferris State University*

Alfredo Louro, *University of Calgary*
Robert March, *University of Wisconsin, Madison*
William E. McCorkle, *West Liberty State College*
Marles L. McCurdy, *Tarrant County Junior College, Northeast*
Daniel McLaughlin, *University of Hartford*
Charles R. Meitzler, *Sam Houston State University*
R. D. Murphy, *University of Missouri*
David Mylander, *California State Polytechnic University*
Melvyn J. Oremland, *Pace University*
B. E. Powell, *State University of West Georgia*
C. W. Price, *Millersville University*
Michele Rallis, *Ohio State University*
Richard W. Robinett, *Penn State University*
Ian Robinson, *University of Champaign, Urbana*
Charles W. Rogers, *Southwestern Oklahoma State University*
Lawrence G. Rowan, *University of North Carolina at Chapel Hill*
Michael Simon, *Houstonic Community Technical College*
Igor Strakovsky, *The George Washington University*
Michael G. Strauss, *University of Oklahoma*
George Strobel, *University of Georgia*
James F. Sullivan, *University of Cincinnati*
Jeffery Sundquist, *Palm Beach Community College*
Andrew Sustich, *Arkansas State University*
John A. Swez, *Indiana State University*
Colin Terry, *Ventura College*
Herman Trivilino, *College of the Mainland*
David Vesper, *Indiana State University*
Chris Viulle, *Embry-Riddle University*
Gail Welsh, *Salisbury State University*
Donald A. Whitney, *Hampton University*
Luc T. Wille, *Florida Atlantic University*
Anthony Zito, *Dutchess Community College*

List of Selected Applications

Life Science

Example 4.1, *Leg traction 100*
Example 5.9, *Blood separation by centrifuge 155*
Example 6.13, *Energy output by a jogger 200*
Example 6.15, *Power of human heart 201*
Physics in Practice, Ch. 6, *Human energy 202*
Example 9.14 *Stable equilibrium of a standing human 274*
Example 9.9, *Biomechanics (deltoid muscle) 277*
Example 9.10, *Compression in weightlifter's femur 281*
Example 10.2, *Intravenous injection 312*
Section 10.2 *Hyperbaric medicine 313*
Example 10.4, *Scuba diving 314*
Physics in Practice, Ch. 10, *Measuring blood pressure 316*
Section 10.3 *Hydrostatic weighing 317*
Physics in Practice, Ch. 10, *Surface tension and the lungs 323*
Example 10.10, *Blood flow in arterioles 328*
Master the Concept, *Heat of vaporization: steam burns and cooling by perspiration 361*
Example 11.12, *Human heat loss by radiation 366*
Example 12.10, *Breathing at high elevation 392*
Example 13.4, *Measuring lung function 411*
Section 13.7, *Thermal pollution 426*
Physics in Practice, Ch. 14, *Walking and running 450*
Section 15.4, *Ultrasonic imaging 468*
Figure 15.13, *Measuring blood flow by Doppler-shifted ultrasonic waves 477*
Physics in Practice, Ch. 15, *Hearing and the ear 488*
Figure 18.15, *Hospital baby warmer 568*
Physics in Practice, Ch. 18, *Electric shock 586*
Physics in Practice, Ch. 19, *Magnetic resonance imaging 601*
Section 20.2, *Magnetic blood flow transducers 633*
Physics in Practice, Ch. 20, *Accelerators for radiation therapy 649*
Example 21.2, *Charging defibrillator capacitor 665*
Physics in Practice, Ch. 21, *Electrocardiography 669*
Section 22.4, *Endoscopes 693*
Section 23.1, *The eye 722*
Example 23.1, *Nearsightedness 724*
Example 23.2, *Farsightedness 723*

Section 23.4, *Microscopes 732*
Section 24.7, *Resolving power of microscopes 764*
Example 24.7, *Human eye resolution 767*
Section 26.5, *X rays 832*
Example 26.6, *Use of the "gamma knife" in medicine 843*
Physics in Practice, Ch. 27, *Photons and vision 866*
Back to the Future, Ch. 28, *Electron microscopes 888*
Example 29.4, *Nuclear medicine 922*
Section 29.7, *Positron emission tomography 927*
Section 29.8, *Detectors of radiation 928*
Section 29.9, *Radiation measurement and biological effects 931*
Example 29.8, *x-ray dosage in dentistry 934*
Section 30.4, *Laser eye surgery 957*

Chemistry

Section 11.6, *Change of phase 360*
Section 12.4, *Ideal gas law 381*
Section 12.6, *Kinetic-theory definition of temperature 388*
Example 14.6, *Atomic force microscope 446*
Section 16.8, *Molecular dipole 516*
Section 24.9, *Spectroscopes and spectra 770*
Section 26.1, *Evidence for atoms 823*
Section 26.3, *Avogadro's number 827*
Example 26.3, *Size of a copper atom 831*
Back to the Future, Ch. 26, *Seeing atoms 839*
Section 27.1, *Spectroscopy 853*
Section 28.9, *Wave theory of the hydrogen atom 898*
Section 31.1, *Types of condensed matter 974*

Astronomy

Section 1.1, *Cosmic background radiation 2*
Back to the Future, Ch. 1, *Echoes of the Big Bang 6*
Section 4.1, *Events leading to Newton's* Principia *97*
Example 5.6, *Earth's force on the moon 153*
Example 5.8, *Artificial gravity on a space station 155*
Section 5.3, *Kepler's laws of planetary motion 157*
Example 5.15, *Period of a satellite 165*
Section 8.6, *Escape speed 252*

Example 8.7, *Speed to project a rocket to the moon 253*
Section 8.6, *Black holes 252*
Example 9.14, *Kepler's second law 290*
Section 22.1, *Electromagnetic spectrum 684*
Back to the Future, Ch. 22, *The speed of light 686*
Section 23.5, *Telescopes 734*
Back to the Future, Ch. 23, *Development of telescopes 737*
Section 25.10, *Relativistic Doppler effect 807*
Example 25.11, *Gravitational effect on radiation 811*
Section 25.12, *Gravitational lens 813*
Back to the Future, Ch. 27, *Fraunhofer and the solar spectrum 856*
Section 32.8, *Cosmology 1019*

Geology

Example 5.14, *Density of the earth 164*
Back to the Future, Ch. 5, *Measuring the density of the earth 167*
Physics in Practice, Ch. 9, *Tides 296*
Example 10.6, *Icebergs 319*
Section 19.2, *Earth's magnetic field 597*
Section 26.8, *Age of the earth 841*

Architecture

Physics in Practice, Ch. 9, *Bridges 280–281*
Example 11.4, *Expansion joints for bridges 351*
Section 11.7, R *value 363*
Example 14.9, *Vibration damping 454*
Physics in Practice, Ch. 15, *Room acoustics 475*
Section 17.8, *Electronic stud finder 545*
Section 18.10, *Home power distribution 583*
Section 30.6, *Light and color 962*

Sports

Example 3.7, *Rowing across a river 74*
Example 3.13, *Baseball throw 85*
Physics in Practice, Ch. 4, *Friction of automobile tires (car racing) 127*
Example 5.10, *Banking of a race track 157*
Example 7.1, *Baseball hit 212*
Example 8.3, *Colliding pool balls 243*
Example 9.1, *Hammer throw 266*
Example 9.5, *Pedaling a bicycle 271*
Section 9.8, *High diver 287*
Example 9.13, *Spinning ice skater 289*
Section 10.8, *Sky diving 329*
Section 10.9, *Baseball pitch (curve ball) 333*

Back to the Future, Ch. 12, *Hot-air balloons 378*
Example 12.10, *Breathing at high elevation 392*

Everyday Life

Figure 1.10, *Relative sizes 16*
Example 4.4, *Runway needed for takeoff 109*
Example 4.8, *Weight in an elevator 114*
Example 5.5, *Fair rides 152*
Master the Concept, Ch. 6, *Energy and automobiles 184*
Example 6.7, *Pile driver 187*
Example 6.11, *Roller coaster 195*
Example 7.3, *Collision of cars of unequal mass 218*
Physics in Practice, Ch. 9, *Tides 296*
Section 10.1, *Tire gauge 308*
Example 10.3, *Hydraulic lift 313*
Physics in Practice, Ch. 10, *Airplane flight 330*
Section 10.8, *Air drag on an automobile 329*
Section 11.2, *Thermometers 346*
Section 11.3, *Thermostat 350*
Example 11.11, *Styrofoam cooler 364*
Example 12.1, *Atmospheric pressure 375*
Example 12.6, *Tire pressure and temperature 383*
Physics in Practice, Ch. 13, *Gasoline engines 416*
Section 13.4, *Refrigerators and heat pumps 417*
Section 15.4, *Ultrasonic range finder 468*
Example 15.8, *Tuning a guitar 483*
Section 15.9, *Musical scales 480*
Physics in Practice, Ch. 16, *Microwave ovens 519*
Section 17.8, *Electronic stud finder 545*
Example 18.5, *Electric hair dryer 568*
Example 18.6, *Electric iron 568*
Section 19.8, *Moving coil meters 614*
Section 20.3, *Electric motors and generators 635*
Example 21.7, *Radio tuner 678*
Example 22.1, *Image in a mirror 688*
Section 23.2, *Magnifying glass 725*
Section 23.3, *Cameras 728*
Example 24.2, *Soap bubbles 756*
Section 24.8, *Rainbows 768*
Section 24.10, *Polarized sun glasses 772*
Section 24.11, *Blue sky 775*
Section 30.2, *Lasers 951*
Physics in Practice, Ch. 30, *White-light holograms 963*
Section 30.6, *Fluorescent lamps 962*
Section 30.7, *Color television 965*
Section 30.7, *Color photography 966*
Physics in Practice, Ch. 31, *Liquid crystal displays 978*
Section 31.9, *Solar cells and light-emitting diodes 993*
Section 31.9, *Laser diodes and CD systems 994*
Back to the Future, Ch. 32, *Aurora Borealis 1007*

1.1 Measurements and Models

Back to the Future: Echoes of the Big Bang

1.2 Units and Standards of Measurement
1.3 Unit Conversions
1.4 Measurements, Calculations, and Uncertainties
1.5 Estimates and Order-of-Magnitude Calculations
1.6 How to Study Physics
1.7 Problem Solving

Measurement, Models, and Analysis

The word *physics* comes from a Greek word meaning "knowledge of nature." Physics attempts to describe the fundamental nature of the universe and how it works, always striving for the simplest explanations common to the most diverse behavior. For example, physics explains why rainbows have colors, what keeps a satellite in orbit, and what atoms and nuclei are made of. The goal of physics is to explain as many things as possible using as few laws as possible, revealing nature's underlying simplicity and beauty.

In achieving their goal, physicists construct models to represent the world around us. To the physicist, a **model** is an idealized description of a physical system or natural phenomenon. Such a model forms a conceptual framework that permits us to reduce complex situations into simpler, more understandable forms. For example, although we cannot see atoms, we can construct useful models of them that enable us to understand their behavior. Usually, such models of physical systems take a mathematical form. It should be understood that these models are by nature incomplete and, therefore, imperfect. For instance, we can describe the main features of the motion of a baseball if we use a model that ignores air resistance. Such a

1

model has its limitations, however, because it does not accurately describe the path of a curve ball thrown by a major league pitcher. We can obtain better agreement with observations by using a model that includes air resistance.

Physics is an experimental science. By this we mean that the acceptance of any physical theory depends on its success in predicting and explaining reproducible observations. To understand physics we must be able to connect our theoretical description of nature with our experimental observations of nature. This connection is made through quantitative measurements. In part, a thorough understanding of physical theories rests on knowing how measurements are made and how reliable the measured information is.

Until this century, scientists assumed that a sufficiently clever observer, given enough time and money, could, in principle, measure any thing or set of things as accurately as necessary. Our understanding of the measurement process is now more refined. We know that we cannot make a measurement that does not in some way affect the system being measured, thereby limiting the precision of our measurement. This limitation is of little or no importance in the everyday measurements with which we are most familiar: the length of a board or the speed of an automobile. However, we will find that when we come to submolecular processes, the interaction of the observer with the measured quantity cannot be ignored. ■

1.1 Measurements and Models

The role of conceptual models in physics can be demonstrated by discussing one in detail. We illustrate here the interplay of measurement and modeling using an example chosen from physics near the end of the last century. This example exhibits the main features of a physical model discussed in the introduction. It is an important model that we will consider in more detail in later chapters for it was a key to the development of twentieth-century physics.

When a solid object is heated to several hundred degrees Celsius, it becomes incandescent; that is, it glows. The radiation emitted by an incandescent object, such as a very hot tungsten filament, forms a continuous range of wavelengths, part of which lies in the visible range. As the filament's temperature is increased, the relative intensities of the light across the visible spectrum change, shifting the observed color from dull red to almost white (Fig. 1.1). Redder (longer) wavelengths correspond to lower energies while whiter or bluer (shorter) wavelengths signal higher energies.

Experiments show that the light emerging from most incandescent objects depends only on the temperature of the object and not on its composition. An ideal object for producing incandescent light is called a blackbody. A good approximation of an ideal blackbody is an enclosed oven or kiln with only a tiny opening for radiation (i.e., light) to get out. When the oven is cold, light from outside that passes into the opening is not reflected back (Fig. 1.2a) and so the

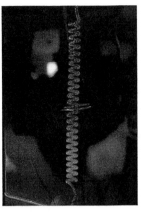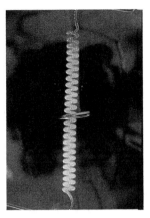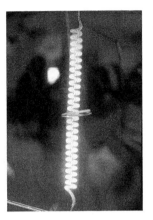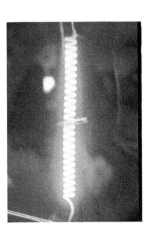

Figure 1.1
As the temperature of a hot filament increases, it emits larger amounts of radiation that peak at shorter and shorter wavelengths. The result is that the color shifts from dark red to bright white.

hole looks completely black. When the oven is very hot, light emitted inside passes out through the hole (Fig. 1.2b). A blackened lamp filament is also a good approximation of an ideal blackbody. Such a blackbody not only is a perfect radiator but also is a perfect absorber that absorbs all radiation falling on it.

During the latter part of the nineteenth century, scientists measured the intensity of the continuous spectrum of light emitted from hot objects. Figure 1.3 shows the radiant energy distribution for a blackbody at several temperatures. The intensity of the radiation is plotted along the vertical axis and wavelength (color) is plotted along the horizontal axis. As the temperature increases, the wavelength of the maximum intensity λ_m shifts to smaller values. The curve for 6000 K (about 5700°C or 10,300°F) corresponds to the approximate temperature

Figure 1.2
A small kiln of the type used to fire ceramics behaves nearly like an ideal blackbody cavity. (a) At a temperature of approximately 300 K, the kiln is very dark inside. Light entering from outside is absorbed. (b) When the kiln is heated to 1400 K, the interior glows brightly and the light emitted inside the cavity passes out through the opening.

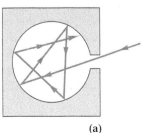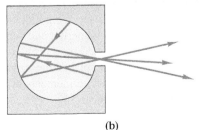

(a)   (b)

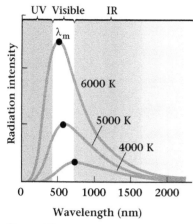

Figure 1.3

Blackbody spectra for several different temperatures. The peak of the curve (λ_m) shifts to shorter wavelengths at higher temperatures. The total amount of energy radiated is proportional to the area under the curve and increases with increasing temperature.

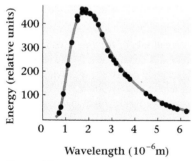

Figure 1.4

Spectral energy distribution of a blackbody at 1596 K. The line is computed from Planck's formula for blackbody radiation. The circles show observation by Coblenz published in *Bulletin of the National Bureau of Standards,* **13,** 436 (1916).

of the sun and has a maximum intensity in the middle (yellow-green) part of the visible spectrum. (The human eye is most sensitive to green light near the maximum of the sun's spectrum.)

In the 1880s and 1890s, numerous attempts were made to explain the shape of the blackbody spectrum. These explanations took the form of conceptual and mathematical models that not only would describe observed spectral curves such as we see in Fig. 1.3 but also would predict curves at wavelengths longer or shorter than visible light. A good model should explain what we can see and measure *and* predict things we have not yet observed. An important part of the scientific method is the construction of experiments to test the predictive value of models. A hundred years ago theoretical models based on the by then well-established—and presumed complete—laws of electromagnetism and thermodynamics failed to reproduce the experimental measurements adequately. The inability to explain blackbody radiation in terms of the framework of physics known in 1890 ultimately led to the development of a new branch of physics, commonly called *modern physics.*

The correct shape of the blackbody radiation curve was first found by Max Planck (1858–1947) as the result of a novel hypothesis. In 1900, Planck reported his discovery of an empirical formula that accurately described the shape of the blackbody spectrum for all observable wavelengths and temperatures. We know that Planck sought a model that would explain his formula (see Section 27.3). His initial model, based on classical theories, assumed that the energy produced through blackbody radiation behaved in a continuous manner. When this model failed to fit the observations, Planck postulated a model in which vibrational energy is *quantized,* that is, limited to certain discrete quantities.

Planck's quantum model was a modification of classical ideas that brought his theory into agreement with experimental observations. (The word *quantum* has the same origin as quantity, and means the smallest possible unit.) Physicists of the time had considerable doubt as to the validity of the quantization of electromagnetic radiation. Planck originally suspected that it was a mathematical trick that did not correspond to reality. However, his formula for blackbody radiation commanded attention because of its striking agreement with observations (Fig. 1.4). The replacement of the model in which energy flowed like a smooth unbroken stream of water, by one in which energy was thought of as coming in little packets, marked the beginning of quantum mechanics and the end of a time in which all physical explanations were in terms of continuous flows or motions.

A fascinating aspect of physics, and science in general, is that an important discovery—like the explanation of blackbody radiation—made years ago can have significance in the present. Though the idea that the universe started with a "big bang" was first proposed in the 1920s, it was not until the 1940s that serious attention was paid to establishing a functional Big Bang theory. Working through the equations that described a hot Big Bang, a few astronomers predicted that there should be surviving radiation from the early universe. Though this radiation initially was superhot and superdense, the expansion of the universe over billions of years should have resulted in the radiation becoming diffuse and cold. The initial prediction placed the temperature of this primordial radiation between 5 K and 50 K.* Later refinements in the early 1960s also indicated that the temperature would be near 5 K.

---

*The letter K is the symbol for the kelvin, the unit of temperature on the Kelvin scale. One kelvin is an interval the same size as the Celsius degree. The zero point of the Kelvin temperature scale is −273.15°C. The temperature of 0 K is called absolute zero.

In 1964, Arno Penzias and Robert W. Wilson discovered microwave radiation with a wavelength of 7.35 cm that was independent of where in the sky their antenna was aimed (see the box: Echoes of the Big Bang). These first measurements and others that soon followed at different wavelengths, were fitted to a Planck radiation curve corresponding to blackbody at a temperature of only 3 K above absolute zero. This radiation is called the cosmic background radiation and its existence is consistent with the prediction made by the Big Bang theory. For their discovery, Penzias and Wilson received the 1978 Nobel prize in physics.

Following Penzias and Wilson's original measurement, other researchers soon measured values at other radio wavelengths to verify the 3 K value. The peak of the blackbody curve for a temperature of 3 K occurs at a wavelength of 1.5 mm. Unfortunately, this wavelength is in the far infrared, which is blocked by the earth's atmosphere. In 1989, NASA launched the Cosmic Background Explorer (COBE) satellite, which proceeded to make a high-precision mapping of the sky (Fig. 1.5). Because the measurements have been so good, the average background temperature of the cosmic radiation is now known to be 2.735 ± 0.06 K.

We see in this example of blackbody radiation the interplay between measurement and analysis. Here, *analysis* means more than graphing the data to observe their essential features. In this context, it means fitting the data to some model (both conceptual and mathematical). Such analysis is almost always done against some background of preconceived ideas. The best models not only explain fully the observations that first led to the model but go on to predict new observations that were previously unexpected. In Planck's case, his original model had to be modified. Others later used his work to predict that the remnant of the radiation left over from the Big Bang would be found within a few

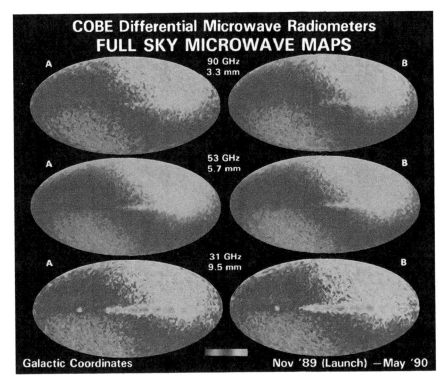

Figure 1.5
All-sky image from the COBE differential microwave radiometers. Two different detectors *A* and *B* operate at three different frequencies marked on the figure. The maps are in galactic coordinates, with the plane of the Milky Way Galaxy horizontal across the middle and the galactic center at the center. The smooth variation from hotter areas (pink) to cooler areas (light blue) is due to the motion of the solar system relative to the distant matter in the universe.

ECHOES OF THE BIG BANG

Figure B1.1 Arno Penzias (right) and Robert W. Wilson with their horn-shaped antenna in the background. Penzias and Wilson won the 1978 Nobel Prize in Physics for their discovery of the cosmic background radiation.

What is cosmic background radiation? How was it discovered? And what does it tell us about the universe?

In 1964, Arno Penzias and Robert W. Wilson of the Bell Telephone Laboratories (Fig. B1.1) began measuring the intensity of radio waves emitted from the gases that surround our galaxy. They used a special 20-foot antenna (called a radio telescope) built for communicating with the Echo and Telstar satellites. The antenna was much more directionally sensitive than were other radio telescopes of that era.

Penzias and Wilson set out to minimize the noise or background signals that had been seen in earlier measurements with the antenna. They considered obvious sources of noise including the Milky Way, the sun, poor antenna joints, even the pigeon droppings that had collected on the antenna. Despite their best efforts, a noticeable radio signal at a wavelength of 7.35 cm was still detected no matter where in the sky the antenna was pointed, the time of day, or the season of the year. The intensity of the signal at that wavelength corresponded to the intensity expected from a thermal radiator (blackbody) at a temperature of about 3 K, that is 3° above absolute zero. This radiation came to be known as the *cosmic background radiation.*

In the spring of 1965, Penzias and Wilson learned of the work of Robert Dicke and James Peebles of Princeton University, who had predicted a residual temperature of 10 K for the universe evolving from a particular point in time in the distant past. This model is referred to as the *Big Bang.* Meanwhile, David Wilkinson and Peter Roll had been building an antenna to look for the remanent radiation at a wavelength of 3.2 cm. The following year, they, too, reported finding radiation corresponding to a temperature of about 3 K.

The cosmic background radiation was first predicted in the late 1940s by George Gamow, Ralph Alpher, and Robert Herman who, in developing a Big-Bang cosmology to explain the formation of the elements, had estimated the necessary temperature and density. They showed that a consequence of their model was the existence of a cosmic background radiation at about 5 K. As the young universe expanded and cooled from its extremely hot beginning, the radiation emitted would survive, although by now it would correspond to a very low temperature. Moreover, the background radiation is isotropic, that is, it is the same in any direction that we observe.

In the years following Penzias's and Wilson's discovery, many measurements of the cosmic background radiation were made at other wavelengths. All of these were fit to the Planck law at the same temperature of about 2.7 K. In 1989, NASA launched the Cosmic Background Explorer (the COBE satellite) designed to measure the cosmic background radiation over a wide range of wavelengths. Orbiting high above the earth's atmosphere, the COBE was able to make better observations than could be made with ground-based radio telescopes. The COBE operated for 10 months, taking many data points in all directions of space. When the data were finally analyzed, they fit precisely a Planck blackbody curve for a temperature of 2.735 ± 0.06 K (Fig. B1.2).

The noise that Penzias and Wilson could not eliminate turns out to be the residual thermal radiation left over from the beginning of the universe. This radiation, which shines on us from every direction, is a uniform glow coming from the most distant regions of the universe. It is the echo of the Big Bang.

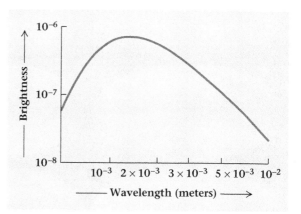

Figure B1.2 Intensity spectrum of the cosmic background radiation detected with the COBE satellite. The data points and their error bars are fit to a Planck curve for $T = 2.735 \pm 0.06$ K.

kelvins of absolute zero. Instruments were then built that could confirm the prediction.

The story of the Big Bang radiation shows how science works—an interplay between measurement and analysis. However, you should remember that even the best models are only as good as the assumptions that go into making them. For this reason we must be careful in applying models to complex situations and not forget the approximations that went into the models.

1.2 Units and Standards of Measurement

When the distance between two objects is measured, that measurement is reported as a number. However, the particular number given depends on the size of the basic unit of measurement. For example, suppose a surveyor needs to measure the distance between two stakes firmly stuck in the ground. If the distance is 25.4 meters, the surveyor must report both "25.4" and "meters." If he reports the distance in centimeters, he says "2540 cm." If he reports the distance in inches, he says "1000 inches."

We say that a measured quantity has **dimensions** when the size of the numerical result depends on the units chosen for measurement. The separation between the two stakes measured by the surveyor has the dimension of length. Time and mass are other familiar dimensions. In order for measurements made in different places and at different times to have meaning, we must first define **base,** or **fundamental, units.** Base units are sometimes referred to as standards.

There are only seven base units, corresponding to the quantities of length, time, mass, electric current, temperature, the amount of substance, and luminous intensity. All measured quantities are expressed in terms of these base units or combinations of them. For instance, a unit of area is meter^2, and a unit of speed is meters per second. Although various systems of units have been used over the years, scientists have generally agreed to use the **International System of Units.** The International System is also known by its abbreviation, SI, which comes from its French name, *Système International.* Table 1.1 lists the SI base units, which are largely based on what is often called the metric system. In the past, this system of units has also been called the mks system, in reference to the base units of meter, kilogram, and second.

Table 1.1 *SI Base Units*

Quantity	Name	Symbol
Length	meter	m
Mass	kilogram	kg
Time	second	s
Electric current	ampere	A
Thermodynamic temperature	kelvin	K
Amount of substance	mole	mol
Luminous intensity	candela	cd

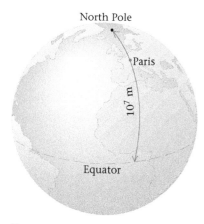

Figure 1.6
The meter was originally chosen to be one ten-millionth of the distance from the equator to the North Pole along a meridian through Paris.

Length

The basic unit of length, the meter, was approved by the first General Conference on Weights and Measures (CGPM) in 1889. It was defined as the distance between two fine lines engraved near the ends of a bar of platinum-iridium alloy when the bar was maintained at 0°C. The original international prototype meter, which is still kept at the International Bureau of Weights and Measures in Sèvres, France, was intended to be one ten-millionth of the distance from the equator to the North Pole along a line of longitude through Paris (Fig. 1.6). To give you some sense of the size of a meter, it is approximately the distance from the tip of your nose to the fingertips of your outstretched arm.

In 1983, the seventeenth General Conference on Weights and Measures redefined the meter in terms of the speed of light: The meter is the length of the path traveled by light in vacuum during a time interval of 1/299,792,458 of a second.

Mass

The base unit of mass, the kilogram, is defined as the mass of a prototype cylinder of platinum-iridium alloy that is kept at the International Bureau of Weights and Measures. Platinum-iridium was chosen because that alloy is particularly stable. The United States has a duplicate of the standard kilogram that is kept by the National Institute of Standards and Technology. In your everyday experience, the mass of a typical baseball bat is about one kilogram.

Time

The base unit for time is the second, which was originally defined as 1/86,400 of the mean solar day. In 1967, the CGPM adopted a standard based on the cesium-beam atomic clock, which can have a stability and accuracy of about one part in 10^{12} or even 10^{13}. The second is defined to be exactly 9,192,631,770 periods of a specified (microwave) radiation from cesium-133 atoms.

Understanding the nature of the atom allows us to use certain periodic properties of atoms as the characteristics that regulate the most modern timekeepers, such as the cesium-beam clocks. Over the years, improvements in timekeepers have often been related to ideas and developments that were in the forefront of science and technology. For example, advances in understanding the thermal properties of materials allowed for the development of temperature-compensated clocks. The use of electromagnets and electric switches brought about still further improvements in pendulum clocks. Studies of the electromechanical properties of quartz led eventually to crystal-controlled clocks that are many times more accurate than mechanical clocks. Figure 1.7 shows the improvement of timekeeping accuracy since the invention of the mechanical clock around the year 1300.

An estimate of the duration of one second is about the time required to say "one Mississippi." The time between human heartbeats is also approximately one second.

Symbols for Units

It is often more convenient to use the shorter symbol for a unit than to use its full name. Thus, we write 10 kg instead of 10 kilograms. Table 1.1 gives the

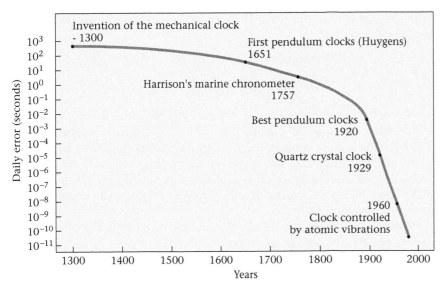

Figure 1.7

The diminishing daily error in clocks is shown as a function of the year in which the improvement was made.

symbols for the seven base units. Several rules govern the writing and use of these unit symbols: Roman (upright) type, generally lowercase, is used for symbols of units; however, if the symbols are derived from proper names, capital roman type is used for the first letter. Unit symbols are not followed by a period (except in. for inch) and do not change in the plural.

A product of two or more units may be indicated by

$$A \cdot m \quad \text{or} \quad A\,m.$$

A unit may also be raised to a power, as

$$m^3 \quad \text{or} \quad cm^2.$$

Units formed from two others by division may be indicated by a horizontal line, a solidus (an oblique line, /), or a negative power; for example,

$$\frac{m}{s}, \quad m/s, \quad \text{or} \quad m \cdot s^{-1}.$$

In complicated cases, negative powers or parentheses should be used; for example,

$$m \cdot kg/(s^3 \cdot A) \quad \text{or} \quad m \cdot kg \cdot s^{-3} \cdot A^{-1}.$$

Prefixes

In physics we frequently encounter numbers that are very large or very small. Such numbers are most easily expressed by the use of **scientific notation**, which uses powers of 10. This notation provides an easier way of writing large and small numbers and of doing arithmetic with them. To illustrate, note that we may write the number "one thousand" in the following way:

$$1000 = 10 \times 10 \times 10 = 10^3.$$

Table 1.2	SI Prefixes	
Factor	Prefix	Symbol
10^{18}	exa	E
10^{15}	peta	P
10^{12}	tera	T
10^{9}	giga	G
10^{6}	mega	M
10^{3}	kilo	k
10^{2}	hecto	h
10^{1}	deka	da
10^{-1}	deci	d
10^{-2}	centi	c
10^{-3}	milli	m
10^{-6}	micro	μ
10^{-9}	nano	n
10^{-12}	pico	p
10^{-15}	femto	f
10^{-18}	atto	a

With this notation, we can conveniently express very large and very small numbers. For example,

$$127{,}000{,}000 = 1.27 \times 100{,}000{,}000 = 1.27 \times 10^{8}$$

and

$$0.00037 = 3.7 \times 0.0001 = 3.7 \times 10^{-4}.$$

Using the scientific notation, 1670 meters can be written as 1.67×10^{3} meters. But this same quantity can also be written 1.67 kilometers—abbreviated as 1.67 km. This is an example of using a prefix to indicate a decimal multiple of a base unit. Here the prefix kilo means one thousand or 10^{3}. Table 1.2 gives the prefixes for other multiples or submultiples of units. Table 1.3 gives the approximate values of various lengths, masses, and times in units with prefixes and expressed in powers of 10.

Numbers expressed in scientific notation may be multiplied and divided according to the usual rules of algebra. Remember that

$$10^{n} \times 10^{m} = 10^{n+m} \quad \text{and} \quad \frac{10^{a}}{10^{b}} = 10^{a-b}.$$

When using numbers with prefixes, they should be converted to scientific notation in the proper units before being used in calculations.

Example 1.1

According to the official rules for international soccer, the minimum size for the rectangular playing field is 100 m by 64 m. Compute the area of a minimum-sized soccer field in units of kilometers squared.

Solution The area of the field is the product of length and width. If we express the length and width in units of km, then the area will be given in km^{2}. Remember that 1 km equals 1000 m so that $1 \text{ m} = 10^{-3}$ km.

$$\text{Area} = (100 \text{ m})(64 \text{ m}) = (0.100 \text{ km})(0.064 \text{ km}) = 0.0064 \text{ km}^{2}$$
$$\text{Area} = 6.4 \times 10^{-3} \text{ km}^{2}.$$

Table 1.3	Approximate Values of Some Physical Quantities			
Quantity		Magnitude		
Radius of a proton	1 femtometer	1 fm	1×10^{-15} m	
Distance from Atlanta to San Diego	3000 kilometers	3000 km	3×10^{3} km $= 3 \times 10^{6}$ m	
Mass of a small marble	5 grams	5 g	5×10^{-3} kg	
Mass of a grain of salt	1 milligram	1 mg	1×10^{-3} g $= 1 \times 10^{-6}$ kg	
Time for light to travel 0.3 m	1 nanosecond	1 ns	1×10^{-9} s	
Time for sound to travel 1.0 m	3 milliseconds	3 ms	3×10^{-3} s	

▼

Example 1.2

What is the volume of a rectangular sheet of paper that is 8.60×10^{-3} cm thick, 21.6 cm wide, and 27.9 cm long?

Solution The volume V of a rectangular-shaped piece of paper is given by the product of the length, width, and thickness:

$$V = \text{length} \times \text{width} \times \text{thickness}$$
$$V = (27.9 \text{ cm})(21.6 \text{ cm})(8.60 \times 10^{-3} \text{ cm}) \approx 5.18 \text{ cm}^3.$$

▼

1.3 Unit Conversions

Frequently you will need to change from one set of units to another. You may have to change a given number of seconds into minutes, or a given number of inches into centimeters or meters. A systematic method for doing this starts with writing a conversion factor, a fraction whose numerator in one set of units equals the denominator in the other set of units. For example, the inch is defined to be exactly 2.54 cm.

$$1 \text{ in.} = 2.54 \text{ cm.}$$

We can rewrite this equation as

$$1 = \frac{2.54 \text{ cm}}{1 \text{ in.}} \quad \text{or} \quad 1 = \frac{1 \text{ in.}}{2.54 \text{ cm}}.$$

Both of these fractions are pure numbers equal to 1. That is, the quantity on the right-hand side of the equation has the value of unity and has no dimensions, since it is equal to the left-hand side. Consequently, we can multiply by 1 in the form of either of these fractions in any equation where they are needed. To change units, you simply multiply the quantity to be converted by the conversion factor chosen so that the undesired units cancel out. Several brief examples of unit conversions will help illustrate the procedure.

▼

Example 1.3

How many centimeters are there in one foot?

Strategy We know that the foot is defined to be exactly 12 in. and that the inch is defined to be exactly 2.54 cm. Thus we can express the foot as 12 in. and then use a conversion factor to take us from inches to centimeters.

Solution We start with the equation

$$1 \text{ ft} = 12 \text{ in.},$$

and multiply the right-hand side by 1 in the form of 2.54 cm/1 in.:

$$1 \text{ ft} = (12 \text{ in.})(1) = (12 \text{ in.})\left(\frac{2.54 \text{ cm}}{1 \text{ in.}}\right) = 30.48 \text{ cm.}$$

Notice that when you use this procedure, the correctness of the units ensures the correctness of the answer.

Example 1.4

How many kilometers are in one mile?

Strategy We know that 1 km is 1000 m, 1 m is 100 cm, and 1 mile is 5280 ft. We can find the number of kilometers in one mile by using these relationships along with the result of Example 1.3 relating cm to ft.

Solution Using the outlined procedure, we obtain

$$1 \text{ mi} = (1 \text{ mi})\left(\frac{5280 \text{ ft}}{1 \text{ mi}}\right)\left(\frac{30.48 \text{ cm}}{1 \text{ ft}}\right)\left(\frac{1 \text{ m}}{100 \text{ cm}}\right)\left(\frac{1 \text{ km}}{1000 \text{ m}}\right)$$

$$1 \text{ mi} = 1.609 \text{ km}.$$

Example 1.5

An automobile has a speed of 30 mi/h. What is its speed in m/s?

Solution Following the method used in the preceding examples, we use a succession of conversion factors to change the units to the desired form:

$$30\frac{\text{mi}}{\text{hr}} = \left(\frac{30 \text{ mi}}{1 \text{ h}}\right)\left(\frac{1 \text{ h}}{60 \text{ min}}\right)\left(\frac{1 \text{ min}}{60 \text{ s}}\right)\left(\frac{1.609 \text{ km}}{1 \text{ mi}}\right)\left(\frac{1000 \text{ m}}{1 \text{ km}}\right)$$

$$\frac{30 \text{ mi}}{\text{hr}} = 13.4 \text{ m/s}.$$

1.4   Measurements, Calculations, and Uncertainties

There is an important difference between how we use numbers in arithmetic and algebra and how we use them in science. This difference arises from the nature of measurement. When we say that a length is 9.2 cm, we mean that this is a length that has been, or can be, measured. Implicit in our statement is information about the precision with which the measurement has been made. By 9.2 cm, we mean a length that is closer to 9.2 cm than to either 9.1 cm or 9.3 cm. Had we estimated between the 0.1-cm divisions, or used a ruler with finer divisions, we might have said the length was 9.23 cm (Fig. 1.8). This means a length closer to 9.23 cm than to 9.22 cm or 9.24 cm. The point is that the last figure in a quoted measurement is in some sense uncertain and lacks the same significance as the figures to its left.

The number of digits reported in a measurement, irrespective of the location of the decimal place, is called the number of **significant figures.** The number of significant figures is a reflection of how well you know a given quantity. For

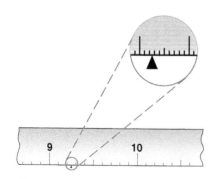

Figure 1.8
Position of a reference mark along a scale. The inset shows a magnified view, which permits greater precision in locating the position of the mark.

example, length is, in the classical sense, assumed to be infinitely divisible. This means that to specify a length "exactly" would require an infinite number of significant figures. Therefore, all numbers that represent lengths are inexact, but they do carry with them information about how well those lengths are known.

Measured values are often used to calculate other quantities. For example, we can determine the circumference C of a circle from a measurement of the radius r of the circle and the expression

$$C = 2\pi r. \tag{1.1}$$

The value of π is well known and has been determined to many significant figures. To seven significant figures, $\pi = 3.141593$. If we had measured the radius of a circle to be 1.60 cm, direct application of Eq. (1.1) would give a numerical answer of

$$C = 10.053098 \text{ cm}.$$

However, this is not a physically meaningful or sensible answer. The circumference can be known only to the same precision as the radius. In this case, the precision is three significant figures. Therefore we must *round off* the answer to the correct number of significant figures:

$$C = 10.1 \text{ cm}.$$

Note that the last figure has been rounded up. The rule we will follow in this book is that if the first digit beyond the last significant figure is 5 or greater, the last significant figure is to be increased by unity (1). All other figures beyond the last significant figure are dropped. If the digit beyond the last significant figure is less than 5, the last significant figure remains unchanged. Thus 10.05 rounds off to 10.1, but 10.04 rounds off to 10.0. (Most pocket calculators that round off automatically use this rule.)

Another numerical example will further illustrate the use of significant figures. Let us calculate the area of a paperback book cover. Suppose the cover is a rectangle whose sides we measure to be 10.6 cm and 17.9 cm. To find the area A of a rectangle, we multiply the length l times the width w:

$$A = l \times w.$$

The product of 10.6 and 17.9 is 189.74. However, it is *not* correct to give the area of the cover as 189.74 cm². To do so would imply that the area is known to be between 189.73 cm² and 189.75 cm², a precision that is unwarranted on the basis of the precision with which the lengths of the individual sides are known.

To see what we mean, notice that the length of the first edge of the cover is between 10.55 cm and 10.64 cm, and the length of the second edge is between 17.85 cm and 17.94 cm. The product of the least of these numbers is 188.3175, and the product of the greater is 190.8816. We see, then, that even the last place *before* the decimal is uncertain, so it would be a mistake to give an answer with more than three figures. Thus, we round off the computed area of 189.74 cm² to 190 cm². The general rule is that your answer must have no more significant figures than is warranted by the least precise of your values (that is, the value with the fewest significant figures).

When multiplying or dividing several quantities, the number of significant figures in the result is the same as the number of significant figures in the factor with the least number of significant figures.

The precision of the sum or difference of two quantities is no better than that of the least-precise quantity. For example,

$$14.1 \text{ cm} + 1.32 \text{ cm} = 15.4 \text{ cm}.$$

Even though both of these numbers have three significant figures, the first number is less precise as it is given only to tenths of cm while the second number is given to hundredths of cm. Consequently, the sum is given only to the nearest tenth of a centimeter. Thus, we have the rule:

When adding or subtracting two quantities, the least significant figure in the result occupies the same position relative to the decimal point as the position of the last significant figure in the number whose least significant figure is farthest to the left.

Sometimes it is not clear whether the final zero or zeros in a number are significant figures or are merely needed to locate the decimal point. In the preceding example, the result of 190 cm was correct to three figures so that the zero was a significant figure. To clearly indicate the number of significant figures, we often express a number in scientific notation. Thus, we write 190 cm as 1.90×10^2 cm. The presence of the final zero indicates that the number is known to three significant figures. We will assume integers of numeration to be precise. Thus, the answer to "What is the cost of 2 hamburgers at $1.89 each?" is $3.78 and not $4.

Example 1.6

Calculate the volume of a cylindrical oatmeal box with a diameter of 10.2 cm and a height of 18.4 cm (Fig. 1.9).

Solution The volume of a cylinder is the product of the height h and the area of the base,

$$V = hA = h\pi\left(\frac{d}{2}\right)^2,$$

where d is the diameter. Upon inserting the values for h, π, and d, we get

$$V = 18.4 \text{ cm} \times 3.14 \times \left(\frac{10.2}{2}\right)^2 \text{ cm}^2.$$

Direct computation with a hand calculator yields

$$V = 1502.75376 \text{ cm}^3 = 1.50275376 \times 10^3 \text{ cm}^3.$$

However, since the dimensions are known to only three significant figures, the answer must be rounded off to give

$$V = 1.50 \times 10^3 \text{ cm}^3.$$

|←— 10.2 cm —→|

18.4 cm

$V = hA = h\pi(d/2)^2$

Figure 1.9
Example 1.6: Calculating the volume of a cylindrical oatmeal box.

| 1.5 | ## Estimates and Order-of-Magnitude Calculations |

As we have just seen, it is important to keep track of uncertainties in measurement when calculating answers to problems. Sometimes, in everyday life as well as in science, we need to solve a problem for which we don't have enough information for a precise answer. We can often obtain a useful answer by estimating the values of the appropriate quantities. These estimates, usually made to the nearest power of ten, are called **order-of-magnitude** estimates. The resulting order-of-magnitude calculation is not exact, but usually it is accurate to within a factor of ten. Just knowing the order of magnitude of physical quantities often provides enough information for us to gain a useful understanding of the physical situation and to be able to make judgments and rough calculations for constructing models. Figure 1.10 shows the range of the magnitudes of lengths encountered in physics.

Making order-of-magnitude estimates is often easy. For example, imagine you are going to college for the first time and that you want to estimate how much money you need for books. You know that the usual load for most students is five courses and that each course requires a textbook. You can estimate the cost of a single book using the following reasoning. You know from experience that $1 is too little and that $100 too much. Even $10 is low. A reasonable estimate might be $50. Thus, the estimated cost of books for one term is 5 × $50 = $250. Although the result is certainly not accurate, it is the right order of magnitude and provides a reasonable estimate to a real problem. The following example further illustrates the application of order-of-magnitude estimates.

When making computations of this sort we often make other approximations as well. Replacing π with 3 or replacing $\sqrt{2}$ with $\frac{3}{2}$ makes little difference in the order of magnitude, but doing so greatly simplifies the calculations. The following examples illustrate the technique.

Example 1.7

Estimate the volume of rubber worn from automobile tires each year in the United States. The average radial tire has a useful tread depth of $\frac{5}{16}$ in. and can be driven 35,000 mi before it is worn out.

Strategy We begin by estimating the number of automobiles in the United States and the average number of miles driven per car each year so that we can find the total number of miles driven per year. From that result we can compute the equivalent number of tires worn out each year. Finally, we compute the volume of rubber lost from each worn out tire and multiply by the number of worn out tires to get the total volume of rubber.

Solution The number of cars can be estimated from the size of the population, which is about 260 million people. We know that not every person has a car and that many families have more than one. If we estimate that there is about one car for every four people, then we get approximately 65 million automobiles. The average number of miles driven/year is about 15,000 mi/year.

10^7 meters
The earth. The average radius of the earth is roughly 6×10^6 m. This is almost twice the radius of Mars, but less than one-tenth the radius of Jupiter.

10^{21} meters
The Andromeda galaxy. This spiral galaxy is our close neighbor within the so-called "Local Group" of galaxies, lying about 2×10^{22} m away from the earth. It is similar in form to our Milky Way galaxy, which contains about 10^{11} individual stars.

10^0 meters
People. Most humans are 1.5–2.0 m tall. The present population of the United States is about 2.6×10^8 people, so if we were all laid out end to end in a straight line, we would cover a distance about 30 times greater than the diameter of the earth.

10^{-5} meters
A red blood cell, or erythrocyte. A human contains about 2.5×10^{13} erythrocytes, which function primarily to transport oxygen within the body. New cells form at a rate of about 10^6 per second to replace dying cells and keep a constant number in the blood.

10^{-10} meters
An atom. This image from an electron tunneling microscope shows individual atoms of silicon, located at the corners of the hexagonal pattern. The nucleus of the atom is only 10^{-14} m in size, so the atom as a whole consists mostly of empty space.

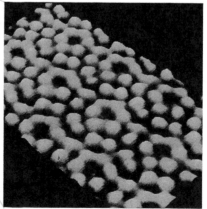

Figure 1.10
The range of sizes in physics is from the very large to the very small. Here we see a range of sizes covering 31 orders of magnitude. Physicists have directly observed distances spanning nearly 41 orders of magnitude, from the diameter of a proton (10^{-15} m) to the most distant galaxies seen by the Hubble Space Telescope (10^{26} m or 12 billion light-years). Extending this range further, particle physicists theorize that quarks, which have not been "seen," have dimensions on the order of 10^{-18} m.

(Surely 1500 mi/year is too low and 150,000 mi/year is too high.) From these numbers we get the number of tire miles per year.

Total tire miles/year ≈ number of cars × 4 tires/car × 15,000 mi/year.

(The symbol ≈ means that the quantity on the left is *approximately* equal to the quantity on the right.) The number N of worn out tires each year is given by

$$N = \frac{\text{total tire miles/year}}{\text{miles/worn out tire}}$$

$$N \approx \frac{(6.5 \times 10^7 \text{ cars})(4 \text{ tires/car})(1.5 \times 10^4 \text{ mi/year})}{3.5 \times 10^4 \text{ mi}} \approx 1.1 \times 10^8 \text{ tires/year.}$$

The volume of rubber worn off each tire is given by

$$V_1 = 2\pi r \times \text{width} \times \text{thickness of tread worn off,}$$

where r = radius of the tire ≈ 15 in. ≈ 38 cm, width ≈ 6 in. ≈ 15 cm, and thickness ≈ $\frac{5}{16}$ in. ≈ 0.8 cm. The total volume of rubber worn from all tires in one year is

$$V_T = NV_1 \times 1 \text{ year}$$
$$V_T \approx (1.1 \times 10^8 \text{ tires/year})(2\pi)(38 \text{ cm})(15 \text{ cm})(0.8 \text{ cm})(1 \text{ year})$$
$$V_T \approx 3.2 \times 10^{11} \text{ cm}^3 \approx 3 \times 10^5 \text{ m}^3.$$

Thus, we estimate that the volume of rubber worn each year from automobiles in the United States is about 3×10^5 m^3.

Discussion Just how big is a pile of rubber 3×10^5 m^3? If it was piled 1 m deep across two lanes of an interstate highway (width ≈ 7 m), it would reach more than 40 km.

Example 1.8

A record store offers a prize to the customer with the guess closest to the correct number of jelly beans that fill a liter jar on a display counter in the store. (One liter is equal to 1000 cm^3.) Estimate what that number should be.

Strategy A careful look at the jar (Fig. 1.11) reveals several things. The jelly beans can be roughly approximated by little cylinders about 2 cm long by about 1.5 cm in diameter. Furthermore, the jelly beans are not tightly packed; perhaps only as much as 80% of the volume of the jar is filled. We can use these observations to estimate the number of beans in the jar.

Solution The number of jelly beans is the occupied volume of the jar divided by the volume of a single jelly bean,

$$\text{number of beans} = \frac{\text{occupied volume of jar}}{\text{volume of 1 bean}}.$$

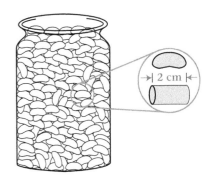

Figure 1.11
Example 1.8: How many jelly beans fill a one-liter jar?

The volume of one jelly bean is approximated by the volume of a small cylinder,

$$\text{volume of 1 bean} = h\pi\left(\frac{d}{2}\right)^2 \approx 2 \text{ cm} \times 3\left(\frac{\frac{3}{2} \text{ cm}}{2}\right)^2 = \frac{27}{8} \text{ cm}^3.$$

Thus the approximate number of beans in the jar is

$$\text{number of beans} \approx \frac{0.80 \times 1000 \text{ cm}^3}{\frac{27}{8} \text{ cm}^3} \approx 240.$$

An actual count, by one of the authors, of the jelly beans filling a quart jar (0.95 liter) gave 255 beans.

▼

| 1.6 | How to Study Physics |

In the first five sections of this chapter, you have seen only a little of what physics is about. Even so, you have probably noticed one thing: words are important. Words are frequently given a more precise meaning in the physical sciences than in ordinary use. To make headway in learning physics, you need to know the meaning of these key words, or terms, as they are used in physics. The key terms in this book have been written in **boldface type** when they are first introduced and defined. As a help in studying, these same terms are gathered together at the end of each chapter in the summary. You should write out the definition of each term, just as you write out vocabulary items when learning a new language. Doing so will help ensure that you learn their precise meanings. Learning the precise meaning of the terms here is just as important as learning the meaning of new words in a language.

In fact, you should always study with a pen or pencil in your hand. (What we are talking about is entirely different from underlining or highlighting part of the text.) You should outline the ideas as they are presented and work out the algebraic steps for yourself. Then you should go on to an example and work through it. By writing out the material you will notice details that reading alone may not convey. Just as words and ideas are important, symbols are important. A lowercase letter, say t, will not stand for the same thing as a capital letter, in this case T. Thus, mA does not mean the same thing as MA. Likewise—as we will see in Chapter 3—the boldface letter $\mathbf{A}$ will not mean the same thing as A. Be careful when writing the Greek letters so that they are not confused with other letters or symbols.

When working for yourself—as well as when working problems to turn in or on a test—you should always help yourself by arranging your work in an orderly way. It is no accident that the equations in a textbook are placed one under another, as in Example 1.7 and elsewhere. This layout makes it easier for you to understand the text. Likewise such a procedure will help you as you try to understand the material. Don't scatter equations around the page, but start at the top and work down going from left to right as you proceed. Furthermore, using a systematic and orderly procedure will help you as you try to tell others—perhaps the graders of your work—about your solutions. Do not make learning more difficult by ignoring purely mechanical procedures.

The mathematical formulas that you will encounter represent more than algebraic equations. The formulas are shorthand for physical situations and therefore represent ideas. You must understand where and when the ideas and the accompanying formulas apply. Always include the units when you substitute a value for a symbol in an equation. With almost no exceptions, all the symbols in equations stand for physical quantities with units. When you are carrying out mathematical manipulations for your private study, for homework, or on a test, it is a good idea to make some comments in words to indicate what you are doing and why. Doing so will make it easier for you when studying and reviewing and will help your grader understand what you did.

When you reach the end of a section in the text, you should ask yourself what key ideas and terms have been introduced. Write them down and compare what you have with the items listed in the summary. After mastering the ideas and concepts of the text, you should work some of the problems at the end of the chapter. Doing so will reinforce the ideas that you have been learning.

1.7   Problem Solving

Learning physics requires more than just learning new terms and definitions and stating the concepts and laws. To find out what physics is really about, you must learn how to apply these concepts and laws to real or hypothetical situations. Experience has shown that this kind of learning cannot occur without practice. For this reason, in a physics course you may spend more time working problems than you do reading the text.

In order to be productive in your study and to make the best use of your time, you must recognize that problem solving is much more than merely substituting numbers in a formula or fitting together the pieces of a jigsaw puzzle. Thumbing through the book to find a formula that seems to fit or a worked-out example that resembles your particular problem is a waste of time and effort. You should begin by studying the ideas, the concepts, and their relationships first. Then you attempt the problems as a way to find out for yourself whether or not you understand the material.

Even though the worked-out examples and problems in this text may sometimes represent an oversimplification of nature—for example, we might ignore the effects of air resistance on a moving body—they illustrate basic ideas, concepts, and techniques that you must master before going on to more complicated situations. The most helpful advice we can offer you is to use the working of problems as a method of studying. When you begin studying a chapter, go over the text examples with pencil and paper, work them out carefully in more detail than the text does, and then proceed to the problems. Although practice is the most important thing, you may find the following general rules to be helpful.

Problem-Solving Guidelines

1. **Read the entire problem carefully.** Then read it again to try and find out what you are being told. Don't worry about the question at first; focus more on what information you are being given.

2. Whenever possible, **draw a diagram of the physical situation.** Label the diagram with the information given in the problem. Be sure to include units, such as meters or kilograms, with the quantities. If some standard symbols have been introduced, label the parts of the diagram with them, too. For example, you might label r for radius, h for height, or l for distance. You might also make a list of the known and unknown quantities involved.

3. Only after you are sure you understand what is given and after you have labeled the diagram should you **tackle the question.** It is often a good idea to briefly write down the question, using symbols.

4. The next step is to **find a mathematical relationship between the known and unknown quantities.** For example, if asked how many dimes make $1.30, you call on your knowledge of the value of a dime. Or, if asked how far an auto goes in 2 hours at 30 kilometers per hour, you call on another type of knowledge. In most cases, you will need to write the relationship between the known and unknown quantities in the form of an equation, or perhaps several equations.

5. Next you should **solve the equation, or equations, for the unknown quantity or quantities.** This means rearranging the formulas in accord with the rules of algebra so that you have an equation with the unknown on the left-hand side of the equals sign and all of the known quantities and constants on the right-hand side.

6. Now, and only now, should you **substitute numerical values into the equation.** Do not substitute just "bare numbers," but substitute both the numerical values *and* the units. As indicated in Example 1.7, units are multiplied and divided as if they were algebraic quantities. Your answer should then come out in the appropriate units. If the units do not come out correctly, you have probably made some basic error. On the other hand, if the units are correct, there is a higher probability that your work is correct. Remember that in giving your final answer you must give the proper number of significant figures.

7. As a final check, you should **consider whether your answer is reasonable.** Does your result have the proper order of magnitude? You may even carry out a quick order-of-magnitude estimate as a way of confirming your work.

As an example of these ideas, let us work a sample problem.

Example 1.9

Suppose you get into your car and travel 25 km due north. Then you turn and travel an unknown distance east. Finally, you travel 32 km directly back to your starting point. How long was the eastern leg of your trip?

Strategy and Solution By reading the problem carefully and drawing a diagram similar to Fig. 1.12, you will have covered steps 1, 2, and 3.

For step 4, recall the relationship between the sides of a right triangle, which is what the diagram shows. This relationship is the Pythagorean theorem: The square of the hypotenuse is equal to the sum of the squares of the other two sides. In terms of the symbols on the diagram, this theorem can be written

$$c^2 = a^2 + b^2.$$

In this equation, the unknown quantity is b and the known quantities are a and c. We may isolate the unknown quantity by subtracting a^2 from both sides to get

$$b^2 = c^2 - a^2.$$

To complete the solution, we take the square root of both sides,

$$b = \sqrt{c^2 - a^2}.$$

The negative solution can be discarded because a negative length is not physically meaningful.

Now, in accord with step 6, we substitute the values and the units for the algebraic symbols:

$$b = \sqrt{(32 \text{ km})^2 - (25 \text{ km})^2}$$
$$b = \sqrt{1024 \text{ km}^2 - 625 \text{ km}^2} = \sqrt{399 \text{ km}^2}$$
$$b = 20 \text{ km}.$$

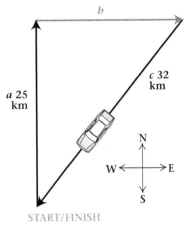

START/FINISH

Figure 1.12
Example 1.9: How long is the distance b?

Discussion Notice how the units were handled and how many significant figures were kept in the answer. The rounding off was done last after all of the calculations were made.

Summary

Useful Concepts

■ A model is an idealized description of a physical system that enables us to form a conceptual framework for understanding that system.

■ There are seven SI base units or standards. The names of the base units for mass, length, and time are kilogram, meter, and second, respectively.

■ Numbers expressed in scientific notation can be multiplied and divided in the following way:

$$(A \times 10^n) \times (B \times 10^m) = (A \times B) \times 10^{n+m}$$
$$\frac{C \times 10^n}{D \times 10^m} = \left[\frac{C}{D}\right] \times 10^{n-m}.$$

■ To convert from one system of units to another, first write the conversion factor as a fraction whose numerator and denominator are physically equal and then multiply this fraction by the quantity to be converted.

■ Numbers arising from measurement convey the precision of the measurement by the number of significant figures used.

■ The results of a calculation may not have more significant figures than is warranted by the least precise of the values used. When multiplying or dividing, the number of significant figures in the result is limited by the number of significant figures in the least-precise value. When adding or subtracting numbers, the number of decimal places in the result is the same as that of the value with the fewest decimal places.

Important Terms

You should be able to write the definition or meaning of each of the following:

model	scientific notation
dimensions	significant figures
base, or fundamental, unit	order of magnitude
International System of Units	

▼
Conceptual Questions

1.1 Suppose you are planning a trip by car to another city and you estimate the time required to get there. Show how this estimate depends on a model, as described in the text. What does the model depend on and how reliable is it?

1.2 Give a personal example of the use of a model for analysis of measured data.

1.3 Make a list of those quantities for which you think it might be helpful to establish standard units. Why?

1.4 Explain the difference between dimensions and units.

1.5 What problems are there in maintaining and using a metal bar as the primary length standard as was done before the meter was redefined in 1983?

1.6 What problems are there in maintaining and using a primary time standard in which the second is defined as 1/86,400 of a mean solar day?

1.7 Explain the basic idea behind unit conversion.

1.8 Discuss the difference in meaning of the three quantities 10 m, 10.0 m, and 10.00 m.

1.9 Estimate the precision of your watch or a clock. You may do this by using radio or television time signals spaced 24 or 48 hours apart.

1.10 Which of the following numbers is given to three significant figures: 0.003 m, 0.32 cm, 0.320 cm, 3.21 mm, or 3.213 mm?

1.11 A student measures a rectangle with a meterstick that measures no better than ±1 mm. She finds the height to be 37 mm and the width to be 46 mm. Why does she then report the area of the rectangle to be 1700 mm^2 instead of 1702 mm^2?

1.12 Estimate the total weight of the population of the United States.

▼
Problems

Section 1.1 Measurements and Models

Hints for Solving Problems

The problems in this section ask you to devise a physical model that explains a given set of observations. In conceiving your model, you may assume a "perfect" world in which friction and other perturbing effects do not influence the working of your model. The model may be conceptual or mathematical.

1.1 What model most simply describes the following observations? (a) A ball placed anywhere on the floor remains at rest. (b) A ball placed anywhere on the floor begins to roll. (c) Give other, less-simple models for these observations.

1.2 A handful of small pebbles is dropped down a large, vertical tube. Only one-half of the pebbles fall out of the lower end. (a) Devise a simple model for a device within the tube that accounts for the observations. (b) Devise another, less-simple model.

1.3 A die is thrown many times with the following results for the number showing on the top face: 1, 63 times; 2, 58 times; 3, 62 times; 4, 63 times; 5, 75 times, and 6, 61 times. What model can you make for the die?

1.4 An insect travels between two fixed points 0.50 meters apart in 4.0 seconds. Another insect travels between fixed points 1.0 meters apart in 2.0 seconds. (a) What is the simplest model for the relationship between the way the insects move? (b) Propose another possible model.

1.5 A metal cube floats in a liquid. What is the simplest model of the cube and liquid? Are there other models?

Section 1.2 Units and Standards of Measurement

1.6 Express 2500 m in kilometers and in centimeters.

1.7 One liter (L) is a volume of 10^3 cm^3. How many cubic centimeters are in 2.5 milliliters?

1.8 How many picoseconds are there in 9.2 microseconds?

1.9 How far will light go in a vacuum in 1.0 nanosecond? (Speed of light = 3.0 × 10^8 m/s)

1.10 What fraction of a kilogram is (a) a milligram and (b) a microgram?

1.11 The black grains in some types of photographic films are about 0.8 μm across. Assume that the grains have a square cross section and that they all lie in a single plane in the film. How many grains are required to completely obscure 1 square centimeter of film?

1.12 The hard-drive memory of a desktop computer used for word processing has a capacity of 2 GByte (GB). (A byte is the amount of memory needed to store one alphabetic character.) A single page of double-spaced text requires about 5 kB of memory and a simple line drawing takes about 15 kB. How many pages of text and drawings can be stored on the hard drive if there is one drawing for every two pages of text material?

1.13 A formula reads $y = \frac{1}{2}at^2$ where y is in meters and t is in seconds. What are the dimensions of a?

1.14• During the total eclipse of the sun, the moon just obscures the sun. The distance from the earth to the moon is 3.84 × 10^8 m and the distance from the earth to the sun is

1.50×10^{11} m. Estimate the relative diameter of the sun and moon.

Section 1.3 Unit Conversions

1.15 What is the height in centimeters of a person who is 5′11″ tall?

1.16 How many minutes make a microcentury?

1.17 What is 40.2 mi expressed in kilometers?

1.18 A cord is a volume of cut wood equal to a stack 4 ft high, 4 ft wide, and 8 ft long. How many cubic meters equals one cord?

1.19 Express 130 km/h in terms of miles per hour.

1.20 (a) Express 75 miles per hour in units of km/h. (b) In units of m/s.

1.21 A store advertises carpet that costs $18.95 per square yard. How much does that carpet cost per square meter?

1.22 As an estimate, you say that your mass in kilograms is numerically equal to one-half your weight in pounds. What is the percent error in this estimate relative to the value computed with the proper conversion factor? (The conversion factor is found in a table in the end papers. The percent error is the ratio of the error to the correct value expressed as a percent.)

1.23 When gasoline sells for $1.069 per gallon, what is the price in dollars per liter? (1 gal = 3.7853 L)

1.24 A student traveling in Hamburg, Germany, finds a radio for sale. The price of the radio is given as 547 marks (DM547). If the exchange rate on that day is $1.00 = DM1.4495, what is the cost of the radio in dollars and cents?

1.25 What is the area in square centimeters of an $8\frac{1}{2}″ \times 14″$ piece of paper?

1.26 The blade on a wood saw has 12 teeth per inch. What is the separation between adjacent teeth in units of mm?

1.27 Wooden slats in a picket fence are spaced 6.0 inches apart, center to center. How many slats are contained in one meter of fence?

1.28 Compute the number of liters in one gallon, given that one gallon is exactly 231 in^3.

1.29 The moon turns on its axis once every $27\frac{1}{3}$ days so that the same face is always toward the earth. Through how many degrees does the moon rotate about its own axis in one hour?

1.30• A clock loses 3.0 s per day. By how many minutes will it be off at the end of one year (365 days)?

1.31• How many revolutions does the second hand of a clock make in three years? Assume no leap years in the interval.

1.32• The AU, the distance from the earth to the sun, is 1.50×10^{11} m, and the speed of light is 3.00×10^8 m/s. (a) How long does it take for light to come from the sun? (b) A light-year is the distance light travels in one year. How far is a light-year in m? (c) How far is a light-year in AU?

1.33• The earth has a mass of 5.98×10^{24} kg and a radius of 6.38×10^6 m. (a) What is the mass per unit volume of the earth in kg/m^3? (b) What is the mass per unit volume of a gold nucleus that has a mass of 3.27×10^{-25} kg and a radius of 6.98×10^{-15} m? (c) What would be the radius of the earth

if its mass were unchanged but it had the same mass per unit volume as the gold nucleus?

Section 1.4 Measurements, Calculations, and Uncertainties

1.34 Calculate the volume of a rectangular cereal box of height 27.5 cm, width 19.2 cm, and depth 5.9 cm. Remember the rule regarding significant figures.

1.35 Calculate the volume of the rectangular board (Fig. 1.13) with height 17.5 mm, width 29.4 cm, and length 115.4 cm. Remember the rule regarding significant figures.

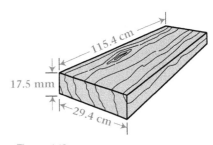

Figure 1.13
Problem 1.35.

1.36 A sphere has a surface area of 0.683 cm^2. What is the volume of the sphere?

1.37 If you measure the sides of a square to be ten centimeters with an accuracy of $\pm$ one percent, what is the area of the square and what is the uncertainty?

1.38 Find the number of seconds in a year and express your answer to two significant places using scientific notation.

1.39 Add the following numbers: 3.57×10^2, 2.43×10^3, and 4.865×10^2.

1.40 A rectangular file cabinet has a height of 133 cm, a width of 37.5 cm, and a length of 72.0 cm. Express its volume in scientific notation. Give your answer in units of cm^3 and m^3.

1.41 The area of the United States is about 9.4×10^6 square kilometers. In early 1996, there were 2.6×10^8 people living in the United States. What was the population density in people per km^2 at that time?

1.42 What error do you make by approximating the length of a football field to be 100 m instead of 100 yards? Give your answer as the percent error, which is defined as
$$\% \text{ error} = \frac{\text{error}}{\text{correct value}} \times 100\%.$$

1.43• A ream of copy paper is 2.00 in. thick. What is the thickness of a single sheet of the paper? Express your answer in m and in mm.

1.44• (a) If the height of the cereal box in Example 1.6 were increased 5%, by what percentage would the volume be increased? (b) If the radius were increased 5%, by what percentage would the volume be increased?

1.45• The speed of an automobile is said to be 103.2784 mi/h on a one-quarter-mile course. How well must the distance be measured for this statement to be accurate?

1.46• The inner edge of a race track is in the form of a rectangle with two semicircular ends on the shorter sides. The rectangle is 87.0 m wide and 137 m long. The race track is 5.25 m wide. What is the difference between the longest path around the track taken by following along the outer edge and the shortest path taken by following along the inner edge?

1.47•• The rectangular floor of a gymnasium has sides of length $x \pm \Delta x$ by $y \pm \Delta y$, where Δx and Δy are the estimated measurement uncertainties and are small compared to x and y. Show by direct computation that the area of the floor and the uncertainty in that area are given by $xy \pm xy\left(\frac{\Delta x}{x} + \frac{\Delta y}{y}\right)$ when very small terms, of order $(\Delta x)^2$, are ignored. (In most cases, this result overestimates the uncertainty in the area, because it does not take into account that the uncertainties in the lengths, Δx and Δy, come from a series of measurements that have a natural spread in their values.)

Section 1.5 Estimates and Order-of-Magnitude Calculations

1.48 How high would the stack reach if you piled one trillion dollar bills in a single stack?

1.49 Estimate the thickness of the pages in this book. Give your result in millimeters.

1.50 How high can you count out loud in half an hour?

1.51 About how many bricks does it take to build a shoulder-high brick wall 100 ft long? Standard bricks are 8 in. long by 2 1/4 in. high and are separated by 3/8 in. of mortar.

1.52 A large power plant burns a 100-car trainload of coal every day. If the coal is 10% ash, estimate the volume of ash generated each year by the power plant.

1.53• Approximately how many gallons of gasoline are used by passenger cars each year in the United States?

1.54•• Approximately what fraction of the area of the continental United States is covered by automobiles?

Additional Problems

1.55 What is the volume in cubic millimeters of a cube 1.00 in. on a side?

1.56 How many square kilometers are there in 10 acres? (1 acre = 43,560 ft^2 or 1/640 mi^2)

1.57 In some countries, the gasoline consumption of an automobile is expressed in liters consumed per 100 km of travel. If an automobile gets 27 miles/gallon, what is its fuel consumption in liters per 100 km? (1 gal = 3.7853 L)

1.58 The equatorial radius of the earth is 6.38×10^6 m. If the time zones are equally spaced, how wide is a time zone at the equator?

1.59 The speed of sound at room temperature is 340 m/s. Express the speed of sound in units of miles per hour.

1.60 The radius of a circle is given as 1.300 cm. When asked to find the area of the circle, a student uses her calculator to arrive at an answer of 5.30998 cm^2. (a) What did she use for the value of π? (b) To how many significant figures was her value of π correct? (c) What is the area, including the correct number of significant figures, when using the best value of π?

1.61• (a) How many milliseconds are there in one minute? (b) How many gigaseconds are there in a century?

1.62• A spherical ball will just pass through a circular hole with an area of 38.2 cm^2. What is the volume of the ball?

1.63• (a) Calculate the height of a cylinder of radius R that has the same volume as a sphere of radius R. (b) Show that the cylinder has a larger surface area than the sphere.

1.64• (a) Calculate the edge length of a cube that has the same volume as a sphere of radius R. (b) Show that the surface area of the cube is greater than the surface area of the sphere.

1.65• Consider a sphere that fits exactly inside a cube. What is the ratio of the volume of the sphere to the volume of the cube?

1.66• (a) By what percentage is the area of a 12.5-cm-radius circle increased if the radius is increased 1.0 cm? (b) By what percentage does the surface area of the side (not the ends) of a 12.5-cm-radius cylinder increase if the radius is increased 1.0 cm?

1.67•• A cylindrical milk shake cup has a measured inside radius of $r \pm \Delta r$ and a height of $h \pm \Delta h$. Show that the volume of the cup is

$$V = \pi r^2 h \pm 2\pi r h \Delta r \pm \pi r^2 \Delta h$$

if very small terms of order $(\Delta r)^2$ are ignored.

2.1 Reference Frames, Coordinate Systems, and Displacement
2.2 Average Speed and Average Velocity
2.3 Graphical Interpretation of Velocity
2.4 Instantaneous Velocity
2.5 Acceleration
2.6 Motion with Constant Acceleration
2.7 Galileo and Free Fall

Back to the Future: Galileo and Experimental Science

Appendix: Solving Quadratic Equations

Motion in One Dimension

This chapter begins our study of motion. You already know a lot about motion from your everyday experience. For example, when you walk briskly along a straight line at a rate of 2 meters per second, you know that in 5 seconds you will travel a distance of 10 meters. We will build on your knowledge to develop methods for accurately describing the positions and motions of objects. To do this we will give precise meaning to terms in everyday use, such as velocity and displacement, and find relationships between them. This study of motion is called kinematics.

The word *kinematics* comes from the Greek word *kinema,* meaning "motion"—the same root from which we get the word *cinema.* **Kinematics** describes the positions and motions of objects in space as a function of time but does not consider the causes of motion. The study of the causes of motion is called **dynamics.** Separating the study of motion into kinematics and dynamics is a great aid in understanding **mechanics,** which is the branch of physics that deals with large-scale

25

(macroscopic) objects. In this chapter, and the next several chapters, we present the basic principles of mechanics.

Kinematics provides the means for describing the motions of such varied things as planets, golf balls, and subatomic particles. Because of its precision and generality, mathematics is the natural language for kinematics. The ideas and techniques of kinematics that you learn here are used throughout the text. The causes and effects of motion are discussed for many seemingly different situations, but the techniques used are the same. The range of these applications runs from gravity to electricity and magnetism to nuclear physics.

We begin our study of kinematics by considering motion in only one dimension. This restriction has the advantage of introducing almost all of the necessary concepts in their simplest form. A mastery of these ideas is necessary for understanding the following chapters, which discuss the motion of objects in two and three dimensions. We start by building on something you already know about motion. ■

2.1 Reference Frames, Coordinate Systems, and Displacement

Your experience teaches you that motion is a relative term. For example, when you ride in a smoothly moving car and toss a ball into the air, the ball goes up and comes back down to your hand. You see only an up-and-down motion (Fig. 2.1a). However, a person standing beside the moving car sees the ball move forward with the car, as well as up-and-down (Fig. 2.1b). Only one thing actually happens, yet different observers see different motions. We can avoid confusion if we carefully specify the location and motion of each observer. We say that the different observers are in different reference frames. A **reference frame** is a physical entity, such as the ground, a room, or a moving car, to which we refer the position and motion of objects.

To adequately describe motion, we must be able to say where something is located within a given reference frame. For example, we can locate the ball in the car by saying it is 0.75 m from the left door, 0.53 m above the floor, and 0.23 m in front of the seat. This choice is not a particularly convenient reference system. However, it does remind us of something: When we say space is three-dimensional, we mean that we need three numbers to completely locate the

Figure 2.1

(a) Motion of a ball thrown vertically by a passenger in a car moving along a straight line at a constant rate, as seen by an observer in the car. The ball's motion appears the same as if the car were not moving. (b) Motion of a ball thrown vertically by a passenger in the moving car, as seen by an outside observer at rest relative to the road. Now the ball has a forward motion equal to that of the car.

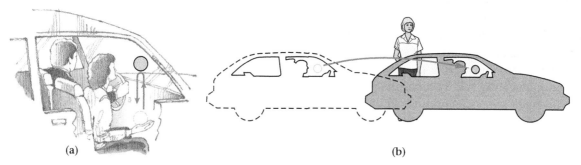

(a)   (b)

position of an object or point. A system for assigning these three numbers, or co-ordinates, to the location of a point in a reference frame is called a **coordinate system.** Most frequently, we will use a *Cartesian (x, y, z)* coordinate system (Fig. 2.2). The Cartesian coordinates in space are often called rectangular coordinates because the axes that define them meet at right angles. Figure 2.3 depicts several reference frames with the coordinate axes shown explicitly. In this chapter, we will only consider motion in one dimension, and so we will align the axis system so that the motion is along the direction of one of the axes, ordinarily the *x* axis.

Because a coordinate system is a mathematical construction, you are free to choose the system that you want, orient it however you wish, and place its origin wherever you prefer. The physical locations of the two people shown in Fig. 2.4, for instance, do not depend on where you place the origin of the coordinate system. However, their positions as *measured* within a coordinate system do depend on where the origin is placed. Two points are worth noting. First, when faced with a physical problem, try to place the origin of the coordinates in a position that will make the problem as easy to solve as possible. Second, having chosen a coordinate system for working the problem, do not change it during the solution.

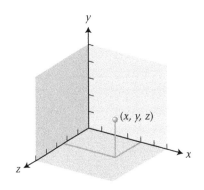

Figure 2.2
A Cartesian coordinate system. The system shown is right-handed.

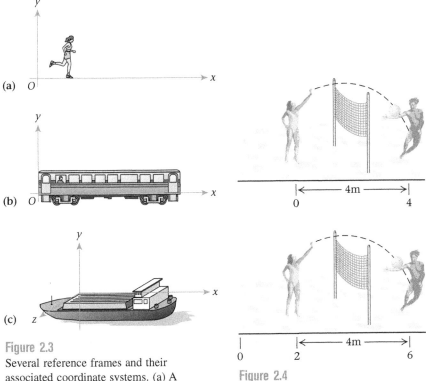

Figure 2.3
Several reference frames and their associated coordinate systems. (a) A runner moves in the reference frame of the earth. (b) A passenger walks in the reference frame of a moving railroad car. (c) A reference frame associated with a floating barge.

Figure 2.4
The location of the two people and, hence, the distance between them does not depend on the location of the origin of the coordinate system used to make the measurements.

$\Delta x = x_{Final} - x_{initial}$
Displacement frum the origin.
Displacement: The change in position, including change of sign.
- motion to the right is positive while motion to the left is neg.

To avoid mistakes later on, you need to be sure of the difference between ~~re~~ frames and coordinate systems. Although the terms have been defined ~~ally,~~ it is helpful to compare the two ideas. ~~The reference frame is the~~ ~~roundings from which the changes in positions of other objects can be~~ ~~l.~~ Within such a frame, the coordinate system permits the measurement ~~ositions.~~

~~ne~~ dimension, the position of an object is given by saying how far it is ~~origin~~ of the coordinate system. The change in position, including the ~~ie change,~~ is called the **displacement.** When something moves from one ~~to another,~~ we say it undergoes a displacement. Thus, the position of an ~~also~~ referred to as its displacement from the origin. Suppose an object ~~ong~~ a line from an initial position x_i to a final position x_f, then the net ~~position~~ (~~its displacement~~) is given by

$$\Delta x = x_f - x_i. \tag{2.1}$$

~~bol~~ Δ (the Greek capital letter delta) is used to indicate a change in ~~g~~—in this case, the position x. The symbol Δx (delta ex) represents one ~~the~~ change in x. Three lines instead of two in an equals sign mean that ~~ity~~ on the left is defined by that equation.

Example 2.1

(a) What is the displacement of the black chess piece if it is moved to the right all the way across the board as shown in Fig. 2.5? (b) What would be the displacement of the white chess piece if it were moved to the left all the way across the board?

Strategy The chessboard can be used as our frame of reference. A coordinate system may be chosen with its x axis aligned parallel to the edge of the board. The solution of the problem can then be found directly from the definition of displacement given in Eq. (2.1). However, we must be careful to specify the initial and final positions correctly in this and all other cases.

Solution (a) We see from Fig. 2.5 that the initial position of the black chess piece is $x_i = 0.00$ m and its final position is $x_f = 0.30$ m, so that we have

$$\Delta x = x_f - x_i = 0.30 \text{ m} - 0.00 \text{ m} = 0.30 \text{ m}.$$

(b) In the case of the white chess piece, using the same coordinate system, we find the initial position of that piece is $x_i = 0.30$ m and the final position is $x_f = 0.00$ m, so that

$$\Delta x = x_f - x_i = 0.00 \text{ m} - 0.30 \text{ m} = -0.30 \text{ m}.$$

Discussion The displacements of the two pieces are not the same because one piece moved to the right while the other one moved to the left. With the coordinate system that we chose, motion to the right is positive while motion to the left is negative. Even though both pieces are moved through the same distance, their displacements are different. Be careful to distinguish between distance and displacement. Also notice that the position of the origin of coordinates does not affect the value or sign of the displacement. You should show this for

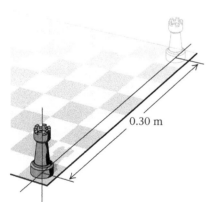

0.30 m

Figure 2.5
Chess pieces are moved on a chessboard. The chessboard provides the frame of reference. A coordinate system is fixed relative to the chessboard with its x axis parallel to the edge of the board as shown. The origin of the coordinate system is chosen to lie under the center of the black chess piece.

yourself by repeating this example with the origin of the coordinates located at some other position along the edge of the chessboard.

Average speed =
$$\frac{\text{total distance traveled}}{\text{time interval of travel}}$$
$$= \frac{s}{t}$$

n you turn around and
again and walk 37 m in the
from your starting point?

corresponding to a dis-
ns of that segment. The to-
ndividual displacements.

irst segment is a displace-
ond segment is −25 m and
otal displacement is

m = 57 m.

splacement is just the alge-
final position is 57 m

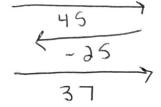

2.2 Average Speed and Average Velocity

You are already familiar with the concept of speed and know that the speed of an object is measured in units such as miles per hour, kilometers per hour, or meters per second. The speed is the ratio of the distance traveled to the time required for the travel. We define the **average speed** as the total distance, s, traveled during a particular time divided by that time interval, t:

$$\text{average speed} \equiv \frac{\text{total distance traveled}}{\text{time interval for travel}} = \frac{s}{t}. \tag{2.2}$$

It is important to recognize that this definition refers to neither the size nor shape nor mass nor any other property of the moving body, nor to how the body is influenced by its surroundings. The definition deals only with the motion itself. In the same way, other definitions in kinematics are restricted to properties of the motion only. If the average speed is the same for all parts of a trip, then the speed is constant.

Example 2.3

On a clear October day, two students take a three-hour automobile trip to enjoy the fall foliage. In the first two hours, they travel 100 km at a constant speed. In the third hour they travel another 80 km, at a different constant speed. What is the average speed for each segment and for the entire trip?

Strategy For each segment we can find the average speed as the distance traveled in that segment divided by the elapsed time. To find the average speed for the whole trip, we must find the total distance and divide it by the total elapsed time.

Solution For the first portion of the trip, the average speed is:

$$\text{average speed} = \frac{\text{distance traveled}}{\text{time elapsed}}$$

$$\text{average speed (1)} = \frac{100 \text{ km}}{2 \text{ h}} = 50 \text{ km/h}.$$

For the second portion of the trip, the average speed is given by the same formula but now with a distance of 80 km and a time of 1 h:

$$\text{average speed (2)} = \frac{80 \text{ km}}{1 \text{ h}} = 80 \text{ km/h}.$$

For the entire trip, the average speed is the *total* distance divided by the *total* time interval:

$$\text{average speed (total)} = \frac{180 \text{ km}}{3 \text{ h}} = 60 \text{ km/h}.$$

Discussion Note that the average speed for the entire trip, in this case 60 km/h, is *not,* in general, the same as the direct average of the individual speeds, which in this case is 65 km/h.

As noted before, in this chapter we limit our study to motion along a line or in one dimension. This limitation makes our definition of speed and related concepts easier to understand. In reality, however, motion is usually not restricted to one dimension, and we must take account of the direction as well as the speed of an object's motion. The name for the quantity that describes both the direction and the speed of motion is **velocity.** Even though we are considering only one-dimensional motion in this chapter, we must still take account of direction (for example, positive versus negative, or east versus west), so we will use the term *velocity.* We will consider two- and three-dimensional motion in the later chapters.

Suppose a car is located at point x_1 at a time t_1, and at another point x_2 at a later time t_2 (Fig. 2.6). Then the car's **average velocity** $\overline{v}$ over the time interval is

$$\overline{v} = \frac{\text{final position} - \text{initial position}}{\text{final time} - \text{initial time}} = \frac{x_2 - x_1}{t_2 - t_1}. \qquad (2.3)$$

Equation (2.3) can be put in words: The average velocity is the displacement divided by the time elapsed during that displacement. In general, a bar over a symbol (as in $\overline{v}$) indicates the average value of that quantity, in this case the average velocity. Note that the average velocity can be either positive or negative. The

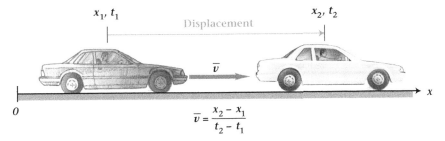

$$\overline{v} = \frac{x_2 - x_1}{t_2 - t_1}$$

Figure 2.6
When the car moves from point x_1 to point x_2, its displacement is given by $x_2 - x_1$. The time interval from t_1 to t_2 is $t_2 - t_1$.

difference between speed and velocity is more than just an algebraic sign; it involves the difference between the total distance traveled (for speed) and the net change in position (for velocity). These two quantities are not necessarily the same. For example, a trip of 30 km away and 30 km back gives a total distance traveled of 60 km, but a net change in position (displacement) of zero.

In the preceding paragraphs, we used the terms *initial position* and *final position,* measuring them from the zero point of our reference system of coordinates. So far we have used a coordinate system that is just the x or y axis with the origin (zero) placed at some convenient point. Most often we have chosen the zero to be the starting point for the motion described. Notice that we can have both positive and negative positions measured from the origin. For example, in one dimension, if we define positions measured to the right of the origin to be positive, then positions measured to the left of the origin are negative. In this case, a positive velocity indicates motion to the right; a negative velocity indicates motion to the left.

The same argument may be made for time, the other basic quantity needed for kinematics. We often say that we "start the clock running" at the moment a process starts or when some particular event happens. In that case we choose the initial time to be zero. Times before that would be negative and all times after the beginning would be positive.

Example 2.4

(a) What is the average velocity of a helicopter: (i) If it takes off from its pad at the hospital and travels 150 km due east in one hour (Fig. 2.7a)? (ii) If, instead, it travels 150 km due west from the hospital in one hour? (iii) If it starts from a location 20 km east of the hospital, travels to a point 50 km due east, then turns around and travels to a spot 80 km west of the hospital in one hour? (b) What would the average speed be in each of these cases?

Strategy (a)   From the statement of the problem, we see that all of the motion is confined to a straight line along the east-west direction. We begin by making a simple diagram to help visualize the situation (Fig. 2.7b). After making the drawing, we must fix the coordinate origin and choose which direction is positive. Here we choose the origin to be at the hospital and choose east to be the

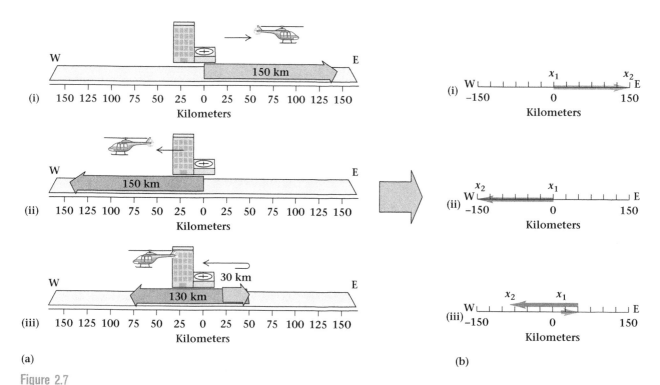

Figure 2.7
Example 2.4: (a) Starting at hospital helicopter pad, (i) the helicopter flies 150 km due east and (ii) the helicopter flies 150 km due west. (iii) Starting 20 km east of the hospital, the helicopter flies first to a position 50 km east of the hospital and then to a position 80 km west of the hospital. (b) Simplified drawing for analysis. We have chosen east as positive and marked the positions of x_1 and x_2 for all three situations.

positive direction and west to be negative. To find the average velocity in each case, we use

$$\bar{v} = \frac{\text{final position} - \text{initial position}}{\text{final time} - \text{initial time}} = \frac{x_2 - x_1}{t_2 - t_1}.$$

Notice that the duration given by the difference between initial and final times is the elapsed time:

$$\bar{v} = \frac{\text{final position} - \text{initial position}}{\text{time elapsed}}.$$

Solution (a) So, for the three cases,

$$(i)\ \bar{v} = \frac{150\ \text{km} - 0\ \text{km}}{1\ \text{h}} = +150\ \text{km/h}.$$

$$(ii)\ \bar{v} = \frac{-150\ \text{km} - 0\ \text{km}}{1\ \text{h}} = -150\ \text{km/h}.$$

$$(iii)\ \bar{v} = \frac{-80\ \text{km} - 20\ \text{km}}{1\ \text{h}} = -100\ \text{km/h}.$$

Strategy (b) Recalling that speed is not the same as velocity and depends on the total distance traveled, we write

$$\text{average speed} = \frac{\text{distance traveled}}{\text{time elapsed}}.$$

Solution (b) For the first two cases,

$$\text{(i) average speed} = \frac{150 \text{ km}}{1 \text{ h}} = 150 \text{ km/h}.$$

$$\text{(ii) average speed} = \frac{150 \text{ km}}{1 \text{ h}} = 150 \text{ km/h}.$$

For the third case, the distance traveled is 30 km east plus 130 km west, for a total distance of 160 km. Thus,

$$\text{(iii) average speed} = \frac{160 \text{ km}}{1 \text{ h}} = 160 \text{ km/h}.$$

Discussion Notice that the average speed is always a positive number. In situation (iii) the magnitude of the displacement and the total distance traveled are not the same. Consequently the numerical value of the average speed is not the same as that of the average velocity.

2.3 Graphical Interpretation of Velocity

We now supplement our algebraic definition of velocity in Eq. (2.3) with a graphical interpretation of velocity. Consider two people, one running and one walking with constant velocity (Fig. 2.8). We plot the elapsed time along the horizontal axis, or **abscissa,** and the velocity along the vertical axis, or **ordinate.** (It is conventional to plot the independent variable along the abscissa and the dependent variable along the ordinate, as we have done here.) The point on the graph that represents the velocity at any time traces out a smooth line as time goes by. In this case, the horizontal line v_A represents the particular constant velocity of the runner. A slower-moving person, but one with constant velocity also, gives rise to the horizontal line v_B.

In Fig. 2.9, we have plotted the positions of the people (their displacement from the origin) against the elapsed time. Our definitions of both velocity and speed show that the displacement at constant velocity or speed is directly proportional to the time. When one variable is directly proportional to the other, as *displacement* is to *time* in this example, a straight line results. For this reason, such relationships are called *linear.* Plotting displacement against time for constant velocity, therefore, will result in a straight line such as A in Fig. 2.9, where we have started at zero displacement at $t = 0$. A graph due to a smaller constant velocity gives rise to another straight line, such as the line B.

In Fig. 2.10 we have plotted displacement against time for a case in which the velocity is not constant. Over the portion of the trip between times t_1 and t_2, the line is straight and the velocity is constant. Between times t_2 and t_3, the velocity remains the same and is still constant. Between times t_4 and t_5, the velocity is constant, but is not the same as between times t_1 and t_2 or between t_2 and t_3. The velocity is not constant for the time interval between t_3 and t_4, nor is it constant overall between times t_1 and t_5. However, we can use Eq. (2.3) to define the average velocity for the time interval t_3 to t_4, t_1 to t_5, or any other interval.

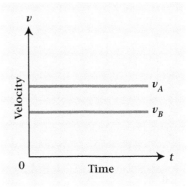

Figure 2.8
Velocity graphed against time for two people moving with different constant velocities. Person A is moving faster than B.

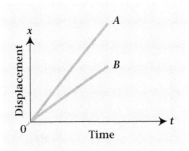

Figure 2.9
Displacement graphed against time for two people moving at different constant velocities. Both people were at zero displacement when the time was zero.

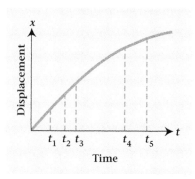

Figure 2.10
Displacement graphed against time for varying velocity.

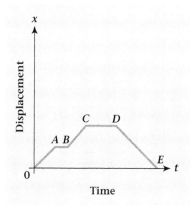

Figure 2.11
Example 2.5: Displacement against time for a drive from home to the store and back.

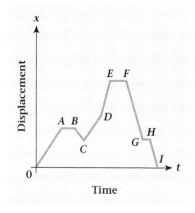

Figure 2.12
Example 2.6: Graph of the displacement against time for a child walking along a path.

▼ Example 2.5

A woman drives her car to the store that is located straight down the street from her home. Halfway there she pauses for a traffic light, then continues to the store. After making her purchase she returns directly home, this time catching the green light so that she doesn't have to stop for the traffic light. Make a graph of the displacement of her car from home against time.

Strategy We can make a simple graph by considering her motion to be one-dimensional and by treating the velocity in each segment to be constant. Then the graph will consist of only straight lines.

Solution Let the origin of the graph be at her home. The first segment (Fig. 2.11) is a straight line showing increasing displacement with increasing time. At point A she stops for the traffic light, so the displacement is constant with time until point B where she resumes moving toward the store. At C she stops upon reaching the store. After completing her shopping (D), she drives toward her home (E); thus the displacement decreases as the time increases until she is again at home.

▼ Example 2.6

The movement of a child walking along a straight path is represented by the graph of displacement against time shown in Fig. 2.12. Describe the motion of the child in words.

Strategy We can interpret the graph if we break it into sections with simple features and analyze each section separately.

Solution The child starts from the origin and walks with constant velocity to point A where she stops. After a short time (B), she begins walking back toward the origin. At C she reverses and starts walking away again. From D to E she walks faster or perhaps runs, stopping at E for a while. Then at the time corresponding to point F, she begins walking back toward home (the origin) until at the point labeled G she stops. At the time corresponding to H, she resumes her return reaching home (I).

To use our graphical method further, we need a more formal definition for the slope of a line. Suppose an object moves with constant velocity so that its position-time graph looks like Fig. 2.13. If the object was at point x_1 at time t_1, and at another point x_2 at a later time t_2, then the net change in position is given by $\Delta x = x_2 - x_1$. Similarly, the change in time is given as Δt (delta tee) $= t_2 - t_1$. The average velocity of the object during the time interval from t_1 to t_2 is then written

$$\overline{v} = \frac{x_2 - x_1}{t_2 - t_1} = \frac{\Delta x}{\Delta t}.$$

As we said earlier, the change in position $\Delta x = x_2 - x_1$ is the displacement of the moving object, including the magnitude of the change and its direction.

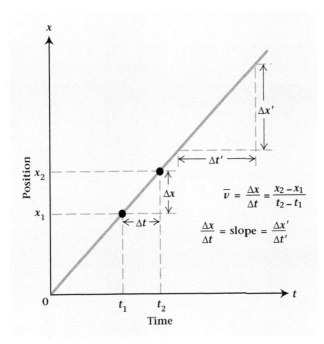

Figure 2.13
The velocity is the slope of the position-time curve. For a straight line, the slope $\Delta x/\Delta t$ is constant and is independent of the particular choice of time interval. This corresponds to constant velocity.

Notice that the position of an object is the same as its displacement from the origin, or zero, of the coordinate system.

An alternative way of defining velocity is to say that velocity is the slope of the position-time curve. The **slope of a line** is defined to be the ratio of the change in the line's ordinate to the corresponding change in the abscissa. For the case of constant velocity (Fig. 2.13), the position-time curve is a straight line and the slope is $\Delta x/\Delta t$. Thus, we can determine the velocity from the slope of the line. Since the distance traveled is proportional to the time, we get the same numerical value for this ratio, $\Delta x/\Delta t$, no matter what interval of time we choose to consider. Thus, in Fig. 2.13 the ratio $\Delta x/\Delta t$ is equal to the ratio $\Delta x'/\Delta t'$. This behavior is characteristic of constant velocity. Notice that the slope, and therefore the velocity, has the dimensions of length/time.

Example 2.7

Find the velocities corresponding to the displacement-time graphs in Fig. 2.14. Then list them in decreasing order starting with the largest velocity.

Strategy We can find the magnitude and sign of the velocity for each distance-time graph by finding the slope of the line using the techniques illustrated in Fig. 2.13.

Solution For the line shown in (a), the velocity is the rise over the run, which is $v = \dfrac{\Delta x}{\Delta t} = \dfrac{8 \text{ m} - 0 \text{ m}}{4 \text{ s} - 0 \text{ s}} = 2 \text{ m/s}.$

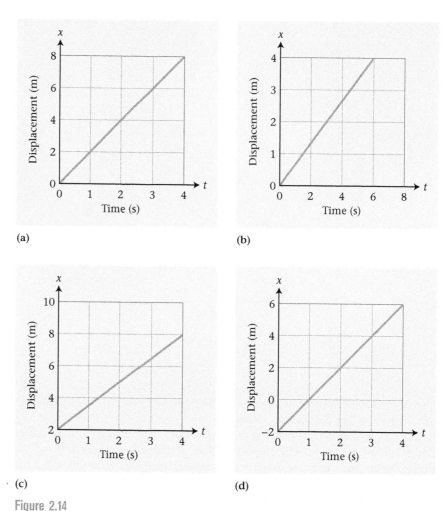

Figure 2.14

Example 2.7: Four graphs of displacement versus time.

For (b) the velocity is $v = \dfrac{\Delta x}{\Delta t} = \dfrac{4 \text{ m} - 0 \text{ m}}{6 \text{ s} - 0 \text{ s}} = \dfrac{2}{3}$ m/s.

For (c) the velocity is $v = \dfrac{\Delta x}{\Delta t} = \dfrac{8 \text{ m} - 2 \text{ m}}{4 \text{ s} - 0 \text{ s}} = 1.5$ m/s.

For (d) the velocity is $v = \dfrac{\Delta x}{\Delta t} = \dfrac{6 \text{ m} - (-2 \text{ m})}{4 \text{ s} - 0 \text{ s}} = 2$ m/s.

To list them in decreasing order, we have (a) and (d) are equal and are the largest, (c) is next, and then (b) is the smallest.

2.4 Instantaneous Velocity

Suppose that a runner's velocity is not constant, but changes as illustrated in the displacement-time graph in Fig. 2.15. Now that the line is curved rather than straight, how do we find the velocity at a particular instant of time? To determine

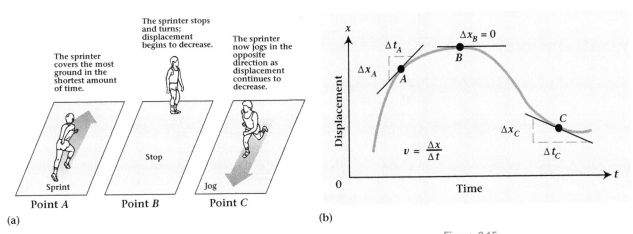

(a)

(b)

Figure 2.15
The slope of a curved line is determined at any point by the slope of the line tangent to the curve at that point. The steepness of the slope corresponds to the magnitude of the velocity. Notice that since Δx_C is negative, the slope at point C is negative, corresponding to velocity in a negative direction (back toward the starting point).

the velocity at point A, for instance, we draw a tangent to the curve at that point. Then the slope of that tangent, which is a straight line, is determined as previously described; it is given by $v_A = \Delta x_A/\Delta t_A$. The subscripts refer to the line tangent to the curve at point A. The velocity measured at any given moment (for example, at point A) is called the **instantaneous velocity.**

At the point of contact, the tangent line is parallel to the displacement-time curve. The average velocity over the time interval Δt that contains A approaches the value of the instantaneous velocity as the interval Δt becomes smaller (Fig. 2.16). We can therefore define the instantaneous velocity as the limiting value of $\Delta x/\Delta t$ as Δt becomes vanishingly small. In symbols, the idea is

$$v = \lim_{\Delta t \to 0} \frac{\Delta x}{\Delta t}. \tag{2.4}$$

The symbol $\lim_{\Delta t \to 0}$ tells us to evaluate the ratio $\Delta x/\Delta t$ in the limiting case of Δt approaching zero. Note that we don't simply set $\Delta t = 0$; rather, we examine the ratio $\Delta x/\Delta t$ as both Δx and Δt get smaller. This ratio goes to a definite value as Δt goes to zero.

The slopes at other points, such as B and C in Fig. 2.15, are determined in the same way. Notice that in the immediate neighborhood of point C the dis-

Figure 2.16
The instantaneous value of the velocity is obtained from the average value as the interval Δt becomes vanishingly small.

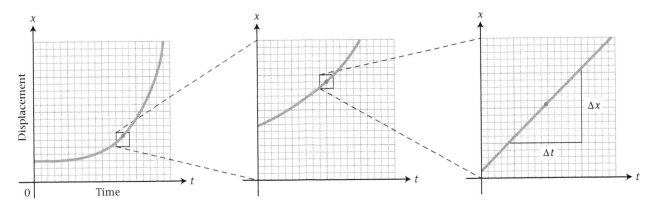

placement from the starting point is decreasing as time increases. Therefore, Δx_C is negative. The slope and the instantaneous velocity are both negative at point C.

The magnitude of the instantaneous velocity is the **speed**; it has no direction and is always taken as positive. Thus, if one car travels east at 60 km/h and another travels west at 60 km/h, both have the same speed but different velocities because they are traveling in different directions. This usage of the term *speed* is different from the *average speed,* defined in Section 2.2 as the total distance traveled divided by the elapsed time. Note that the average speed is not the magnitude of the average velocity. An object that oscillates back and forth through the origin, like the pendulum of the clock, has an average velocity of zero because it spends equal times with equal positive and negative velocities. But its average speed is not zero.

Example 2.8

Estimate the relative size and sign of the velocity corresponding to the displacement-time graph shown in Fig. 2.17(a). Then make a sketch of the velocity-time graph.

Strategy We can estimate the relative size of the velocity at the points marked from the slope of the curve at each point.

Solution The curve seems to be starting at point A with zero slope. At point B the slope is the most negative and at C it is zero again. Point D has a positive slope and point E has an even greater slope. The corresponding graph of velocity versus time should look like Fig. 2.17(b)

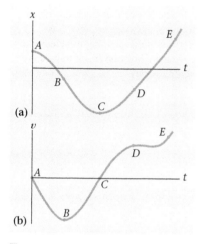

Figure 2.17
Example 2.8: (a) Graph of displacement versus time. (b) Graph of velocity versus time corresponding to the slope of (a).

Example 2.9

At the start of a 100-m race, a sprinter is poised for action. When the starter fires the gun, the sprinter pushes off the starting block and quickly reaches maximum velocity. The graph in Fig. 2.18 shows a sprinter's displacement as a function of the time elapsed after the starting signal. Determine the instantaneous velocity of the sprinter at 0.50 s, 1.50 s, and 2.50 s.

Solution The graph in Fig. 2.18 shows tangent lines drawn through the points corresponding to $t = 0.50$ s, 1.50 s, and 2.50 s. Therefore, Δt and Δx can be read directly from the graph.

At $t = 0.50$ s we have

$$v = \frac{\Delta x}{\Delta t} = \frac{2.0 \text{ m}}{0.50 \text{ s}} = 4.0 \text{ m/s}.$$

At $t = 1.50$ s,

$$v = \frac{4.0 \text{ m}}{0.50 \text{ s}} = 8.0 \text{ m/s}.$$

At $t = 2.50$ s,

$$v = \frac{4.8 \text{ m}}{0.50 \text{ s}} = 9.6 \text{ m/s}.$$

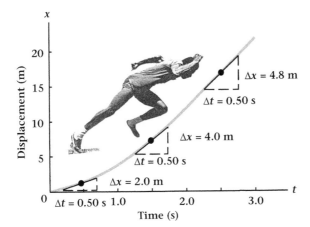

Figure 2.18
Example 2.9: Graph of displacement versus time for a sprinter. The slope of the curve at any time is measured from the line tangent to the curve at that time. The tangents shown correspond to times of 0.50 s, 1.50 s, and 2.50 s.

Discussion In this example, we see that the velocity changes with time. The velocity increases rapidly as the runner springs from the starting block but begins to level off as he approaches maximum velocity.

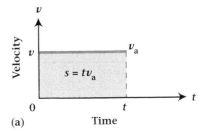

(a)

In addition to being used for specific examples, graphical techniques can also help us obtain general relationships between variables. Let us consider one example of such a procedure. The example is specific to kinematics, but we will use the idea and technique many times again.

Figure 2.19(a and b) shows velocity-time graphs for an object moving at constant velocity. The length of a vertical line from the horizontal axis to the line v_a (or v_b) is equal to the velocity. The line v_a is higher than the line v_b, indicating a greater velocity for the object represented in Fig. 2.19(a). Note that the area of the rectangle under the line v is given by tv, where t is the elapsed time and v is the velocity. However, this quantity is also the net distance traveled, s, which is the displacement. We can extend this observation to state a general principle: *The area under any velocity-time curve between two times is equivalent to the displacement during that time interval.*

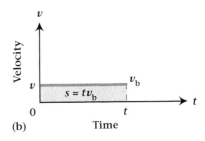

(b)

To see that this last statement is true, consider the velocity-time graph of Fig. 2.19(c), for which the velocity is not constant. We can divide the total time into small time intervals of duration Δt. Over each of these intervals, we may approximate the velocity by a constant value, given by the average of the initial and final velocities for the interval. Then for each interval, we have, as before, a rectangle whose area is equivalent to the displacement during that interval. The total displacement is then represented by the sum of all the areas of these rectangular strips—that is, the total area under the velocity-time curve. Thus

$$\text{total displacement} = \bar{v}_1 \Delta t_1 + \bar{v}_2 \Delta t_2 + \bar{v}_3 \Delta t_3 + \cdots,$$

where $\bar{v}_1$ is the average velocity during the first interval, $\bar{v}_2$ is the average velocity during the second interval, and so on.

If the intervals Δt are too long, or if the velocity changes too much during each interval, this approximation is unsatisfactory because we assume that the velocity is constant for each time interval Δt. However, if we make the intervals smaller and smaller, this approximation becomes more accurate. Also, as the

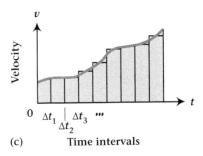

(c)

Figure 2.19
Graphs of velocity versus time for three moving objects: (a), and (b) Constant velocity; (c) Time-varying velocity. The area under the velocity curve is equivalent to the displacement of the object during the time interval.

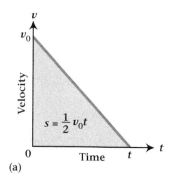

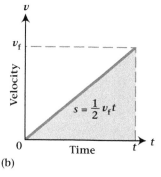

Figure 2.20
Calculating displacement from velocity-time graphs. (a) Velocity decreasing uniformly with time. (b) Velocity increasing uniformly with time.

intervals become smaller, more of them fit into a given range. The techniques of calculus, but not algebra, allow us to make the intervals as small as we want— even approaching zero time duration—and still keep track of the areas of the tremendous number of strips. We will not use calculus techniques in this text, but we will make use of two basic concepts from calculus: the meaning of the slope of a curve and that of the area under a curve.

Since the area under the velocity-time curve always represents the displacement of the moving body, we can deal with cases of nonuniform velocity. Figure 2.20(a) represents a case in which the velocity decreases from some initial value, v_0, to zero in a linear way. This graph might represent the slowing down and stopping of a car when you apply the brakes. The area under the curve, and therefore the distance traveled, is easily determined by noting that the required area is that of a right triangle. The area of the triangle is one-half the height times the base, so distance traveled $= \frac{1}{2}v_0 t$.

Instead of starting with a car in motion and smoothly bringing it to rest, we could consider a car initially at rest and smoothly increase its velocity to some final value v_f (Fig. 2.20b). The distance traveled during the time the velocity is increasing is given by $s = \frac{1}{2}v_f t$.

Example 2.10

Traveling on the German Autobahn in your BMW at a speed of 166 km/h, you smoothly brake to a halt in 12 s. How far do you travel after first applying the brakes?

Solution Using the result from Fig. 2.20(a), we have

$$s = \tfrac{1}{2}v_0 t = \tfrac{1}{2}(166 \text{ km/h})(12 \text{ s})$$

$$s = \frac{1}{2}\left(\frac{166 \text{ km} \times 12 \text{ s}}{\text{h}}\right)\left(\frac{1 \text{ h}}{60 \text{ min}}\right)\left(\frac{1 \text{ min}}{60 \text{ s}}\right)$$

$$s = 0.277 \text{ km}.$$

Because the time is known to only two significant figures, we round the answer to

$$s = 0.28 \text{ km}.$$

2.5   Acceleration

In Section 2.2 we defined the average velocity of an object as its change in position divided by the time elapsed, $\bar{v} = \Delta x/\Delta t$. This tells us how the object's position changes with time. From our discussion in the last section, it is reasonable to define a quantity that indicates how the object's velocity changes with time. We define the **average acceleration,** $\bar{a}$, as the change in velocity divided by the time required for the change. The average acceleration can be written as

$$\bar{a} \equiv \frac{v_2 - v_1}{t_2 - t_1} = \frac{\Delta v}{\Delta t}. \tag{2.5}$$

The dimensions of acceleration are velocity divided by time, which is the same as length divided by time squared. In the SI system, the unit of acceleration is m/s^2. Acceleration, like velocity, has a direction as well as a magnitude.

The following two examples illustrate the meaning of average acceleration and the use of Eq. (2.5).

Example 2.11

A bicyclist starts from rest and increases his velocity at a constant rate until she reaches a speed of 4.0 m/s in 5.0 s (Fig. 2.21). What is his average acceleration?

Strategy We can use the definition, Eq. (2.5), to find the acceleration because the statement of the problem gives us the initial and final velocities and the time interval. Since the bicycle starts from rest, the initial velocity is 0. The final velocity is 4.0 m/s and the time interval is 5.0 s.

Solution The correct relationship is

$$a = \frac{v_2 - v_1}{t}.$$

Inserting the numerical values gives

$$a = \frac{4.0 \text{ m/s} - 0 \text{ m/s}}{5.0 \text{ s}} = 0.80 \frac{\text{m/s}}{\text{s}},$$

or

$$a = 0.80 \text{ m/s}^2.$$

Figure 2.21
Example 2.11: A bicyclist accelerating from rest at a constant rate reaches a speed of 4.0 m/s in 5.0 s.

Discussion Notice that the units of acceleration are m/s². We have a new unit that is derived from the previously defined base units for length and time.

Example 2.12

A motorcyclist starts from rest and accelerates in one direction with a constant acceleration of 4.0 m/s² for 12 s. What is the rider's velocity at the end of the 12 s?

Strategy Here we are given a constant acceleration and a time interval and need to find the change in velocity. We can rewrite Eq. (2.5) in the form

$$v_2 = \bar{a}(t_2 - t_1) + v_1,$$

which will give us the final velocity (v_2) in terms of the known quantities.

Solution Inserting the values of $\bar{a} = 4.0$ m/s², $t_2 - t_1 = 12$ s, and $v_1 = 0$ into this equation gives

$$v_2 = 4.0 \text{ m/s}^2 \times 12 \text{ s} + 0 = 48 \text{ m/s}.$$

Discussion Again notice the units. In working problems you should always insert the units and perform the algebraic operations on them as well as on the numbers. After all, a number without any units is just a number. But if it represents a physical quantity, it should be accompanied by the appropriate units. Furthermore, if the units have the correct form, you probably have the correct answer. For example, if you get units of m/s for velocity, you have probably worked the problem correctly, but if you get units of m/s², then you know that something has gone amiss.

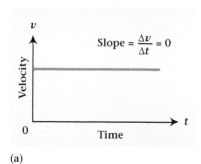

(a)

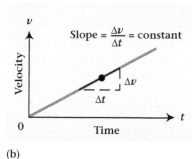

(b)

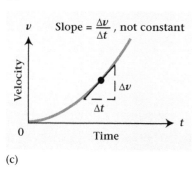

(c)

Figure 2.22
Acceleration is the slope of the curve of velocity versus time. (a) Zero acceleration. (b) Constant nonzero acceleration. (c) Variable acceleration.

A graphical approach offers further insight into the relationships between acceleration, velocity, time, and distance. From the definition of average acceleration in Eq. (2.5), we see that acceleration may also be described as the slope of the curve of velocity versus time. In Fig. 2.22(a), the horizontal line (zero slope) corresponds to an object moving with constant velocity and therefore zero acceleration. In Fig. 2.22(b), the slope of the line is everywhere the same, indicating that the velocity is increasing at a constant rate. Therefore, the acceleration is positive and constant. But suppose the velocity changes as shown in Fig. 2.22(c). How can we determine the acceleration at any particular instant of time? We can define the **instantaneous acceleration** in a manner similar to the way we defined the instantaneous velocity. The instantaneous acceleration is the limiting value of $\Delta v/\Delta t$ as the time interval Δt becomes vanishingly small. In symbols, the instantaneous acceleration is

$$a = \lim_{\Delta t \to 0} \frac{\Delta v}{\Delta t}. \tag{2.6}$$

In the limit that the time interval Δt approaches zero, the ratio $\Delta v/\Delta t$ becomes the value of the instantaneous acceleration. Recall that the slope of a curved line at any point is determined by the line tangent to the curve at that point. Thus, the slope of a velocity-time curve at any point of time equals the instantaneous acceleration at that point.

Example 2.13

A sprinter, at rest ($v = 0$) at the start of a race, quickly accelerates to maximum velocity (Fig. 2.23). Determine the instantaneous acceleration of the sprinter at 0.50 s, 1.50 s, and 2.50 s. Notice that the data here are related to those in Example 2.9.

Solution The results can be read directly from the graph of Fig. 2.23, where we have drawn the tangent lines through the points corresponding to $t = 0.50$ s, 1.50 s, and 2.50 s.

At $t = 0.50$ s we have

$$a = \frac{\Delta v}{\Delta t} = \frac{3.0 \text{ m/s}}{0.50 \text{ s}} = 6.0 \text{ m/s}^2.$$

At $t = 1.50$ s we have

$$a = \frac{1.25 \text{ m/s}}{0.50 \text{ s}} = 2.5 \text{ m/s}^2.$$

At $t = 2.50$ s we have

$$a = \frac{0.40 \text{ m/s}}{0.50 \text{ s}} = 0.80 \text{ m/s}^2.$$

Discussion As expected, we find that the acceleration decreases with time as the sprinter approaches maximum velocity (see the inset). Compare this

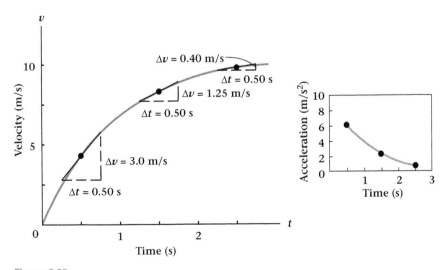

Figure 2.23
Example 2.13: Graph of the velocity of a sprinter versus time.

example with Example 2.9 and Fig. 2.18. Be sure you clearly understand how the shapes of these two curves are related.

2.6 Motion with Constant Acceleration

Many situations occur in which an object's acceleration is constant. The most common case is the motion of a freely falling object when air resistance is negligible. Because of the numerous motions that can be described by constant acceleration, we will assume constant acceleration for the remainder of this chapter. This restriction to constant acceleration allows us to develop some simple relationships among four kinematic quantities—displacement, velocity, acceleration, and time.

First, let us find an expression for the average velocity of an object moving with constant acceleration. Figure 2.24 shows a velocity-time graph of this situation. The velocity is increasing from v_1 to v_2, as discussed in Section 2.4. The displacement is the total area under the velocity-time curve and is equal to the sum of the areas of rectangle $ABCD$ and triangle BCE. The average velocity is then

$$\overline{v} = \frac{\text{displacement}}{\text{time elapsed}} = \frac{\text{area of } ABCD + \text{area of } BCE}{\Delta t}$$

$$\overline{v} = \frac{v_1 \Delta t + \frac{1}{2}(v_2 - v_1)\Delta t}{\Delta t} = \frac{v_1 + v_2}{2}.$$

We see that for the special case of constant acceleration, and *only* for this case, the average velocity is one-half the sum of the initial and final velocities.

We can use this result, along with the definition of average velocity (Eq. 2.3) and the definition of acceleration (Eq. 2.5), to get another useful relationship. [We can use Eq. (2.5) because the instantaneous and average accelerations are the same when the acceleration is constant.] The resulting equations are simpler if we measure time in terms of elapsed time. In this case we set the initial time $t_1 = 0$, and t_2 becomes any later time t. Thus,

$$t_2 - t_1 = t - 0 = t.$$

We also let x_0 represent the initial position (at time $t = 0$) and let x be the position at time t. Using these quantities, we can represent the distance x in terms of the average velocity (from Eq. 2.3) as

$$x - x_0 = \overline{v}t.$$

If we also let v_0 represent the initial velocity when $t = 0$ and let v be the velocity at time t, then the average velocity is

$$\overline{v} = \frac{v_0 + v}{2}.$$

Inserting this value of $\overline{v}$ into the equation for displacement, we find

$$x - x_0 = \frac{1}{2}(v_0 + v)t. \tag{2.7}$$

This equation expresses the change in displacement (distance traveled) of an object in terms of its initial and final velocities and the elapsed time of motion.

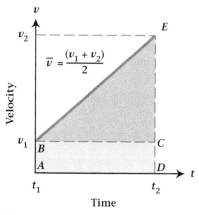

Figure 2.24

Velocity-time graph for constant acceleration, starting with an initial velocity $v_1 \neq 0$.

To express the distance traveled in terms of the acceleration rather than the final velocity v, we rewrite Eq. (2.5) in terms of v, v_0, and t, solving for v:

$$v = v_0 + at.$$

Then we substitute this result into Eq. (2.7), getting

$$x = x_0 + v_0 t + \tfrac{1}{2}at^2. \qquad (2.8)$$

You should carry out these steps to assure yourself that Eq. (2.8) is correct.

Equation (2.8) can also be obtained by examining Fig. 2.24. The term $v_0 t$ represents the area of rectangle $ABCD$, and the term $\frac{1}{2}at^2$ represents the area of the triangle BEC. Equation (2.8) is one of the more important and useful kinematic expressions, as we shall see in Chapter 3. The following examples illustrate the use of this relationship.

Example 2.14

A Boeing 777 airliner, initially at rest, undergoes a constant acceleration of 2.3 m/s² down the runway for 34 s before it lifts off (Fig. 2.25). How far does it travel down the runway before taking off?

Strategy The distance the airplane travels is given by Eq. (2.8):

$$x = x_0 + v_0 t + \tfrac{1}{2}at^2.$$

If we choose the coordinates so that the airliner is at rest at the origin at $t = 0$ and the direction of the acceleration is along the positive x axis, then the numerical values are $x_0 = 0$, $v_0 = 0$, $a = 2.3$ m/s², and $t = 34$ s.

Solution Using these values the distance is then

$$x = \tfrac{1}{2} \times 2.3 \text{ m/s}^2 \times (34 \text{ s})^2 = 1329.4 \text{ m}.$$

Because the acceleration and time are known to only two significant figures, we round off the answer to

$$x = 1.3 \times 10^3 \text{ m} = 1.3 \text{ km}.$$

Figure 2.25
Example 2.14: An airliner accelerates down the runway to gain enough speed to become airborne.

Example 2.15

A drag racer travels one-quarter mile in 10 s from a standing start. Calculate the acceleration in ft/s², under the assumption that it is constant. Choose the origin to be at the starting point and the direction of travel along the positive x axis.

Solution Setting $v_0 = 0$ in Eq. (2.8) and solving for the acceleration gives

$$a = \frac{2(x - x_0)}{t^2}.$$

Next, we insert the numerical values for the distance $x - x_0$ and t.

$$a = \frac{2(0.25 \text{ mi} - 0 \text{ mi})}{(10 \text{ s})^2} = 0.0050 \text{ mi/s}^2.$$

Since we are asked to calculate the acceleration in units of ft/s^2, we need to convert the units from miles to feet. We do so by multiplying a by the conversion factor of 5280 ft/mi:

$$a = 0.0050 \text{ mi/s}^2 \times 5280 \text{ ft/mi} = 26 \text{ ft/s}^2.$$

▼

Example 2.16

Suppose a child driving a go-cart is traveling 4.0 m/s when she crosses a line 4.0 m from her starting point. She continues, with a steady acceleration of 0.40 m/s^2, until she crosses a mark 40 m from the starting point. How long does it take for her to go from the 4.0-m mark to the 40-m mark?

Strategy The problem gives us the initial velocity v_0, the acceleration a, and the displacement $x - x_0$, and it asks us to compute the time. These quantities are all related in Eq. (2.8),

$$x = x_0 + v_0 t + \frac{1}{2} a t^2.$$

We can rearrange this equation into the general form of a quadratic equation in the variable t:

$$\tfrac{1}{2} a t^2 + v_0 t + (x_0 - x) = 0.$$

The values of the coefficients can now be inserted into the quadratic formula to find t. (See the appendix to this chapter for a review of using the quadratic formula.)

Solution On comparing the last equation with the quadratic formula, we get

$$t = \frac{-v_0 \pm \sqrt{v_0^2 - 4(\frac{1}{2}a)(x_0 - x)}}{2(\frac{1}{2}a)}.$$

Notice that the a in Eq. (2.7) is not the same as the a of the quadratic formula. Inserting the numerical values leads to

$$t = \frac{-4.0 \text{ m/s} \pm \sqrt{(4.0 \text{ m/s})^2 - 4(0.20 \text{ m/s}^2)(4.0 \text{ m} - 40 \text{ m})}}{0.40 \text{ m/s}^2}$$

$$t = \frac{-4.0 \text{ m/s} \pm \sqrt{44.8 \text{ m}^2/\text{s}^2}}{0.40 \text{ m/s}^2} = \frac{-4.0 \pm 6.69}{0.40} \text{ s}.$$

Discussion The quadratic equation gives two answers: $t = 6.7$ s and $t = -27$ s, where we have rounded the answer to two significant figures. We discard the negative time because, although it does satisfy the algebraic equation, it has no physical meaning in this case. The meaningful answer is that the child took 6.7 s to reach the 40-m mark after she passed the 4.0-m mark. Notice that units are handled just like numbers or symbols.

We can derive another useful expression relating velocities and distances for motion with constant acceleration by combining Eqs. (2.5) and (2.7). Again using t to stand for elapsed time, we may rewrite Eq. (2.5) as

$$t = (v - v_0)/a.$$

Inserting this into Eq. (2.7) and rearranging, we get

$$v^2 = v_0^2 + 2a(x - x_0). \tag{2.9}$$

This equation gives us a way of calculating distances, velocities, or acceleration without needing to know the elapsed time involved. (It is another basic equation of constant-acceleration kinematics that shows how our definitions of the quantities fit together consistently.)

For convenience, we summarize the important kinematic equations for straight-line motion with constant acceleration in Table 2.1.

Table 2.1	Summary of Kinematic Equations for Constant Acceleration In One Dimension

$$x = x_0 + \bar{v}t$$
$$x = x_0 + \tfrac{1}{2}(v_0 + v)t$$
$$x = x_0 + v_0 t + \tfrac{1}{2}at^2$$
$$v = v_0 + at$$
$$v^2 = v_0^2 + 2a(x - x_0)$$

In these equations we have taken the initial values of time, position, and velocity to be 0, x_0, and v_0, respectively.

Example 2.17

You are driving your new sports car at a velocity of 90 km/h, when you suddenly see a dog step into the road 50 m ahead (Fig. 2.26). You hit the brakes hard to get maximum deceleration of 7.5 m/s²: that is, $a = -7.5$ m/s². How far will you go before stopping? Can you avoid hitting the dog?

Strategy In this problem, we choose the positive x axis as the direction of travel. We are looking for distance in terms of velocity and acceleration. To find the distance we can rearrange Eq. (2.9) to give the stopping distance:

$$x - x_0 = \frac{v^2 - v_0^2}{2a}.$$

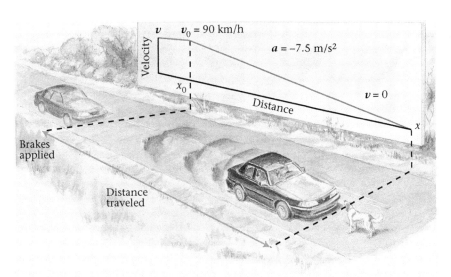

Figure 2.26
Example 2.17: Can you stop quickly enough to avoid hitting the dog?

Solution The values of the known quantities are $v_0 = 90$ km/h, $v = 0$, and $a = -7.5$ m/s^2. Before inserting the known quantities into the equation, we should express v_0 in units of m/s:

$$v_0 = 90 \text{ km/h} \times 1000 \text{ m/km} \times 1 \text{ h/3600 s} = 25 \text{ m/s}.$$

The stopping distance can now be evaluated:

$$x - x_0 = \frac{0^2 - (25 \text{ m/s})^2}{2 \times (-7.5 \text{ m/s}^2)} = 42 \text{ m}.$$

Fortunately, you are able to stop without hitting the dog.

Discussion In solving this problem we have ignored the very real effects of perception time (the time required for the driver to perceive a hazard) and reaction time (the time required to react by moving the foot to the brake pedal). Including these times would change the results of the calculation.

2.7 Galileo and Free Fall

We now discuss in some detail a familiar and important example of constant acceleration: we examine the work by Galileo Galilei on **freely falling bodies,** objects that are moving freely under the influence of gravity. One of Galileo's earliest scientific studies of motion is illustrated in Fig. 2.27. The data for this experiment are recorded in Galileo's notes. Galileo held a ball at the top of an inclined, grooved board and marked its position. Releasing the ball, he marked its position at the end of equal intervals of time. This is much like dropping a ball from a height, except that the effect of gravity has been "reduced" by allowing the ball to roll slowly down the inclined board rather than fall straight down. The positions as measured by Galileo are given in Table 2.2. The observations show what was already known qualitatively to Galileo and others of his time—that a rolling (or falling) object picks up speed as it continues to roll (or

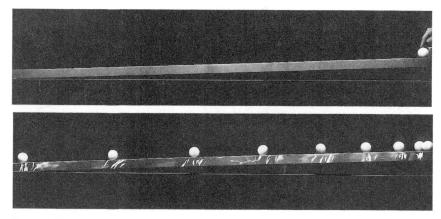

Figure 2.27
Reconstruction of Galileo's experiment on accelerated motion. The distance traveled by the ball rolling down the plane is proportional to the square of the elapsed time.

Table 2.2	Galileo's Results for a Ball Rolled Down an Inclined Plane		
Time t (Equal Intervals)	t^2	Distance x (Points)	x/t^2
1	1	33	33.0
2	4	130	32.5
3	9	298	33.1
4	16	526	32.9
5	25	824	33.0
6	36	1192	33.1
7	49	1620	33.1
8	64	2104	32.9

Distances were measured in points, a unit that equals 29/30 mm.

Source: This experiment is described by Stillman Drake, "The Role of Music in Galileo's Experiments," *Scientific American,* June 1975, p. 98.

fall). However, the debt we owe to Galileo is for his careful measurements and his quantitative (mathematical) interpretation of the data.

Galileo's object was to find a general rule describing how distances increase with increasing time of fall. After some trial and error, and with considerable insight, Galileo realized that the distance traveled was proportional to the square of the elapsed time. That is, with $x_0 = 0$,

$$x \propto t^2,$$

where the symbol $\propto$ means "is proportional to." The fourth column in Table 2.2 lists the ratio of distance to the square of the time, which is seen to be essentially constant. It was experiments like this, rather than the legendary Tower of Pisa experiment, that led to Galileo's conclusion that the distance a falling body moves is proportional to the square of the elapsed time.

Galileo further deduced from his observations that heavy objects fall in the same way that light objects do. Some thirty years later, Robert Boyle, in a series of experiments made possible by his new vacuum pump, showed that this observation is strictly true for bodies falling without the retarding effect of air resistance. This experiment was also demonstrated in 1971 by an astronaut on the moon. There a hammer and a feather both fell with the same acceleration when they were dropped from rest in the airless space around the moon. Figure 2.28 illustrates this effect.

Therefore, we can write the relation between distance and time squared as an equality, where the proportionality constant k does not depend on the nature of the falling object:

$$x = kt^2.$$

For the case of an object released from rest at $x_0 = 0$, Eq. (2.8) reduces to $x = \frac{1}{2}at^2$. (For an object initially at rest $v_0 = 0$.) Thus, the constant $k = \frac{1}{2}a$, and we say that all bodies fall with the same acceleration. This acceleration is called the **acceleration of gravity** and is usually denoted by g. Its standard value is 9.80665 m/s^2, or approximately 9.81 m/s^2. In British units, g is about 32.2 ft/s^2.

(a) In air   (b) In airless space

Figure 2.28

An apple and a feather are dropped simultaneously from the same height. (a) The feather falls more slowly than the apple due to the effects of the air. (b) The feather and the apple fall at the same rate when dropped in the airless space on the moon.

Up to now, the relationships between kinematic quantities such as velocity and acceleration were not dependent upon any property of nature, but rather on how they were defined. Here, for the first time, we have introduced a quantity, the acceleration of gravity, which reflects a property of nature. We cannot calculate the acceleration of gravity from just our knowledge of the kinematical relationships, but rather it must be measured. The value we measure depends on the coordinate system and, hence, the units of measurement. But the fact that all things fall with the same acceleration (in the absence of air friction) is a consequence of natural law.

As we will see later in Chapter 5, the acceleration of gravity near the earth's surface is slightly different at different locations on earth. The acceleration depends on latitude because of the earth's rotation. It also depends on altitude. But for any given location, the acceleration there is the same for all objects.

Galileo knew that there was an effect on motion due to air resistance. However, his statement, even neglecting air resistance, was in much better agreement with his observations and measurements than was the generally believed (but untested) conclusion from Aristotle, namely, that a body ten times the weight of another would fall to the ground in one-tenth the time. We see here the importance of extracting from a series of observations the essence of what is important and setting aside or holding for later the less important aspects. It was the genius of Galileo that enabled him to see what was important and what was of secondary concern.

The measurements quoted here are not the ones Galileo referred to in *Discourses on Two New Sciences,* published in 1638, but are taken from his unpublished notes. For the published presentation of his ideas, Galileo discussed experiments in which he marked off distances in equal intervals and measured the time for those distances. He measured the short time intervals with a water clock. The result was that x/t^2 was constant, no matter which method was used. Galileo publicly described an experiment that differed from his real discovery experiment for just the same reason that scientists often do so today: to make the results more easily understood and to give the appearance that a logical mode of inquiry has been followed throughout. That a logical sequence of inquiry is often not the case is one of the important lessons in the history of science.

An extension of Galileo's experiments with inclined planes led to another extremely important qualitative result. Galileo positioned two inclined planes facing each other so that after a ball rolled down one, it would roll up the other. From his experiments with this setup, Galileo concluded that under ideal conditions (lack of friction and air resistance), the ball would roll up the second plane to a height above the base equal to the height from which it had been released on the first plane. If the upper end of the second track was lowered, the ball would roll farther along it in order to reach the same height. As the track was lowered more, the ball would travel farther, with less deceleration each time. Thus, on a level plane the ball would have no deceleration and its speed would be constant (in the absence of friction). By this reasoning, Galileo discovered the essence of what is called the law of inertia, later stated in full by Newton (see Chapter 4). Galileo realized that his experiment showed, at least for bodies on the earth, that it was not necessary to constantly apply a force in order to move an object. He concluded that rest and motion are both "natural" states of a body.

This conclusion was in direct and complete opposition to most beliefs of the time. The need for a force to keep a body in motion was accepted by some as a proof of the existence of God. The conclusions from Galileo's work in mechanics were not published for many years, in part because of the contradictions they presented with Aristotle's views.

Master the Concept

Velocity and Acceleration in Free Fall

Question: A ball thrown vertically upward rises to a maximum height and then falls to the ground. What are the ball's velocity and acceleration at the instant it reaches its maximum height?

Answer: When the ball is released, it has an initial upward velocity. It also has a constant downward acceleration due to gravity. As it moves up its (upward) velocity steadily decreases because of the downward acceleration until at one instant the velocity is zero. Afterward, the velocity becomes increasingly negative (that is, directed downward) and the ball moves down. At the instant the velocity becomes zero the ball has reached its maximum height; thereafter it falls back toward the ground. Thus, at the maximum height the ball has zero velocity and a downward acceleration of gravity g.

Example 2.18

At Six Flags Over Georgia near Atlanta, Free Fall riders seated four abreast in a padded gondola are taken to the top of a 10-story tower (Fig. 2.29a). Then the gondola is dropped 30 m down a vertical track that curves near the bottom, where the gondola slows to a stop. (a) How long does it take to fall from top to bottom? (b) What maximum speed is reached?

Strategy (a) First we make a simplified sketch of the situation (Fig. 2.29b). We approximate the situation to be entirely vertical motion along an x coordinate that is vertically oriented with positive direction down. In this case we have chosen the origin at the top of the ride so that $x_0 = 0$. Then with the direction of travel chosen as positive, the gondola drops from rest and falls with a positive acceleration almost equal to that of all freely falling objects, 9.81 m/s². The relation between time, acceleration, and distance is Eq. (2.8) with $v_0 = 0$,

$$x - x_0 = \tfrac{1}{2}at^2.$$

This equation can be rearranged to give

$$t^2 = \frac{2(x - x_0)}{a}.$$

Solution (a) If we insert the values for x, x_0, and a (30 m, 0 m, and 9.81 m/s^2, respectively), we get the time to fall:

$$t = \sqrt{\frac{2(x - x_0)}{a}} = \sqrt{\frac{2(30 \text{ m})}{9.81 \text{ m/s}^2}} = \sqrt{6.116 \text{ s}^2} = 2.5 \text{ s}.$$

Strategy (b) The maximum speed is reached near the bottom of the ride. We can determine the speed from Eq. (2.9), which relates the final velocity to the initial velocity, the acceleration, and the displacement. In this case, the initial velocity is zero and the equation simplifies to

$$v^2 = 2a(x - x_0),$$

or

$$v = \sqrt{2a(x - x_0)}.$$

Solution (b) Inserting the numerical values, we find

$$v = \sqrt{2(9.81 \text{ m/s}^2)(30 \text{ m})} = 24 \text{ m/s}.$$

This speed is equivalent to 54 mi/h. The riders attain this speed because the gondolas are in free fall until slowed at the bottom of the ride.

Discussion In computing both of these solutions we had to find the square root. Mathematically, we should allow for both positive and negative values. However, since we chose the initial time to be zero and we can't make time run backward, only the positive value was reported for the time. Similarly, for positive displacement down the track with constant positive acceleration, the velocity must also be positive. Note also that the results for t and v are limited to two significant figures because the displacement was given only to two significant figures.

Figure 2.29
Example 2.18: (a) Free Fall, an experience that's like falling off a 10-story building. (b) Simplified diagram for analysis of the problem.

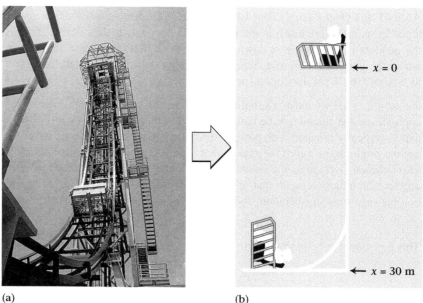

(a)   (b)

GALILEO AND EXPERIMENTAL SCIENCE

What makes science different from other human activities? Perhaps the principal distinction is the role of experiments that can be reproduced by other scientists around the world. Although people had previously tested their ideas of nature with observations, Galileo Galilei (Fig. B2.1) was one of the first to make the experimental process central to science. His influence, which persists to the present day, is in large measure due to his literary skill in describing his theories and experiments so clearly and beautifully that quantitative methods became attractive and fashionable. Galileo, as he is universally known, played a uniquely pivotal role in history. His breakthrough way of linking theory with experiment influenced all subsequent scientific thought, and, to some extent, nonscientific thought as well.

Galileo's work on falling bodies is an important early study of how nature works. This work also illustrates the modern view of how one should arrive at scientific conclusions. It is an example of what is sometimes called the scientific method.

An experiment believed to have been first conducted by Galileo in 1604 was reconstructed for *Scientific American* in 1975 by photographer Ben Rose according to specifications supplied by Stillman Drake. The objective of this modernized test was to measure the distances traveled from rest by a ball rolling down an inclined plane at the ends of eight equal times (in this case, at 0.55-s intervals). The grooved inclined plane was fitted with a stop at the higher end, against which a 2-in. steel ball could be held.

Galileo lived before the development of accurate clocks, and could not

Figure B2.1   Galileo Galilei (1564–1642).

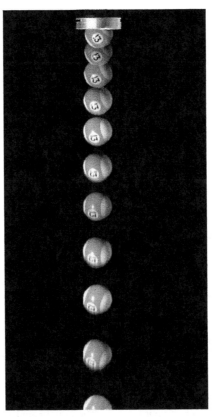

Figure B2.2   High-speed multiflash photograph of a freely falling billiard ball.

have measured time accurately if it had been necessary to measure the elapsed time. However, he needed to determine only equal intervals of time, not total elapsed time. Galileo was especially suited to do this because of his known ability as a musician. Even people who have no training in music are able to detect small differences in timing.

In the modern reconstruction of Galileo's experiment, the time intervals were established by singing the song "Onward Christian Soldiers" at a tempo of about two beats per second. At one beat the ball was released, and the positions of the ball at subsequent beats were marked with chalk; for comparison, the exact 0.55-s positions were also captured by multiple-flash photography (Fig. 2.27). A rubber band was then put around the plane at each chalk mark and the positions adjusted so that the audible bump made by the ball in passing each band would always come exactly at a beat of the march. The ratios of the successive measured distances were found to agree closely with a set of figures recorded by Galileo.

You may easily repeat his experiment by using a long board with rubber bands stretched around it, and tilting it at about two degrees to the horizontal. Hold a heavy ball lightly in place with your finger until you are ready to release it. You will hear a slight thump as the ball rolls over each of the rubber bands. When the thumps are regular, the time intervals are of equal length. Sing a song with a good strong beat and place the rubber bands so as to keep time with the music. The results depend only on whether the beat is regular.

Today's experimental techniques are far more sophisticated than anything Galileo could have imagined. For example, the development of high-speed photography, pioneered by Dr. Harold Edgerton, has enabled us to measure time intervals as small as 10^{-6} s. These techniques have led to calculations of speed and distance not otherwise obtainable (Fig. B2.2).

▼ Summary

Useful Concepts

■ A reference frame is a physical entity to which we refer the position and motion of objects.

■ A coordinate system is used to specify the location of a point in a reference frame.

■ Average speed is the total distance traveled divided by the elapsed time interval.

■ Average velocity is given by

$$\overline{v} = \frac{\Delta x}{\Delta t},$$

where $\Delta x = x_f - x_i$ is the object's displacement. Velocity has direction as well as magnitude.

■ Instantaneous velocity is the limiting value of $\frac{\Delta x}{\Delta t}$ as Δt becomes vanishingly small; that is,

$$v = \lim_{\Delta t \to 0} \frac{\Delta x}{\Delta t}.$$

Alternatively, it is the slope of the tangent to the displacement-time curve at a point.

■ The area under the velocity-time curve between two time intervals is equivalent to the displacement during that time interval.

■ Average acceleration is the change in velocity divided by the time required for the change,

$$\overline{a} = \frac{\Delta v}{\Delta t}.$$

■ Instantaneous acceleration is the limiting value of $\frac{\Delta v}{\Delta t}$ as Δt becomes small; that is,

$$a = \lim_{\Delta t \to 0} \frac{\Delta v}{\Delta t}.$$

Alternatively, it is the slope of the tangent to the velocity-time curve at a point.

■ All bodies near the earth's surface fall with the same acceleration due to gravity, $g = 9.81$ m/s^2. If released from rest and if air resistance is not important, they traverse the same distance in the same amount of time.

■ The most frequently used kinematic equations for motion with constant acceleration are

$$x = x_0 + \overline{v}t \qquad\qquad v = v_0 + at$$
$$x = x_0 + v_0 t + \tfrac{1}{2}at^2 \qquad v^2 = v_0^2 + 2a(x - x_0)$$

Important Terms

You should be able to write the definition or meaning of each of the following terms:

kinematics	abscissa
dynamics	ordinate
mechanics	slope of a line
reference frame	instantaneous velocity
coordinate system	speed
displacement	average acceleration
average speed	instantaneous acceleration
velocity	freely falling bodies
average velocity	acceleration of gravity

▼ Conceptual Questions

2.1 Carefully distinguish between speed and velocity.

2.2 Can an object have zero velocity but nonzero acceleration? Can it have zero acceleration and nonzero velocity? Give examples of each if the answer is yes.

2.3 Sketch a curve of velocity versus time for the displacement-time curve of Fig. 2.15. Sketch the acceleration-time curve also.

2.4 Sketch graphs to represent the following situations: (a) A car driven for 1 hour at a constant speed of 37 km/h (b) A person runs as fast as possible to the corner mailbox and immediately runs back as fast as possible (c) The motion of your hand as you wave it up and down

2.5 Discuss the qualitative relationship between the total national debt, the increase per year, and the rate of change of the increase per year. Use a graphical method. Which would you judge to be affected more by national and world events?

2.6 The distance-time curve for a hypothetical journey has the shape of an equilateral triangle with the base along the time axis. Discuss the velocity *and* acceleration necessary to bring about such a journey. Comment on whether or not this is a realistic journey.

2.7 What is meant by the word *slope* in the term *ski slope*?

2.8 Use a graphical method to answer the following question. The initial population of snowy egrets on a barrier island was 100 on January 1. Each January 1 thereafter, the population was 5% more than for the previous year. What was the population at the end of 15 years? Is the rate at which the population grew a constant? (Recall the graphical meaning of constant velocity.)

2.9 In a common parlor trick, one person holds a dollar bill so that it hangs vertically. A second person places his hand so that the dollar is between but does not touch his thumb and forefinger. When the dollar is dropped, the second person tries to catch it but fails. Estimate the minimum reaction time of the second person.

2.10 Summarize your concept of the scientific method as you understand it from considering the work of Galileo.

2.11 Describe another observation or experiment that shows Galileo was correct in concluding that both straight-line motion and rest are "natural states" for a body (that is, they do not require the application of an external force).

2.12 A car's speedometer is correctly calibrated for tires of a specific size. If larger-diameter tires are substituted, what will be the effect on the speedometer reading?

Problems

You may find it helpful to review the steps for solving problems that were given in Chapter 1 on pp. 19 and 20. In addition, be sure to choose the positive direction for the coordinate system used in each problem and apply the signs consistently to displacement, velocity, and acceleration. Be careful in converting units. (A conversion table is included inside the front cover.) Check your answers to see whether they are reasonable.

Section 2.1 Reference Frames, Coordinate Systems, and Displacement

2.1 A helicopter leaves its base and travels 20.0 km north. After a brief stop, it flies 35.7 km south, pauses briefly and then flies 17.0 km north. Finally it flies 6.0 km south and lands. At the end of the trip, what is the displacement of the helicopter from its base?

2.2 A scale is marked off in cm on a long table. A coin initially at the position labeled 100 cm is moved to the position marked −30 cm. What is the displacement of the coin?

2.3 The cursor on a computer screen is moved with a "mouse" resting on a 6.0-cm-wide pad. Two "swipes" completely across the pad move the cursor from the extreme left to the extreme right of the 25-cm-wide screen. Suppose that initially the cursor is at the left of the screen and the mouse is in the center of the mouse pad. Then the mouse is moved to the right edge of the pad, picked up and placed on the left edge of the pad and then moved all the way across the pad to the right edge. Where is the cursor?

2.4 Figure 2.30 shows the position of an object as a function of time. (a) At which point is the displacement from zero greatest? (b) At what point is the distance from zero greatest? Explain your answer.

2.5 Figure 2.31 shows position-time graphs for three different objects A, B, and C. (a) Which object is farthest from the origin at time $t = 0$? (b) Which object is at rest at time $t = 2.5$ s? (c) Which object moves the greatest distance away from the

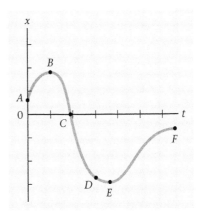

Figure 2.30
Problem 2.4.

origin? (d) How far from the origin is object C at $t = 2.0$ s? (e) Which object is farthest from the origin at $t = 3.0$ s? (f) Where is object B at 1.5 s?

2.6• You move 3.27 m ahead, 2.00 m ahead, 7.95 backward, 2.34 m ahead, 4.56 m backward, and 4.90 m ahead. (a) What is your final displacement? (b) What is your maximum displacement? (c) What is your minimum displacement?

2.7• A bike has a displacement of 1.27 km after a trip consisting of three segments x_1, x_2, and x_3 along a straight line. The sum of the first two segments is 3.79 km, the sum of the last two segments is −7.82 km. How long is each segment?

Section 2.2 Average Speed and Average Velocity

2.8 (a) What is the speed in kilometers per hour of a car traveling at a constant speed of 60 mi/h? (b) What is the speed of the car in meters per second? (1 mi = 1.609 km.)

2.9 What is the average speed for a trip of 157 km that requires 2.45 h?

2.10 How far will an automobile go in 3.5 h at a constant speed of 95 km/h?

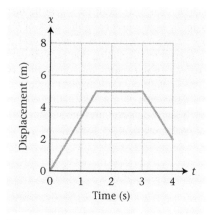

(A)

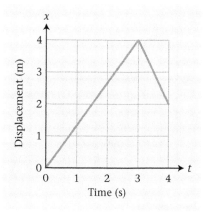

(B)

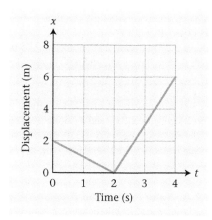

(C)

Figure 2.31
Problem 2.5.

2.11 How long can you afford to stop for lunch if you can drive a steady 104 km/h on the highway and must make a 260-km trip in $3\frac{1}{2}$ h?

2.12 What is the linear speed of the earth in its orbit around the sun? Give your answer in meters per second. (Consider the earth's orbit to be a circle of radius 1.5×10^{11} m.)

2.13 It takes 2.51 s for a laser signal to go from the earth's surface to the moon and back. How far is the lunar surface from the earth's surface? The light travels at a speed of 3.00×10^8 m/s.

2.14 The speed of light is 3.0×10^8 m/s and the speed of sound is 340 m/s. Find the value of the integer n in the following statement: "If you start counting seconds when you see something happen and stop when you hear it happen, for every n seconds counted the event was about 1 km away."

2.15 When a batter hits a baseball its velocity is changed from 128 km/h due west to 136 km/h due east. (a) What is the change in speed? (b) What is the change in velocity?

2.16 Which of the displacement-time graphs in Fig. 2.32 correspond to each of the physical situations listed? (a) A ball rolled along the floor toward the origin, (b) a book at rest on a table, (c) a ball rolling along the floor away from the origin hits a wall and bounces straight back, (d) a ball rolling away from the origin at constant speed, (e) a ball rolled along the floor toward a wall at the origin, the ball then rebounds, and (f) an object rolling toward the origin that suddenly stops.

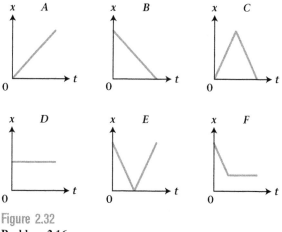

Figure 2.32
Problem 2.16.

2.17 A medivac helicopter travels 78 km due south of its base to pick up a patient. The helicopter then travels 93 km due north to a hospital. The entire trip takes 1.22 h. (a) What is the average velocity? (b) What is the average speed?

2.18 A long-distance runner starts at a given place and runs around a circular track of 50 m radius at a speed of 6.0 m/s in the clockwise direction for 60 s. Then the runner reverses direction and runs in the counterclockwise direction at 4 m/s for 120 s. At the end, how far around the track is the runner from the starting point?

2.19 Two children cross a starting line at the same time, one running with a velocity of +3.5 m/s and the other with a velocity of −4.0 m/s. How far apart are they after 12 s?

2.20• A commuting student leaves home and drives to school at an average speed of 40 km/h. After 24 min he realizes that he has forgotten his homework and returns home to get it at the same average speed. It takes 10 min to find the report, after which the trip to school 40-km away to the east is resumed at the same speed as before. (a) What is the average speed for the entire trip? (b) What is the average velocity for the entire trip?

2.21• If a greyhound runs in a straight line for 3.0 min at a velocity of 40 m/s, what must its velocity be in order to return to its starting point in 2.5 min?

2.22• Runner A, who runs with an average speed of 3.0 m/s, starts out at 3:00 P.M. Runner B, who runs with an average speed of 4.0 m/s, starts after A from the same place exactly 5 min later. (a) At what time will runner B catch up with runner A? (b) If the runners stop when B catches A, how far do they run?

2.23• A 9.0-h trip is made at an average speed of 50 km/h. If the first half of the distance is covered at an average speed of 45 km/h, what is the average speed for the second half of the trip?

2.24• Two automobiles travel in opposite directions from the same starting point. If the speed of one is twice the speed of the other and they are 200 km apart at the end of 1 hour, what is the speed of each car?

Section 2.3 Graphical Interpretation of Velocity

Hints for Solving Problems

Remember that the slope of a line is the ratio of the rise to the run, or $\Delta y/\Delta x$.

2.25 Plot the points given in the following table and sketch a curve through them. Determine the slope of the curve at $x = 5$ and at $x = 10$.

x	0	1	2	3	4	5	6	7
y	6.7	6.3	6.0	5.9	6.0	6.5	7.3	8.5

x	8	9	10	11	12	13
y	10.2	12.0	14.2	15.0	14.4	12.4

2.26 You are driving a car with initial speed v_0. At time $t = 0$, you begin to increase your speed at a constant rate. Twenty seconds later you are traveling at a speed of 80 km/h. At $t = 60$ s you are traveling at a speed of 140 km/h. (a) What was your initial speed v_0? (b) What was your speed at $t = 40$ s? Use a graphical method to arrive at the answers.

2.27 Figure 2.33 is an observed position-time graph. Sketch the corresponding velocity-time curve.

2.28 Match the velocity time graphs in the second row of Fig. 2.34 to the distance-time graphs in the first row.

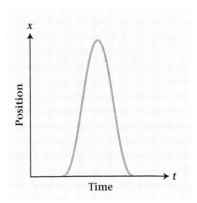

Figure 2.33
Problem 2.27.

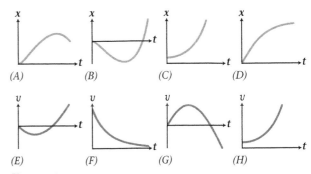

Figure 2.34
Problem 2.28.

2.29 Figure 2.35 contains pairs of distance-time and velocity-time graphs. In each of the four cases, identify which is the distance-time and which is the velocity-time graph.

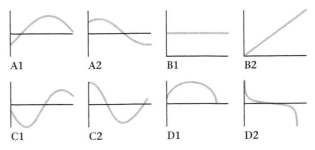

Figure 2.35
Problem 2.29.

2.30• Use the following data to plot a distance-time curve. Determine the velocity (slope) at each second and plot a velocity-time graph.

Time (s)	1	2	3	4	5	6	7	8	9
Distance (m)	2	4	6	8	9.2	9.8	10	10	10

2.31• A test car driver, starting with zero speed at time zero, drove in such a way that the speed-time graph is approximately an isosceles triangle with the base along the time axis. The maximum speed was 30 m/s, and the total elapsed time was 50 s. What distance did she travel?

Section 2.4 Instantaneous Velocity

2.32 The velocity-time graph of part of a cyclist's trip consists of a straight line between $v = 20$ m/s at $t = 10$ s and $v = 0$ at $t = 20$ s. What distance was covered during this portion of the trip?

2.33 Figure 2.36 shows the displacement of an object as a function of time. At which time is the velocity greatest? Explain your answer.

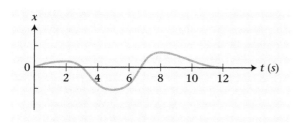

Figure 2.36
Problem 2.33.

2.34• Sketch an approximate distance-time curve for an object that has a velocity given by

$$v = (4.0 + 4.0t^{1/2})\text{m/s}$$

for the first five seconds of motion, where t is given in seconds.
2.35• The velocity-time graph of a jogger's trip is approximated by a triangle that starts at $v = 0$ at $t = 0$, rises to a maximum at $t = 6$ s, and then returns to $v = 0$ at $t = 10$ s. If the maximum speed was 6 m/s, how far did the jogger go?
2.36• (a) Plot the curve corresponding to $y = 3x^2 + 7$ and find the slope at $x = 5$ by graphical means. (b) Find the area under the curve between $x = 0$ and $x = 10$.

Section 2.5 Acceleration

2.37 A motorist traveling at 90 km/h applied the brakes for 5.0 s. If the braking acceleration was -2.0 m/s^2, what was her final speed?
2.38 The 542 hp Jaguar XJ220 can accelerate from 0 to 60 mi/h (26.8 m/s) in 4.0 s. What is the average acceleration during this time interval?
2.39 A Dodge Stealth turbo can accelerate from 0 to 60 mi/h (26.8 m/s) in 5.0 s. What is the average acceleration during this time interval?
2.40 A motorcycle rider moving with an initial velocity of 8.0 m/s uniformly accelerates to a speed of 17 m/s in a distance of 30 m. (a) What is the acceleration? (b) How long does this take?

2.41 Figure 2.37 shows the speed-time graph for a compact car under acceleration from a standing start. Use graphical techniques to determine the acceleration at 10 s and 30 s.

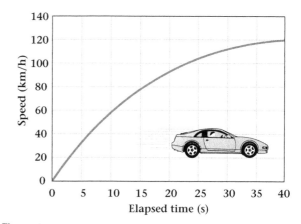

Figure 2.37
Problem 2.41: Graph of speed versus elapsed time for a compact car under acceleration from rest.

2.42 Describe in words the three types of motion represented in Fig. 2.38(a).

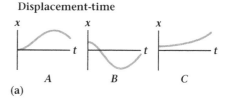
Displacement-time

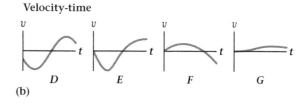
Velocity-time

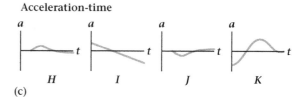
Acceleration-time

Figure 2.38
Problems 2.42 and 2.43: (a) Displacement-time curves. (b) Velocity-time curves. (c) Acceleration-time curves.

2.43• Figure 2.38 shows displacement-time curves for three different straight-line motions (*A*, *B*, *C*). Figure 2.38 also shows velocity-time curves for four different motions (*D*, *E*, *F*, *G*), three of which correspond to the motion shown in the displacement curves. (a) Match the three displacement curves to the appropriate velocity curves. (b) Match the three displacement curves to the appropriate acceleration curves shown as parts *H*, *I*, *J*, and *K*. (*Hint:* Use the velocity curves when looking for the accelerations.)

2.44• Starting from rest, a Mazda MX-6 reaches 48 km/h in 3.2 s and 96 km/h in 8.4 s. (a) Calculate the average acceleration needed to reach 48 km/h. (b) Calculate the average acceleration during the time it takes to go from 48 to 96 km/h. (c) Calculate the average acceleration during the time it takes to go from 0 to 96 km/h.

Section 2.6 Motion with Constant Acceleration

Hints for Solving Problems

You may find it helpful to refer to Table 2.1 to select the proper relationship between the quantities given in a problem and what you need to find. Remember that the equations in the table apply only to motion with constant acceleration. Include units in your work.

2.45 A motorcyclist moving with an initial velocity of 8.0 m/s undergoes a constant acceleration for 3.0 s, at which time his velocity is 17.0 m/s. (a) What is the acceleration? (b) How far does he travel during that 3.0-s interval?

2.46 The nominal stopping distances of a Nissan Sentra SE Sport Coupe are (a) 147 ft from 60.0 mi/h and (b) 264 ft from 80.0 mi/h. Determine the value of the acceleration for each case, assuming that it is constant during each event. Give your answer in units of m/s^2.

2.47 An object at rest is subject to a constant acceleration of 2.00 m/s^2 for 10.0 s. For the next 10.0 s there is no acceleration. Finally the object undergoes an acceleration of -2.00 for 10.0 s. (a) What is the final speed? (b) How far did the object go during the 30.0 s?

2.48• A soccer ball is released from the top of a smooth incline. After 4.22 s the ball travels 10.0 m. One second later it has reached the bottom of the incline. (a) Assume the ball's acceleration is constant and determine its value. (b) How long is the incline?

2.49• A speeding motorist passes a stopped police car. At the moment the car passes, the police car starts from rest with a constant acceleration of 4.28 m/s^2. The speeding motorist continues with constant velocity until caught by the police car 14.8 s later. How fast is the speeding car going?

2.50• Most state driver's handbooks contain a table of stopping distances for cars with good brakes and tires. The tables frequently include the braking distance for several speeds. The braking distance is the distance to stop after the brakes have been applied. Typical values of braking distances for a number of initial speeds are given in the following table. (a) Do these stopping distances represent approximately the same acceleration for each initial speed? (b) If the accelerations are constant, determine the stopping distance from 60 mi/h.

Initial speed (mi/h)	20	30	40	50
Stopping distance (ft)	20	45	80	125

2.51• You are driving down the street when you suddenly see a child dart out in front of you. Assuming that it takes 0.75 s for you to apply the brakes, compute the total stopping distance (braking distance plus distance traveled while moving your foot to the brake pedal) for initial speeds of 20 mi/h, 40 mi/h, and 50 mi/h. Use the information about braking distances given in Problem 2.50.

2.52• A Nissan Sentra can accelerate from 0 to 48 km/h in 3.6 s and from 0 to 96 km/h in 10.2 s. In addition, under constant acceleration from rest it crosses the 0.40-km marker at a speed of 130 km/h. (a) Calculate the average acceleration needed to reach 48 km/h. (b) Calculate the average acceleration during the time it takes to go from 48 to 96 km/h. (c) What constant acceleration would be required to reach a speed of 130 km/h over the 0.40-km course when starting from rest?

2.53• A motorcycle traveling with a constant acceleration of 2.00 m/s^2 crosses a 100-m-long bridge in 4.23 s. (a) What was the velocity at the beginning of the bridge? (b) What was the velocity at the end of the bridge?

2.54•• (a) A slowly moving train with 12-m-long flatcars is passing a station at 10 km/h. A person on the station platform tosses rocks onto the moving flatcars at the rate of once every second. (a) If the first rock just hits the front edge of one car, how many rocks will fall onto that car? (b) How many rocks will fall onto that car if the train begins to accelerate at 0.50 m/s^2 just as the first rock hits the car?

2.55•• Two motocross bikes start from one corner of a square field and go to the corner diagonally opposite in the same time *t*. They both start from the same place and take different routes. One travels along the diagonal with constant acceleration *a*, and the other accelerates momentarily and then travels along the edge of the field with constant speed *v*. What is the relationship between *a* and *v*? Assume a negligible acceleration time for the biker traveling along the edge.

Section 2.7 Galileo and Free Fall

2.56 A cannonball is dropped from the top of a building. If the point of release is 32.0 m above the ground, what is the speed of the cannonball just before it strikes the ground?

2.57 How long would it take an object to fall to the ground from the top of the Leaning Tower of Pisa (height = 54.6 m)?

2.58 Make a table of the velocity and total distance fallen at the end of each half-second during the first 3 s for an apple dropped from rest from the top of a very tall building. Make a graph of distance versus time and velocity versus time.

2.59 What is the acceleration of gravity on a planet where an object released from rest falls 54.2 cm in 1.08 s.

2.60• A ball is allowed to roll from rest down an inclined plane, and the distances are marked every 2.0 s. If the second mark is made 1.60 m from the starting point, where are the first and fourth marks?

2.61• A ball is thrown straight up so that it reaches a height of 25 m. How fast was it going when it was 5 m high? (*Hint:* Use the symmetry of the upward and downward paths.)

2.62• A small parachute dropped from a 30-m-high cliff falls with a constant velocity of 1.2 m/s. Twenty seconds after the parachute is dropped, a stone is dropped from the cliff. Will the stone catch up with the parachute before it reaches the ground?

2.63• The hollow cylinder shown in Fig. 2.39 is free to rotate about a horizontal axis. One hole is cut in the side of the cylinder. The object of a game is to spin the cylinder so fast that an object dropped through the hole when it is in the uppermost position will fall through the same hole when it has rotated to the bottom position. If the diameter of the cylinder is 0.50 m, how many revolutions per second must it make? (*Hint:* First calculate the time for the object to fall the appropriate distance, then use that result to determine the number of revolutions per second.)

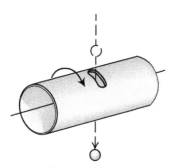

Figure 2.39
Problem 2.63.

2.64•• A professor drops one lead sinker each second from a very high window. (a) How far has the first sinker gone when the second one is dropped? (b) Does the distance between the first and second sinker remain constant? Explain your answer.

2.65•• A loose bolt falls from a high-flying helicopter that is rising at a constant 8.76 m/s. How far is the bolt below the helicopter 3.05 s later?

2.66•• A ball is dropped from a height *h* directly above a base toward which a fielder is running with speed *v*. When the ball is dropped, the glove on the fielder's outstretched hand is a distance *d* from the base. Find an expression for *v* so that the fielder just catches the ball if her glove is a height *y* above the base.

Additional Problems

2.67 A 3.0-h trip was made at an average speed of 75 km/h. For the first hour, the average speed was 90 km/h. What was the average speed for the remainder of the trip?

2.68 Figure 2.40 shows the speed curve for a sports coupe under maximum acceleration from a standing start. From the graph, determine the acceleration at a number of points, and make your own graph of acceleration versus time over the range from 0 to 40 s.

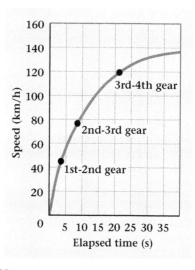

Figure 2.40
Problem 2.68: Graph of speed versus elapsed time for a sports coupe under maximum acceleration from rest.

2.69 (a) The flying time of the Concorde airplane from New York to London (5564 km) is approximately 3 h. What is the Concorde's average speed in km/h? (b) The Wright brothers' first sustained powered flight at Kitty Hawk, North Carolina, lasted 12 s and covered approximately 120 ft. What was their average speed in kilometers per hour? (c) How many times faster is the Concorde than the Wrights' first powered flight?

2.70• Starting from rest, you move with a constant acceleration of 2.0 ft/s^2 for 12 s and then move with an acceleration of −2.0 ft/s^2 for another 12 s. (a) What is your maximum speed attained? (b) How far do you go during the whole trip? (c) What is your average speed?

2.71• With what initial velocity must you throw a ball from a second-story window ($h = 4.0$ m) in order for it to reach the ground in half the time it would have taken if it had been dropped and not thrown?

2.72• A rock is dropped from rest from a height above a strange planet, and a strobe-light photograph is taken. The image is damaged in transmission to earth so that an unknown part of the top of the picture is lost. However, five successive images of the falling rock can be seen. The spacing between the remaining images corresponds to 0.70, 0.90, 1.10, and 1.30 m, and the flash rate is 4.0 flashes per second. Calculate the acceleration of gravity on that planet.

2.73•• Two cyclists start in opposite directions at the northernmost point of a circular track of 25 m radius. (a) If the speed of each bike is constant and is 10 km/h for cyclist A and 15 km/h for cyclist B, where will they meet? (b) Where will the cyclists meet the second time? Assume that they go around the track on essentially the same path, with cyclist A initially headed west and cyclist B initially headed east.

2.74•• A Boeing 767 is initially moving down the runway at 4.5 m/s preparing for takeoff. The pilot pulls on the throttle so that the engines give the plane a constant acceleration of 1.8 m/s^2. The plane then travels a distance of 1700 m down the runway before lifting off. How long does it take from the application of the acceleration until the plane lifts off, becoming airborne?

2.75•• A person can throw a ball with an upward velocity v_0 so that it will just reach the top of a 20-m-tall building. If the same person stands on top of the building and throws the ball downward with velocity v_0, how much sooner does it reach the ground than if it were merely dropped from the same height?

2.76•• A model rocket is fired upward. The rocket's average initial acceleration is 37.5 m/s^2 until the fuel burns out in 0.845 s. How high does the rocket go? Ignore the effects of air friction.

2.77•• A stone is dropped from rest from a height of 20 m. At the same time, a stone is thrown upward from the ground with a speed of 17 m/s. At what height do their paths intersect?

2.78•• A ball bearing is dropped from rest at a point A. At the instant it passes a mark 10 m below A, another ball bearing is released from rest from a position 11 m below A. (a) At what time after its release will the second ball bearing be overtaken by the first? (b) How far does the second bearing fall in that time?

2.79•• An electric-powered model car starts from rest and moves in a straight line for 4 s. The relationship between time and position is approximated by

$$x^2 + 2t^2 = 32,$$

where x is in centimeters and t is in seconds. Using graphical methods, find the velocity at $t = 1$ s and at $t = 3$ s.

2.80•• A ball dropped from the top of a tower reaches a velocity v_f just before it reaches the ground. An automobile traveling toward the tower with constant speed v_f just reaches the tower when the ball strikes the ground. Show that at the instant the ball was released, the distance of the car from the tower was twice the height of the tower.

2.81•• A ball is dropped from the top of a tower at the same time that one is thrown upward from the ground below. They collide at the top of the second ball's trajectory 2.0 s after the ball is thrown upward. How tall is the tower? Neglect the height of the thrower. (*Hint:* A ball thrown upward with speed v acquires the same speed v when it returns again to the ground.)

Solving Quadratic Equations

Any quadratic equation can be put in the form

$$ax^2 + bx + c = 0,$$

where a, b, and c are constants. An equation in this form has solutions for x given by the quadratic formula:

$$x = \frac{-b \pm \sqrt{b^2 - 4ac}}{2a}.$$

Thus, a particular quadratic equation such as

$$7x^2 + 4x - 3 = 0,$$

has values of $a = 7$, $b = 4$, and $c = -3$, which can be substituted into the quadratic formula to give

$$x = \frac{-4 \pm \sqrt{(4)^2 - (4)(7)(-3)}}{2(7)}$$

$$x = \frac{-4 \pm 10}{14}.$$

There are two values of x: the first one corresponds to the + sign and the second one corresponds to the − sign. Our final answers are

$$x = 0.429 \quad \text{and} \quad x = -1.00.$$

Both values satisfy the original equation.

| Example 2.19 |

A student riding a skateboard down an incline is traveling 3.0 m/s when she crosses a mark on the sidewalk. She continues down the incline, with a steady acceleration of 0.50 m/s^2, until she crosses another mark 20 m from the first one. How long does it take for her to go from the first mark to the second one?

Strategy The position of the student is given by Eq. (2.8):

$$x = x_0 + v_0 t + \tfrac{1}{2}at^2.$$

Subtracting x from both sides of the equation and rearranging the order gives a quadratic equation in the variable t:

$$\tfrac{1}{2}at^2 + v_0 t + (x_0 - x) = 0.$$

On comparing this with the quadratic formula we get

$$x = \frac{-v_0 \pm \sqrt{v_0^2 - 4(\tfrac{1}{2}a)(x_0 - x)}}{2(\tfrac{1}{2}a)}.$$

Notice that the a in Eq. (2.8) is not the same as the a of the quadratic formula.

Solution If we let the first mark represent the origin, then the numerical values become $x_0 = 0$, $x = 20$ m, $v_0 = 3.0$ m/s, and $a = 0.50$ m/s^2. Inserting these numerical values gives

$$t = \frac{-3.0 \text{ m/s} \pm \sqrt{(3.0 \text{ m/s})^2 - 4(0.25 \text{ m/s}^2)(0 \text{ m} - 20 \text{ m})}}{0.50 \text{ m/s}^2}$$

$$t = \frac{-3.0 \text{ m/s} \pm \sqrt{29 \text{ m}^2/\text{s}^2}}{0.50 \text{ m/s}^2} = \frac{-3.0 \pm 5.39}{0.50} \text{s}.$$

This gives two answers: $t = 4.8$ s and $t = -17$ s, where we have rounded the answer to two significant figures. We discard the negative time because, although it does satisfy the algebraic equation, it has no physical meaning in this case. (We assumed $t = 0$ when $x = x_0$, and that time only increases in one direction. That is, t must be positive.) Thus, the meaningful answer is that the student took 4.8 s to go from the first mark to the second mark. Notice that units are handled just like numbers or symbols.

3.1   Vectors
3.2   Addition of Vectors
3.3   Resolution of Vectors
3.4   Relative Velocity in One Dimension
3.5   Relative Velocity in Two Dimensions
3.6   Kinematics in Two Dimensions
3.7   Projectile Motion

Appendix: Review of Trigonometry

Motion in Two Dimensions

Galileo's studies of motion went beyond the case of free fall in one dimension to explore the two-dimensional motion of projectiles, such as shells fired from a cannon. However, before we can analyze projectiles, we need to understand more about the description of motion in two and three dimensions.

The motion of a runner in an open field is two dimensional. In order to describe the runner's velocity, we need to know how fast and in what direction the runner is going. Quantities, such as velocity, that have both direction and magnitude are called vectors. The vector techniques presented here are useful in physics and will be used often throughout the remainder of the text.

We will use the example of a projectile, such as a thrown baseball, as an illustration to show that it is possible to treat independently the horizontal and vertical components of the motion of a body. These ideas will appear again in the chapters that follow, especially those on mechanics, electricity, and magnetism. ■

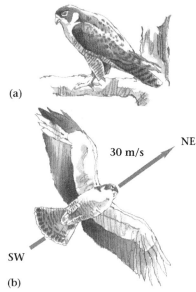

(a)

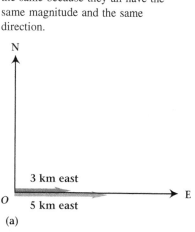

NE

30 m/s

SW

(b)

Figure 3.1

Direction and magnitude. (a) A quantity with magnitude but no direction, such as the falcon's mass, is a *scalar.* (b) The speed and direction of the falcon's flight result in a quantity with both magnitude and direction, called a *vector.*

Figure 3.2

(a) The magnitude of a vector is indicated by the length of the arrow representing the vector. (b) Arrows representing displacements of 5 km east and 5 km north. The vectors have the same magnitude but different directions. (c) The three vectors are the same because they all have the same magnitude and the same direction.

3.1 Vectors

Many physical quantities can be completely specified by their magnitude alone. Such quantities are called **scalars.** Examples include such diverse things as distance, time, speed, mass, and temperature. Another physically important class of quantities is that of **vectors,** which *have direction as well as magnitude.* For example, if we say a grocery store is ten miles from home, we have not completely specified its location unless we state its direction from us—north, south, east, or west. The distance and the direction together constitute a vector called the displacement. Without knowing the direction, we do not know the displacement even when we know the distance.

Many other physical quantities are vectors besides displacement, including velocity and acceleration, which were introduced in Chapter 2. Force and momentum, which will be defined in later chapters, are also vector quantities. Often an object (such as the falcon shown in Fig. 3.1) can have both scalar properties (mass) and vector properties (velocity) at the same time. Because we live in a three-dimensional world, we need vectors to describe the motions of objects. In this chapter, as in Chapter 2, we will consider only the way in which objects move. In the next and subsequent chapters, we will inquire into the causes of motion and the relationships between the various motions and their causes.

In printed materials such as this text, we represent a vector quantity in bold-face roman type, **A**. If we are referring only to the magnitude of that quantity, we use the same letter in lightface italic type, *A*. For your own purposes in working problems and taking notes, you may find that a letter with an arrow drawn over it ($\vec{A}$) is a useful symbol for a vector.

In diagrams we frequently use an arrow to represent a vector. The arrow is drawn so that it points in the direction of the vector and its length is proportional to the magnitude of the vector. For instance, we might represent a displacement of 5 km east by an arrow 25 mm long (Fig. 3.2a). To represent a displacement of 3 km east, we would draw a second arrow parallel to the first but shorter, in the ratio of 3:5 or 15 mm. A vector representing 5 km north is directed 90° counterclockwise from a vector representing 5 km east (Fig. 3.2b). Because a vector is denoted by its length and direction, it remains the same vector when translated to a new starting point (Fig. 3.2c).

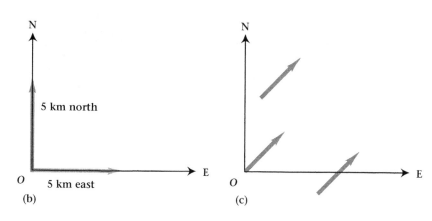

(a) (b) (c)

The **magnitude of a vector** quantity is represented by the same letter used for the vector, but in lightface italic type instead of boldface type. An alternative notation for the magnitude is the vector symbol with vertical bars on both sides. Thus

$$\text{magnitude of } \mathbf{A} = A = |\mathbf{A}|.$$

By definition, the *magnitude of a vector quantity is a scalar and is always positive*.

▼

3.2 Addition of Vectors

Addition of scalars uses just simple arithmetic: 3 kg + 5 kg = 8 kg, for example. Addition of vectors, however, must be different to take account of the directions of the quantities. To illustrate vector addition, let us first take a simple example, after which we will state the general rule. Consider the following problem: If a woman walks 4 km north and 3 km east, how far and in what direction is she from the starting point?

Figure 3.3 is a scale map of this walk. The initial northward walk is a displacement and hence is represented by a vector, which we have labeled **A** in the figure. The eastward journey results in a displacement represented by vector **B**. After traveling north and east, the walker arrives at point *P*. However, a more direct way to reach the same point would be to walk along the straight line *OP*. This line, which represents the resultant displacement, is represented by vector **C** and measures 5 km at an angle of 36.9° east of north. (The distance and angle may be determined either by measuring on a scale drawing or by calculating with geometry and trigonometry.)

Whether the walker takes the indirect or the direct route, she ends up in the same place. Thus, the displacement represented by the sum of the two vectors **A** + **B** equals the displacement represented by the vector **C**:

$$\mathbf{A} + \mathbf{B} = \mathbf{C}.$$

We say that the vector **C** is the **vector sum**, or **resultant**, of the two vectors **A** and **B**.

Two important points are worth mentioning before proceeding. First, note that although the sum of the magnitudes of the individual parts of the trip is 7, this is not the magnitude of the resultant vector. The sum of two vectors depends on their directions as well as their magnitudes (Fig. 3.4). The second point is that

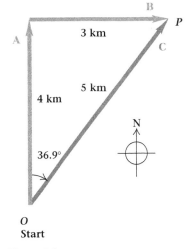

Figure 3.3
Addition of vectors. The displacement that results from walking along vectors **A** and **B** is equal to that of vector **C**. However, the sum of the magnitudes of **A** and **B** is not the same as the magnitude of **C**.

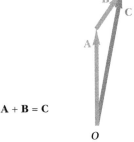

Figure 3.4
Variations in magnitude and direction. If vectors **A** and **B** are of constant magnitude but their direction changes, then the magnitude and direction of **C** will also change.

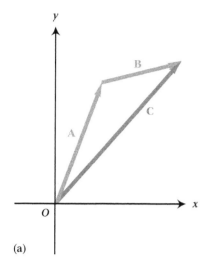

(a)

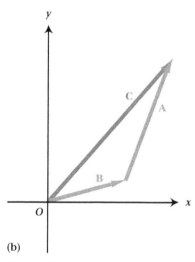

(b)

Figure 3.5
(a) Vector **C** is the vector sum **A** + **B**.
(b) Vector **C** is also the sum **B** + **A**.
Vector addition is commutative.

the technique for adding vectors is the same for all vectors, whether they represent displacement or any other vector quantity—just as the rules for adding all scalars are the same, no matter whether they represent time, money, mass, or pure numbers.

Graphical Methods

To add two vectors graphically, make a scale drawing and place the vectors "head to tail"—that is, with the tail (origin) of the second vector starting from the head (end point) of the first. Then draw the resultant vector from the origin of the first vector to the end point of the second vector. Finally, measure the length (magnitude) and direction of the resultant vector directly from the scale drawing. This method is called the *triangle method of addition.*

Now consider an object that undergoes a displacement **A**, followed by a second displacement **B** (Fig. 3.5a). If we make the displacements in reverse order, as in Fig. 3.5b, with displacement **B** followed by **A**, the resultant is the same. We conclude that the order in which we add the vectors may be reversed without changing the result:

$$\mathbf{A} + \mathbf{B} = \mathbf{B} + \mathbf{A}.$$

We express this behavior by saying that vector addition is commutative. Moreover, commutation is a general rule for the addition of any two vectors.

In the previous example of a woman walking 4 km north and then 3 km east, she would reach the same end point if she reversed the order in which she made the two parts of the trip. The final distance and direction between her ending point and her starting point are the same in both cases.

Vectors may be moved (translated) without changing their value, so long as their directions and magnitudes are not changed. The vector **A** in Fig. 3.5a is identical to the vector **A** in Fig. 3.5b. Similarly the two vectors **B** are identical. Their resultants **C** are also identical in both direction and magnitude.

An alternative graphical method for adding two vectors is shown in Fig. 3.6. If the two vectors **A** and **B** are drawn with their tails joined together, their resultant **C** is the diagonal (bisector) of the parallelogram constructed with **A** and **B** as its sides. This method is known as the *parallelogram method of addition.*

To add more than two vectors together, we repeat the rule by adding successive vectors head to tail (Fig. 3.7). If we wish to add three vectors **A**, **B**, and **C**, we first add **A** and **B** to get a resultant **D**. Then we add **C** to **D** to give **E**. Additional vectors could also be added one at a time. It is not necessary to draw the intermediate sum **D**; we may simply add **C** by placing it next to **B**, as shown in the figure.

Negative of a Vector

The negative of vector **A** is a vector of the same magnitude and parallel to **A** but pointing in the opposite direction (Fig. 3.8). The negative of **A**, represented as −**A**, can be obtained by adding 180° to the angle that specifies vector **A**. The vector and its negative are equal in magnitude and opposite in direction.

Subtracting Vectors

The subtraction of one vector from another, such as

$$\mathbf{A} - \mathbf{B} = \mathbf{C},$$

can be considered as the addition of the first vector to the negative of the second, as

$$A + (-B) = C.$$

Figure 3.9 illustrates the procedure.

Multiplication of a Vector by a Scalar

The result of multiplying a vector by a scalar is another vector. For example, the vector 2**A** has a magnitude twice as great as that of **A** and points in the same direction as **A**. The vector −2**A** is also twice as great as **A**, but it points in the opposite direction.

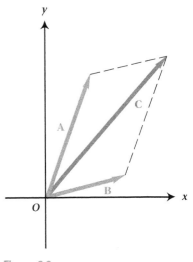

Figure 3.6
The sum of two vectors may be found from the diagonal of the parallelogram formed with the vectors for its sides.

Example 3.1

A vector **A** has a magnitude of 7 units and a direction of 30° measured counterclockwise from the positive *x* axis. The vector **B** has a magnitude of 11 units and a direction of 140° measured counterclockwise from the positive *x* axis. What is the vector sum of **A** and **B**?

Strategy First we draw a careful scale diagram. Then using the triangle method of addition, the vectors **A** and **B** are drawn head to tail (Fig. 3.10a). Then the resultant vector **C** is drawn from the tail of **A** to the head of **B**. This diagram corresponds to

$$A + B = C.$$

Solution After making the diagram, we determine the magnitude of **C** by measuring its length on the drawing and converting it to the appropriate number of units by using the scale indicated. Always indicate on the diagram the scale you use. In this case, the magnitude of **C** is 10.8 units. The direction of **C** can be measured with a protractor and is 103° from the positive *x* axis.

Alternate strategy We can also find the sum by using the parallelogram method of addition (Fig. 3.10b). Again we make a careful scale drawing, but this time both vectors are drawn with their tails at the origin of the coordinates.

Solution We complete the parallelogram and draw the diagonal from the origin to the opposite corner. This diagonal is the resultant **C**. As before, we measure the length of the **C** with a ruler and its angle from the *x* axis with a protractor to find a magnitude of 10.8 units and an angle of 103°.

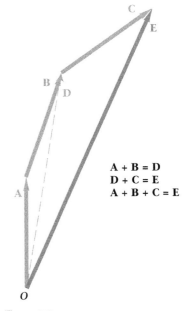

$$A + B = D$$
$$D + C = E$$
$$A + B + C = E$$

Figure 3.7
Addition of three vectors.

Example 3.2

Your friend standing at point *P* wishes to join you at point *Q* located a distance of 200 m due north across a lake (Fig. 3.11). Your friend decides to go around the lake by traveling along two straight-line paths, **A** and **B**. If the first path **A** is 150 m at an angle of 25° east of north, what are the distance and the direction of the second path?

Strategy The distance across the lake is the **C**, the sum of two contributing vectors **A** and **B**. We know **C** and one vector **A**, so to find the other vector **B**, we must subtract **A** from **C**.

Figure 3.8
The negative of a vector has the same magnitude but is directed in the opposite direction.

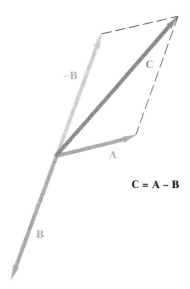

Figure 3.9
Subtraction of vectors. We can obtain the difference between two vectors such as **A** and **B** by adding the first vector to the negative of the second.

Figure 3.10
Example 3.1: Addition of vectors by (a) the triangle method and (b) the parallelogram method.

Solution We may formulate this vector relation as

$$\mathbf{B} = \mathbf{C} - \mathbf{A},$$

where **C** is 200 m to the north and **A** is 150 m at 25° to north. Figure 3.11 is a scale diagram from which we may determine the answer by direct measurement. The second path **B** is found to be 90 m at an angle of 45° west of north.

3.3 Resolution of Vectors

It is often useful to think of a vector as the sum of two or three other vectors. We call these other vectors *components*. Usually we choose components at right angles to each other. Resolving vectors into their components makes it easier to carry out mathematical manipulations such as addition and subtraction.

In two dimensions, we frequently choose the component vectors to lie along the x and y axes of a rectangular (Cartesian) coordinate system. For example, consider the vector **A** lying in the xy plane (Fig. 3.12). We can construct two component vectors by drawing lines from the end of **A** perpendicular to the x and y axes. The two vectors that lie along the x and y directions add to form **A**. When we find the magnitude of these two vectors, we say that we have *resolved* the vector **A** into its x and y components.

Since the known vector and its component vectors form a right triangle, we may use trigonometry to resolve the vector into its components. (A review of basic trigonometry is found in the appendix to this chapter.) This is why components at right angles are particularly convenient. Thus, for the vector of magnitude A that makes an angle θ with the x axis, the component A_x along the x direction and the component A_y along the y direction are given by

$$A_x = A \cos \theta, \qquad A_y = A \sin \theta. \tag{3.1}$$

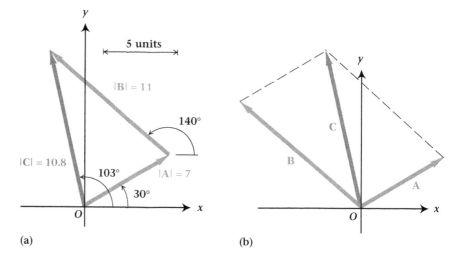

(a)

(b)

If we know the components A_x and A_y of a vector, then we can obtain the magnitude and direction of the vector by applying trigonometry. The magnitude A of the vector is computed from the Pythagorean theorem as

$$A = \sqrt{A_x^2 + A_y^2}. \tag{3.2}$$

The angle θ between the vector $\mathbf{A}$ and the x axis is determined from

$$\tan \theta = \frac{A_y}{A_x}. \tag{3.3}$$

Note that for a given ratio A_y/A_x there are two possible values for the angle. Your calculator will give an angle θ between $-90°$ and $+90°$. The other value is $\theta + 180°$. You must inspect each situation to know which value is correct.

Example 3.3

Swimming at an angle of $27°$ from the horizontal, an angelfish has a velocity vector $\mathbf{v}$ with a magnitude of 25 cm/s (Fig. 3.13). Find the x and y components of $\mathbf{v}$.

Strategy Choose a coordinate system with the x axis along the horizontal. Then we can resolve the velocity into its x and y components by applying Eq. (3.1).

Solution To resolve vector $\mathbf{v}$ into its x and y components, we use Eq. (3.1):

$$v_x = v \cos \theta = (25 \text{ cm/s}) \cos 27° = 25 \text{ cm/s} \times 0.891 = 22 \text{ cm/s},$$
$$v_y = v \sin \theta = (25 \text{ cm/s}) \sin 27° = 25 \text{ cm/s} \times 0.454 = 11 \text{ cm/s}.$$

Adding Vector by Components

Adding or subtracting vectors by resolving them into perpendicular components simplifies the mathematics by enabling us to add vectors in the same directions. This way we avoid having to make careful scale drawings or using trigonometry for every manipulation of vectors. The way to add or subtract two or more vectors is first to resolve each vector into components. Then add the components

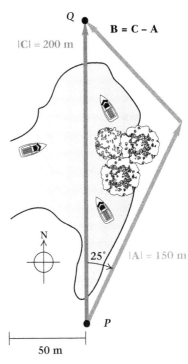

Figure 3.11
Example 3.2: Subtraction of vectors.

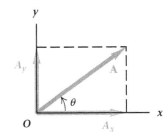

Figure 3.12
A vector $\mathbf{A}$ lying in the xy plane has components A_x along the x direction and A_y along the y direction. From trigonometry we see that $A_x = A \cos \theta$ and $A_y = A \sin \theta$.

Figure 3.13
Example 3.3: Resolution of a vector into components along x and y.

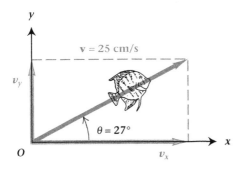

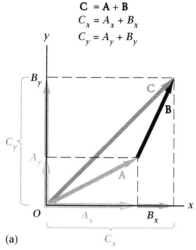

$$C = A + B$$
$$C_x = A_x + B_x$$
$$C_y = A_y + B_y$$

(a)

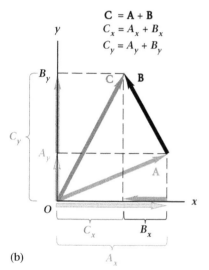

$$C = A + B$$
$$C_x = A_x + B_x$$
$$C_y = A_y + B_y$$

(b)

Figure 3.14

Adding two vectors **A** and **B** to form a new vector **C**. (a) We add the x components to form C_x and the y components to form C_y. (b) If the x component of B is directed along the negative direction, the x component of C is less than A_x.

along the x direction to form the x component of the resultant vector. Similarly, add the y components to get the y component of the resultant vector. For example, the vectors **A** and **B** add together to form a new vector **C** (Fig. 3.14a) whose components are

$$C_x = A_x + B_x, \qquad C_y = A_y + B_y.$$

We can obtain the magnitude and direction of the new vector **C** from Eqs. (3.2) and (3.3) using the new components C_x and C_y. In the case illustrated in Fig. 3.14(b), the x component of vector **B** points in the negative direction, so the sum of the x components is less than A_x.

If we want to subtract two vectors **A** and **B**, we can use the same procedure of resolving each vector into components and subtracting them in proper order. Then we use the resulting components to find the magnitude and direction of the new vector **C**.

▼

Problem-Solving Strategy

Adding Vectors

1. Start by choosing a coordinate system and sketching the vectors. Use graphical techniques to get a qualitative estimate of the resultant.
2. Resolve the vectors into x and y components and be careful to keep their algebraic signs.
3. Add the x components algebraically to find the resultant x value and add the y components algebraically to find the resultant y value.
4. Then find the magnitude of the resultant vector using Eq. (3.2) and find the angle θ from the x axis using Eq. (3.3).

Example 3.4 ▼

Vector **A** has a length of 14 cm at 60° with respect to the x axis, and vector **B** has a length of 20 cm at 20° with respect to the x axis. Add the vectors by first resolving them into components and then adding the components.

Strategy We find the x and y components of each vector. Then we add the x components to get the x component of the resultant and add the y components to get the y component of the resultant. Then the magnitude and direction of the resultant is computed from the value of its components.

Solution Figure 3.15 shows this situation. The components of the vectors are

$$A_x = A \cos \theta_A \qquad\qquad A_y = A \sin \theta_A$$
$$= 14\ \text{cm} \times \cos 60° \qquad\qquad = 14\ \text{cm} \times \sin 60°$$
$$= 14\ \text{cm} \times 0.500 = 7.00\ \text{cm}; \qquad = 14\ \text{cm} \times 0.8660 = 12.12\ \text{cm};$$

$$B_x = B \cos \theta_B \qquad\qquad B_y = B \sin \theta_B$$
$$= 20\ \text{cm} \times \cos 20° \qquad\qquad = 20\ \text{cm} \times \sin 20°$$
$$= 20\ \text{cm} \times 0.9397 = 18.79\ \text{cm}; \qquad = 20\ \text{cm} \times 0.3420 = 6.840\ \text{cm}.$$

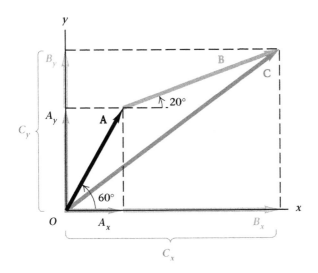

Figure 3.15
Example 3.4: Adding **A** and **B** by components.

The sum is given by

$$C = A + B,$$

where

$$C_x = A_x + B_x = 25.79 \text{ cm}, \qquad C_y = A_y + B_y = 18.96 \text{ cm}.$$

The magnitude of **C** is then found from the Pythagorean theorem as

$$C = \sqrt{C_x^2 + C_y^2},$$
$$C = \sqrt{(25.79 \text{ cm})^2 + (18.96 \text{ cm})^2} = 32 \text{ cm}.$$

The angle of **C** with respect to the x axis is given by

$$\tan \theta = \frac{C_y}{C_x} = \frac{18.96}{25.79} = 0.735$$
$$\theta = 36°.$$

Discussion Notice that we carried out all the computations before rounding off the answers to two significant figures. This is consistent with the rules given in Chapter 1.

To this point we have considered the addition or subtraction of two vectors that lie in the same plane. Other cases occur in nature in which the vectors occupy three dimensions, rather than two. Although we will not deal with such cases very often in this text, we will state the basic principle for adding and subtracting vectors in three dimensions. The vectors to be added (or subtracted) are resolved into components along the x, y, and z axes, and the components are added (or subtracted). This procedure is the same as that used for vectors lying in a plane except that there are three, rather than two, dimensions. Figure 3.16 shows the resolution of a vector into components in three dimensions.

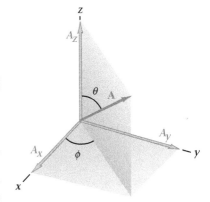

Figure 3.16
Components of a vector in three dimensions.

3.4 Relative Velocity in One Dimension

Now that we've seen how to add and subtract vectors, let's look at some examples of vectors in physics. A good example is velocity, which is the rate of change of displacement. As we have seen, velocity is not an absolute quantity but is measured relative to other objects. For example, when you hear about a pitcher throwing a baseball 85 mi/h, you normally assume that it means a velocity relative to the earth. Thus, to measure any object's velocity we must specify the coordinate system or reference frame in which the measurement is to be made. Ordinarily the origin of the coordinate system is fixed in some other body. In the example of the baseball, the earth was the other body.

When we say that an automobile is traveling 90 km/h (55 mi/h), we usually mean that it is going 90 km/h relative to the road. Imagine that you are driving down the highway at 90 km/h when another car passes you at 100 km/h. Although both cars are moving rapidly down the road, the faster car appears to overtake you very slowly. Relative to a coordinate system fixed on your car, the passing car is going only 100 km/h − 90 km/h = 10 km/h.

When two objects are traveling along the same line, the **relative velocity** of one to the other is obtained simply by ordinary subtraction. (Recall that the negative of a vector is a vector of the same magnitude pointing in the opposite direction.) To clarify the frame of reference of a particular object, we will use the notation $\mathbf{v}_{AB}$ to indicate the velocity of object A with respect to object B. Then if we have a velocity $\mathbf{v}_{AB}$ of A with respect to B and a velocity $\mathbf{v}_{BC}$ of B with respect to C, the velocity of A relative to C is found by vector addition,

$$\mathbf{v}_{AC} = \mathbf{v}_{AB} + \mathbf{v}_{BC}.$$

Example 3.5

A freight train pulling several flatcars is slowly passing a highway intersection at 10 km/h. A hobo on one of the flatcars is walking toward the engine at 5 km/h (Fig. 3.17). What is the velocity of the hobo relative to an observer waiting in a truck stopped at the crossing?

Strategy In this example both velocities are in the same direction. We choose a coordinate system oriented with the positive direction in the direction of the train's motion. The hobo walks toward the engine with a velocity $\mathbf{v}_{he} = 5$ km/h. At the same time, the train moves past the observer with velocity $\mathbf{v}_{eo} = 10$ km/h. We want to find $\mathbf{v}_{ho}$, the velocity of the hobo relative to the observer.

Solution We can write the expression for the velocity of the hobo relative to the observer as

$$\mathbf{v}_{ho} = \mathbf{v}_{he} + \mathbf{v}_{eo}.$$

Since $\mathbf{v}_{he}$ and $\mathbf{v}_{eo}$ are in the same direction, we can simply add their magnitudes to get the magnitude of $\mathbf{v}_{ho}$.

$$v_{ho} = v_{he} + v_{eo}.$$

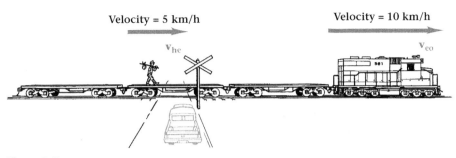

Figure 3.17
Example 3.5: A hobo walking with velocity $\mathbf{v}_{he}$ on a train moving with velocity $\mathbf{v}_{eo}$ passes a stationary observer with a velocity equal to the sum of the two velocities.

When we insert the numerical values we get

$$v_{ho} = 5\ \text{km/h} + 10\ \text{km/h} = 15\ \text{km/h}.$$

The direction of $\mathbf{v}_{ho}$ is positive.

Example 3.6

Suppose the hobo in Fig. 3.17 turns around and walks away from the engine at 5 km/h. What is his velocity with respect to the observer then?

Strategy If we choose the direction of the engine's velocity as positive, then for this case the hobo's velocity must be negative.

Solution The velocity of the hobo relative to the observer is computed just as before.

$$\mathbf{v}_{ho} = \mathbf{v}_{he} + \mathbf{v}_{eo}.$$

Because the direction of $\mathbf{v}_{he}$ is opposite to that of $\mathbf{v}_{eo}$, the indicated sum of the magnitudes is

$$v_{ho} = -v_{he} + v_{eo}.$$

Upon inserting the numerical values we get

$$v_{ho} = -5\ \text{km/h} + 10\ \text{km/h} = 5\ \text{km/h}.$$

Discussion This example illustrates the need for choosing a coordinate system and sticking with it throughout the problem. The difference between this example and the previous one is that the hobo is walking away from the engine. Since we choose the engine's velocity to be positive, the hobo's velocity relative to the engine was necessarily negative.

3.5 Relative Velocity in Two Dimensions

We have seen that when two objects are traveling along the same straight line, the relative velocity of one to the other is obtained by ordinary addition or subtraction. However, if the two velocities are not along the same line, then we need to use vector addition to determine the relative velocity. In particular, we make use of the resolution of vectors into components.

▼
Problem-Solving Strategy

Relative Velocity

1. Identify all velocities and make a vector diagram.
2. Use double subscripts to specify the velocities. For example, use $\mathbf{v}_{AB}$ to indicate the velocity of A relative to B.
3. Then use the techniques of vector addition to find the needed velocity.

▼
Example 3.7

A person who can row a boat at 5.0 km/h in still water tries to cross a river whose current moves at a rate of 3.0 km/h (Fig. 3.18a). The boat is pointed straight across the river, but its progress includes a downstream motion due to the river current. (a) What is the velocity of the boat with respect to the bank? (b) If the river is 200 m wide, how far downstream does the rower land?

Strategy (a) Velocity is the rate of change of displacement, a vector quantity. Hence, velocity is also a vector and has both direction and magnitude. Thus, the rule for adding relative velocities is a rule of vector addition. First make a scale

Figure 3.18
Example 3.7: (a) A boat crossing a stream with a current. (b) Vector diagram of the velocities. The boat travels downstream as it crosses the river.

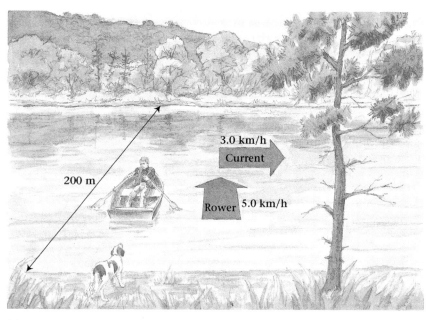

(a)

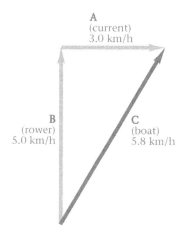

(b)

drawing of the vector diagram that corresponds to the physical situation. It should look like Fig. 3.18(b).

Solution (a) Once you have the scale diagram, it is relatively simple to use a ruler and protractor to get the answer of 5.8 km/h at an angle of 59° with respect to the river's motion. It is equally correct to give the direction as 31° with respect to a line straight across the river. You should do this example for yourself on paper, using a scale different from the one used in the text.

Strategy/Solution (b) The displacement of the boat is proportional to its velocity. Consequently, the ratio of the distance that the boat drifts downstream to the width across the river is the same as the ratio of the magnitude of the river's velocity to the magnitude of the velocity of the boat in still water:

$$\frac{\text{distance along bank}}{\text{width of river}} = \frac{\text{downstream current}}{\text{velocity across river}} = \frac{3.0\ \text{km/h}}{5.0\ \text{km/h}} = \frac{3.0}{5.0}.$$

Thus, the boat lands downstream a distance given by

$$\text{distance} = \frac{3.0}{5.0} \times \text{width} = \frac{3.0}{5.0}\ (200\ \text{m})$$

$$\text{distance} = 120\ \text{m}.$$

▼

Example 3.8

A small airplane flies with an air speed of 200 km/h. A novice pilot wishing to fly from Columbia to Charlotte heads along a path that is due north. The wind is blowing from northwest to southeast at 28 km/h. What is the resultant ground speed of the plane and what is the direction in which the plane actually travels?

Strategy We begin by sketching a vector diagram indicating the velocity of the plane when no wind is present and indicating the velocity of the wind. For simplicity we choose a coordinate system with the y axis oriented north. The plane's velocity $\mathbf{v}_p$ in still air is along the y axis (Fig. 3.19a). The wind velocity $\mathbf{v}_w$ is

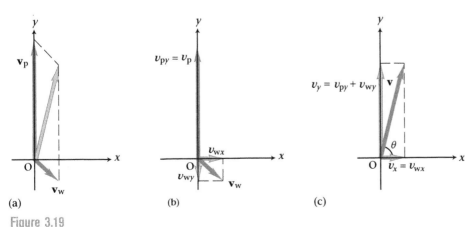

(a) (b) (c)

Figure 3.19
Example 3.8: (a) Vector diagram showing the velocity of the plane in still air and the velocity of the wind. (b) Resolving the wind velocity into components. (c) Finding the resulting velocity.

directed to the southeast, that is, at a 45° angle below the $+x$ axis. We can then use the parallelogram method to get a sense of the magnitude and direction of the resultant vector. The numerical values can be computed by resolving the wind velocity into x and y components (Fig. 3.19b) and then adding to get the components of the vector that represents the net motion of the plane.

Solution The components of the wind velocity are

$$v_{wx} = v_w \cos \theta = (28 \text{ km/h})\cos(-45°) = 19.8 \text{ km/h},$$
$$v_{wy} = v_w \sin \theta = (28 \text{ km/h})\sin(-45°) = -19.8 \text{ km/h}.$$

The plane's velocity $\mathbf{v}_p$ lies along the y axis so that

$$v_{py} = v_p = 200 \text{ km/h},$$
$$v_{px} = 0.$$

The y component of the resultant velocity is (Fig. 3.19c)

$$v_y = v_{wy} + v_{py} = -19.8 \text{ km/h} + 200 \text{ km/h} = 180 \text{ km/h}.$$

The x component is

$$v_x = v_{wx} = 19.8 \text{ km/h}.$$

The resultant velocity has a magnitude

$$v = \sqrt{v_x^2 + v_y^2} = \sqrt{(19.8 \text{ km/h})^2 + (180 \text{ km/h})^2} = 181 \text{ km/h},$$

The angle is found from

$$\tan \theta = \frac{v_y}{v_x} = \frac{180 \text{ km/h}}{19.8 \text{ km/h}} = 9.09$$

$$\theta = 83.7° \approx 84°.$$

Example 3.9

A dolphin traveling at 10 km/h in still water enters a tidal current at an angle of 30° and swims in that direction. The current is moving parallel to the shore at a speed of 3.0 km/h. What is the dolphin's velocity relative to the shore?

Strategy Let us begin by looking at a diagram of the situation (Fig. 3.20a). The velocity of the water relative to the shore is shown as $\mathbf{v}_{ws}$. The velocity of the dolphin relative to the water is $\mathbf{v}_{dw}$, which makes an angle of 30° with $\mathbf{v}_{ws}$. The vector sum of these two velocities ($\mathbf{v}_{dw} + \mathbf{v}_{ws}$) is the velocity of the dolphin relative to the shore, which we call $\mathbf{v}_{ds}$.

To calculate this quantity, we first choose a coordinate system so that $\mathbf{v}_{ws}$ is in the x direction. Then we resolve $\mathbf{v}_{dw}$ into components along x and y, that is, parallel and perpendicular to $\mathbf{v}_{ws}$ (Fig. 3.20b). The dolphin's total speed parallel to the shore is just the sum of $\mathbf{v}_{ws} + v_{dw_x}$. The total speed perpendicular to the shore is v_{dw_y}. The total velocity $\mathbf{v}_{ds}$ of the dolphin relative to the shore is the vector sum of these components.

Solution The parallel component of the dolphin's velocity relative to the water is

$$v_{dw_x} = v_{dw} \cos(-30°) = (10 \text{ km/h}) \cos(-30°) = 8.66 \text{ km/h}.$$

The perpendicular component is

$$v_{dw_y} = v_{dw} \sin(-30°) = (10 \text{ km/h}) \sin(-30°) = -5.00 \text{ km/h}.$$

The dolphin's total speed parallel to the shore is $v_{ws} + v_{dw_x} = 11.66$ km/h and its speed perpendicular to the shore is -5.00 km/h. The magnitude of $\mathbf{v}_{ds}$ is given by the Pythagorean theorem as

$$v_{ds} = \sqrt{(11.66 \text{ km/h})^2 + (-5.00 \text{ km/h})^2}$$
$$v_{ds} = 13 \text{ km/h}.$$

The magnitude of $\mathbf{v}_{ds}$ is the speed of the dolphin relative to the shore. The resulting direction is

$$\tan \theta = \frac{v_{ds_y}}{v_{ds_x}} = \frac{-5.00}{11.66},$$
$$\theta = -23°.$$

Discussion The direction of the dolphin's velocity is $-23°$ away from the direction of the current (Fig. 3.20c) because one of its components is in the negative y direction. You should verify these results both by repeating the calculations yourself and by making a scale drawing and measuring with a ruler and protractor.

··· ■

Figure 3.20

Example 3.9: (a) A dolphin swims in a tidal current at an angle of 30° from the direction in which the water is flowing. (b) Components of the dolphin's velocity relative to the water velocity $\mathbf{v}_{ws}$. (c) The velocity of the dolphin relative to the shore is $\mathbf{v}_{ds}$, the vector sum of $\mathbf{v}_{ws}$ and $\mathbf{v}_{dw}$.

(a)

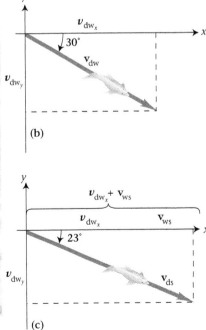

(b)

(c)

3.6   Kinematics in Two Dimensions

We can now rephrase our earlier kinematic definitions in vector form. The one-dimensional kinematic equations developed in Chapter 2 are for motion along a straight line. The vector equation defining average velocity is

$$\bar{\mathbf{v}} \equiv \frac{\Delta \mathbf{r}}{\Delta t} = \frac{\mathbf{r} - \mathbf{r}_0}{t - 0}, \tag{3.4}$$

where $\mathbf{r}_0$ and $\mathbf{r}$ are the initial and final position vectors, t is the final time, and the initial time is set equal to zero. Here $\mathbf{r}$, $\mathbf{r}_0$, and $\mathbf{v}$ represent vectors that can have components along the directions of x, y, and z.

Now we can see that the average velocity is distinct from the average speed, which depends on the total distance traveled. For example, imagine a round trip in which a bee moves a distance of 5 cm and then returns to its starting point in 1 s. During that time interval, the bee travels a total distance of 10 cm and has an average speed of 10 cm/s. However, its net change in vector displacement is zero, since $\mathbf{r}_0$ (the position at the start) and $\mathbf{r}$ (the position at the end) are the same. Therefore, the bee has an average velocity of zero.

As in the case for one dimension, the instantaneous velocity $\mathbf{v}$ is given by the limiting value of $\Delta \mathbf{r}/\Delta t$ as Δt becomes vanishingly small:

$$\boxed{\mathbf{v} \equiv \lim_{\Delta t \to 0} \frac{\Delta \mathbf{r}}{\Delta t}.} \tag{3.5}$$

Similarly, the components of the instantaneous velocity vector are the limiting values of the component displacements divided by Δt as Δt becomes vanishingly small:

$$v_x = \lim_{\Delta t \to 0} \frac{\Delta x}{\Delta t}, \qquad v_y = \lim_{\Delta t \to 0} \frac{\Delta y}{\Delta t}.$$

The magnitude of the instantaneous velocity is given by

$$v = \sqrt{v_x^2 + v_y^2}.$$

The direction of motion is the direction of the instantaneous velocity, *not* the direction of the displacement.

The average acceleration is defined by

$$\bar{\mathbf{a}} \equiv \frac{\Delta \mathbf{v}}{\Delta t} = \frac{\mathbf{v} - \mathbf{v}_0}{t - t_0}. \tag{3.6}$$

Notice that an acceleration can arise from a change in the velocity's direction as well as from a change in its magnitude or speed (Fig. 3.21). In particular, a body moving in a circle may have constant speed, yet it will be accelerating because its velocity is continuously changing direction. We will study uniform circular motion in Chapter 5.

The instantaneous acceleration vector $\mathbf{a}$ is given by the limiting value of $\Delta \mathbf{v}/\Delta t$ as Δt becomes vanishingly small:

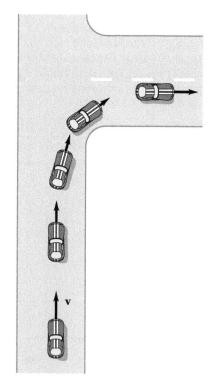

Figure 3.21
The magnitude of the car's velocity changes as the car slows for the turn and the direction of the velocity changes as the car turns. Both of these effects contribute to the car's acceleration.

$$a \equiv \lim_{\Delta t \to 0} \frac{\Delta \mathbf{v}}{\Delta t}. \tag{3.7}$$

As in the case of velocity, the instantaneous acceleration can be resolved into components of acceleration a_x and a_y,

$$a_x = \lim_{\Delta t \to 0} \frac{\Delta v_x}{\Delta t}, \qquad a_y = \lim_{\Delta t \to 0} \frac{\Delta v_y}{\Delta t}.$$

The magnitude of the instantaneous acceleration is given by

$$a = \sqrt{a_x^2 + a_y^2}.$$

The direction of the acceleration depends on the direction of change of velocity, *not* on the direction of the velocity.

The kinematic equations for motion with constant acceleration can be extended to vector form. Galileo found that the horizontal and vertical components of motion can be treated separately. Thus, we can express the vector equations of motion in terms of their separate components. For example, Eq. (2.8) written for two dimensions becomes

$$x = x_0 + v_{0x}t + \tfrac{1}{2}a_x t^2, \tag{3.8a}$$

$$y = y_0 + v_{0y}t + \tfrac{1}{2}a_y t^2, \tag{3.8b}$$

where x_0 and y_0 are the components of initial position, v_{0x} and v_{0y} are the components of initial velocity, and a_x and a_y are the components of acceleration. We can apply the same reasoning to extend these equations to the case of three dimensions.

Example 3.10

A particle is confined to move in a horizontal plane. Its location at time $t = 0$ is chosen as the origin of a coordinate system. The particle has an initial velocity along the x direction of 10 cm/s and is subject to a constant acceleration along the y direction of 2 cm/s^2. (a) Determine the path of the particle by computing its position at $t = 1, 2, 3, 4,$ and 5 s and graphing the result. (b) What is the displacement of the particle from the origin at time $t = 5$ s, and (c) what is its velocity?

Strategy (a) Since the acceleration is constant, we can use Eq. (3.8a,b) to find the x and y coordinates of the particle at the times specified:

$$x = x_0 + v_{0x}t + \tfrac{1}{2}a_x t^2 \quad \text{and} \quad y = y_0 + v_{0y}t + \tfrac{1}{2}a_y t^2.$$

A graph of these values gives the path of the particle.

Solution (a) Substituting the values $x_0 = 0$, $v_{0x} = 10$ cm/s, $a_x = 0$, $y_0 = 0$, $v_{0y} = 0$ and $a_y = 2$ cm/s^2 into the equations for x and y, we obtain the equations

$$x = 0 + (10 \text{ cm/s})t + 0 \quad \text{and} \quad y = 0 + 0 + \tfrac{1}{2}(2 \text{ cm/s}^2)t^2.$$

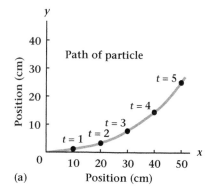

(a)

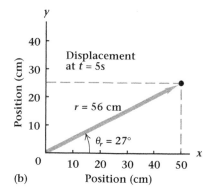

(b)

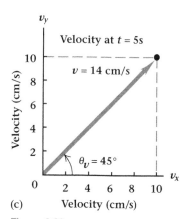

(c)

Figure 3.22

Example 3.10: (a) Path of the particle described. (b) Displacement of the particle at time $t = 5$ s. (c) Velocity of the particle at $t = 5$ s.

We can compute the coordinates x and y of the particle at each second along its path by inserting the values for the time in these equations:

t	x	y
0	0	0
1	10 cm	1 cm
2	20 cm	4 cm
3	30 cm	9 cm
4	40 cm	16 cm
5	50 cm	25 cm

These points, plotted on the graph in Fig. 3.22(a), show the path taken by the particle.

Solution (b) The displacement of the particle from the origin at $t = 5$ s is the vector $\Delta \mathbf{r} = \mathbf{r} - 0$ whose coordinates are $x = 50$ cm and $y = 25$ cm. Its magnitude is

$$r = \sqrt{x^2 + y^2} = \sqrt{(50)^2 + (25)^2} \text{ cm} = 56 \text{ cm}.$$

The direction of the displacement with respect to the x axis is given by the angle θ_r, where

$$\tan \theta_r = \frac{y}{x} = \frac{25}{50}.$$

This corresponds to an angle $\theta_r = 27°$ (Fig. 3.22b).

Strategy (c) The equation for velocity as a function of acceleration and time can be expressed in component form as

$$v_x = v_{xo} + a_x t \quad \text{and} \quad v_y = v_{yo} + a_y t.$$

For the case at hand we are seeking v_x and v_y at $t = 5$ s.

Solution (c) Upon inserting the numerical values we get

$$v_x = 10 \text{ cm/s} + 0 \quad \text{and} \quad v_y = 0 + (2 \text{ cm/s}^2)(5 \text{ s})$$
$$v_x = 10 \text{ cm/s} \qquad\qquad v_y = 10 \text{ cm/s}.$$

The velocity vector at $t = 5$ s, shown in Fig. 3.22c, has a magnitude

$$v = \sqrt{v_x^2 + v_y^2} = \sqrt{(10)^2 + (10)^2} \text{ cm/s} = 14 \text{ cm/s}.$$

The velocity vector is directed at an angle θ_v given by

$$\tan \theta_v = \frac{v_y}{v_x} = \frac{10 \text{ cm/s}}{10 \text{ cm/s}} = 1.0$$
$$\theta_v = 45°.$$

Discussion The direction in which the particle is traveling is the direction of its instantaneous velocity. Notice that this is not the same as the direction of the displacement from the origin. To help understand two-dimensional motion, you should extend this computation out to $t = 10$ s.

3.7 Projectile Motion

In the last part of his work *Discourses on Two New Sciences,* Galileo published a particularly useful idea that arose in connection with the motion of projectiles. Galileo observed that we could think of a projectile's motion as consisting of a horizontal part with constant speed and a vertical part with constant downward acceleration. Each of these motions is independent of the other, but their combination describes the overall motion of the projectile. For example, a ball projected horizontally falls with the same downward acceleration as a ball that is simply dropped (Fig. 3.23). The downward motion is unaffected by the horizontal motion. Thus, if air resistance is negligible, a ball projected horizontally reaches the floor at the same time as a ball dropped vertically, a result predicted by Galileo.

Galileo also used the example of a stone dropped from the mast of a ship moving with constant speed. To a shipboard observer the stone appears to travel straight down alongside the mast, falling with constant acceleration. However, to an observer on the shore, the path of the falling stone on the moving ship is equivalent to projecting it horizontally from a stationary point with an initial velocity equal to the velocity of the ship.

It is important to understand that the motion seen from the shore consists of two independent parts: the downward motion with constant acceleration and the horizontal motion with constant velocity. (In this discussion we neglect the effect of air resistance.) Experiments have confirmed the independence of the horizontal and vertical components. The reason for this will become clear in Chapter 4. To clarify the idea of independent components of motion, study the following example.

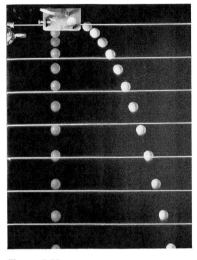

Figure 3.23
Photograph of two balls illuminated with a flashing strobe light. The balls are released at the same time. The ball projected horizontally has the same downward acceleration as the ball that is simply dropped.

Problem-Solving Strategy

Projectile Motion

1. Choose a coordinate system and stick with it while solving the problem.
2. Identify the initial position, initial velocity, and acceleration and resolve these quantities into x and y components.
3. Identify the quantities that you know and those that you need to find.
4. Write the appropriate kinematic equations in component form and solve them separately making use of the fact that the time of flight is the same for both components of motion.

Example 3.11

A ball is thrown horizontally from the Leaning Tower of Pisa (Fig. 3.24) with a velocity of 22 m/s. If the ball is thrown from a height of 49 m above ground,

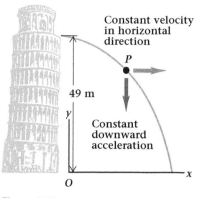

Figure 3.24
Example 3.11: A ball thrown from the Leaning Tower of Pisa.

how far from the point on the ground directly below the launch point does the ball strike the ground?

Strategy We can treat the x and y motions independently, and we know that the time it takes the ball to reach the ground will be the same for both motions. So, knowing the vertical height through which the ball falls, we can solve the equation of vertical motion for the time of fall and then use this value in the equation for horizontal motion to determine the horizontal distance.

Solution Choose a coordinate system with x along the horizontal and the positive y axis up. The time for the ball to reach the ground depends on the height h and the constant vertical acceleration a_y. (In Section 2.7 we discussed the motion of a body falling freely under the acceleration of gravity.) For motion in the vertical direction, we may use Eq. (3.8b),

$$y = y_0 + v_{0y}t + \tfrac{1}{2}a_yt^2,$$

where the initial y coordinate position is $y_0 = h$ and the acceleration in the y direction is $a_y = -g$. The negative sign is used since the positive y direction is upward and the acceleration of gravity is downward. Because the initial velocity is horizontal, the initial velocity in the y direction is $v_{0y} = 0$. The time t for the ball to reach the ground is given by this equation with $y = 0$ (the height of the ground) and the values for y_0, v_{0y}, and a_y inserted. The equation then becomes

$$0 = h + 0 - \tfrac{1}{2}gt^2.$$

Solving for t and inserting the numerical values gives

$$t = \sqrt{\frac{2h}{g}} = \sqrt{\frac{2 \times 49 \text{ m}}{9.81 \text{ m/s}^2}}$$
$$t = 3.162 \text{ s} \approx 3.2 \text{ s}.$$

This is the elapsed time before the ball strikes the ground after it has been thrown horizontally. We have chosen the positive square root because time increases as the ball falls.

The gravitational acceleration acts downward and does not affect the horizontal component motion. Thus, the horizontal component of acceleration is zero ($a_x = 0$) and the ball continues to travel with a constant x component of velocity until it strikes the ground. The horizontal distance traveled in time t at constant velocity v_{0x} is

$$x = v_{0x}t = 22 \text{ m/s} \times 3.162 \text{ s}$$
$$x = 70 \text{ m}.$$

Thus, the ball strikes the ground 70 m from the point directly below the launch point.

The combined effect of horizontal motion with constant velocity and vertical motion with constant acceleration is that the body moves in a parabolic path. In the following discussion, we prove that the path of a projectile thrown horizontally (as in Example 3.11) is a parabola. We then extend our discussion to cases in which the body is projected at any angle, not just horizontally. If you need to review some of the properties of a parabola, refer to page A–3 of Appendix A.

Consider an object, like a golf ball, projected horizontally (Fig. 3.25). For the y (vertical) component of motion, the initial velocity is zero and the acceleration is that of gravity, giving

$$y = -\frac{1}{2}gt^2.$$

We use the minus sign because the acceleration of gravity is downward and we have chosen the upward direction to be positive in the figure. The projected object starts at $y = 0$ and falls to negative values of y.

The horizontal component of motion has an initial velocity but is not accelerated, so

$$x = v_0 t.$$

Solving this equation for t and inserting the value of t into the equation for y, we get

$$y = -\frac{g}{2v_0^2}x^2. \tag{3.9}$$

Equation (3.9) has the same form as the equation for a parabola. In both cases the factor that is multiplied by x^2 on the right-hand side is a constant for a particular problem. Thus, we conclude that projectile motion is parabolic.

A more detailed analysis would take account of air resistance, which causes a departure from a true parabolic path in many real situations. In this book, we will consider air resistance to be negligible unless stated otherwise. Although the assumption does not correspond to physical reality, it often gives a good approximation. The mathematical model needed to include the effects of air resistance is more complicated than we wish to analyze here.

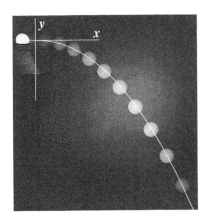

Figure 3.25
A photograph of a golf ball illuminated with a flashing strobe light and given an initial horizontal velocity. Superimposed on the photograph is a section of a parabola drawn from Eq. (3.9). Whether an object is thrown horizontally, upward, or downward, the principle remains the same: the object follows a parabolic path.

Master the Concept

Projectile Motion

Question: Will a ball dropped from rest reach the ground quicker than one launched from the same height but with an initial horizontal velocity?

Answer: In both cases, the balls have zero initial velocity in the vertical direction and are accelerated downward with gravitational acceleration g. The vertical motion is unaffected by the horizontal motion. The time to fall depends only on the initial height and g. Thus the time to reach the ground is the same for both balls.

Example 3.12

A boy aims his slingshot directly at an apple hanging in a tree. At the moment he shoots a pebble, the apple drops. Show that the pebble hits the target.

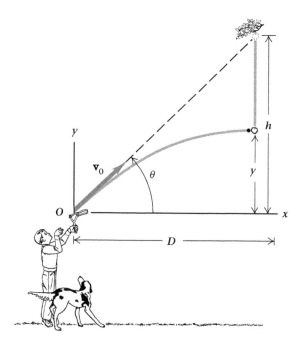

Figure 3.26

Example 3.12: Shooting a pebble at an apple that drops at the instant the pebble is fired.

Strategy For the pebble to hit the apple, they both need to be at the same place at the same time (Fig. 3.26). We know the horizontal distance the pebble must travel, namely D, so we need to calculate the time t required for that to happen. Then we can use that value of time in the equation for the pebble's vertical motion to determine its height when it reaches the horizontal distance D. Finally, we substitute this same time into the apple's equation of motion to see if it's at the same height as the pebble.

Solution For convenience, we place an x-y coordinate system with its origin at the slingshot (Fig. 3.26). We first consider the motion of the projectile. Let θ be the firing angle measured from the horizontal. Then the horizontal component of the pebble's velocity is $v_0 (\cos \theta)$. In a time t the pebble travels the horizontal distance D given by

$$D = v_0 (\cos \theta)\, t,$$

or

$$t = \frac{D}{v_0 \cos \theta}.$$

The vertical component of the pebble's initial velocity is $v_0(\sin \theta)$, so the vertical distance traveled by the pebble during the same period of time is given by Eq. (3.8b):

$$y = v_0(\sin \theta)t - \tfrac{1}{2}gt^2.$$

By substituting the value of t from the equation above, we get

$$y = D \tan \theta - \tfrac{1}{2}gt^2.$$

Examination of the diagram shows that $D \tan \theta$ is the initial height of the apple h, so that the height reached by the pebble in time t is

$$y = h - \tfrac{1}{2}gt^2.$$

Next we find the position of the apple at time t, which is given by

$$y = y_0 + v_{0y} + \tfrac{1}{2}a_y t^2.$$

Since $y_0 = h$, $v_{0y} = 0$, and $a_y = -g$, the position of the apple at time t is

$$y = h - \tfrac{1}{2}gt^2.$$

This height is just exactly the point that the pebble reached in time t. So, the pebble hits the apple.

Discussion This result is independent of the speed v_0, so collision occurs for any projectile (pebble, bullet, arrow, or whatever) as long as the projectile travels a distance D before hitting the ground. For the case shown in Fig. 3.26, the projectile was still rising when it hit the target. However, the collision would still occur even if the projectile were past its maximum height. This example is often the basis for a classroom demonstration experiment.

Example 3.13

A baseball thrown upward leaves the player's hand at a height of 1.60 m above a level playing field (Fig. 3.27). The ball has an initial speed of 28.0 m/s at an angle of 45.0° above the horizontal. How far from a point on the ground directly below the point of release will the baseball strike the field?

Strategy Again we can treat the x and y motions independently. We know that the time it takes the ball to reach the ground is the same for both motions. We can solve the equation of vertical motion for the time of fall and then use this value of time in the equation for horizontal motion to determine the horizontal distance. This is the same strategy that we used in Example 3.11, only in this case the ball's initial velocity has an upward component.

Solution The ball has an initial component of velocity in the vertical (y) direction given by $v_{0y} = v_0 \sin 45.0° = 28.0 \text{ m/s} \times 0.707 = 19.8 \text{ m/s}$. We can use Eq. (3.8b) to find the time of flight of the ball since we know the initial

Figure 3.27
Example 3.13: A baseball thrown with an initial velocity making an angle of 45° with the horizontal is released at a height of 1.60 m above the ground.

velocity, the initial position $y_0 = 1.60$ m, the final position $y = 0$, and the vertical acceleration $a_y = -g = -9.81$ m/s^2. The equation may be put in the form

$$\tfrac{1}{2}a_yt^2 + v_{0y}t + (y_0 - y) = 0,$$

which is quadratic in t. When the proper values are inserted for the coefficients, we get

$$(-4.91 \text{ m/s}^2)t^2 + (19.8 \text{ m/s})t + 1.60 \text{ m} = 0.$$

Upon applying the quadratic formula, we obtain two values for the time t: $+4.11$ s and -0.0792 s. Since the elapsed time is positive, we choose the positive value, $t = 4.11$ s.

Now that we know the time of flight of the ball, we can compute the horizontal distance traveled from the product of the horizontal velocity component with the time:

$$x = v_{0x}t = v_0 \cos 45.0° \, t$$
$$x = (28.0 \text{ m/s})(0.707)(4.11 \text{ s}) = 81.4 \text{ m}.$$

The ball travels a horizontal distance of 81.4 m before it hits the ground.

Example 3.14

Find an expression for the *horizontal range* of a projectile, the horizontal distance it travels during the time it rises and returns to its initial height. Ignoring the effects of air resistance, show that the range depends on the initial velocity (both the magnitude and the launch angle) in a relatively simple way.

Strategy Figure 3.28 depicts the parabolic path of a football projected upward. The football's initial velocity $\mathbf{v}_0$ makes an angle θ with the horizontal. The horizontal component of velocity is $v_0 \cos \theta$ and is constant because there is no horizontal acceleration. (As usual, we have neglected air resistance.) The initial vertical or y component of velocity is $v_0 \sin \theta$. The vertical component of velocity changes with time as a result of gravitational acceleration. As the

Figure 3.28

Range of a projectile (football) with initial velocity $\mathbf{v}_0$ directed at an angle θ with respect to the horizontal.

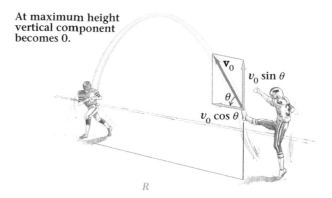

At maximum height vertical component becomes 0.

object rises, it slows down and its vertical component of velocity v_y at any time t is

$$v_y = v_0 \sin \theta - gt,$$

where the initial vertical velocity is $v_0 \sin \theta$ and the acceleration is $-g$.

The time for an object thrown upward from the ground to reach its maximum height and the time for it to fall to the ground again are the same, provided the initial and final positions are on the same level. This symmetry in the upward and downward parts of the path results from the fact that the acceleration of gravity, g, is constant and is the same for upward and downward motion at any height. The time required for the object to reach its maximum height is then half the total time T that it is in the air. Also, at the maximum height, the vertical component of velocity becomes zero; that is, the projectile stops rising before it begins to fall down. (It continues moving horizontally at this point.) Thus, at the maximum height, $v_y = 0$, and $t = T/2$.

Solution At the maximum height the velocity equation in the vertical direction becomes

$$0 = v_0 \sin \theta - g\frac{T}{2}.$$

Upon rearranging to find the time T,

$$T = \frac{2v_0 \sin \theta}{g}.$$

The horizontal range R, indicated in Fig. 3.28, is the horizontal distance traveled in the time T. It is given by $v_x t$, with $v_x = v_0 \cos \theta$ and $t = T$:

$$R = v_0(\cos \theta)T.$$

If the previous equation is used for the time T, the expression for the range becomes

$$R = \frac{2v_0^2}{g} \sin \theta \cos \theta.$$

Making use of the trigonometric identity $2 \sin \theta \cos \theta = \sin 2\theta$, we can express the range as

$$R = \frac{v_0^2}{g} \sin 2\theta.$$

Discussion The horizontal range derived here does not include the effects of air resistance. In cases where air resistance plays a role, the range is usually less than the amount given by this expression. An obvious exception is the Frisbee, a light disk that acquires a lifting force from the air passing over its surface.

Figure 3.29 shows the paths of an object projected upward at various angles with the same initial speed. Figure 3.30 is a graphical representation of the expression for the range. From either figure we can see that the maximum range occurs when $\theta = 45°$. (At this value of θ, $\sin 2\theta$ has its maximum value of 1.) The expression for the maximum range $R_{\max}$ is then

$$R_{\max} = \frac{v_0^2}{g}.$$

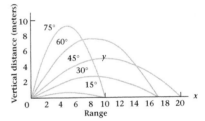

Figure 3.29

Trajectories of an object thrown upward with the same initial speed at various angles of inclination.

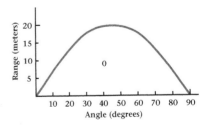

Figure 3.30

Range versus angle with respect to the horizontal for the same initial speed.

▼ Summary

Useful Concepts

■ We can determine the sum of two vectors by using geometry, algebra, or trigonometry. However, it is a good idea, especially at the outset, to always make a scale drawing.

■ Vectors are added graphically by making a scale drawing. In the triangle method, the vectors are placed head to tail and the resultant is drawn from the origin (tail) of the first vector to the head of the last vector. In the parallelogram method, two vectors are placed with their tails joined together. A parallelogram is constructed and the diagonal is the resultant.

■ In two dimensions, a vector **A** may be resolved into its components:

$$A_x = A \cos \theta, \qquad A_y = A \sin \theta.$$

■ The angle θ is measured counterclockwise from the positive x axis.

■ Vectors may be added together by adding their components. The magnitude and direction of a vector **A** in terms of its components are

$$A = \sqrt{A_x^2 + A_y^2} \quad \text{and} \quad \tan \theta = \frac{A_y}{A_x}.$$

■ The instantaneous velocity vector is

$$\mathbf{v} \equiv \lim_{\Delta t \to 0} \frac{\Delta \mathbf{r}}{\Delta t}.$$

■ The instantaneous acceleration vector is

$$\mathbf{a} \equiv \lim_{\Delta t \to 0} \frac{\Delta \mathbf{v}}{\Delta t}.$$

■ A projectile launched with an initial velocity $\mathbf{v}_0$ at an angle θ with the horizontal has initial x and y components of velocity

$$v_x = v_0 \cos \theta \quad \text{and} \quad v_y = v_0 \sin \theta.$$

■ The path of a projectile is a parabola (neglecting air resistance).

Important Terms

You should be able to write out the definitions or meanings of the following terms:

scalar	vector sum
vector	resultant
magnitude of a vector	relative velocity

▼ Conceptual Questions

3.1 List as many vector quantities as you can think of.

3.2 How is the meaning of the word *vectorcardiography* connected with our definition of a vector? Can you give any other compound words containing *vector* or any uses of the word outside of mathematics and physics?

3.3 What do we mean when we say that a weather map indicating temperatures represents a scalar field but a map indicating winds represents a vector field?

3.4 Show how you would add the following three vectors: 10 units north, 10 units south, and 10 units straight up.

3.5 Find an expression or procedure for finding the length of a vector with components along the x, y, and z axes.

3.6 In Galileo's example, if the stone had been thrown downward from the top of the mast rather than dropped from rest, what would the path have looked like to observers on the ship and on the shore?

3.7 If the object had been thrown horizontally from the mast of the ship in Galileo's example, what type of path would a person on the ship have observed? What type of path would a person on shore have observed? Be as explicit as you can for both cases.

3.8 A waiter in the dining car of a smoothly riding train pours a glass of water for a passenger. How would his task be affected if the velocity of the train is zero, if the velocity is nonzero but constant, and if the train is accelerating?

3.9 Can a group play volleyball on the deck of a ship moving at 15 km/h without taking into account the motion of the ship?

3.10 A child on a moving train rolls a ball down the aisle toward the back of the train. The ball travels 9.0 m along the floor in 3.0 s while the train moves forward at a constant speed of 18 m/s. Discuss the displacement of the ball during the 3-second interval from the point of view of the child and from the point of view of someone standing on the ground beside the track.

Problems

Section 3.2 Addition of Vectors

Draw scale diagrams carefully. Choose a scale that gives you plenty of room to work. Indicate your scale on the diagram.

3.1 (a) If you walk three city blocks east and then four blocks north, how many blocks are you from your starting place? (b) What direction are you from the starting point? Give your answer as an angle measured from due east.

3.2 A jogger runs directly east for 3.0 km, then turns and goes northwest for 5.0 km. He then travels directly south for 2.0 km. How far and in what direction is he from the starting point? (Northwest is the direction lying exactly half way between north and west.)

3.3 A motorist travels directly north for 36 km, then turns to the west and goes 18 km. How far is she from the starting point and in what direction? Give the angle with respect to east.

3.4 Vector **A** has a magnitude of 13 units at a direction of 250°, and vector **B** has a magnitude of 27 units at a direction of 330°, both measured with respect to the positive *x* axis. (a) What is the vector sum of **A** and **B**? (b) What is the vector **C** = **A** − **B**? Find your answers by graphical analysis.

3.5 Add the following vectors graphically in the order given, then add them in reverse order on a separate diagram, thereby testing that vector addition is commutative: **A** = 5 units at 60° and **B** = 7 units at 180°.

3.6 A vector **A** has a magnitude of 25 units at 200°, and a vector **B** has a magnitude of 30 units at 45°. What is the vector difference **A** − **B**?

3.7● The vectors diagrammed in Fig. 3.31 have the same magnitude, *A*. Find: (a) **B** + **C**, (b) **A** + **B** + **C**, (c) **B** − **C**, (d) **A** − **B** − **C**.

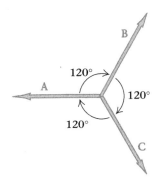

Figure 3.31
Problem 3.7.

3.8● Four ropes are tied to a stake, and each is pulled toward a compass direction, N, S, E, or W. A force of 10 lb is applied to the rope pulled toward the east. Forces of 20, 30, and 40 lb are applied toward the south, west, and north, respectively. What is the net force exerted on the stake by the ropes and in what direction is it? (Forces are vector quantities. The net force is the vector sum of the individual forces.)

3.9● A motorcyclist rides a given distance due north, then rides twice that far to the west. At the end of the trip, the direct distance from the starting point is 112 m. What is the length of each leg of the trip and in what direction is the end point with respect to due north?

3.10● A salesperson made a trip starting from the home office. The trip was made in two straight-line parts, one of which was 20 km long to the east. The end point of the trip was 80 km from the starting point at a direction of 45° southeast. Describe the other leg of the trip. Work this as a problem in vector subtraction.

Section 3.3 Resolution of Vectors

Solve the following vector problems using trigonometry. A review of trigonometry is found in the appendix at the end of this chapter.

3.11 A vector with a magnitude $V = 16$ makes an angle of 50° with the *x* axis. Resolve the vector into its *x* and *y* components.

3.12 A vector with magnitude $V = 24$ makes an angle of −36° with the *x* axis. Find the *x* and *y* components of the vector.

3.13 What are the magnitude and direction of the vector with $A_x = 4.8$ and $A_y = -6.2$?

3.14 A vector has components of 9.0 units along the *x* axis and 12 units along the *y* axis. (a) What is the magnitude of the vector? (b) What is the angle between the vector and the *x* axis?

3.15 A helicopter takes off from pad #1 at ground level and rises straight up to an altitude of 327 m. The helicopter then flies in a straight level flight to a point directly above pad #2 on top of a building that is 873 m horizontally away from pad #1. The helicopter then descends in a straight line to pad #2. What is the helicopter's final displacement from pad #1 if pad #2 is 180 m above the ground level?

3.16 A person rides a motorbike 150 m along a road that slants upward at 4.50° from the horizontal. (a) How much higher will the rider be at the end of the trip? (b) How far has the rider gone in the horizontal direction?

3.17 The direction of a vector is 118° from the positive *x* axis, and its *y* component is 18.0. Find the *x* component and the magnitude of the vector.

3.18 Vector **A** has a magnitude of 8.0 at an angle of 60° from the x axis. Vector **B** has a magnitude of 6.0 at an angle of −30° from the x axis. Determine the vector sum **C = A + B** by resolution into components.

3.19 Find the difference **D = A − B** for the vectors given in Problem 3.18.

3.20 Find the vector **V = 2A − B** for **A** and **B** given in Problem 3.18.

3.21 (a) Find the sum **C** of the two vectors **A** and **B** given by $A_x = 3.0$, $A_y = 7.0$ and $B_x = 10.0$, $B_y = -9.0$. (b) Find the difference **D = A − B**.

3.22• If a vector has a magnitude of 18 and an x component of −7.0, what are the two possibilities for its y component and direction?

3.23•• A woman traveling due north makes a detour around a large lake in the following manner (Fig. 3.32). At point *A* she turns 46° toward the west and travels 4.91 km to *B*. At *B* she turns to the north and travels a distance of 8.27 km to *C*. At *C* she turns 60° to the east and travels a distance of 4.08 km to *D*. At *D* she turns to the north and continues her trip. (a) Are the initial and final northward paths along the same line? (b) What is the distance between *A* and *D*.

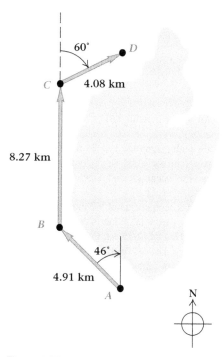

Figure 3.32
Problem 3.23.

Section 3.4 Relative Velocity in One Dimension

Hints for Solving Problems

You will find it helpful to use subscripts on the velocities similar to those used in Example 3.5.

3.24 A vendor on a train moving in the forward direction at 2.00 m/s pushes her cart toward the rear of the train at 0.47 m/s while an ant on a sandwich crawls toward the front of the train at 0.01 m/s. What is the velocity of the train station with respect to the ant.

3.25 Two airplanes are flying side by side at the same altitude. Plane A is slowly overtaking plane B at 4 km/h. A flight attendant in plane A is walking toward the rear of the plane at a speed of 2 km/h and a passenger is walking toward the front at 2 km/h. What are their speeds relative to a passenger watching them from plane B?

3.26 A boat is traveling in a river with a current of 3.0 km/h. The boat is capable of traveling at 10.0 km/h in still water. (a) How long will it take the boat to travel 7.0 km upstream? (b) How long will it take to travel 7.0 km downstream?

3.27 A boat capable of making 9.0 km/h in still water is traveling upstream in a river flowing at 4.0 km/h (Fig. 3.33). An object lost overboard is not missed for 30 minutes. (a) If the boat is then turned around, how long will it take to overtake the floating lost object? (b) What total distance will the boat travel relative to the shore from the point of turnaround to the point of overtaking the object?

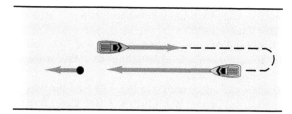

Figure 3.33
Problem 3.27.

3.28• A passenger rushing to catch a plane at the airport walks on a moving sidewalk at a speed of 3.0 km/h relative to the sidewalk in the direction that the sidewalk is moving. The sidewalk is 100 m long and moves with a steady velocity of 1.0 km/h. (a) How long does it take for the passenger to get from one end of the sidewalk to the other, that is, to cover the 100 m? (b) How much time does the passenger save by taking the moving sidewalk instead of just walking beside it? (c) Through what distance does the passenger walk relative to the moving sidewalk? (d) If the passenger's stride is 80 cm, how many steps are taken in going from one end of the moving sidewalk to the other?

3.29• Two cars approach each other on the highway. Car A moves north at 90 km/h, car B moves south at 70 km/h. (a) What is the velocity of car A as seen from car B? (b) What is the velocity of car B as seen from car A? (c) What are their velocities relative to car C, which is traveling north at 100 km/h?

Section 3.5 Relative Velocity in Two Dimensions

3.30 A small airplane flies with a speed relative to the ground (ground speed) of 208 km/h in a direction 18.0° to the east of north. If the plane is headed due north and the deviation from that direction is due to a crosswind blowing from west to east (Fig. 3.34), what is the speed of the wind?

Figure 3.34
Problem 3.30: An airplane headed due north is blown off course by a crosswind blowing due east.

3.31 A small airplane has a cruising speed of 260 km/h in still air. The pilot heads the plane in an easterly direction on a day when the wind is blowing at 25 km/h in a direction 60° north of east. In what direction will the plane move and what will be its ground speed?

3.32• An airplane with a maximum air speed of 320 km/h takes off and heads to its destination, which is due east of its starting point, when a 70 km/h crosswind starts blowing from the north. The schedule calls for the plane to travel a distance of 1590 km between airports in a time of 5.0 h. Will the plane arrive on schedule?

3.33• An airplane heading south with an air speed of 200 km/h is in a cross wind of 10 km/h blowing toward the west. How far does the airplane go in two hours and in what direction?

3.34• A boat capable of making 9.0 km/h in still water is used to cross a river flowing at a speed of 4.0 km/h. (a) At what angle must the boat be directed so that its motion will be straight across the river? (b) What is its resultant speed relative to the shore?

Sections 3.6 and 3.7 Kinematics in Two Dimensions and Projectile Motion

Hints for Solving Problems

Choose a coordinate system and stick with it throughout the problem. Remember that horizontal and vertical components of motion are independent of each other, but they take place during the same time interval. Pay careful attention to signs and apply them consistently throughout the problem. Assume that air resistance can be ignored for these problems.

3.35 A student touring Japan accidentally drops a 500-yen coin from a height of 1.20 m above the floor of the Bullet Train, which is traveling at 250 km/h (Fig. 3.35). (a) How long does it take for the coin to hit the floor? (b) Where does the coin land with respect to the floor of the train? (c) How far along the track does the train go during the time it takes for the coin to fall?

Figure 3.35
Problem 3.35: The Bullet Train.

3.36 A rock thrown horizontally from the top of a radio tower lands 17.0 m from the base of the tower. If the speed at which the object was projected was 9.50 m/s, how high is the tower?

3.37 A monkey on a cliff throws a coconut horizontally from a height of 17 m with a speed of 2.1 m/s. If the ground below the cliff is level, how far from the base of the cliff does the coconut strike the ground?

Hints for Solving Problems

Problems 3.38 to 3.42 can be solved using the techniques and results of Example 3.14.

3.38 A rock thrown with an initial velocity of 32.5 m/s at an angle of 50° with respect to the horizontal has a range of 985 m on a certain planet. What is the acceleration of gravity on this planet?

3.39 An astronaut playing golf on earth consistently hits a golf ball 170 m. Using the same swing, how far could the astronaut hit golf balls on the moon? (*Hint:* The gravitational acceleration on the moon is approximately 1/6 that on the earth.)

3.40 (a) How far will a stone travel over level ground if it is thrown upward at an angle of 30.0° with respect to the horizontal and with a speed of 12.0 m/s? (b) What is the maximum range that could be achieved with the same initial speed?

3.41 Locusts have been observed to jump horizontal distances up to 80 cm on a level floor. Photographs of their jump show that they usually take off at an angle of about 55° from the horizontal. Calculate the initial velocity of a locust making a jump of 80 cm with a takeoff angle of 55°.

3.42• If you can throw a ball vertically upward to a height $h = 20$ m, what is the maximum horizontal range over which you can throw the same ball, assuming you throw it at the same initial speed?

3.43• Plot the path of an object in the xy plane that moves according to

$$x = (2 + 3t + 2t^2) \text{ cm},$$
$$y = (2t + 5t^2) \text{ cm}$$

from $t = 0$ to $t = 4$ s.

3.44• A cougar leaps horizontally from the top of a cliff with an initial velocity of 8.25 m/s. The cliff is 6.43 m tall. (a) Sketch the path of the cougar. (b) What are the magnitude and direction of the velocity when the cougar is halfway to the ground?

3.45• A ball thrown horizontally from a 13-m-high building strikes the ground 5.0 m from the building. With what velocity was the ball thrown?

3.46• A ball is thrown upward from a platform 5.2 m high with a speed of 15 m/s at an angle of 40° from the horizontal. What is the magnitude of its velocity when it hits the ground?

3.47• A monkey throws a coconut horizontally out of a tree at 5.36 m/s. The coconut leaves his hand 13.4 m above the level ground. The coconut lands on the ground by falling directly into a cylindrical basket tilted so that the coconut goes to the bottom without touching the sides. (a) How far is the basket horizontally from the point directly below the release point for the coconut? (b) At what angle is the basket tilted?

3.48• A third baseman makes a throw to first base 39.0 m away. The ball leaves his hand with a speed of 38.0 m/s at a height of 1.50 m from the ground and making an angle of 20.0° with the horizontal. How high will the ball be when it gets to first base?

3.49•• A third baseman makes a throw to first base 39.0 m away. (a) If the ball leaves his hand traveling horizontally with a speed of 38.0 m/s at a height of 1.20 m from the ground, how far will it go before striking the ground? (b) At what angle must he throw the ball so that it reaches the first baseman's glove at a height of 1.20 m above the ground?

3.50•• A cannon sitting on the battlement of a castle is aimed away from the castle at an angle θ above the horizontal. Find an equation for the time for the cannonball to hit the level ground below in terms of the height of the battlement, the magnitude and direction of the initial velocity, and the acceleration of gravity.

3.51•• An object on a horizontal plane starts at the origin and moves with velocity $v_x = 10.0$ cm/s, $v_y = -5.0$ cm/s, and acceleration $a_x = 0$, $a_y = 4.0$ cm/s². (a) How far is it from the origin after 5.0 s? (b) In what direction is it from the origin? (c) In what direction is it moving?

3.52•• A Hollywood daredevil plans to jump the canyon shown in Fig. 3.36 on a motorcycle. If he desires a 3.0-second flight time, what is (a) the correct angle for his launch ramp, (b) his correct launch speed, (c) the correct angle for his landing ramp, and (d) his predicted landing speed? (Neglect air resistance.)

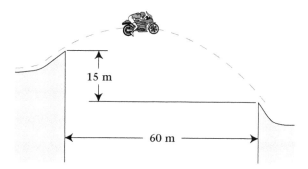

15 m

60 m

Figure 3.36
Problem 3.52: Motorcycle daredevil jumping canyon.

3.53•• An intramural quarterback throws a football with an initial speed of 9.7 m/s at an upward angle of 38° above a horizontal playing field. (a) How long will the ball remain in the air before falling to the ground if it leaves his hand at a point 1.5 m above the ground? (b) What horizontal distance will the ball travel before striking the ground?

Additional Problems

3.54 Five vectors of equal magnitude radiate outward from the center of a regular pentagon, one vector pointing toward each vertex (Fig. 3.37). Show by a graphical treatment that the sum of all five vectors is zero.

3.55 A ladder leans against a house at an angle of 76° from the horizontal. The base of the ladder is 1.48 m from the

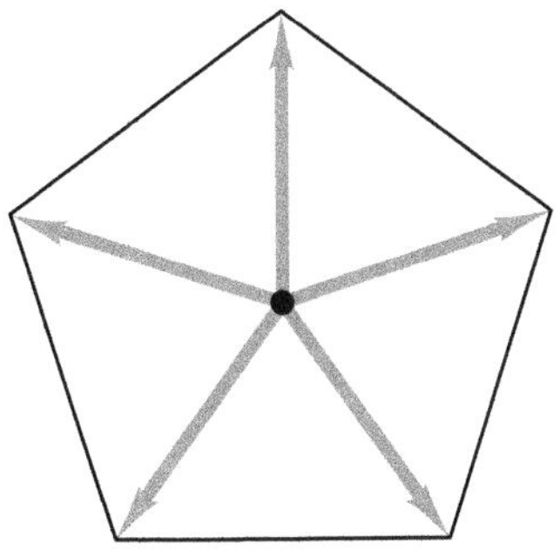

Figure 3.37
Problem 3.54.

house. (a) How long is the ladder? (b) How far up the wall does the ladder touch the house?

3.56 A guy wire bracing a power pole makes an angle of 53° with the ground. How long is the guy wire if it attaches to the pole at a height of 5.50 m above the ground?

3.57 A vector **A** has a magnitude of two units at 30° with respect to the horizontal. Vector **B** has a magnitude of five units at 90°. Calculate **C = 3A + 2B.**

3.58 A physics student standing on the top floor of a building sights downward to a newspaper box on the ground below. The line of sight to the box makes an angle of 75° with respect to the horizontal. After coming down, the student measures the distance from the building to the box to be 40.5 m. How high above the ground were the student's eyes when he was looking at the box from the top floor?

3.59 Observations are made of a distant television tower from each end of a 100-m base line. From each position the angle between the line of sight and the base line is 85.5°. How far is the tower from the center of the line?

3.60 Three vectors have the same magnitude of 14 units. They make angles of θ, 2θ and 3θ with respect to the x axis, where $\theta = 20°$. What is their vector sum?

3.61 (a) How far will a stone travel over level ground if it is thrown upward at an angle of 30.0° with respect to the horizontal and with a speed of 12.0 m/s? Assume the stone is launched at a height of 2.0 m above the ground. (b) What is the maximum horizontal range that could be achieved with the same initial speed? Refer to Example 3.14.

3.62• A ladder that is 4.00 m long is leaning against a wall at an angle of 64° with respect to the ground. If the base of the ladder is moved 0.30 m away from the wall, how far will the top of the ladder go down?

3.63• An arrow was fired horizontally from a platform above the ground. Exactly 3 s after it was released, it struck the ground at an angle of 45° from the horizontal. (a) With what speed and (b) from what height was it launched?

3.64• This problem helps to illustrate how important the effects of aerodynamic forces can be. A golf ball hit at a speed of 67 m/s will carry (achieve its maximum flight distance of) 183 meters when driven at a launch angle of 11°. What would be its horizontal range in a vacuum if launched at the same speed and (a) at the same angle and (b) at a 45° angle?

3.65•• A baseball player standing on a platform throws a baseball out over a level playing field. The ball is released from a point 3.50 m above the field with an initial speed of 14.3 m/s at an upward angle of 27° from the horizontal. How far from a point on the ground directly below the point of release will the baseball strike the field?

3.66•• A spring-loaded cannon aimed at 47° above the horizontal is on the last car of a long train of flat cars. The train has an initial velocity of 54.3 km/h. At the moment the train begins to accelerate forward at 0.325 m/s², the cannon fires a projectile at 180 m/s. The cannon points in the direction that the train is moving. (a) What is the horizontal range observed by a person standing on the ground? (b) How far on the train from the cannon does the projectile land? Neglect air resistance.

3.67•• Show that the maximum height h to which a football rises when kicked from the ground at an angle θ is given by $h = \frac{1}{4}R \tan \theta$, where R is the range.

3.68•• A cannon is adjusted for maximum range R_{max} on level ground. How high is the cannonball when its horizontal distance from the cannon is $\frac{3}{4}R_{max}$?

3.69•• How high does a golf ball rise when projected for maximum range? Express your answer in terms of the range.

3.70•• Galileo's great-great-great-…grandchild drops a Chianti bottle from the top of a vertical tower 54.6 m tall.
(a) How long does it take for the bottle to fall to the ground?
(b) What is the velocity of the bottle as it hits the ground?
(c) If the bottle is thrown straight out horizontally from the tower with a speed of 12.3 m/s, how far does it land from a point on the ground directly beneath the point from which it was launched? (d) What is the bottle's horizontal component of velocity, and (e) what is the magnitude of its velocity just before it strikes the ground for the situation in (c)?

Review of Trigonometry

This brief outline of basic trigonometry, together with a few other relationships introduced later, includes most of the mathematics you need to know for this text.

It may be intuitively obvious to you (or you may remember a formal proof from geometry) that in the right triangle ABC of Fig. A3.1, the *ratio* of side AC to the hypotenuse AB does not depend on the physical size of the triangle, but only on the angles. For instance, in the two similar triangles ABC and ADE in Fig. A3.1, we see that

$$\frac{BC}{AB} = \frac{DE}{AD}.$$

This ratio uniquely characterizes the angle marked θ in the diagram. This ratio is called the sine of the angle θ and is written

$$\sin \theta = \frac{BC}{AB}.$$

More generally, for any right triangle,

$$\sin \theta = \frac{\text{length of the side opposite the angle } \theta}{\text{length of the hypotenuse}}.$$

Two other trigonometric functions, the cosine of the angle and the tangent of the angle, are defined as

$$\cos \theta = \frac{\text{length of the side adjacent to the angle}}{\text{length of the hypotenuse}}.$$

and

$$\tan \theta = \frac{\text{length of opposite side}}{\text{length of adjacent side}}.$$

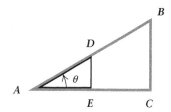

Figure A3.1
Two similar right triangles, ABC and ADE, with a common angle θ.

The tangent may seem somewhat superfluous, since $\tan \theta = \sin \theta/\cos \theta$, but its use is often convenient. A scientific pocket calculator can give you the value of the sine, cosine, or tangent of any given angle. There are other trigonometric functions, but they will not be needed in this text.

We always measure angles in the counterclockwise direction from the positive x axis (Fig. A3.2). Angles measured in the clockwise direction are negative. Our definitions of sine, cosine, and tangent do not change for angles greater than 90°; however, the sign of the trigonometric function changes from quadrant to quadrant. For 150° the hypotenuse is positive (as always), the side opposite the angle is positive, but the adjacent side (in the negative x-direction) is negative. Thus, the sine of an angle in the second quadrant (that is, an angle between 90° and 180°) is positive, but the cosine is negative. The signs of the sine and cosine functions are marked in each quadrant of Fig. A3.2.

If you know the value of the sine of an angle, you can also use your calculator to find the value of the an-

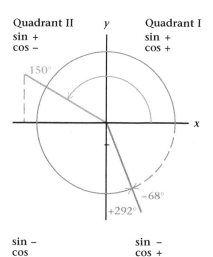

Figure A3.2
Angles are measured relative to the positive x axis. The signs of the sine and cosine functions are indicated for each quadrant.

gle. The angle θ whose sine is equal to A is written as $\theta = \sin^{-1}A$, where $\sin^{-1}$ is read as the inverse sine. The values of $\cos^{-1}$ and $\tan^{-1}$ can be obtained in a similar manner.

You can use your calculator to verify numerically that, for any angle,

$$\sin^2\theta + \cos^2\theta = 1.$$

We can show from Fig. A3.1 that this equation is true in general. The Pythagorean theorem gives

$$(BC)^2 + (AC)^2 = (AB)^2.$$

Dividing both sides by $(AB)^2$, we get

$$\frac{(BC)^2}{(AB)^2} + \frac{(AC)^2}{(AB)^2} = 1$$

$$\left(\frac{BC}{AB}\right)^2 + \left(\frac{AC}{AB}\right)^2 = 1,$$

or

$$\sin^2\theta + \cos^2\theta = 1.$$

Example 3.15

Standing on top of a tall building, you see a friend walking at a distance. The angle between your line of sight and the horizontal is 15°. How far from you is your friend? Assume the road is level and your eyes are 40.8 m above the ground.

Solution Let BC be the distance from the ground to your eyes and AB the distance from you to your friend. The angle θ in Fig. A3.3 is given as 15°. The sine of θ is

$$\sin \theta = \frac{BC}{AB},$$

or

$$AB = \frac{BC}{\sin \theta}.$$

Inserting the numerical values gives

$$AB = \frac{40.8 \text{ m}}{0.259} = 158 \text{ m}.$$

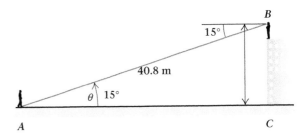

Figure A3.3
Example 3.15: How far away is your friend?

Example 3.16

Three narrow strips of wood, having lengths of 30, 40, and 50 cm, are arranged on a table top to form a right triangle (Fig. A3.4). What is the angle between the 40-cm side and the 50-cm side?

Solution Using the definition of the cosine, we write

$$\cos \theta = \frac{40 \text{ cm}}{50 \text{ cm}} = 0.80.$$

The value of the angle θ is

$$\theta = \cos^{-1}(0.80) = 37°.$$

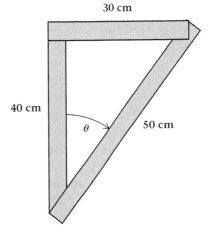

Figure A3.4
Example 3.16: How large is the angle θ?

4.1   Events Leading to Newton's *Principia*
4.2   What Is a Force?

Back to the Future: The Writing of the Principia

4.3   Newton's First Law—Inertia
4.4   Newton's Second Law
4.5   Weight
4.6   Newton's Third Law
4.7   Some Applications of Newton's Laws
4.8   Friction

Physics in Practice: The Friction of Automobile Tires

4.9   Static Equilibrium
4.10   The Laws of Motion as a Whole

Appendix: Solving Simultaneous Equations

Force and Motion

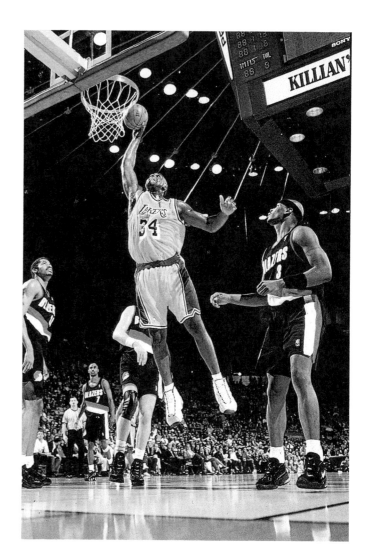

In the last three chapters you learned to describe motion. In this chapter we discuss the underlying causes of motion, a study called *dynamics*. **Newtonian mechanics,** or classical mechanics as it is also called, is the branch of physics that deals with the kinematics and dynamics of large-scale (macroscopic) objects. The essence of Newtonian mechanics, which is widely used to describe the motion of objects as different as golf balls and spacecraft, is found in Newton's three laws of motion. These laws, first clearly stated by Isaac Newton more than 300 years ago in his book the *Principia,* tell us how forces affect the motion of objects. The same laws apply whether the object is a mosquito zigzagging through the air or a planet moving about the sun. Although Newton's laws do not apply in the domain of the very small (that is, to atoms and molecules) and the very fast (to objects moving at speeds near the speed of light), they apply to almost everything else. Thus, the concepts introduced in this chapter form the basis for our understanding of much of physics and are essential to al-most all of wh · at follows in this course. ■

4.1 Events Leading to Newton's *Principia*

In the sixteenth century, the idea that the earth was the fixed center of the universe was firmly ingrained in astronomical thought and had become an article of religious faith. Nicolas Copernicus (1473–1543) published in his last year a workable scheme for the solar system with the sun at the center and the planets in orbits about it. His idea was initially rejected, but the work of Galileo and Johannes Kepler (1571–1630) helped to bring about its adoption. Such a model is called a heliocentric theory, from the Greek word *helios,* for sun.

By Kepler's time, it was known that the orbits of the planets were not exact circles and that the sun was not at the exact center of the orbits. Kepler analyzed Tycho Brahe's (1546–1601) astronomical observations and found that the planets closer to the sun moved faster than those farther away, and that a single planet moved faster when it was closer to the sun than when it was farther away. He proposed that the sun was the cause of the planet's motion and that the sun's influence might decrease with increasing distance from it. With these ideas as guidelines and Tycho's detailed observations as his raw material, Kepler constructed a model of the solar system that was compatible with both ideas.

Kepler's laws of planetary motion were among the first "laws of nature" in the modern sense. The first of these laws, published in 1609, states that the planets move in elliptical orbits with the sun at one focus (Fig. 4.1).* (This law and Kepler's other two laws are discussed in detail in Chapter 5.) Though Kepler's laws could be considered statements about the geometry and kinematics of the solar system, Kepler himself was not content with this and thought that one should look for the cause of planetary motion. Many, including Kepler, held that the planets' orbits were due to some influence of the sun.

By the 1660s and 1670s, there was some reason to believe that the sun attracted each planet with a force that depended in a simple way on the distance between them: The force was thought to be proportional to the reciprocal of the square of this distance. That is,

$$F \propto \frac{1}{r^2},$$

where r is the distance between the sun and planet and F is the attractive force. Such a force is called an **inverse-square force.** This terminology means that if the force were, say, 36 units for a distance of 6000 m, then doubling the distance to 12,000 m would make the force become one quarter as much, or 9 units. Similarly, if the distance were halved to 3000 m, the force would increase by a factor of 4, to 144 units. The reasons for accepting the idea of an inverse-square force for the sun-planet attraction are developed later in Chapter 5.

One of the principal events that led to the writing of the *Principia* was Newton's deduction that an inverse-square force was responsible for the observed

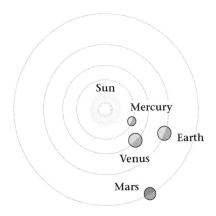

Figure 4.1
The orbits of the four innermost planets of the solar system. Relative distances from the sun are correct. On this scale the difference between the true ellipse and a circle cannot be detected. The size of the planets is exaggerated.

---

*A review of the properties of the ellipse is found on page A–2 of Appendix A.

orbits of the planets. Further, he identified the action of the inverse-square force as the law of gravitation and showed it to be universal by applying it to the moon, the planets, and objects on earth.

Newton's ideas about the way the universe worked, as expressed in the *Principia,* transcended science and influenced Western thought in general. The idea that a mechanical universe obeyed a single set of laws suggested that all observed behavior could be explained in mechanical terms. Within the last hundred years, physicists have found that it is not possible to take this deterministic viewpoint and that nature is much more subtle than it was imagined to be in Newton's day. We will discuss the contemporary viewpoint later in this book, when we get to relativity and quantum theory.

4.2   What Is a Force?

Understanding the concept of force forms the basis for understanding Newton's laws. In everyday language, a **force** is a "push" or a "pull." When we push a lawnmower or a grocery cart, we exert a force on it. When we pull open a drawer, we exert a force on the drawer. When we drop something, it falls, and we say that the force, or pull, of gravity made it fall. A roller coaster plunges downhill because of the force of gravity and moves through turns and loops because of the forces exerted on it by the track (Fig. 4.2). However, forces do not always cause motion. A book resting on a table experiences the downward force of gravity even though the book does not move.

Notice that force is not a property of an object, like mass, but rather it is an interaction of the object with an external agent. Consequently, for a force to act

Figure 4.2
A roller coaster moves in response to forces acting on it.

THE WRITING OF THE *PRINCIPIA*

The writing of the *Principia* came about from an argument over physics. The discussion was on the nature of gravitational force, and took place in January 1684 among three men: Christopher Wren (1632–1723), remembered today as an architect of churches and public buildings, especially St. Paul's Cathedral in London; Robert Hooke (1635–1703), who was curator of the Royal Society* at that time; and Edmund Halley (1656–1742), a young astronomer and mathematician. It was Halley (rhymes with Sally) who in 1705 predicted the return of the comet of 1682, which, upon its next appearance in 1758, was given his name.

Wren offered a prize to whichever of the other two could produce a proof that the force between the sun and the planets obeyed an inverse-square law. Hooke maintained that he had done so, but failed to produce evidence within a reasonable span of time. So Halley sought the help of Isaac Newton (Fig. B4.1), at that time a professor at Cambridge University. During the visit, Halley asked Newton what would be the orbit of planets attracted to the sun in an inverse-square manner. Newton replied that they would be ellipses and further said that he had produced a mathematical proof of this. Newton promised to repeat the calculation and send it to Halley, and the manuscript arrived in November. This so excited Halley that he suggested that Newton make his results public by sending them to the Royal Society. Newton did so in the form of a tract, *De Motu,* based in part on earlier calculations. In this work he proved that if "a body revolves in an ellipse . . . the law of the centripetal force . . . is reciprocally as the square of the distance." Here was the solution to the physical problem of planetary orbits, the first real answer to the question, "What *must* be the force that gives rise to the observed planetary orbits if the sun is the attracting body?"

Figure B4.1 Isaac Newton (1642–1727). As an old man, Newton recollected that his peak years were 1665 and 1666. While the black plague swept through England, Newton retreated to his family's farm. There he invented calculus, completed much of the preparatory work for his theory of gravity, and discovered that white light is composed of many colored rays—all in the span of 18 months!

Figure B4.2 Saturn's rings as seen by *Voyager* 2 in August 1981. The colors are computer enhanced.

After presenting *De Motu* to the Royal Society, Halley, with the support of the society, invited Newton to write a more comprehensive version. Newton finished the complete work within 18 months, an incredibly short time for such a monumental work. The first edition of the *Principia* was available by July 5, 1687.

Newton wrote the *Principia* for an elite audience who understood science and mathematics. In many ways he tried to make it as difficult and inaccessible as possible. He is said to have boasted to a friend that he made the *Principia* "abstruse" so that he would not have to argue with those of lesser learning. In contrast to Galileo's use of everyday language, Newton wrote the *Principia* in Latin, the international language of learning. Newton never attempted to produce an English version, though he lived forty more years and brought out revised editions in 1713 and 1723. The first, and only, complete English translation was published by Andrew Motte in 1729.

The *Principia* was and is a difficult book, so difficult that one historian has said "it is doubtful whether any work of comparable influence can ever have been read by so few persons." Like major scientific works in other times, it had strong proponents as well as strong detractors. However, the Newtonian concepts were admitted to the general body of scientific knowledge because of their utility and precision.

Newtonian mechanics is still important today. For example, when coupled with modern computer technology, Newtonian physics allows us to make the calculations necessary to guide probes to the outer planets of the solar system. In the 1970s and 1980s, Voyager spacecraft sent back dramatic pictures of Saturn, Jupiter, Uranus, and Neptune (Fig. B4.2).

---

*The Royal Society of London is one of the oldest scientific societies in the world. Founded in 1660, the society is still active publishing scientific journals.

on an object there must be something external other than the object itself that causes the force. For example, the force that moves a grocery cart is the result of an interaction between a person and the cart, and the force of gravity that keeps the moon in its orbit is an interaction between the earth and the moon.

Because force has direction as well as magnitude, it is a vector quantity. The **net force** is the *vector sum* of all forces acting simultaneously on an object. We often refer to the net force as the *resultant force* or the unbalanced force. *It is the net force that determines the motion of the object.*

Example 4.1

A patient with a fractured femur is placed in Russell's traction to help in the proper healing of the bone (Fig. 4.3a). The ropes and pulleys are positioned so that the resultant force is parallel to the upper leg. The downward force *F* exerted by gravity on the hanging mass is applied to the knee by a flexible rope that passes through the pulleys. The force on the knee has magnitude *F* and is directed upward along the rope. The force on the heel has magnitude 2*F* because there are two ropes leading to the heel pulley, each pulling with a force *F*. This force is directed horizontally away from the heel. The angle between the horizontal force and the upward force is 122°. What is the magnitude of the net, or resultant, force that pulls parallel to the upper leg?

Strategy We first draw a vector diagram (Fig. 4.3b) with the force on the knee represented by the vector **A** and the force on the heel by the vector **B**. If we measure the angles with respect to the positive *x* axis as shown, then vector **A** makes an angle of 58°. From the statement of the problem, we know that

Figure 4.3
(a) Russell's traction. (b) Vector diagram for Russell's traction.

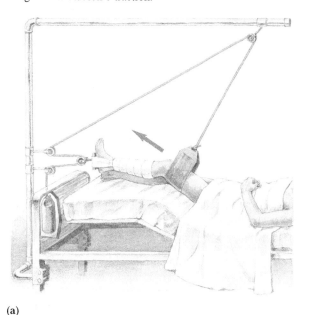

(a)

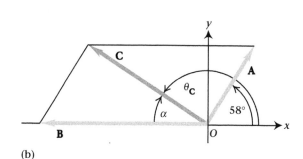

(b)

$A = F$ and $B = 2F$. Because forces are vector quantities, we use the vector addition techniques of Chapter 3 to find the magnitude of the resultant force. We resolve each force **A** and **B** into horizontal (x) and vertical (y) components. Then we add the x components together to get the x component C_x of the resultant vector and add the y components to get C_y. Finally, we use the Pythagorean theorem to obtain the magnitude C of the resultant. As a check of our work, we will also calculate the direction and verify that our answer agrees with the diagram.

Solution The components of the vectors are

$$C_x = A_x + B_x \qquad\qquad\qquad C_y = A_y + B_y$$
$$C_x = A \cos \theta_A + B \cos \theta_B \qquad C_y = A \sin \theta_A + B \sin \theta_B$$
$$C_x = F \cos 58 + 2F \cos 180 \qquad C_y = F \sin 58 + 2F \sin 180$$
$$C_x = F(0.530) + 2F(-1.00) = -1.47F \qquad C_y = F(0.848) + 0 = 0.848F.$$

The magnitude of the force vector **C** is then

$$C = \sqrt{C_x^2 + C_y^2}$$
$$C = \sqrt{(-1.47F)^2 + (0.848F)^2} = 1.70F.$$

Thus, the force applied parallel to the upper leg is $1.70F$, where F is the magnitude of the force due to the action of gravity on M. Measurement of the length of **C** on the diagram confirms that this is the magnitude of the applied force.

   We can check our work by calculating the direction of the resultant force **C**. Because C_y is a positive quantity and C_x is a negative quantity, the head of the vector **C** will lie in the second quadrant. That is, the angle θ_C lies between 90° and 180°. The angle of **C** with respect to the horizontal direction is given by

$$\tan \theta_C = \frac{C_y}{C_x} = \frac{0.848F}{-1.47F} = -0.577.$$

Direct computation with a pocket calculator gives $\theta = -30°$. However we know that the vector lies in the second quadrant, so we must add 180°, making the correct answer

$$\theta_C = 150°.$$

Discussion When you use a calculator to determine the angle whose tangent is -0.577, you will get an answer of $-30.0°$. This happens for the following reason. Because the tangent is the ratio y/x, the value of the tangent can be negative in two situations, either because x is positive and y is negative or because y is positive and x is negative. For positive x and negative y, the angle is in the fourth quadrant, but in the case of negative x and positive y, the angle is in the second quadrant, as we know our answer to be in this instance. However, a calculator cannot distinguish between the two cases and is designed to give you the smaller angle. This is another reason why you must always draw a diagram and use it as part of your calculational procedure.

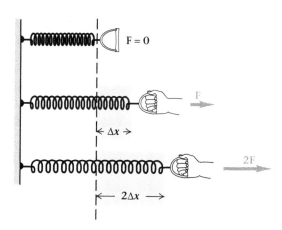

Figure 4.4

A spring attached to a fixed wall stretches through a distance proportional to the force applied to the ends. If a force **F** stretches the spring a distance Δx, then a force of 2**F** extends the spring a distance $2\Delta x$.

How can you measure a force? Consider that when you pull on the ends of a coiled spring (Fig. 4.4), the spring stretches. The harder you pull, the more the spring is extended. When you pull with a force **F**, the spring extends a length Δx; when you pull with twice the force (2**F**), the spring extends a length $2\Delta x$. If you calibrate the extension of the spring, you can use the distance the spring stretches to measure the magnitude of the applied force. Spring scales that use this principle are commonly available. Once the scale is calibrated, you can use it to measure forces of different origins, such as forces resulting from muscular effort, gravitation, or magnetism.

When you pull or push a spring, you exert a *contact force,* a force in which two bodies interact directly by contact between their surfaces. The force you feel on your hand when you push a door and the force you feel on your feet when you walk are familiar contact forces. Although contact forces are common, they are not considered fundamental forces in the physical world.

A dropped stone falls because of the force of gravity. In this case the stone falls freely without being in contact with anything. The force involved is an example of a field force; the force is exerted without actual contact between the bodies but acts through space. The gravitational field is discussed in the next chapter.

The gravitational force is one of the four *fundamental forces* in nature (Table 4.1). The other fundamental forces are the electromagnetic force, the strong force, and the weak force. The gravitational force is responsible for the weight of bodies on the earth as well as for the motion of the planets. It acts between all masses. We will study gravitation in detail in Chapter 5.

The electromagnetic force includes both electric and magnetic forces and is relatively strong. It is the electric force that you observe if you run a comb through your hair and then use the comb to pick up bits of paper. You see the magnetic force act when you pick up a pin with a magnet. The electromagnetic force is responsible for holding atoms and molecules together and for the structure of matter. Contact forces are actually large-scale manifestations of fundamental electromagnetic forces. We discuss electromagnetic forces in Chapters 16–21.

The strong force holds together the constituents of the atomic nucleus. It is sometimes called the nuclear force. Chapters 29 and 32 include material on the strong force.

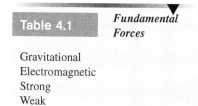

Table 4.1	*Fundamental Forces*
Gravitational	
Electromagnetic	
Strong	
Weak	

The weak force acts between all matter, but is so weak that it plays no direct part in ordinary observable behavior. It is important, however, in the interactions between subnuclear particles.

Current theories have been partially successful in unifying the basic forces of nature. We now understand the electric and weak force to be separate manifestations of one force. However, efforts to fully unify the forces of nature under a single theory have not yet been successful.

4.3 Newton's First Law—Inertia

Because of our past experience, we can readily believe that a body at rest remains at rest unless some action is taken. However, it is not so easily seen from everyday experience that once a body is moving with nonzero constant velocity (constant speed in a straight line), it continues to do so without any additional outside effort. Your first reaction may be that this idea goes against common sense. Let's consider a glider moving along an air track with very little friction shown in the time exposure photograph in Fig. 4.5(a). While holding the glider at the left end of the track, the photographer sets off a regularly flashing light, opens the camera shutter, and gives the glider a push to the right. The constant spacing of the glider in the picture shows that the velocity of the glider remained essentially constant.

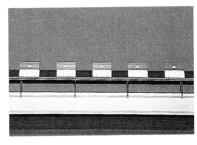

(a)

Newton understood this idea of constant velocity and incorporated it in his laws of mechanics. A paraphrase of an example given by one of Newton's acquaintances is understandable. Suppose you exert a certain force to roll a bowling ball on an unmowed lawn, and it rolls 20 yards. (In Newton's time, bowling took place on lawns, called bowling greens.) With the same force, you might roll it 30 yards if the grass were cut. Further smoothing of the grass surface would increase the ball's range. Since the range increases as obstacles are removed, we conclude that the removal of *all* retarding influences (forces) would allow the ball to continue rolling forever, with neither its speed nor direction changed. Once the ball is given a speed and direction by the bowler, the ball continues in its original state until acted on and retarded. In many cases, the major retarding force is friction.

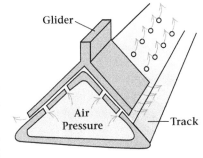

(b)

Newton's first law of motion is his embodiment of the idea we have just described that motion does not require a force. A paraphrase of Newton's first law is: *Every object continues in its state of rest, or of uniform motion in a straight line, unless compelled to change that state by forces acting on it.* Notice that this law is a cause-and-effect statement relating force and motion. A force causes a change in the state of motion. A statement of **Newton's first law** in more concise language, is: **An object has a constant velocity unless there is a net force acting on it.** A velocity of zero corresponds to the case of an object at rest.

Newton's first law is also known as the *law of inertia.* The word *inertia* is from the Latin word for *sluggish* or *inactive.* In modern terms, **inertia** is the property of matter that causes objects to resist changes in motion. You experience the effect of inertia when you set a bowling ball in motion. Likewise, you experience inertia when you try to stop the ball from moving. By the time Newton wrote the *Principia,* it was fairly well established that the kind of motion that

Figure 4.5

(a) A glider moving with a constant velocity on an air track. The regular spacing of the glider's successive positions indicates a constant velocity, which means that the horizontal force on it is negligible. (b) A typical linear air track is made from a hollow triangular rail that has tiny holes drilled in its upper surfaces. When it is pressurized, a cushion of escaping air supports a carefully fitted glider on the track. The glider floats nearly friction free along a straight line on this air cushion.

would continue indefinitely without any additional "push" was linear motion. The first law is a clear statement of this principle.

Inertial Frames of Reference

In Chapter 2 we discussed the necessity for a frame of reference to which we refer the position and motion of objects. The concept of a reference frame is central to Newton's laws of motion. Imagine yourself in an airliner in level flight at a constant velocity (Fig. 4.6a). You are at rest relative to the seat and to the other parts of the aircraft. A ball placed in the aisle will remain motionless relative to the airplane. A coin dropped from your hand will fall straight down. If we take the airplane as a frame of reference, everything within the cabin will behave as expected by Newton's first law. Such a reference frame in which Newton's first law is valid is called an **inertial reference frame.**

Now consider the very different circumstances of an airliner accelerating down a level runway for takeoff (Fig. 4.6b). You are at rest relative to the seat and the rest of the aircraft. However, you feel the force of the seat back that is accelerating you forward along with the plane. If the same ball is placed at rest in the aisle, it would begin rolling toward the back of the plane. Likewise, a coin dropped from your hand would not appear to fall straight down. Such motion is not consistent with the law of inertia (Newton's first law), so in this case the airplane is *not* an inertial frame. Reference frames such as the accelerating airplane, in which the law of inertia (Newton's first law) does not hold, are called *noninertial* reference frames.

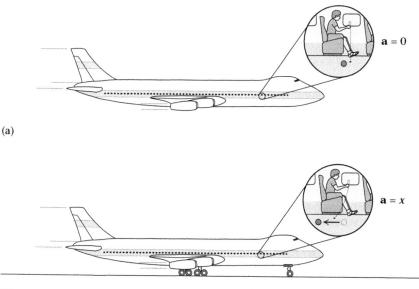

(a)

(b)

Figure 4.6
(a) An airliner in level flight at constant velocity is an inertial reference frame.
(b) An airliner accelerating down a level runway is not an inertial reference frame.

We usually consider Newton's laws to be valid on the face of the earth, even though, because it rotates, the earth is not truly an inertial reference frame. The effects of the rotation are not large and for most purposes Newton's laws apply. The effects of rotation can be calculated by using Newton's laws and an external inertial reference frame. Such calculations help explain the motion of the atmosphere and the formation of hurricanes and tornadoes.

▼

4.4 Newton's Second Law

Newton's first law describes what happens when the net force acting on an object is zero. In that case, the object either remains at rest or continues in motion with constant speed in a straight line. Newton's second law describes the change of motion that occurs when a nonzero net force acts on the object.

To get a sense of what Newton's second law is about, imagine that you pull a child in a wagon along a smooth, level sidewalk. If you pull with a constant force, the wagon accelerates, moving faster as you continue to pull. If a friend helps pull so that the force is greater, the rate at which the speed increases is also greater; the larger force gives rise to a larger acceleration. This effect is predicted by Newton's second law.

The original translation of **Newton's second law** was, *The alteration of motion is ever proportional to the motive force impressed; and is made in the direction of the right line in which that force is impressed.* Elsewhere in the *Principia* Newton was clear that by "motion" he meant the product of the velocity and the mass. For the moment, it is sufficient to use Newton's identification of mass as the "quantity of matter." The modern name of the product of mass m and velocity $\mathbf{v}$ is **momentum.** (We consider momentum more fully in Chapter 7.) Using this term, we restate the second law:

The rate of change of momentum with time is proportional to the net applied force and is in the same direction:

$$\frac{\Delta(m\mathbf{v})}{\Delta t} \propto \Sigma\, \mathbf{F}, \tag{4.1}$$

where $\Sigma\, \mathbf{F}$ is the net force—that is, the vector sum of all forces acting on a body*—and the change in the momentum $\Delta(m\mathbf{v})$ is in the direction of $\Sigma\, \mathbf{F}$.

If we include a proportionality constant, the proportion becomes an equation. The value of the proportionality constant depends on the choice of units for force, mass, velocity, and time. If we choose the units appropriately, the proportionality constant can have the value 1. In that case the equation simply becomes

$$\boxed{\frac{\Delta(m\mathbf{v})}{\Delta t} = \Sigma\, \mathbf{F}.} \tag{4.2}$$

---

*The symbol Σ (the Greek letter sigma) indicates a summation. In Eq. (4.1), $\Sigma\, \mathbf{F}$ indicates the sum of all forces $\mathbf{F}$ acting on the body of mass m.

In the majority of real situations, the mass of an object does not change appreciably, so the change in momentum is just the mass times the change in velocity. Then

$$\frac{\Delta(m\mathbf{v})}{\Delta t} = m\,\frac{\Delta \mathbf{v}}{\Delta t} = m\mathbf{a}.$$

Thus Newton's second law may be expressed as

$$\mathbf{a} = \frac{\Sigma\,\mathbf{F}}{m}. \tag{4.3}$$

Rearranging, we have the most common statement of the second law in the form

$$\boxed{\Sigma\,\mathbf{F} = m\mathbf{a}.} \tag{4.4}$$

Although this last equation is mathematically correct, you should use care in interpreting it. *It is the force that causes the acceleration, not vice versa.*

Equation (4.4) is a vector equation. It is equivalent to a set of three equations, one for each component:

$$\Sigma\,F_x = ma_x, \qquad \Sigma\,F_y = ma_y, \qquad \Sigma\,F_z = ma_z. \tag{4.5}$$

These equations relate three components of acceleration of a mass m to the three components of the net force causing the mass to accelerate.

Once we know the velocity and acceleration of an object, we can predict its motion. The ability to predict the motion of a body from a knowledge of the forces acting on it is one of the most useful accomplishments of physics. Not only is it useful for predicting the motion of bodies under mechanical or gravitational forces, but also it allows us to calculate the motion when the force is due to other causes, such as magnetism or electricity. Conversely, when the force is not known it may sometimes be deduced from a knowledge of the motion.

Before we go on to examples of the second law, it is worth noting that Newton's meaning of the second law is properly represented by Eq. (4.1). Equation (4.4), or even $\mathbf{F} \propto \mathbf{a}$, as it is sometimes stated, is a restricted special case for objects with constant mass. In this case, *the acceleration is proportional to the force, and the direction of the acceleration is the same as the direction of the force.*

Compare the glider moving with no horizontal force on it (Fig. 4.5) to the photo in Fig. 4.7(a). In this case, a constant horizontal force has been applied to the same glider in the manner shown in Fig. 4.7(b). The increased spacings between positions recorded by flashes at equal time intervals indicate that the glider accelerates as it moves to the right.

Measurements taken from a photograph similar to Fig. 4.7 are listed in Table 4.2. They show that over each equal interval of time the velocity increases by the same amount; that is, the acceleration is constant. In this demonstration, a constant force has given rise to a constant acceleration. In another experiment similar to this one, the horizontal force on the glider was increased by hanging another mass alongside the first. Measurements on the photograph again showed motion with constant acceleration.

(a)

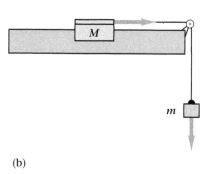

(b)

Figure 4.7

(a) An air-track glider moving under the influence of a small hanging mass. The photograph was made by the same technique used in Fig. 4.5. The increased spacing between the positions of the glider for successive strobe flashes indicates acceleration. (b) A simplified drawing of the air track showing the hanging mass. As the mass falls, it pulls the glider along with a constant force.

Table 4.2		The Motion of an Air-track Glider Subjected to a Constant Force	
Time	x (cm)	$\Delta x/\Delta t$ (cm/time interval)	$\Delta(\Delta x)/(\Delta t)^2$ [cm/(time interval)^2]
0	131.4		
		8.4	
1	139.8		3.0
		11.4	
2	151.2		3.2
		14.6	
3	165.8		3.1
		17.7	
4	183.5		3.0
		20.7	
5	204.2		3.1
		23.8	
6	228.0		

Time intervals were uniformly spaced. The position given is x, the location of the front of the glider. There is some uncertainty in the fourth digit. The change in x is Δx, which is proportional to the velocity. The acceleration is proportional to the change in $\Delta x/\Delta t$ and is given by $\Delta(\Delta x)/(\Delta t)^2$. From the table we see that the acceleration is constant.

Indeed, using a range of accelerating forces and a number of different gliders, we always observe that for a given total mass (glider plus hanging mass), the acceleration is proportional to the net force. Rearrangement of the mathematical statement of Newton's second law gives

$$m = \frac{F}{a}.$$

Then we can call on common experience and this equation to tell us that what we have called **mass** is a quantitative measure of the inertia of a body. Finally, we say that the more massive a body, the larger the force necessary to give it a particular acceleration.

In the SI system of units, the unit of mass is the kilogram. The present standard of mass is a platinum-iridium cylinder whose mass is defined to be, by international agreement, one kilogram. This standard is kept at the International Bureau of Weights and Measures near Paris. Other bodies are assigned their mass value by a comparison with the standard. If, when Eq. (4.4) is used, the unit of mass is the kilogram and the unit of acceleration is the meter/second^2, then the unit of force becomes the kilogram · meter/second^2. This combination of units is given the name **newton** (N). We say: **A force of one newton acting on a one-kilogram mass gives it an acceleration of one meter/second^2.** Some familiar forces and their approximate magnitudes in newtons are shown in Fig. 4.8.

Although we shall use SI units almost exclusively in this text, other systems of units are still in use. Principal among these are the British system and the centimeter-gram-second (CGS) system of units. The units of force, mass, and acceleration in these three systems are summarized in Table 4.3.

Force exerted by a weightlifter: 2000 N

Gravitational force (weight) on a person: 600 N

Force to flip a light switch: 3 N

Figure 4.8
Some familiar forces.

Table 4.3	Units of Force, Mass, and Acceleration		
System of Units	Force	Mass	Acceleration
SI	newton (N)	kilogram (kg)	m/s^2
CGS	dyne (dyn)	gram (g)	cm/s^2
British*	pound (lb)	slug	ft/s^2

*1 lb = 1 slug · ft/s^2 = 4.448 N

Example 4.2

Safety regulations require that all cars traveling at a given speed be able to stop within a given distance. What must be the relationship between the minimum braking forces allowed by law for two cars whose masses have the ratio of 3 to 2?

Strategy We can use Newton's second law to relate the force to mass and acceleration. From your knowledge of kinematics, you know that the requirement for stopping in equal distances from the same initial speed for both cars means they must both have the same acceleration.

Solution We can write the two accelerations in terms of the braking forces F_1 and F_2 and the masses m_1 and m_2 as

$$a_1 = \frac{F_1}{m_1} \quad \text{and} \quad a_2 = \frac{F_2}{m_2}.$$

When we set the accelerations equal we find

$$\frac{F_1}{m_1} = \frac{F_2}{m_2},$$

so

$$\frac{F_1}{F_2} = \frac{m_1}{m_2} = \frac{3}{2}.$$

Discussion This result tells us that a larger braking force is needed to stop a larger (more massive) car in the same distance that a smaller (less massive) car is stopped.

Example 4.3

(a) What force is necessary to give a 0.80-kg air-track glider a horizontal acceleration of 1.5 m/s^2 if the force is directed horizontally along the length of the level air track? (b) What is the acceleration of the glider when the applied force is 1/3 the value found in part (a)?

Solution (a) We can find the magnitude of the force from Newton's second law:

$$F = ma = 0.80 \text{ kg} \times 1.5 \text{ m/s}^2 = 1.2 \text{ N}.$$

(b) We can also use the second law to find the acceleration when the force applied is 1/3 the value just found in part (a). Then the magnitude of the acceleration is

$$a = \frac{F}{m} = \frac{\frac{1}{3}(1.2 \text{ N})}{0.80 \text{ kg}} = 0.50 \text{ m/s}^2.$$

Example 4.4

A fully loaded Lockheed L-1011 with a mass of 2.17×10^5 kg accelerates at full throttle down a level runway (Fig. 4.9). The engines push with a combined constant horizontal net force of 753 kN. If the plane starts from rest, how far will it go during the 33.5 s that it takes to reach liftoff velocity?

Strategy The problem asks us to find the distance traveled by an airplane accelerating from rest. We can use our knowledge of kinematics to find that distance if we know the acceleration. Because we are given the mass of the plane and the force of the engines, we can use Newton's second law to find the acceleration.

Remember to put all numerical values in SI units. For example, the force of the engines is

$$F = 753 \text{ kN}\left(\frac{1000 \text{ N}}{1 \text{ kN}}\right) = 753000 \text{ N} = 7.53 \times 10^5 \text{ N}.$$

Solution The acceleration is found from Newton's second law in the form of Eq. (4.3):

$$a = \frac{F}{m} = \frac{7.53 \times 10^5 \text{ N}}{2.17 \times 10^5 \text{ kg}} = \frac{7.53 \times 10^5 \text{ kg} \cdot \text{m/s}^2}{2.17 \times 10^5 \text{ kg}} = 3.47 \text{ m/s}^2.$$

This value of acceleration is then used with the kinematic equation for displacement,

$$x = v_0 t + \tfrac{1}{2}at^2.$$

Since the plane starts from rest, $v_0 = 0$. Inserting the values for a and t we get

$$x = \frac{1}{2}\left(\frac{7.53 \text{ m}}{2.17 \text{ s}^2}\right)(33.5 \text{ s})^2 = \frac{1}{2}(3.47)(1122 \text{ m})$$

$$x = 1947 \text{ m} \approx 1.95 \text{ km}$$

Figure 4.9
Example 4.4: An airliner accelerates under constant force.

4.5 Weight

One important example of Newton's second law is the expression for an object's weight. The **weight** of an object on earth is the gravitational force exerted on it by the earth. In Galileo's time, most scholars held Aristotle's belief that heavy (weightier) objects fall faster than light ones, just because they are heavier. As we saw in Chapter 2, Galileo showed that reasoning to be incorrect. Some objects do fall less swiftly than others because of air resistance, which slows the fall of objects such as feathers and leaves. More compact objects such as stones fall faster because, for a given mass, they offer a smaller area to the air, thus reducing the effect of air resistance to a negligible amount. In a vacuum, all objects fall with the same acceleration, regardless of their weight.

As a result, we know that near the earth's surface, when we neglect air resistance, the acceleration is the same for all falling bodies. This constant acceleration is known as the acceleration of gravity, **g**, and has the standard value 9.807 m/s².* When an object is dropped near the earth's surface, it is accelerated by the gravitational force (equal to its weight) with an acceleration **g**. Thus, by Newton's second law, the weight **w** becomes

$$\mathbf{w} = \mathbf{mg}. \tag{4.6}$$

We see in this equation the relation between mass and weight: *Weight is a force proportional to the mass of a body and g is the constant of proportionality.*

Example 4.5

What is the weight of a textbook whose mass is 1.85 kg?

Solution The weight may be computed from Eq. (4.6),

$$w = mg,$$

where the numerical value of g is 9.81 m/s². The weight becomes

$$w = 1.85 \text{ kg} \times 9.81 \text{ m/s}^2 = 18.1 \text{ kg} \cdot \text{m/s}^2 = 18.1 \text{ N}.$$

Discussion The weight of the book is 18.1 N. Notice that the unit of weight is the unit of force. Using the information in Table 4.3, you should show for yourself that this SI force of 18.1 N corresponds to 4.07 lb.

When you stand on a scale, the scale reading gives the magnitude of your weight. Because most of the force that comprises your weight is due to the gravitational attraction between you and the earth, we have described weight as the force of gravity. However, because the earth rotates, your weight is slightly less than it would be if the earth were not rotating. Consequently, we need a more precise definition of weight. It is: *The weight of a body in a specified reference frame is the force which, when applied to the body, would give it an acceleration equal to the local acceleration of free fall in that reference frame.* On the earth, the local acceleration of free fall is **g**. We still use Eq. (4.6) to express the relationship between mass and weight.

If we take an object to the moon, the force of gravity exerted on it by the moon is less than the force of gravity on it when it was on the earth. Thus, its

---

*Although the value of g is the same for all objects in a given locality, it is measurably different at other localities. There is about 0.5% variation with latitude, with g being smaller at the equator than at the poles. An additional variation depends on altitude and on the underlying geological formation. For example, the value of g in Denver, Colorado, is 9.796 m/s², while the value in Greenwich, England, is 9.812 m/s².

weight on the moon is different from its weight on the earth, even though its mass remains constant.

The Normal Force

When an object such as a brick rests on the ground, the gravitational force continues to act on the brick, even though it is not accelerating. According to Newton's second law, the net force on the brick at rest must be zero. There must be another force acting on the brick that opposes the gravitational force. This force is provided by the ground (Fig. 4.10a). The force provided by the ground is perpendicular to the surface of contact and is known as the **normal force.** (In geometry, the word *normal* means "perpendicular.") The normal force is simply the resistance of the ground to the motion of the brick acted upon by gravity. It is this normal force that keeps the brick from sinking into the ground.

If the brick rests on an inclined surface, the gravitational force *m***g** acting on the brick is still directed downward. The normal force **N** acts perpendicular to the surface, and since the surface is inclined, the normal force must also be inclined (Fig. 4.10b). If we introduce a coordinate system with components parallel and perpendicular to the surface, then we can resolve the gravitational force into components along these directions. The component of gravitational force perpendicular to the surface must be opposed by an equal but opposite normal force if the brick is not to sink into the surface. If there are no other forces acting on the brick, then the component of gravitational force parallel to the surface will be unopposed and will cause the brick to slide down the slope. Notice that in this case the component of gravitational force parallel to the surface is the net force. That is, it is the vector sum of *m***g** and **N**. The brick will then accelerate down the incline at a rate determined by this net force and the brick's mass.

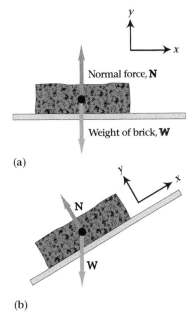

(a)

(b)

Figure 4.10
The normal force is always perpendicular to the contact surface. (a) The normal force is equal to the weight of the brick. (b) The normal force is less than the weight of the brick.

Example 4.6

A furniture van has a smooth ramp for making deliveries. The ramp makes an angle θ with the horizontal. A large crate of mass m is placed at the top of the ramp. Assuming the ramp is a frictionless plane, what is the acceleration of the crate as it moves down the ramp?

Strategy To find the acceleration of the crate we must first find the net force acting on it. The gravitational force *m***g** acts downward on the crate (Fig. 4.11). The plane supports the crate with a normal force **N** perpendicular to the plane. We assume that the ramp is rigid and that the crate can slide freely over the surface, so there are no other forces acting on the crate. The net force is the vector sum of the two forces *m***g** and **N**. We can find the net force and divide by the mass of the crate to obtain the acceleration of the crate.

Solution In this case it is convenient to choose a coordinate system with one axis parallel to the surface of the inclined plane. Then we can resolve the gravitational force vector into components parallel and perpendicular to the surface. We choose the positive x direction to be upward along the plane, and the positive y direction perpendicular to it as indicated in the figure. The resulting components of the gravitational force along the x and y directions are

$$F_x = -mg \sin \theta$$

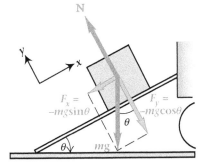

Figure 4.11
Example 4.6: A large crate slides down a slippery incline. The weight of the crate is *m***g**, the normal force is **N**, which is perpendicular to the surface of the incline.

parallel to the surface of the plane and

$$F_y = -mg \cos \theta$$

perpendicular to the plane.

There is no acceleration perpendicular to the plane, so the net force in the y direction must be 0:

$$F_{y \text{ net}} = N - mg \cos \theta = 0.$$

The only force in the x direction is a component of the gravitational force,

$$F_{x \text{ net}} = -mg \sin \theta.$$

Because there are no other forces along the x direction, this force is the net force along x that causes the crate to move down the plane. The acceleration is given by Newton's second law:

$$a_x = \frac{F_{x \text{ net}}}{m} = \frac{-mg \sin \theta}{m} = -g \sin \theta.$$

Discussion The negative sign indicates that the crate accelerates to the left in the figure. Notice that the acceleration of the crate depends only on the acceleration of gravity (g) and on the angle of the inclined plane, and not on the mass of the crate. The crate moves with the same acceleration if it contains heavy furniture or if it is empty.

| 4.6 | ▼ Newton's Third Law |

Newton's **third law** of motion may be stated as: **For every action (force) there is a reaction force and the action and reaction forces are equal in magnitude, opposite in direction, and act upon different bodies.** Newton's own words help us understand the third law a little better. "Whatever draws or presses another is as much drawn or pressed by that other. If you press a stone with your finger, the finger is also pressed by the stone. If a horse draws a stone tied to a rope, the horse will be equally drawn back towards the stone; for the distended rope, by the same endeavor to relax or unbend itself, will draw the horse as much toward the stone as it does the stone toward the horse . . ."

Restating the third law in more quantitative terms, we have (Fig. 4.12)

**If body A exerts a force F_{AB} on body B,
then B exerts a force F_{BA} on A, so $F_{AB} = -F_{BA}$.**

The action and reaction forces of Newton's third law are equal in magnitude, opposite in direction, and *act upon different bodies*. Newton's third law tells us that forces always occur in pairs.

We should point out that when applying Newton's *second* law we consider only one of these forces at a time. Body A is subjected to the applied force F_{BA}. The acceleration of A is thus proportional to F_{BA} and inversely related to its own mass m_A. Similarly, body B is subjected to the force F_{AB} and is accelerated by it.

It is important to remember that the third-law action-reaction pair of forces have equal magnitudes. Thus, when a large person pulls on a much smaller per-

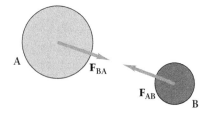

Figure 4.12
Body A exerts a force F_{AB} on body B, then B exerts a force F_{BA} on A. The two forces are equal in magnitude and opposite in direction.

(a)

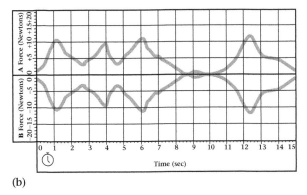

(b)

Figure 4.13
(a) Two people holding force sensors pull against each other. (b) Graph showing that the measured forces on the two people are equal in magnitude and opposite in direction.

son, the action-reaction forces are exactly the same size even though they act in the opposite directions (Fig. 4.13).

Example 4.7

An apple rests on an upturned basket (Fig. 4.14). What forces act on the apple and on the basket? Identify all of the action-reaction pairs.

Strategy There are two types of forces involved here, gravitational and contact forces. We can isolate each object and examine the forces on it. (We will consider the earth to be an inertial frame so that the gravitational force and the weight are the same.)

Solution There are two forces that act on the apple (Fig. 4.14b), a downward gravitational force $\mathbf{F}_{EA}$ of the earth (E) acting on the apple (A) and a contact force $\mathbf{F}_{BA}$, the normal force due to the basket (B) that pushes the apple up. For the apple to be at rest, those two forces must be equal and opposite so that their sum is zero.

$$\mathbf{F}_{EA} + \mathbf{F}_{BA} = 0.$$

The basket is subject to three forces (Fig. 4.14c), the contact force $\mathbf{F}_{AB}$ due to the apple pushing down, the gravitational force $\mathbf{F}_{EB}$ of the earth pulling it down, and a contact force $\mathbf{F}_{GB}$, the normal force of the ground (G) pushing it up. For the basket to be at rest, the sum of these three forces must also be zero.

$$\mathbf{F}_{AB} + \mathbf{F}_{EB} + \mathbf{F}_{GB} = 0.$$

Now, which forces are action-reaction pairs? Start with the apple. The two forces $\mathbf{F}_{EA}$ and $\mathbf{F}_{BA}$ cannot be an action-reaction pair because they act on the same object. Since the force $\mathbf{F}_{EA}$ is due to the earth's attraction for the apple, there must be an equal and opposite reaction force $\mathbf{F}_{AE}$ due to the apple acting on the earth (Fig. 4.14b). So, $\mathbf{F}_{AE} = -\mathbf{F}_{EA}$. The force $\mathbf{F}_{BA}$ of the basket on the apple and the force $\mathbf{F}_{AB}$ of the apple on the basket are an action-reaction pair, so

$$\mathbf{F}_{BA} = -\mathbf{F}_{AB}.$$

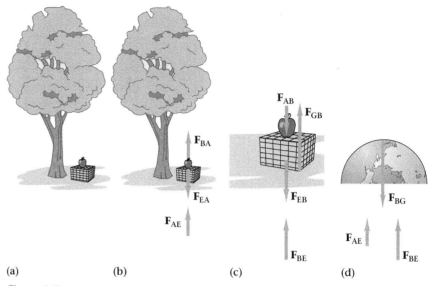

Figure 4.14

Example 4.7: (a) An apple resting on a basket resting on the ground. (b) Two forces act on the apple and (c) three forces act on the basket. (d) Three forces act on the earth, two gravitational forces upward and a contact force downward.

Similarly, the gravitational force $\mathbf{F}_{EB}$ of the earth acting on the basket and the force $\mathbf{F}_{BE}$ of the basket attracting the earth (Fig. 4.14c) are an action-reaction pair:

$$\mathbf{F}_{EB} = -\mathbf{F}_{BE}.$$

Finally, the reaction force to the contact force $\mathbf{F}_{GB}$ of the earth's surface pushing up on the basket is a force $\mathbf{F}_{BG}$ of the basket pushing down on the earth. Thus

$$\mathbf{F}_{GB} = -\mathbf{F}_{BG}.$$

Discussion Notice that action-reaction forces always act on different bodies. The reaction to the contact force of the ground on the basket is the force of the basket on the ground. Even though the two forces $\mathbf{F}_{EA}$ and $\mathbf{F}_{BA}$ acting on the apple are equal and opposite, they are not an action-reaction pair because they act on the same object, the apple. You can show from the equations here that the vector sum of the three forces acting on the earth is zero as it should be (Fig. 4.14d).

Example 4.8

A 68-kg passenger rides in an elevator that is accelerating upward at 1.0 m/s^2 because of external forces. What is the force exerted by the passenger on the floor of the elevator?

Strategy Only two forces act on the passenger (Fig. 4.15a): the gravitational force $m\mathbf{g}$, pulling down, and the force $\mathbf{F}_{FP}$ of the floor on the passenger, pushing up. The force $\mathbf{F}_{FP}$ of the floor on the passenger and the force $\mathbf{F}_{PF}$ exerted by the passenger on the floor are an action-reaction pair of forces (Fig. 4.15b). From the third law we know that the action-reaction forces are equal and opposite. We can find the force $\mathbf{F}_{FP}$ from Newton's second law by observing that the vector sum of the forces $\mathbf{F}_{FP}$ and $m\mathbf{g}$ is the net force that provides the upward acceleration of the passenger, which is the same as the acceleration of the elevator. From our knowledge of the mass and acceleration of the passenger, we can find the force $\mathbf{F}_{FP}$. Then the force exerted by the passenger on the elevator floor is obtained from the third law.

Solution By Newton's second law, the net force on the passenger is

$$\mathbf{F}_{net} = \mathbf{F}_{FP} + m\mathbf{g} = m\mathbf{a}.$$

Taking into account the directions of the forces and choosing up as the positive direction, the magnitude of the net force is

$$F_{net} = F_{FP} - mg = ma.$$

Upon rearranging, we find the upward force of the floor on the passenger,

$$F_{FP} = ma + mg = m(a + g)$$
$$F = 68 \text{ kg} \times (1.0 + 9.81) \text{ m/s}^2 = 740 \text{ N}.$$

From Newton's third law, the passenger exerts a downward force of 740 N on the floor of the elevator.

Discussion If the passenger were standing on a scale placed on the elevator floor, the 740-N force would be the force read on the scale. This force is the passenger's weight in the reference frame of the elevator. If the elevator were at rest or moving with a constant speed, the scale would read

$$F = mg = 68 \text{ kg} \times 9.81 \text{ m/s}^2 = 670 \text{ N}.$$

If the elevator were accelerating downward, the weight of the passenger would be less than normal:

$$F = m(g - a).$$

You can feel this change in weight when riding in an elevator. If you walk around in the elevator, when it accelerates as it starts to ascend (or comes to a stop during a descent), you will notice how much more effort is needed to walk naturally. On the other hand, as the elevator begins to descend (or comes to a stop when moving upward), you will feel lighter and sense an additional spring in your step as you walk.

According to Example 4.8 and our definition of weight, when an elevator moves with a downward acceleration a, the weight of a passenger decreases as measured in the reference frame of the elevator. If you were riding in the elevator, you would say that your weight was less than normal. If the downward acceleration increased, your weight would also decrease. If the downward acceleration of the elevator reached g, the condition of free fall, your weight measured by a scale would become zero:

$$F = m(g - a) = m(g - g) = 0.$$

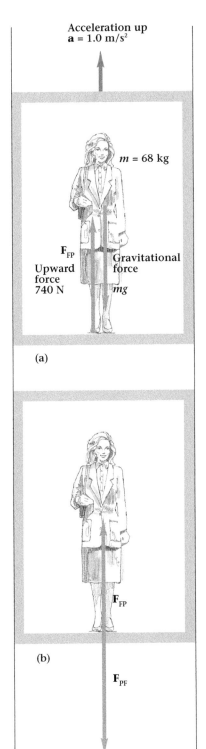

Figure 4.15

Example 4.8: A passenger in an accelerating elevator has an apparent weight different from her real weight.

Figure 4.16
Two astronauts demonstrate the effects of weightlessness.

This condition is called **weightlessness.** Notice that your mass is unchanged. The gravitational force on you is also unchanged, even though your weight becomes zero. Because you and the elevator are both falling with the same acceleration, you are free to float within the elevator. A slight push against the floor sends you to the ceiling. Because there is no net force between you and the floor, the concepts of "up" and "down" with respect to the elevator no longer apply. You are just as comfortable with your head toward the floor or lying on your side as with your head toward the ceiling.

Weightlessness is experienced by the occupants of orbiting artificial satellites like the space shuttle. In that case, the satellite and its occupants are both in free fall, just as in the case of the accelerating elevator. During weightlessness the occupants of artificial satellites move around freely (Fig. 4.16). Remember, the explanation is that the satellite and its occupants have the same acceleration because of gravity. There is no force acting between them, but the force of gravity still acts on all of them.

▼

| 4.7 | **Some Applications of Newton's Laws** |

A useful device for illustrating Newton's second law was devised by George Atwood (1746–1807), nearly a century after the *Principia* appeared. His original device had an elaborate wheel work to reduce frictional forces and a pendulum to measure time. In the simplified diagram (Fig. 4.17a), Atwood's machine is a flexible cord connecting two masses, m_1 and m_2, that runs over a pulley that turns freely without friction. Since the masses of the pulley and the cord are very small in comparison with the masses m_1 and m_2, we can disregard them in our analysis.

We include the force provided by the cord, which we have labeled with the symbol **T**. The magnitude of this force is called the **tension** in the cord. (Recall

Figure 4.17
(a) A simplified version of an Atwood's machine in which two masses are suspended by a cord passing over a frictionless pulley.
(b) Free-body diagrams, showing the forces acting on the two single masses, m_1 and m_2. The downward forces are due to the weight of the masses and the upward forces are due to the tension (**T**) in the cord.

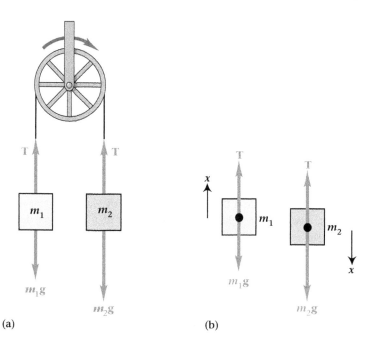

Newton's example of a horse pulling a stone with a rope, mentioned in the previous section.) We begin by making a separate vector diagram for each body, showing all the forces that act on that body. Such a diagram is called a **free-body diagram.** For example, in Fig. 4.17(b) we see that two forces act upon mass m_2: a downward force m_2g and an upward tension force T provided by the cord. We choose the downward motion of mass m_2 as the positive direction (that is, we assume $m_2 > m_1$). Since m_1 must move up when m_2 moves down, the corresponding positive direction for m_1 is upward. The net downward force on m_2 is therefore

$$F_2 = m_2g - T = m_2a.$$

The acceleration is positive (downward) when m_2g exceeds T. The net upward force on m_1 (as seen in Fig. 4.17b) is

$$F_1 = T - m_1g = m_1a.$$

The acceleration a must be the same for m_1 and m_2, since they are joined by the cord and we assume that the cord does not stretch. The tension T in the cord is the same at each end if we neglect all effects of the pulley.

We now have two equations involving two unknown quantities T and a. Both of these equations must be satisfied at the same time. For this reason they are called *simultaneous equations.* The appendix to this chapter reviews how to solve simultaneous equations. Note that you cannot solve either equation alone for either of the two variables.

Upon rearranging the two equations, we get

$$T = m_2g - m_2a \quad \text{and} \quad T = m_1g + m_1a.$$

▼

Problem-Solving Strategy

Free-body Diagrams

Free-body diagrams show all of the forces acting on an object. When there is more than one object involved, use of free-body diagrams helps us to isolate the forces acting on each object separately. Thus, the free-body diagram becomes a very useful tool for analyzing the motion of a physical situation. The following three steps illustrate the method.

1. Choose the object you wish to isolate and draw it along with whatever geometry and dimensions are important to solving the problem. Show objects as simple particles or blocks and keep your diagrams simple and uncluttered.
2. Draw all forces acting on the object as vector arrows, in approximately correct size and direction. Label all forces clearly.
3. Indicate a coordinate system and show the positive direction of displacement, velocity, or acceleration, depending on the problem. If you resolve vectors into components, mark out the original vector so that you don't count it twice.

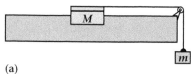

(a)

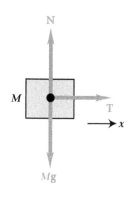

(b)

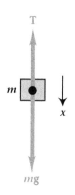

(c)

Figure 4.18
(a) An air-track glider of mass M connected to a small mass m by a light cord passed over a frictionless pulley. (b) A free-body diagram for the glider. The forces are the downward force of gravity $M\mathbf{g}$, the upward support $\mathbf{N}$ due to the air track (equal and opposite to $M\mathbf{g}$), and the horizontal force $\mathbf{T}$ due to the tension in the cord. (c) A free-body diagram for the small mass m.

The right-hand sides of these equations may be set equal and solved to find the acceleration,

$$a = \frac{m_2 - m_1}{m_2 + m_1} g.$$

We can now compute the tension T from the acceleration by inserting the expression for a into either of the equations for T,

$$T = \frac{2m_1 m_2}{m_1 + m_2} g.$$

Notice that when $m_1 = m_2$, the tension T equals the weight mg and there is no acceleration.

As another example of analysis using free-body diagrams, let's consider an air-track glider of large mass M moving on a frictionless air track (Fig. 4.18a). A small mass m is attached to M by a light cord that passes over a frictionless pulley of negligible mass. The forces on M are shown in the free-body diagram of Fig. 4.18(b). The gravitational force Mg is equal and opposite to the supporting force N provided by the air track because there is no vertical acceleration. An unbalanced horizontal force T, exerted by the string, accelerates the mass to the right:

$$T = Ma.$$

The forces acting on the smaller mass m (Fig. 4.18c) are a downward gravitational force mg and the upward force T, the tension in the string:

$$mg - T = ma.$$

Combining these two simultaneous equations, we find that

$$a = \frac{m}{m + M} g.$$

We can find the tension T by substituting for a in either of the force equations above,

$$T = \frac{mM}{m + M} g.$$

The tension T is always less than the downward force of gravity on the hanging mass m, and the acceleration is always less than g.

Example 4.9

Suppose an air-track glider of 1.000-kg mass is connected to a mass of 0.015 kg as in Fig. 4.18(a). What is the acceleration of the glider?

Strategy Because the two masses are joined by the light cord, they must move with identical speed and acceleration. We assume that the cord is so light that its mass may be neglected. Then the only force causing the masses to move is the gravitational force on the mass m. But, because of the cord, that force causes both masses to move.

Solution The acceleration of the glider is obtained from Newton's second law,

$$a = \frac{F_{\text{net}}}{m_{\text{total}}},$$

where F_{net} is given by mg and the total mass is the sum of the masses, $m + M$. Thus

$$a = \frac{mg}{m + M}$$

$$a = \frac{0.015 \text{ kg} \times 9.81 \text{ m/s}^2}{1.015 \text{ kg}} = 0.14 \text{ m/s}^2.$$

▼

Problem-Solving Strategy

Newton's Laws

You will need to work problems in order to deepen your understanding of the laws of motion. Developing your skills for problem solving requires practice. To help you solve problems, we summarize here the problem-solving guidelines from Chapter 1 as they apply to problems involving Newton's laws.

1. Read the entire problem carefully. Then read it again, focusing on what you are being told.
2. Draw and label a diagram of the physical situation. Draw a free-body diagram where appropriate. Choose a coordinate system and indicate it on your drawing. Include units, such as meters or kilograms, with the quantities. The diagram is more than a simplified picture, it is part of the solution. In complicated situations, drawing several free-body diagrams separates the problem into manageable pieces so that you can find the appropriate equations.
3. After you understand what is given and after you have labeled the diagram, then tackle the question. Briefly restate the question, perhaps in symbols, on your paper. It may help to make a list of the known quantities given in the problem as well as the unknown quantities being sought.
4. State the basic principles or concepts that apply. Find a mathematical relationship between the known and unknown quantities and write it in the form of an equation, or perhaps several equations.
5. Solve the equation for the unknown quantity (or quantities) so that you have an equation with only the unknown on the left-hand side of the equals sign and all of the known quantities and constants on the right-hand side.
6. Now substitute the numerical values into the equation if the problem has a numerical solution. Include both the numerical value *and* the units for each quantity. Then compute the numerical answer.
7. As a final check you should ask whether your answer is reasonable.

Example 4.10

Suppose that a block of mass M on an inclined plane is joined to a mass m by a cord over a pulley (Fig. 4.19a). The block slides on a frictionless surface and the effects of the pulley are negligible. What are the magnitude and direction of the acceleration of the block if the surface is inclined at 20° and $m = \frac{1}{2}M$?

Strategy We choose a coordinate system for block M with the positive x direction up the ramp, and we resolve the gravitational force on the block into components parallel and perpendicular to the surface of the inclined plane, as we did in Example 4.6. We choose a coordinate system for the mass m with the positive x coordinate directed downward so that when m moves in the positive x direction, M will also move in the positive x direction.

For block M, the perpendicular component of the weight is balanced by the normal force N of the plane supporting the block (Fig. 4.19b):

$$N - Mg \cos \theta = 0.$$

Two forces act on the block in the direction parallel to the plane: the gravitational component $-Mg \sin \theta$ and the tension force T due to the cord. Applying Newton's second law to the mass of the block, M, we find the net force along x to be

$$F_{\text{net(block)}} = T - Mg \sin \theta = Ma.$$

From the free-body diagram of the hanging mass (Fig. 4.19c) the net force is

$$F_{\text{net(mass } m)} = mg - T = ma,$$

Figure 4.19
Example 4.10: (a) External forces acting on mass M cause it to move on a frictionless surface inclined at angle θ. (b), (c) Free-body diagrams for masses M and m, respectively.

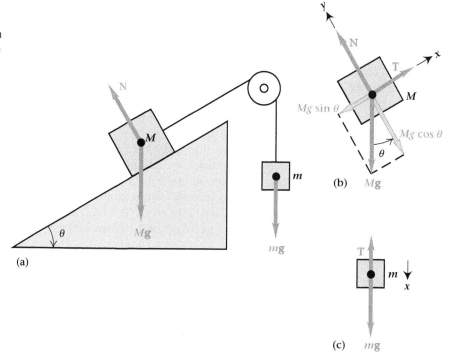

where a positive net force corresponds to the mass m accelerating downward and M accelerating up the incline. We now have two equations that must be solved simultaneously for the two unknowns a and T.

Solution We can add these two equations to eliminate T, resulting in an equation for the acceleration in terms of the masses and the gravitational acceleration g:

$$mg - Mg \sin \theta = (m + M)a.$$

The acceleration is then

$$a = \frac{(m - M \sin \theta)g}{m + M}.$$

If we insert the values $m = \frac{1}{2}M$ and $\theta = 20°$, we get

$$a = \frac{Mg(\frac{1}{2} - \sin 20°)}{\frac{3}{2}M},$$

or

$$a = \frac{2}{3}g(0.5 - 0.34) = 0.11 \text{ g} = 1.0 \text{ m/s}^2.$$

The direction of the acceleration of block M is up the incline.

▼

Example 4.11

Two blocks of masses m_1 and m_2 are connected by a light string passing over a pulley (Fig. 4.20). The blocks are at rest on inclined frictionless surfaces, and the effects of the pulley are negligible. Which way and how far do the blocks move in 0.750 s after being released?

Strategy We can draw free-body diagrams for the two blocks and use them to find an equation for their acceleration. Once we have the acceleration, we can use the kinematic relationship between acceleration, time, and distance to determine how far they slide in 0.750 s.

Starting with block m_1, we resolve the gravitational force into components parallel and perpendicular to the inclined plane on which m_1 moves, just as we did in the previous example. We choose a reference coordinate system as indicated in Fig. 4.20(b), with the positive x axis directed up the left-hand plane. The component of the weight perpendicular to the plane is balanced by the normal force N_1. The component of the weight parallel to the plane is directed down the plane, and the tension T in the string is directed up the plane. Applying Newton's second law to m_1, we find the net force to be along the x axis,

$$F_{1net} = T - m_1 g \sin \theta_1 = m_1 a.$$

For the second block, we see again that the normal component is equal and opposite to the component of the weight perpendicular to the surface (Fig. 4.20c). Using the indicated coordinate system so that motion of the block m_2 down the plane is positive, we see that the component of the weight parallel to the plane is in the positive x direction and the tension T in the string is in the negative x direction. Applying Newton's second law to

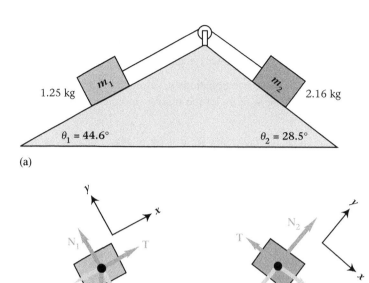

Figure 4.20
Example 4.11: (a) Two blocks rest on frictionless surfaces. (b), (c) Free-body diagrams for the two blocks.

m_2, we find the net force to be

$$F_{2\text{net}} = m_2 g \sin \theta_2 - T = m_2 a.$$

We now have two equations with two unknowns. We can solve them simultaneously to find the acceleration a.

Solution We eliminate T by adding the two equations from the free-body analysis to get

$$(m_2 \sin \theta_2 - m_1 \sin \theta_1)g = (m_1 + m_2)a.$$

The acceleration then becomes

$$a = \frac{(m_2 \sin \theta_2 - m_1 \sin \theta_1)g}{(m_1 + m_2)}.$$

We now insert the values $m_1 = 1.25$ kg, $m_2 = 2.16$ kg, $\theta_1 = 44.6°$, and $\theta_2 = 28.5°$ to get

$$a = \frac{[(2.16 \text{ kg})(\sin 28.5°) - (1.25 \text{ kg})(\sin 44.6°)]9.81 \text{ m/s}^2}{2.16 \text{ kg} + 1.25 \text{ kg}}$$

$$a = +0.440 \text{ m/s}^2.$$

The positive value of the acceleration tells us that the motion of the two blocks is in the positive x direction (to the right in the diagram). That is, block m_1 slides up its incline while block m_2 moves down.

Now that we know the acceleration, we can compute the distance the blocks move in the time $t = 0.750$ s by applying the kinematics expression

$$x = x_0 + v_0 t + \tfrac{1}{2}at^2$$

to either block. Taking mass m_1, we can choose the initial position to be $x_0 = 0$, and since they start from rest, $v_0 = 0$. The distance traveled becomes

$$x = \tfrac{1}{2}at^2 = \tfrac{1}{2}(+0.440 \text{ m/s}^2)(0.750 \text{ s})^2 = +0.124 \text{ m}.$$

Discussion The positive value for x indicates that the motion of the mass m_1 is up the plane, as we expected from the sign of the acceleration. In making our free-body diagrams, we arbitrarily chose the positive direction for m_1 to be up the plane on the left. We then chose the positive x direction for m_2 to be down the plane on the right, so that their positive motions were both to the right. Finally, with careful attention to these directions in writing down the equations and with careful algebra, we computed the acceleration and the displacement, complete with sign.

<table>
<tr><td>4.8</td><td></td></tr>
</table>

Friction

So far we have been careful to ignore the effects of friction. However, when one object slides over the surface of another, its motion is always opposed by a retarding force that resists this motion. This force is called **friction.** Frictional forces are especially important to us in our everyday lives, for without them we could not walk or hold things with our hands; cars would be unable to start or stop; nails and screws would be useless. We first examine frictional forces and show how to work problems that include friction. Then we present a description of the causes of friction. Frictional forces are not fundamental forces like gravity or electromagnetism, but arise as reaction to other applied forces.

Consider the motion of a solid object in contact with a horizontal surface. The object might be a brick on the floor or a telephone on a tabletop (Fig. 4.21). Initially the telephone of weight **w** rests on the horizontal surface. If we pull on the telephone's cord with a small horizontal force **T** parallel to the surface, the telephone does not slide; instead it remains at rest. According to Newton's second law, there must be another force acting on the telephone that is equal and opposite to **T** so that the net force is zero and the telephone remains stationary. This force is the frictional force $\mathbf{F}_{fr}$ exerted on the telephone by the surface. If **T** is made smaller, the frictional force must also decrease so that the two remain equal but opposite. When the applied force **T** becomes large enough, the telephone begins to slide in the direction of the applied force. The frictional force is still present and directed opposite to the applied force, but is no longer equal in magnitude to **T**. The net difference in these forces causes the telephone to accelerate.

The general principles of frictional behavior have been known for nearly 500 years. (1) For objects in relative motion—that is, sliding or rolling—the force of friction always acts in a direction opposite to the direction of motion. (2) The frictional force is proportional to the perpendicular (or normal) force between the two surfaces in contact. (3) For solid objects, the frictional force is approximately independent of the area of contact between the surfaces. (4) The frictional force depends on the particular materials that make up the surfaces. These empirical rules usually hold to a good approximation. However, they are not "laws" in the same sense as Newton's laws; they simply sum up the approximate behavior under some simple conditions. Yet, in some situations the usual rules of friction do not apply. We consider one such situation on p. 127.

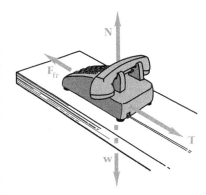

Figure 4.21
A telephone of weight **w** rests on a horizontal surface. When a horizontal force **T** is applied through its cord, the telephone's motion is opposed by a frictional force $\mathbf{F}_{fr}$.

Let's put these statements about friction in quantitative form. For the static case, in which there is no relative motion between the surfaces, the magnitude of the frictional force is

$$F_{fr} \leq \mu N, \qquad \text{[static friction]} \qquad (4.7a)$$

where N is the magnitude of the normal force and the proportionality constant μ is the (dimensionless) **coefficient of friction.** The value of μ depends on the objects involved and on the condition of their surfaces. Table 4.4 lists typical values of μ for a few cases.

Equation (4.7a) actually sets an upper limit for the frictional force $\mathbf{F}_{fr}$ since, as we have seen, when an object is at rest the frictional force must be equal and opposite to the applied tangential force, that is, to the force parallel to the surface. If no tangential force is applied, there is no opposing frictional force. As the tangential force increases, the frictional force increases to oppose it. Ultimately, the frictional force reaches the maximum value expressed by Eq. (4.7a). If a still greater external force is applied, the object no longer remains at rest but begins to slide. For this case, in which the surfaces slide against each other, the magnitude of the frictional force is

$$F_{fr} = \mu N \qquad \text{[kinetic friction]} \qquad (4.7b)$$

Notice that the expression of Eq. (4.7b) is an equality and not an inequality as given in Eq. (4.7a). Although the coefficient of friction is not truly constant, Eqs. (4.7a) and (4.7b) are good empirical rules for approximating the force needed in many practical situations.

The magnitude of the frictional force depends on whether the two surfaces are in relative motion. For identical surface conditions and constant pressures, the coefficient of friction generally decreases slowly with increasing relative speed. If the normal force or the speed becomes too large, Eq. (4.7b) no longer applies. It is important to realize that an empirical law such as this has its limitations, beyond which it does not work.

Sometimes two frictional coefficients are given: μ_s for static friction and μ_k for kinetic, or sliding, friction. However, because the coefficient of friction depends on speed, and because it varies greatly as a result of conditions such as

Table 4.4	*Coefficients of Friction*	▼
Materials	**Conditions**	μ
Glass on glass	Clean	0.9–1.0
Wood on wood	Clean and dry	0.25–0.5
Wood on wood	Wet	0.2
Steel on steel	Clean	0.58
Steel on steel	Motor oil lubricant	0.2
Rubber on solids	Dry	1–4
Teflon on steel	Clean	0.04
Waxed hickory on dry snow		0.03–0.06
Brass on ice		0.02–0.08

Values are approximate. Frictional coefficients vary with surface conditions and cleanliness.

surface moisture, cleanliness, and wear, such coefficients are poorly known and not very reproducible. For these reasons we have not drawn a distinction between static and kinetic coefficients in the examples and in the problems. You should bear in mind that the values of the coefficients given in the table are only approximate. Ordinarily, for identical surface conditions, μ is slightly greater for static friction than it is for sliding (kinetic) friction. The situation is very complicated. As Richard Feynman observed,

> Many people believe that the friction to be overcome to get something started (static friction) exceeds the force required to keep it sliding (sliding friction), but with dry metals it is very hard to show any difference. The opinion probably arises from experiences where small bits of oil or lubricant are present, or where blocks, for example, are supported by springs or other flexible supports so that they appear to bind.*

Example 4.12

A horizontal force **T** of 100 N is applied to a box of books of mass 20 kg resting on a wooden table (Fig. 4.22). Does the box slide if the coefficient of friction of the box on the table is 0.40? If the box moves, find its acceleration.

Strategy We can compute the maximum frictional force and compare it to the horizontal force **T**. If the maximum friction force exceeds T, the box stays at rest. If the friction force is less than T, the box will accelerate.

Solution The normal force between the box and the table is just equal to the weight of the box, mg = 196 N. The maximum frictional force is

$$F_{fr} = \mu N = 0.40 \times 196\ \text{N} \approx 78\ \text{N}.$$

This force is less than the applied force, so the box slides in the direction of **T**.
The box is accelerated by the net force $F_{net} = T - F_{fr}$. Thus from Newton's second law we get

$$a = \frac{F_{net}}{m} = \frac{(T - F_{fr})}{m}$$

$$a = \frac{(100 - 78)\text{N}}{20\ \text{kg}} = 1.1\ \text{m/s}^2.$$

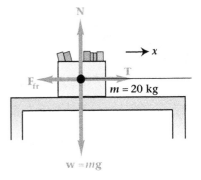

w = mg

Figure 4.22
Example 4.12: A box of books moves only if the applied force **T** is greater than the force of friction between the books and the table.

What are the causes of frictional forces and how do we know about them? It is often supposed that frictional effects originate in the roughness of the surfaces in contact with one another. In fact, experiments have shown that friction does not generally increase with roughness. For example, two pieces of smooth, flat glass show much more frictional drag than two pieces of rough, ground glass. The frictional forces arise primarily from molecular forces in the regions of real contact. Thus, friction is determined not so much by the effect of the roughness

---

*R. P. Feynman, R. P. Leighton, and M. Sands, *The Feynman Lectures on Physics* (Reading, Mass.: Addison-Wesley, 1964), Vol. I, p. 12-5.

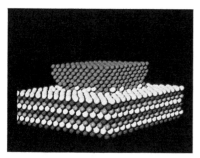

(a)

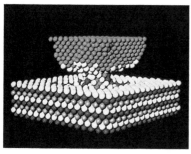

(b)

(c)

Figure 4.23
Friction at the atomic level as modeled by computer simulation for a nickel tip (red) and a surface of gold. (a) The tip is pressed into the surface. (b) The tip is slowly raised, forming an intermetallic bond. (c) Gold atoms continue to cling to the tip after it is well above the surface.

Master the Concept

Friction and Newton's Laws

Question: According to Newton's laws, an external force is needed to stop a car when the brakes are applied. Where is this force and what is its origin? Be careful to distinguish between internal forces and external forces.

Answer: You know that a car is slowed by applying pressure to the brake pedal causing a frictional force between the brake pads and the wheel. But these forces are internal forces and cannot stop the car. If the car is rolling smoothly in a straight line with no brake applied, the forces between the tires and the road are essentially only normal forces. The operation of the brakes retards the rotation of the wheels resulting in frictional forces between the tires and the road. These friction forces are parallel to the road surface. The tires push forward on the road and the road pushes backward on the tires. This behavior not only is true for skidding when the wheels are locked, but also is true even when the wheels are rolling. This backward or retarding force of the road on the tires is an external force acting on the car. Except for air resistance, there are no other external forces along the line of motion, so the net force opposes the forward motion of the car causing it to slow to a stop.

or smoothness of the surfaces as by the molecular forces in the area of actual contact.

Studies of blocks sliding on blocks show that friction is generally independent of the contact area of the blocks. This area, which is determined by multiplying length times width, is more properly thought of as the apparent area of coverage. Because objects that appear smooth may be microscopically rough, the apparent area of coverage is usually much larger than the actual area of contact. As the normal force increases, the actual contact area also increases because of deformations of the two surfaces at their interface. It is this increase in contact area with increasing load that gives the apparent connection between friction and normal force.

In dealing with surfaces that are easily deformed, an increase in apparent area may closely approximate an increase in the actual area of contact. For this reason the width (and hence area) of tires can make a significant difference in how an automobile drives. This effect (of dependence on area) stands in sharp contrast to that seen in experiments with metal blocks sliding over metal surfaces, where changes in the apparent area of the block make little difference in the observed friction.

Whenever you measure the friction of one metal block sliding against another block of the same metal, it is not really a case of pure metal sliding on pure metal. The surfaces of each block contain oxides and other impurities. If the surfaces are carefully cleaned in a high vacuum and are touched together, they will stick, forming a cold weld (Fig. 4.23). This surprising result happens when microscopically clean surfaces touch, since the bonding at the interface is then the same as it is anywhere else within the metal. Thus, the friction that we normally

THE FRICTION OF AUTOMOBILE TIRES

How do tires affect your safety when you drive your car along the highway? What factors help to prevent skidding and allow you to control your car when turning and stopping? What does friction have to do with this?

The tread pattern of rubber tires plays a major role in determining their friction, or skid resistance. Under dry conditions on paved roads, a smooth tire gives better traction than a grooved or patterned tread because a larger area of contact is available to develop the frictional forces. For this reason, the tires used for auto racing on the tracks at Darlington, Indianapolis, Talladega, and elsewhere have a smooth surface with no tread design (Fig. B4.3). Unfortunately, a smooth tire develops very little traction under wet conditions because the frictional mechanism is reduced by a lubricating film of water between the tire and the road. A patterned tire provides grooves or channels into which the water can squeeze as the tire rolls along the road, thus again providing a region of direct contact between tire and road (Fig. B4.4). A patterned tire gives typical dry and wet frictional coefficients of about 0.7 and 0.4, respectively. These values represent a compromise between the extreme values of about 0.9 (dry) and 0.1 (wet) obtained with a smooth tire.

Classical friction theory must be modified for tires because of their structural flexibility and the stretch of the tread rubber. Instead of depending solely on the coefficient of friction at the tire-road interface (which is determined by the nature of the road surface and the tread rubber compound), maximum stopping ability also depends on the resistance of the tread to tearing under the forces that occur during braking.

When a car is braked to a hard stop on a dry road, the maximum frictional force developed can be greater than the strength of the tread. The result is that instead of the tire

Figure B4.4 Tires used on racing cars driven only on dry tracks have a solid contact area, like that of the race tires shown. Grooved tires designed for general use provide traction under wet conditions by channeling water away from the tire. Because it has no similar tread pattern, the racing tire cannot be driven on a wet track.

merely sliding along the road, rubber is torn off the tread at the tire-road interface. Undoubtedly the tread resistance to this tearing is a combination of the rubber strength and the grooves and slots that make up the tread design.

The weight of the car is unevenly distributed over the tire-road contact area, creating areas of high and low pressure. (This is much like what you feel when you step on a pebble while walking in thin-soled shoes.) The resistance of the tread to tearing increases in the areas of higher pressure, where the tread is more compressed, causing an effective increase in traction.

Further, the size of the contact area is very important in car tires because the traction is dynamic rather than static; that is, it changes as the tire rolls along. The maximum coefficient of friction can occur anywhere in the contact area, so that the greater the area, the greater the likelihood of maximum traction. Thus, under identical load and on the same dry surface, the wider tire has a greater contact area and develops higher traction, resulting in greater stopping ability.

Next time you need to buy tires, think about what kind of climate you live in, what kind of roads you drive on, and what speeds you drive. If you live in a region with good paved roads, you may not need tires with extra tread. If you drive in areas with mud or snow, you need a tread designed for those conditions.

Figure B4.3 Race cars driven on the superspeedways are equipped with wide, smooth tires known as "racing slicks."

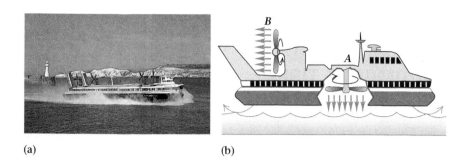

(a)   (b)

Figure 4.24
(a) Hovercraft vehicles use powerful blowers to maintain a cushion of air beneath them to float over land and sea with little frictional drag. (b) Fan *A* provides the air cushion and fan *B* provides the horizontal thrust.

observe is due principally to the surface layer of contaminants that is always present and that serves to reduce the intermolecular forces at the interface.

A thin layer of oil is often placed between surfaces to make motion easier. This idea is not new; lubrication with fats and oils has been common for thousands of years. The principal effect of a lubricating film is to diminish the attractive forces of the sliding surfaces and thereby reduce their cohesion. Even an invisible layer of oil can reduce the friction of dry surfaces by several orders of magnitude.

A different effect occurs when the lubricating film separating two sliding surfaces is thick compared to the dimensions of molecules. Then the friction depends on the properties of the film rather than on the surfaces. A striking example of this is the use of a thin layer of air to support heavy objects. Because the friction of the air is so small, the objects appear to glide along almost without friction. This effect has been put to use in the air track of Fig. 4.5. Its application to air bearings has made possible the modern high-speed drills used by dentists. Hovercraft vehicles that float on a cushion of air are in regular service across the English Channel (Fig. 4.24).

▼

4.9   Static Equilibrium

We have seen that a body subjected to a net force has an acceleration proportional to that force. But what if the vector sum of the forces acting on the body is zero? This is the condition of translational **equilibrium,** a state of motion in which the velocity of the body is constant. If the body is in motion with constant velocity, then we say it is in **dynamic equilibrium.** If the velocity of the body is zero, then the body is at rest and is said to be in **static equilibrium.**

In addition to translational motion, a body can also have rotational motion. However, these two types of motion can be separated and treated independently. We shall defer discussion of rotational motion and rotational equilibrium until Chapter 9. Our immediate concern is with static equilibrium of translational motion.

We begin by examining the forces on a refrigerator resting on a horizontal floor (Fig. 4.25). We know that for a refrigerator of mass m, a gravitational force $m\mathbf{g}$ pulls down on it, as illustrated in the figure. But from observation and Newton's laws, we have come to expect the refrigerator to remain at rest. Therefore, another force must be present, equal and opposite to the gravitational force. If this were not so, a net unbalanced force would be acting on the refrigerator and

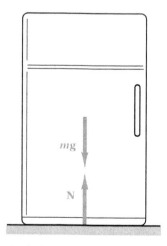

Figure 4.25
A refrigerator rests in static equilibrium on a horizontal floor. Therefore, its weight must be balanced by an upward normal force.

it would accelerate. This equal and opposite force is provided by the floor, which pushes up on the refrigerator with a normal force **N**.

The condition of translational equilibrium for any object is given mathematically by the statement that the vector sum of all forces acting on that object must be zero. That is,

$$\mathbf{F}_{net} = \mathbf{F}_1 + \mathbf{F}_2 + \mathbf{F}_3 + \cdots = 0.$$

We can represent this summation more compactly as

$$\mathbf{F}_{net} = \sum_i \mathbf{F}_i = 0, \tag{4.8}$$

where i stands for the indices 1, 2, 3, 4, ... and the symbol $\sum_i$ represents the sum over all values of i. Here the forces $\mathbf{F}_i$ all act on the same object. This study of objects and forces in equilibrium is a special case of dynamics called *statics*. The vector Eq. (4.8) can be easily handled by resolving the forces into components along the vertical (y) direction and the horizontal (x) direction. If the forces are in equilibrium, then their x components and their y components must also be in equilibrium separately. The resulting equilibrium conditions are

$$\sum_i F_{ix} = 0 \quad \text{and} \quad \sum_i F_{iy} = 0.$$

Example 4.13

A child sits on a sled that rests on a snow-covered hill making an angle θ with the horizontal. If the coefficient of friction is 0.10, what is the maximum angle at which the sled remains at rest? (Assume the hill can be approximated by an inclined plane.)

Strategy We begin by making a sketch of the situation (Fig. 4.26). Then we treat the child and sled as a single free body and make a diagram showing the three forces that act on this "free body." These forces are the weight acting vertically downward, the normal force due to the surface and the frictional force that acts parallel to the surface and opposite to the direction of motion. At the maximum angle at which the sled remains stationary, the frictional force is maximum and equals the coefficient of friction times the normal force. We can use the equilibrium equations in directions parallel and perpendicular to the incline to express the friction force and the normal force in terms of the sled's weight and the angle of the hill. Then by combining these equations we can find a simple expression for the angle of the hill in terms of the coefficient of friction.

Solution We can resolve the weight of the sled plus child, $m\mathbf{g}$, into components parallel and perpendicular to the incline (Fig. 4.26). The perpendicular component of the weight is equal and opposite to the normal force **N**. The parallel component F_x down the incline is opposed by the friction force $\mathbf{F}_{fr}$. From Fig. 4.26 we see that the relations between **N**, F_x, and $m\mathbf{g}$ are

$$N = mg \cos \theta \text{ and } F_x = mg \sin \theta.$$

For the sled to be at rest, the condition of equilibrium requires that the vector sum of the forces must be zero in each direction. Thus, the magnitude

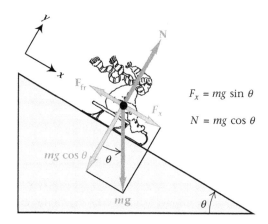

Figure 4.26
Example 4.13: How steep can the hill be before the sled slides down?

of $\mathbf{F}_x$ must be equal to the magnitude of the force of friction $\mathbf{F}_{fr}$. The maximum value for F_{fr} is μN. Thus

$$F_x = \mu N$$

at the maximum angle. Inserting the relations for F_x and N into the equation $F_x = \mu N$, we obtain

$$F_x = mg \sin \theta = \mu N = \mu mg \cos \theta,$$

or

$$\mu = \tan \theta.$$

When $\mu = 0.10$, $\theta = 5.7°$.

For angles less than $5.7°$, the sled remains stationary on the incline, regardless of its weight. For angles greater than $5.7°$, the sled slides down.

Example 4.14

A lantern of mass m is suspended by a string that is joined to two other strings as shown in Fig. 4.27(a). What is the tension in each string if they make equal angles of $35°$ from the support beam as shown? Ignore the mass of the string.

Strategy Since we assume that the lantern and strings are at rest, we have static equilibrium. We can apply the equilibrium condition, Eq. (4.8), to obtain three equations containing the three unknown tensions.

Solution First make a free-body diagram of the mass m, which is acted on by a downward gravitational force $m\mathbf{g}$ and by an upward force of tension in the string $\mathbf{T}_1$ (Fig. 4.27b). For the lantern to be in static equilibrium,

$$T_1 = mg.$$

This equation gives the tension in the lower string, but how do we find the relationships for the other strings? The answer is to make a free-body diagram for the knot connecting the three strings (Fig. 4.27c). At the knot, the tension $\mathbf{T}_1$ in the lower string is downward. The tensions in the other two strings are $\mathbf{T}_2$ and $\mathbf{T}_3$ in the directions indicated. According to Eq. (4.8), the condition for the equilibrium can be expressed as

$$\mathbf{T}_1 + \mathbf{T}_2 + \mathbf{T}_3 = 0.$$

Treating the horizontal components first, we get

$$\Sigma\, T_x = T_{2x} + T_{3x} = 0.$$

Taking the positive direction to the right, we see that

$$T_{3x} = T_3 \cos 35° = 0.819T_3$$

and

$$T_{2x} = -T_2 \cos 35° = -0.819T_2.$$

Upon inserting these values in the equilibrium equation, we find that $T_2 = T_3$, something we might have suspected from the symmetry of the situation.

We now have enough information to evaluate T_2 (and T_3) in terms of T_1 by summing the vertical components in equilibrium:

$$\Sigma\, T_y = T_{1y} + T_{2y} + T_{3y} = 0.$$

If we take the positive direction to be upward, then

$$T_{3y} = T_3 \sin 35° = 0.574T_3,$$
$$T_{2y} = T_2 \sin 35° = 0.574T_2 = 0.574T_3,$$

and

$$T_1 = -mg,$$

so

$$\Sigma\, T_y = -mg + 0.574T_3 + 0.574T_3 = 0.$$

This gives

$$T_3 = T_2 = \frac{mg}{1.15} = 0.87\ mg.$$

In summary, the three tensions are $T_1 = mg$, $T_2 = 0.87\ mg$, and $T_3 = 0.87\ mg$.

Example 4.15

A child of mass M sits in a light swing suspended by a rope of negligible mass. His sister pushes him forward by a horizontal force until the rope makes an angle θ with the vertical (Fig. 4.28). What is the tension in the rope and how much horizontal force is required to hold the child in that position?

Solution We solve the problem by essentially the same method used in Example 4.14. First we sum the vertical components of force,

$$\Sigma\, F_y = T \cos\theta - Mg = 0.$$

There are only two vertical components, since the force $\mathbf{F}$ is purely horizontal. We obtain the tension immediately as

$$T = \frac{Mg}{\cos\theta}.$$

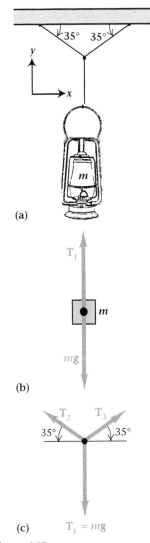

(a)

(b)

(c) $T_1 = mg$

Figure 4.27
Example 4.14: (a) A lantern of mass m suspended by one string joined to two other strings. (b) A free-body diagram for the mass m. (c) A free-body diagram for the knot joining the strings.

Figure 4.28
Example 4.15: A horizontal force **F** pushes a child in a swing until the rope makes an angle θ with the vertical.

The condition of equilibrium for the horizontal forces gives

$$\Sigma F_x = F - T \sin \theta = 0,$$

or

$$F = T \sin \theta.$$

The horizontal force F can be expressed in terms of Mg by inserting the value for T found above:

$$F = \frac{Mg \sin \theta}{\cos \theta} = Mg \tan \theta.$$

Discussion Notice that for $\theta = 0$, $F = 0$. For $\theta = 45°$, the force becomes $F = Mg$. As θ approaches $90°$, F must increase toward infinity; that is, a purely horizontal force can never make the rope become perfectly horizontal as long as it has to support the downward weight.

4.10 The Laws of Motion as a Whole

We have introduced Newton's laws and some of their limitations. But the real content of these laws is that forces have some independent properties in addition to that expressed in the law $F = ma$. Not only can we use the laws to calculate acceleration when a given force acts on a mass, but we can use Newton's laws to investigate the forces observed in nature. By studying accelerations, we can find how forces depend on other quantities, such as distance. In this way Newton's laws become a tool for understanding nature.

In Newton's *Principia* the laws of motion are in a section called "Axioms, or Laws of Motion." As with axioms in geometry, we may postulate a set of axioms for dynamics that give rise to an abstractly satisfactory scheme of dynamics, just so long as the axioms are not contradictory. However, Newton wanted to explain nature as it was observed. This desire determined his choice of axioms. Strictly speaking, the success of Newtonian dynamics rests not on verification of individual axioms, but on the success of the entire scheme in predicting what we observe.

In this chapter, "what we observe" has meant "ordinary-sized things moving with ordinary velocities." If, instead, we want to explain observations that include a much wider range of sizes and velocities, alternative or modified axioms are needed. In particular, if the range of observed velocities is to include those comparable to the velocity of light, then we need the postulates of Einstein's relativity (Chapter 25). If we go to small dimensions comparable to atomic sizes, then the postulates of quantum mechanics are required (Chapter 28). Figure 4.29 illustrates the domain of Newtonian physics. The overall success of Newtonian dynamics in its proper domain is evident from the great variety of situations covered and the enormous range of sizes, from the motion of the solar system to the motion of helium atoms in a gas.

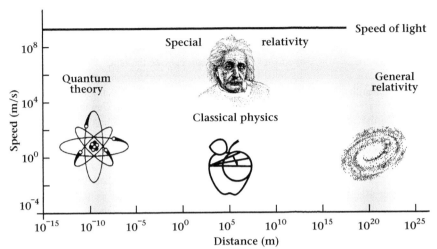

Figure 4.29
(A speed-distance diagram illustrating the range of applicability of Newtonian mechanics. (Note that the scales chosen are not linear, but logarithmic.) The laws of classical physics (center area) are consistent with observations of everyday life. However, when dealing with very small or very large distances or with very high speeds, these laws do not adequately describe what we observe. In those regions, we need the laws of quantum mechanics and relativity instead of Newton's laws to describe and predict the physical observations.

Summary

Useful Concepts

■ Newton's laws tell us that a body in motion stays in motion at constant velocity along a straight line unless acted upon by an external force; that a net force applied to a body causes it to change its motion by accelerating, and similarly, an accelerating body does so because a net force is applied; and that every action has an equal and opposite reaction, applied to different bodies. The mathematical statements of Newton's laws of motion are usually given as follows:

1. A body has a constant velocity unless there is a net force acting on it.
2. The rate of change of momentum with time is proportional to the net applied force and is in the same direction,

$$\frac{\Delta(m\mathbf{v})}{\Delta t} = \Sigma\,\mathbf{F}.$$

For the case of constant mass, Newton's second law is

$$\Sigma\,\mathbf{F} = m\mathbf{a}.$$

3. If a body A exerts a force $\mathbf{F}_{AB}$ on a body B, then B exerts a force $\mathbf{F}_{BA}$ on A, so that $\mathbf{F}_{AB} = -\mathbf{F}_{BA}$.

■ One newton is the force acting on one kilogram to give it an acceleration of one meter/second^2.

■ The weight of an object is proportional to its mass and to the free-fall acceleration,

$$\mathbf{w} = m\mathbf{g}.$$

■ The frictional force of one object sliding on another is

$$F_{\text{fr(static friction)}} \leq \mu N; \qquad F_{\text{fr(kinetic friction)}} = \mu N$$

■ For a body to be in translational equilibrium, the sum of all the forces acting on it must be zero:

$$\Sigma\,\mathbf{F}_i = 0.$$

Important Terms

You should be able to write the definition or meaning of each of the following terms:

Newtonian mechanics	normal force
inverse-square force	weightlessness
force	tension
net force	free-body diagram
inertia	friction
inertial reference frame	coefficient of friction
momentum	equilibrium
mass	static equilibrium
newton	dynamic equilibrium
weight	

Conceptual Questions

4.1 Why do packages slide off the seat of a car when the brakes are applied quickly and forcefully?

4.2 A book rests motionless on a table. Does that mean there are no forces acting upon it?

4.3 A child sits in a swing that is not moving. Describe all forces present and identify all action-reaction pairs.

4.4 A tennis ball thrown against the wall bounces back toward the thrower. Where does the force come from that sends it back?

4.5 Imagine a large adult and a small child on roller skates. Describe their motions if they push off each other.

4.6 Given the existence of a standard mass, devise a way of dynamically comparing other masses with the standard.

4.7 Suspend a heavy weight from a light string and attach a similar string below it (Fig. 4.30). If you pull on the lower string with steadily increasing force, the upper string will break; if you pull the lower string with a jerk, the lower string will break. Explain both cases.

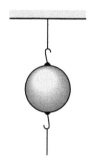

Figure 4.30
Question 4.7.

4.8 Two teams of students are having a tug-of-war. The rope passes through a small hole in a high fence that separates the two teams. Neither team can see the other. Both teams pull mightily, but neither budges. As lunchtime approaches, the members of one team decide to tie their end of the rope to a stout tree while they take a lunch break. Can the other team tell that the first is not pulling on the motionless rope? Analyze the forces in this problem.

4.9 Describe the difference between mass and weight.

4.10 Would a 5.0-kg mass on the earth still be a 5.0-kg mass if it were on the moon? If the mass weighed 49 N on the earth, would it weigh 49 N on the moon?

4.11 A spring scale is used to weigh beans on an elevator. How will the readings for a given amount of beans change when the elevator is (a) going down with constant velocity, (b) moving with a constant downward acceleration less than g, (c) moving upward with a constant velocity, (d) accelerating upward with an acceleration a?

4.12 A man goes over Niagara Falls in a barrel with windows in the side. During the descent, the man takes out an apple, holds it up in front of his face and releases it. Describe what is seen by (a) an observer on the bank looking through the window and (b) the man in the barrel.

4.13 A person on an upward-moving elevator is throwing darts at a target on the elevator wall. How should she aim the dart if the elevator has (a) constant velocity, (b) constant upward acceleration, (c) constant downward acceleration?

4.14 Describe some of your everyday activities that would be seriously hindered, if not impossible, if there were no friction.

4.15 According to Newton's laws, an external force is needed to stop a car when the brakes are applied. Where is this force and what is its origin? Be careful to distinguish between internal forces and external forces.

4.16 When a moving car is slowed to a stop with its brakes, what is the direction of its acceleration vector? Describe the path of a ball dropped by a passenger during the time the car is slowing down.

Problems

Section 4.2 What Is a Force?

4.1 A man pushing a lawn mower exerts a force of 436 N on the handle (Fig. 4.31). The handle makes an angle of 40° with the horizontal. What is the horizontal force applied to the mower?

4.2 Two horses pull horizontally on ropes attached to a tree stump (Fig. 4.32). Each horse pulls with a force of magnitude F. If the resultant force is 1.79 F, what is the angle between the two ropes?

4.3 Two horses pull horizontally on ropes attached to a tree stump (Fig. 4.32). Each horse pulls with a force of magnitude F. If the angle between the two ropes is 126°, what is the resultant force?

4.4• Three coplanar forces act on a 7.0-kg mass: 14 N directed at 0°, 14 N at 138°, and 18 N at 275°. What are the magnitude and direction of the force?

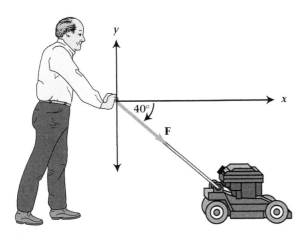

Figure 4.31
Problem 4.1.

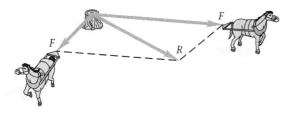

Figure 4.32
Problems 4.2 and 4.3.

Section 4.4 Newton's Second Law

Hints for Solving Problems

An object's acceleration is proportional to the net applied force. Because forces are vectors, they should be added vectorially to find the net force. Unless directed otherwise take all acceleration and all forces in this section to be constant and all motions to be along a straight line.

4.5 A force of 45.6 N is applied to a 2.00-kg discus. What is the acceleration of the discus?

4.6 (a) Find the net force that produces an acceleration of 6.4 m/s² for an 0.50-kg cantaloupe. (b) If the same force is applied to a 20-kg watermelon, what will its acceleration be?

4.7 A German Inter City Express train initially at rest accelerates to a speed of 200 km/h in 3 min 20 s (Fig. 4.33). What steady net force must be exerted by the engine if the total mass of the train is 8.63×10^5 kg?

4.8 An Inter City Express train traveling at 250 km/h is braked to a stop in a distance of 4820 m. If the mass of the train is 8.63×10^5 kg, what is the average braking force?

4.9• The total horizontal force exerted between the tires of a 1500-kg automobile and the ground is 980 N. If the car starts from rest, how far will it go in 5.0 s?

Figure 4.33
Problem 4.7.

4.10• A 400-kg ice boat moves on runners on essentially frictionless ice. A steady wind blows, applying a constant force to the sail. At the end of an 8.0-s run, the acceleration is 0.50 m/s². (a) What was the acceleration at the beginning of the run? (b) What was the force due to the wind? (c) What retarding force must be applied at the end of 4.0 s to bring the ice boat to rest by the end of the next 4 s? (The wind is still blowing. Assume the boat was at rest at time $t = 0$.)

4.11• A toy truck of 1.0 kg is at rest on a horizontal frictionless surface. At time $t = 0$ there are no horizontal forces acting on the truck. At $t = 1.0$ s the truck is suddenly acted upon by a force $F = 1.0$ N. This force is maintained until $t = 2.0$ s, when the force becomes 2.0 N. At $t = 3.0$ s the force becomes 3.0 N, and so on. Construct a graph of the velocity as a function of time. From this make a graph of displacement versus time.

4.12• A Lufthansa A320 accelerates from rest to liftoff speed of 73.7 m/s in 27.1 s. Each of the plane's two jet engines provides a forward force (thrust) of 111 kN. (a) What is the mass of the plane and (b) how far does it travel down the runway before liftoff?

4.13• A net force of 5.34 N acting for 4.23 s on a mass initially at rest causes it to travel 4.75 m in a straight line. What is the mass?

4.14•• A 7.31-g bullet is moving at 579 m/s as it leaves the 0.610-m-long barrel of a rifle. What is the average force on the bullet as it moves down the barrel? Assume that the acceleration is constant.

Section 4.5 Weight

Hints for Solving Problems

Assume the value of $g = 9.81$ m/s² unless stated otherwise in the problem.

4.15 What is the mass in kilograms of a bag of sugar that weighs 5.00 lb? (1 N = 0.2248 lb.)

4.16 A force of 1 newton is equal to 0.2248 lb. (a) Compute the weight in newtons of a 150-lb man. (b) Compute the mass of the man.

4.17 What is the weight of a 48.9-kg girl?

4.18 A brass block of mass m resting on a horizontal frictionless surface is given a horizontal acceleration of 4.5 m/s^2 by a force of 8.7 N. (a) What is the mass of the block? (b) What is the weight of the block?

4.19 A standard kilogram mass was prepared in Paris, where $g = 9.81$ m/s^2, and sent to Washington, where $g = 9.80$ m/s^2. What was the percentage change in the weight of the standard?

4.20 A 24-kg block is pushed up a frictionless inclined plane that makes an angle of 23° with the horizontal direction. What force is needed to move the block with constant speed? Assume that the force is parallel to the surface of the plane.

4.21• The free-fall acceleration on earth is about 9.81 m/s^2. On the moon the same quantity is 1.62 m/s^2. An astronaut in a space suit has a mass of 145 kg. (a) What is the astronaut's weight on earth? (b) On the moon? (c) What is the astronaut's mass on the moon?

4.22• A Saturn-Apollo launch rocket has a mass of 5.40 × 10^5 kg. What is the initial acceleration of the rocket if the thrust at liftoff is 7.40 × 10^6 N?

4.23• A force of 8.7 N is applied to a steel block initially at rest on a horizontal frictionless surface. The force, which is directed at an angle of 30° below the horizontal, gives the block a horizontal acceleration of 5.3 m/s^2. (a) What is the mass of the block? (b) What is the normal force of the surface acting on the block?

Section 4.6 Newton's Third Law

Hints for Solving Problems

Remember that action-reaction pairs act on different objects.

4.24 A large 500-kg magnet exerts a constant force of 3.00 N on a 0.250-kg bar magnet. What magnitude force does the bar magnet exert on the big magnet?

4.25 What force must be exerted at A to give an upward force of 32 N on the cervical traction device in Fig. 4.34?

4.26 The starship Enterprise is on a mission into deep space, where no human has gone before. It encounters an alien spacecraft, and Captain Kirk orders activation of the tractor beam to pull the alien craft to the starship. The alien ship is made of a super-dense alloy so its mass is 8 times the mass of the starship. Assuming the two craft have zero relative ve-

Figure 4.34
Problem 4.25.

locity at the time the tractor beam is activated, describe their motions by comparing the acceleration of the Enterprise to that of the alien craft as seen by a distant stationary observer.

4.27 An 59-kg woman stands in an elevator. What force does she exert on the floor of the elevator under the following conditions? (a) The elevator rises with a constant velocity of 2.0 m/s. (b) The elevator accelerates upward at 1.8 m/s^2. (c) The elevator goes down with a constant velocity of 4.0 m/s. (d) The elevator descends with a downward acceleration 2.8 m/s^2. (e) While going down, the elevator decelerates at 1.5 m/s^2.

4.28 An 75-kg man stands in an elevator. What force does he exert on the floor of the elevator under the following conditions? (a) The elevator is stationary. (b) The elevator accelerates upward at 2.0 m/s^2. (c) The elevator rises with constant velocity of 4.0 m/s. (d) While going up, the elevator accelerates downward at 1.5 m/s^2. (e) The elevator goes down with constant velocity of 7.0 m/s.

4.29 An unabridged dictionary of mass m rests on a weak table. (a) What is the reaction force to the force of the book on the table? (b) What is the reaction force to the force of gravity on the book? (c) The tabletop collapses under the book's weight. Answer (a) and (b) for the conditions while the table is collapsing.

4.30• A bird is placed on a perch in a large closed box that is sitting on a spring scale. What will happen to the scale reading when (a) the bird jumps off the perch, (b) the bird is flying, (c) the bird lights on the perch again?

4.31• A person weighing 650 N stands on spring scales in an elevator that is moving downward with constant speed of 3.6 m/s. The brakes suddenly grab, bringing the elevator to a stop in 1.8 s. Describe the scale readings from just before the brakes grab until after the elevator is at rest.

Section 4.7 Some Applications of Newton's Laws

Hints for Solving Problems

Be sure to draw a properly labeled free-body diagram for each problem.

4.32 Figure 4.35 shows a graph of distance along a straight course as a function of time for a 1000-kg dragster. Construct a graph of the horizontal force between the tires and ground (no slipping) as a function of time. (*Hint:* First construct a plot of velocity, taking points, say, every 0.5 s.)

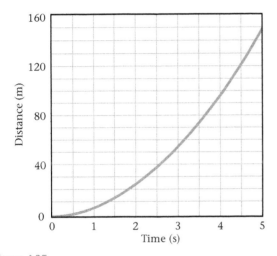

Figure 4.35
Problem 4.32.

4.33 (a) A 17.0-kg bucket is lowered by a rope with constant velocity of 0.500 m/s. What is the tension in the rope? (b) A 17.0-kg bucket is lowered with a constant downward acceleration of 1.00 m/s^2. What is the tension in the rope? (c) A 10.6-kg bucket is raised with a constant upward acceleration of 1.00 m/s^2. What is the tension in the rope?

4.34● A 0.0050-kg bullet traveling with a speed of 200 m/s penetrates a large wooden fence post to a depth of 0.030 m. What was the average resisting force exerted on the bullet?

4.35● A 0.0048-kg bullet traveling with a speed of 400 m/s penetrates into a large wooden fence post. If the average resisting force exerted on the bullet was 4.5×10^3 N, how far did the bullet penetrate?

4.36● Two air-track gliders m_1 and m_2 are joined together with a light string (Fig. 4.36). A constant horizontal force of 4.0 N to the right is applied to mass m_2. (a) If $m_1 = 1.5$ kg and $m_2 = 0.50$ kg, what is the acceleration of the gliders? (b) What is the tension in the cord joining them?

4.37● Find the accelerations and the tension for the situation of Problem 4.36 given that $m_1 = 0.50$ kg and $m_2 = 1.5$ kg.

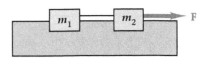

Figure 4.36
Problems 4.36 and 4.37.

4.38●● An 8.0-kg mass rests on an inclined frictionless surface as shown in Fig. 4.37. A light string runs parallel to the surface from the mass over a light, frictionless pulley to a 3.6-kg mass. Find (a) the acceleration of the masses and (b) the tension in the string.

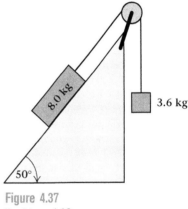

Figure 4.37
Problem 4.38.

4.39●● A simple Atwood machine composed of a single pulley and two masses m_1 and m_2 is on an elevator. When $m_1 = 44.7$ kg and $m_2 = 45.3$ kg, it takes 5.00 s for mass m_2 to descend exactly one meter from rest relative to the elevator. What is the elevator's motion? (That is, is it moving with constant velocity or accelerating up or down?)

4.40●● A classroom demonstration is done with an Atwood machine. The masses are $m_1 = 1.00$ kg and $m_2 = 1.10$ kg (Fig. 4.38). If the larger mass descends a distance of 3.00 m from rest in 3.6 s, what is the acceleration of gravity at that place? (Ignore the effects of pulley mass and friction.)

Section 4.8 Friction

4.41 A 9.75-kg lead brick rests on a level wooden table. If a force of 46.4 N is required to slide the brick across the table at a constant speed, what is the coefficient of friction?

4.42 A horizontal force pulls a 50.0-kg bag of fertilizer across the floor. What is the minimum force required if the coefficient of friction is 0.37?

4.43 A 5.00-g nickel coin sliding along a level table top with an initial velocity of 200 cm/s comes to a stop after traveling

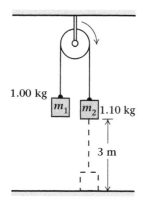

Figure 4.38
Problem 4.40.

50.0 cm. (a) What is the acceleration of the coin? (b) What is the coefficient of friction between the coin and the table?

4.44 A horizontal force of 3.00 N is applied to a 1.00-kg radio, initially at rest on a table with a level surface. (a) Will the radio move if the coefficient of friction is 0.45? (b) What is the coefficient of friction if it just begins to move? (c) What is its acceleration if the coefficient of friction is only 0.20?

4.45 A 5.00-kg concrete block rests on a level table. The coefficient of friction between the block and the table is 0.55. A 4.00-kg weight is attached to the block by a string of negligible mass passed over a light frictionless pulley (Fig. 4.39). What is the acceleration of the block when the 4.00-kg weight is released?

over a light, frictionless pulley (Fig. 4.39). If the acceleration of the block is measured to be 1.00 m/s², what is the coefficient of friction between the block and the table?

4.47• A crate starts from rest and slides 8.35 m down a ramp. When it reaches the bottom it is traveling at a speed of 5.25 m/s. If the ramp makes an angle of 20.0° with the horizontal, what is the coefficient of friction between the crate and the ramp?

4.48• A block of mass 4.7 kg slides 20 m from rest down an inclined plane making an angle of 30° with the horizontal. If the block takes 10 s to slide down the plane, what is the retarding force due to friction?

4.49• A 4.0-kg wooden block rests on a level table. The coefficient of friction between the block and the table is 0.40. A 5.0-kg mass is attached to the block by a horizontal string passed over a frictionless pulley of negligible mass. (a) What is the acceleration of the block when the 5.0-kg mass is released? (b) What is the tension in the string during the acceleration?

4.50• Determine the acceleration and the tension for the situation in Problem 4.49 when the coefficient of friction between the block and the table is 0.25.

4.51•• Two clay pots joined together by a light string rest on a table (Fig. 4.40). The frictional coefficient between the pots and the table is 0.35. The pots are also joined to a 4.0-kg mass by a string of negligible mass passed over an ideal pulley as shown in the figure. (a) Calculate the acceleration of the system when the 4.0-kg mass is released. (b) Also find the tensions T_1 and T_2 in the strings during acceleration.

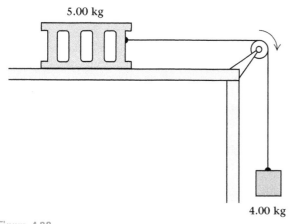

Figure 4.39
Problems 4.45 and 4.46.

4.46 A 5.00-kg concrete block rests on a level table. A 4.00-kg mass is attached to the block by a string passing

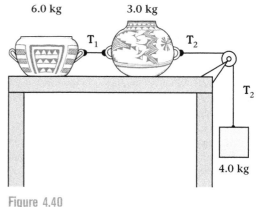

Figure 4.40
Problems 4.51 and 4.52.

4.52•• Consider the situation shown in Fig. 4.40 but with the 4.0-kg mass replaced by a 6.5-kg mass. Find the acceleration of the system and the tensions T_1 and T_2 assuming that the frictional coefficient is 0.35.

Section 4.9 Static Equilibrium

Hints for Solving Problems

In static equilibrium problems, the equilibrium condition applies independently in each direction. In inclined-plane problems, it is often helpful to resolve forces into components parallel and perpendicular to the plane.

4.53 A steel paperweight rests on a clean dry steel incline making an angle θ with the horizontal. Find the maximum angle θ for the paperweight to remain at rest.

4.54 A glass cube rests on a glass incline making an angle θ with the horizontal. The coefficient of friction between the cube and the incline is 0.92. Find the maximum angle θ for the cube to remain at rest.

4.55 When the archer in Fig. 4.41 pulls on the bow string with a force of 267 N, the bow string makes angles of 62° with the arrow. What is the tension in the string?

Figure 4.41
Problem 4.55.

4.56 A 52.6-kg high-school student hangs from an overhead bar with both hands. (a) What is the tension in each arm if the bar is gripped with both arms raised vertically overhead? (b) What is the tension in each arm when the arms make an angle of 33° with respect to the vertical?

4.57 A 60-lb child is seated in a swing of negligible mass. How much horizontal force is required to pull the child and swing aside so that the support rope makes an angle of 30° with the vertical? See Fig. 4.28. (p. 132)

4.58 Three equal masses are suspended from frictionless pulleys as shown in Fig. 4.42. What are the angles of the strings with respect to the horizontal when the system comes to equilibrium?

4.59• Suppose that the masses in Problem 4.58 are not identical. What are the angles θ_1 and θ_2 if $m_1 = m_2 = 2.0$ kg and $m_3 = 3.0$ kg?

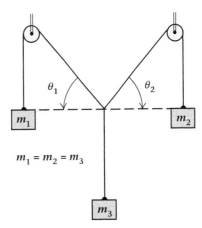

Figure 4.42
Problems 4.58 and 4.59.

4.60• A physicist finds that her car is stuck in the sand and cannot be driven out. Unable to push it out, she ties a strong rope from the front of the car to a large tree 30 m away and directly in front of the car. She then pushes on the middle of the rope with a force of 400 N in a direction perpendicular to the length of the rope. If the midpoint of the rope is displaced by 3.0 m, what is the force applied to the car?

4.61• A fish of mass m is suspended by a string as shown in Fig. 4.43. The string is fastened securely at point C but will pull loose from the wall at A when the string tension exceeds 22 N. What is the maximum mass of the fish that can be supported by the string?

4.62• What is the force exerted by the string on the wall at point A in Fig. 4.43 if the suspended fish has mass $m = 0.35$ kg?

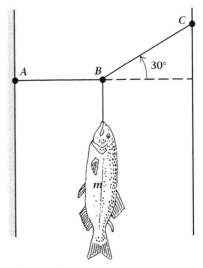

Figure 4.43
Problems 4.61 and 4.62.

4.63• A plant is hung from wires as shown in Fig. 4.44. What is the tension in each wire if the plant weighs 20.0 N? Ignore the weight of the wire.

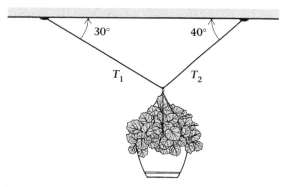

Figure 4.44
Figure 4.44
Problem 4.63.

4.64• Suppose that the weight w_2 in Fig. 4.45 is 400 N. What must be the values of the weights w_1 and w_3?

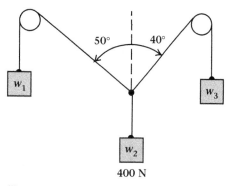

Figure 4.45
Problem 4.64.

4.65•• A 10.0-kg block is placed on a frictionless inclined plane and connected to a 5.0-kg block as shown in Fig. 4.46. (a) What would the angle θ have to be for the blocks to remain motionless? (b) What would be the acceleration of the blocks if $\theta = 37°$?

Additional Problems
4.66 A 1000-kg car is moving at 30 m/s. A braking force of 6000 N is applied for 4.0 s. What is the velocity of the car when the brakes are released?
4.67 What is the coefficient of friction between a sled and a plane inclined at 30° from the horizontal if the sled just slides without accelerating when given an initial push?

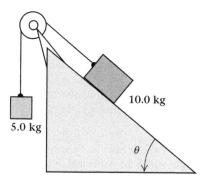

Figure 4.46
Problem 4.65.

4.68 A single cable supports an 837-kg elevator car. What is the tension in the cable when the car is moving with (a) constant speed, (b) an upward acceleration of 3.21 m/s², and (c) a downward acceleration of 3.21 m/s²?
4.69 A truck loaded with heavy cartons is forced to stop suddenly with a deceleration of 5.0 m/s². Calculate the minimum coefficient of friction between the cartons and the truck bed given that the cartons do not slide.
4.70 Assume that the Atwood's machine of Fig. 4.17 (a) (p. 116) is in static equilibrium. Make a diagram showing all forces. What must be the relationship of mass m_1 to mass m_2?
4.71 A 10-kg block is placed on a frictionless table and connected to a 5.0-kg block by a string that extends horizontally across the table over a pulley and down to the 5.0-kg block. What is the acceleration of the blocks? Ignore friction in the pulley.
4.72• For the accompanying diagram (Fig. 4.47), describe what will happen and what the spring scale S will read if (a) $m_1 = m_2 = 1$ kg; (b) $m_1 = 1.2$, $m_2 = 1$ kg. (Ignore the mass of the scale.)

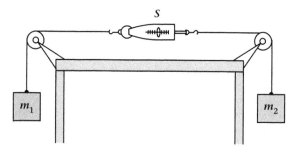

Figure 4.47
Problem 4.72.

4.73• A 500-kg trailer being pulled behind a car is subject to a 100-N retarding force due to friction. What force must the car exert on the trailer if (a) the trailer is to move forward at a constant speed of 25 km/h; (b) the trailer is to move forward with an acceleration of 2.0 m/s²; (c) starting from rest, the trailer and car are to travel 150 m in 10 s?

4.74• An Inter City Express locomotive pulls fourteen cars, each with a mass of 53,000 kg. What is the tension in the coupling between the third and fourth cars when the acceleration of the train is 0.26 m/s²?

4.75• (a) What is the minimum time in which one can hoist a 1.00-kg rock a height of 10.0 m if the string used to pull the rock up has a breaking strength of 10.8 N? Assume the rock to be initially at rest. (b) If the string is replaced by one that is 50% stronger, by what percentage will the minimum time for the hoist be reduced?

4.76• What minimum force is required to drag a carton of books across the floor at constant speed if the force is applied at an angle of 45° to the horizontal (Fig. 4.48)? Take the mass of the carton as 40 kg and the coefficient of friction as 0.60.

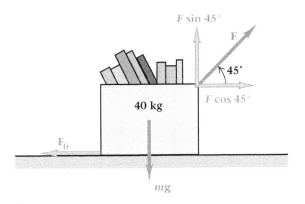

Figure 4.48
Problem 4.76.

4.77• A 65-kg skier goes down a 30° slope. (a) What would be the acceleration of the skier if friction could be neglected? (b) A skier continues to accelerate until gravitational force is balanced by the normal force and by the frictional forces due to the skis on the snow and the air resistance. What must be the frictional forces if the skier is no longer accelerating?

4.78• An elevator with a mass of 2500 kg carries four passengers with a combined mass of 260 kg. (a) What is the tension in the supporting cable when the elevator starts from rest and moves upward with constant acceleration until reaching a speed of 5.0 m/s in 2.0 s? (b) What is the tension in the cable when the elevator starts down with the same load and acceleration of the same magnitude?

4.79• Two blocks are connected by a light string passing over a pulley (Fig. 4.49). The inclined surfaces are frictionless and the effects of the pulley can be ignored. If the values are mass $m_2 = m_1 = 1.00$ kg, $\theta_1 = 46°$, and $\theta_2 = 34°$, what is the acceleration of the blocks?

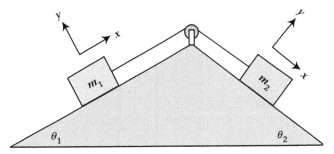

Figure 4.49
Problems 4.79, 4.85, and 4.86.

4.80•• A 400-N kangaroo exerts a constant force on the ground during the first 0.60 m of a vertical jump. After the kangaroo's feet leave the ground it rises an additional 1.8 m. When the kangaroo carries a baby kangaroo in its pouch and jumps with the same force, it can rise only 1.65 m higher after its feet leave the ground. What is the weight of the baby kangaroo?

4.81•• A 0.840-kg glider on a level air track is joined by strings to two hanging masses (Fig. 4.50). The strings have negligible mass and pass over light, frictionless pulleys. (a) Find the acceleration of the masses and (b) the tension in the strings.

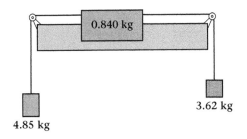

Figure 4.50
Problems 4.81 and 4.82.

4.82•• A 0.840-kg glider on a level air track is joined by strings to two hanging masses (Fig. 4.50). The strings have negligible mass and pass over light, frictionless pulleys. (a) Find the acceleration of the masses and (b) the tension in the strings when the air flow is turned off and the coefficient of friction between the glider and the track is 0.47.

4.83•• A monkey clinging to one end of a rope that passes over a frictionless pulley is balanced by a mirror of exactly equal weight on the other end of the rope (Fig. 4.51). When the monkey begins to climb the rope, it sees itself in the mirror. (a) Can the monkey climb up or down to escape the image? (b) After the monkey has traversed 4.0 m of rope, he stops. How high has he climbed? (c) What will happen if the monkey lets go of the rope? If you need additional information, make a specific assumption and answer the question in that light.

$M_m = M_b$

M_b

M_m

Figure 4.51
Problem 4.83.

4.84•• A 0.50 kg air-track glider has an initial speed of 0.25 m/s as it passes through a photoelectric gate that starts a timer. As it passes through, a constant force of 0.40 N is applied in the direction of motion. (a) What is the acceleration of the glider? (b) The glider then passes through a second gate that stops the timer at 1.3 s. What is the distance between the two gates? (c) The 0.40-N force is applied by means of a string attached to the glider. The other end of the string passes over a frictionless pulley and is attached to a hanging mass m. How big is the mass m? (d) Derive an expression for the tension T in the string as a function of the mass M of the glider, the mass m of the hanging mass, and the acceleration of gravity g.

4.85•• Two blocks are connected by a light string passing over a pulley (Fig. 4.49). The inclined surfaces are frictionless and the effects of the pulley can be ignored. The value of $m_1 = 1.05$ kg, $\theta_1 = 30°$, and $\theta_2 = 40°$. If the blocks accelerate to the left with acceleration $a = 0.010$ m/s^2, what is the value of m_2?

4.86•• Two blocks are connected by a light string passing over a pulley (Fig. 4.49). The inclined surfaces are frictionless, and the effects of the pulley can be ignored. The value of $m_1 = m_2 = 1.00$ kg and $\theta_2 = 40°$. If the blocks accelerate to the right with acceleration $a = 0.206$ m/s^2, what is the value of θ_1?

Solving Simultaneous Equations

Physics problems often lead to two or more equations that need to be solved at the same time to get the required answers. We call these equations simultaneous equations. The following problem illustrates how we solve simultaneous equations: A bicyclist heads north at a steady speed of 15 km/h from a point 3 km from a park. Three hours before the cyclist departed, a walker started walking north from the park along the same path at 5 km/h. When and where does the bicyclist overtake the walker?

Let y be the distance from the park where the bicyclist overtakes the walker. Then for the bicyclist

$$y = (15 \text{ km/h})t + 3 \text{ km},$$

where t is the cyclist's elapsed time in hours. The walker, having traveled for $t + 3$ h, goes the same distance,

$$y = (t + 3 \text{ h})5 \text{ km/h} = (5 \text{ km/h})t + 15 \text{ km}.$$

Each of these equations contains two unknown quantities, y and t. Neither equation alone can give us the answers, but we can solve them simultaneously to obtain both unknowns.

There are several techniques for solving simultaneous equations, all using only simple algebra and all giving the same result for a given problem. When you use these techniques to solve physics problems, be sure you take proper care of the units. However, because our intent here is to review the mathematical techniques, we will simplify them by omitting the units.

To solve the two equations just developed, let's write them again without units. We can eliminate the variable y by subtracting the second equation from the first. They become

$$
\begin{array}{r}
y = 15t + \ \ 3 \\
- \quad y = \ \ 5t + 15 \\
\hline
0 = 10t - 12.
\end{array}
$$

This new equation involves only t and may be rearranged to give

$$10t = 12.$$

Thus

$$t = \frac{12}{10} = 1.2.$$

Now that we have a value for t, it may be substituted into either of the original equations to give

$$y = 15t + 3 = 15(1.2) + 3 = 21$$
$$y = 5t + 15 = 5(1.2) + 15 = 21.$$

Notice that we get the same answer in both cases. Only one is necessary, but you may want to compute both as a check on your work. The physical answer to the original problem is that the cyclist overtakes the walker 1.2 h after the cyclist started. They meet at a position 21 km from the park.

We can solve the same pair of equations by eliminating t first. To do so we multiply the first equation by 5 and the second equation by 15. This procedure gives two new equations with the same coefficient of t. If we subtract the lower equation from the upper one, we get

$$
\begin{array}{r}
5y = 75t + \ \ 15 \\
- \quad 15y = 75t + 225 \\
\hline
-10y = \qquad -210.
\end{array}
$$

Thus

$$y = 21.$$

This is the same result as before. If you substitute this value of y into either original equation and solve for t, you will again get $t = 1.2$.

These examples are called the *addition and subtraction* method. Strictly speaking we used subtraction in both examples. Suppose the physical process had given equations of the type

$$z = 12x + 20$$

and

$$z = -2x + 7.$$

Then we could solve them by multiplying the second equation by 6 and adding the two equations:

$$
\begin{aligned}
z &= 12x + 20 \\
+\ 6z &= -12x + 42 \\
\hline
7z &= 62.
\end{aligned}
$$

The unknown quantity z is then

$$
z = \frac{62}{7} = 8.86.
$$

The value for x can be found by substituting z into one of the original equations.

Another technique for solving simultaneous equations makes use of substitution. For example, in the problem of the cyclist and walker, we could rewrite the first equation to express t in terms of y:

$$
t = \frac{1}{15} y - \frac{1}{5}.
$$

We then substitute this value of t into the second equation to get

$$
y = 5 \left(\frac{1}{15} y - \frac{1}{5} \right) + 15
$$

$$
y = \frac{1}{3} y - 1 + 15
$$

$$
y \left(1 - \frac{1}{3} \right) = \frac{2}{3} y = 14
$$

$$
y = \frac{14}{2/3} = 21.
$$

As before, we can substitute this value of y into either original equation to get the value for t.

If your simultaneous equations include the square of an unknown quantity, you should use these same techniques to eliminate all but one variable. If the resulting equation still contains a squared term, it may be necessary to use the quadratic formula to find the solution. In some cases—for instance, the two-dimensional elastic collision of two objects (Chapter 8)—you will have three simultaneous equations to be solved for three unknown quantities. By applying any of the procedures we have just described, you can sequentially eliminate variables and thus reduce the number of equations to a single equation in one variable. The resulting solution can then be used to determine the other unknowns. In general, the number of independent equations you will need must be at least as great as the number of unknowns.

5.1 Uniform Circular Motion
5.2 Force Needed for Circular Motion
5.3 Kepler's Laws of Planetary Motion
5.4 The Law of Universal Gravitation

Back to the Future: Johannes Kepler

5.5 The Universal Gravitational Constant *G*
*5.6 Gravitational Field Strength

*Back to the Future: Henry Cavendish and the
Density of the Earth*

Uniform Circular Motion and Gravitation

We saw in Chapter 4 how we can use Newton's laws to calculate the motion of an object once we know the forces acting on it. The ability to do so does not depend on the nature or origin of the forces involved. We will see that in addition to the contact forces we have already discussed, there are other forces arising from gravity, electricity, magnetism, etc. Once we know the details of the particular force, we may then use Newton's laws to predict the motion of the object.

In this chapter we introduce Newton's law of universal gravitation, which was the first example of a fundamental force of nature expressed in mathematical form. The second force to be described mathematically was the electrostatic force, almost 100 years later (see Chapter 16). This process of mathematical development continues today for nuclear and subnuclear forces (see Chapters 29 and 32).

We observe that planets move in elliptical paths around the sun. In many cases these ellipses are almost circles. Therefore, we can improve our understanding of the motion of planets and satellites in their orbits if we first examine the dynamics of circular motion. Circular motion is quite common in nature and can be found in varied settings from orbiting satellites to charged particles moving in a magnetic field to fair rides to cars rounding a curve. Furthermore, circular motion is closely related to vibrations and waves. Thus, the concepts learned here will be put to use in other areas. ■

5.1 Uniform Circular Motion

You know from experience that when you tie an object to a string and swing it in a circle around your head, you exert a force on the string. Because the string is flexible, the force that acts on the object is directed along the string toward your hand. According to Newton's second law, there is an acceleration in the same direction as this force. In this section we will show that any object moving in a circle at constant speed has an acceleration toward the center of the circle.

Before we begin the derivation, let us introduce a unit of angular measure, the radian. If we measure the length of an arc along the circumference of a circle (Fig. 5.1), we find that the arc length s is proportional to the angle θ subtended by the arc.* For a given angle, the arc length increases in direct proportion to increases in the radius of the circle. We define the angle in **radians,** θ, to be the ratio of the arc length s to the radius r:

$$\theta \equiv \frac{s}{r}. \tag{5.1}$$

Thus, one radian is the angle subtended by an arc length equal to the radius of the circle.

If we let the arc length become the entire circumference of the circle, then $s = 2\pi r$. (Recall that π is just a number, equal to 3.14159 . . .) Thus the angle in radians generated in going around a complete circle is 2π. We can say that the angular change in a full rotation is either 360° or 2π radians, depending on which unit of angular measure is used.

The relationship between the radian and the degree is

$$2\pi \, \text{rad} = 360°,$$

where we have used the symbol rad for the unit of radian. If we divide both sides by 2π, we find that

$$1 \, \text{rad} = \frac{360°}{2\pi} = 57.3°.$$

We could have divided both sides by 360 and found that

$$1° = \frac{2\pi}{360} = 0.0175 \, \text{rad}.$$

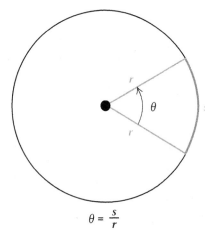

$$\theta = \frac{s}{r}$$

$s = $ circumference
$s = 2\pi r$

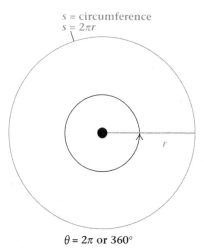

$\theta = 2\pi$ or 360°

Figure 5.1
Angular measure in radians. The radian measure of an angle is the ratio of the subtended arc length to the radius. If the arc length is the entire circumference of a circle, then the angle in radians is 2π.

---

*In a triangle or sector of a circle, a line *subtends* the angle opposite to it; that is, the line extends across the entire angle.

Example 5.1

Eratosthenes (ca. 276–196 BC) knew that when the sun was directly overhead at Syene (modern Aswan) in southern Egypt, the sun was about 7° away from directly overhead in Alexandria (Fig. 5.2). Using the known distance between the two observing points, he was able to determine the circumference of the earth. Use a figure of 770 km for the distance to perform the same calculation.

Strategy From the figure we see that the distance from Syene to Alexandria is an arc length that subtends an angle of 7°. If we express the angle in radians, we can use the definition of Eq. (5.1) to determine the radius of the earth and, hence, the circumference.

Solution The angle measured in radians is

$$\theta = (7°)\left(\frac{2\pi\,\text{rad}}{360°}\right) = 0.122\,\text{rad}.$$

The radius of the earth, given by $r = s/\theta$, where s is the arc length of 770 m, is

$$r = \frac{s}{\theta} = \frac{770\,\text{km}}{0.122\,\text{rad}} = 6300\,\text{km}.$$

The circumference of the earth is found from

$$C = 2\pi r = 2\pi(6300\,\text{km}) = 40{,}000\,\text{km}.$$

Discussion The modern value for the average radius of the earth is 6380 km, barely 1% greater than Eratosthenes's measurement.

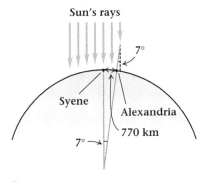

Figure 5.2
When the sun is directly overhead at Syene, it is about 7° away from directly overhead in Alexandria.

Now, consider a point particle moving along a circular path of radius r with constant speed v. A particle moving in this manner is said to undergo **uniform circular motion.** By a "particle" we mean an object of negligible size and constant mass. We use the idea of a particle as a way of creating a simplified model of a real physical situation. However, the resulting equations apply to real situations, such as a dot of paint on the rim of a wheel rotating at a steady rate. To a good approximation, we can extend our description of a point in uniform circular motion to a merry-go-round ride or to a satellite revolving around the earth.

As we learned in our study of kinematics (Chapter 2), a particle's speed is determined by measuring the distance traveled along its path and dividing by the elapsed time. Although the dot moves along its circular path with a constant speed v, its instantaneous velocity vector is constantly changing because the direction of its motion is constantly changing. (Remember that the speed is the magnitude of the instantaneous velocity.) At any moment of time, the instantaneous velocity is tangential to the circle. In a time interval Δt, the object moves along the circular path from one point, say P in Fig. 5.3(a), to another point, Q. The instantaneous velocity vectors at points P and Q, given by $\mathbf{v}_P$ and $\mathbf{v}_Q$, respectively, have the same magnitude but differ in direction. Each instantaneous velocity is tangent to the circle and perpendicular to the radius r at the point in question.

Because the velocity is constantly changing, there must be an acceleration. (Remember, acceleration occurs whenever the velocity changes in magnitude or

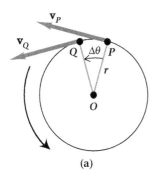

(a)

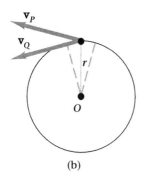

(b)

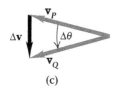

(c)

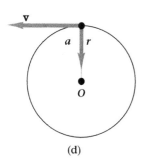

(d)

Figure 5.3
(a) The instantaneous velocity vector at points P and Q for a particle moving in a circular path. The velocity vector at a later time is shown at point Q.
(b) Vectors $\mathbf{v}_P$ and $\mathbf{v}_Q$ are translated to a common origin for comparison.
(c) The vector $\Delta\mathbf{v} = \mathbf{v}_Q - \mathbf{v}_P$. As $\Delta\theta$ becomes very small, $\Delta\mathbf{v}$ becomes perpendicular to both $\mathbf{v}_Q$ and $\mathbf{v}_P$.
(d) The moving particle has an instantaneous velocity tangential to the circle and an acceleration directed toward the center of the circle.

direction.) During the time interval Δt, the velocity changes by an amount $\Delta\mathbf{v} = \mathbf{v}_Q - \mathbf{v}_P$. The definition of average acceleration is

$$\bar{\mathbf{a}} \equiv \frac{\Delta\mathbf{v}}{\Delta t}. \tag{5.2}$$

To evaluate the acceleration we translate the vectors $\mathbf{v}_P$ and $\mathbf{v}_Q$ to a common origin (Fig. 5.3b). The change in velocity $\Delta\mathbf{v}$ is shown in Fig. 5.3(c). As the time interval Δt is made smaller, points P and Q are found closer together, reducing $\Delta\theta$, the angle between them. You can see that this angle is also the angle between the two velocity vectors. Eventually the angle $\Delta\theta$ becomes so small that $\mathbf{v}_P$ and $\mathbf{v}_Q$ are almost parallel and their difference $\Delta\mathbf{v}$ is almost perpendicular to both of them. In the limit that Δt goes to zero, $\Delta\mathbf{v}$ is exactly perpendicular to $\mathbf{v}$. Hence, the instantaneous acceleration, which is in the same direction as $\Delta\mathbf{v}$, is directed radially toward the center of the circular path. Therefore *a particle moving with constant speed around a circle is always accelerated toward the center* (Fig. 5.3d). In this special case, the particle has uniform circular motion, and its acceleration is always perpendicular to the velocity. This acceleration is called the **centripetal** (center-seeking) **acceleration.**

The centripetal acceleration can be readily evaluated. The angle $\Delta\theta$ between $\mathbf{v}_P$ and $\mathbf{v}_Q$, when measured in radians, is the ratio of the arc length to the radius. The arc length is the product of the speed and the time interval, so the angle becomes

$$\Delta\theta = \frac{\text{arc length}}{\text{radius}} = \frac{v\Delta t}{r}. \tag{5.3}$$

From the geometry of Fig. 5.3(c), we see that as $\Delta\theta$ gets smaller, the magnitude of $\Delta\mathbf{v}$ (indicated by $|\Delta\mathbf{v}|$) is approximately the same as the arc length made by turning a vector of magnitude $|\mathbf{v}_P|$ through the angle $\Delta\theta$. Thus $\Delta\theta$ may also be expressed as the ratio

$$\Delta\theta \approx \frac{|\Delta\mathbf{v}|}{|\mathbf{v}_P|}.$$

Since the magnitude of the velocity is constant, $|\mathbf{v}_P| = |\mathbf{v}_Q| = v$ and we can write

$$\Delta\theta \approx \frac{|\Delta v|}{v}.$$

The magnitude of the average acceleration becomes

$$|\bar{a}| = \frac{|\Delta\mathbf{v}|}{\Delta t} \approx \frac{v\Delta\theta}{\Delta t}.$$

Upon substituting Eq. (5.3) for $\Delta\theta$, we find that, in the limit of very small angles, we have

$$\boxed{a_c = \frac{v^2}{r},} \tag{5.4}$$

where the subscript c denotes centripetal acceleration. The velocity of a point in uniform circular motion is always tangential to the circle, and the acceleration always points to the center of the circle.

Example 5.2

A bicycle racer rides with constant speed around a circular track 25 m in diameter (Fig. 5.4). What is the acceleration of the bicycle toward the center of the track if its speed is 6.0 m/s?

Solution Since the speed around the circle is constant, we can compute the acceleration directly from Eq. (5.4):

$$a_c = \frac{v^2}{r} = \frac{(6.0 \text{ m/s})^2}{12.5 \text{ m}} = 2.9 \text{ m/s}^2.$$

Remember that this acceleration is directed toward the center of the circle as the bicycle moves at a constant speed around the circular track.

Sometimes it is more convenient to describe circular motion in terms of other quantities. For example, suppose that we know an object's **period** T, which is the time it takes the object to complete one revolution around its circular path. During this time, the object travels with constant speed v along a distance equal to the circumference of the circle, $vT = 2\pi r$. We can rearrange this last equation to find v, and then insert the result into Eq. (5.4) to get the centripetal acceleration in terms of r and T,

$$a_c = \frac{4\pi^2 r}{T^2}$$

The **frequency** f is the number of complete revolutions, or cycles, an object makes per unit of time. The frequency f is the reciprocal of the period T. If an object takes a time T to complete one revolution around the circle, then the number of revolutions per unit time, the frequency, is

$$\boxed{f = \frac{1}{T}.} \qquad (5.5)$$

Frequency has the dimension of inverse time, that is, 1/time. The SI unit of frequency is the **hertz,** abbreviated Hz:

$$1 \text{ Hz} = 1/\text{s} = 1 \text{ s}^{-1}.$$

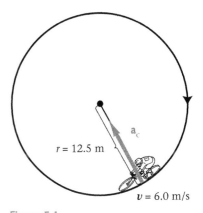

Figure 5.4
Example 5.2: Bicycle racer on a circular track.

Example 5.3

An industrial grinding wheel with a 25.4-cm diameter spins at a rate of 1910 revolutions per minute (Fig. 5.5). What is the linear speed of a point on the rim?

Solution The speed of a point on the rim is the distance traveled, $2\pi r$, divided by T, the time for one revolution. However, we are given the frequency, which is the reciprocal of the period. Thus, the speed of a point on the rim, a distance

Figure 5.5
Example 5.3: A grinding wheel.

r from the axis of rotation, is

$$v = \frac{2\pi r}{T} = 2\pi r f.$$

Inserting the values of r and f, we get

$$v = (2\pi)\left(\frac{25.4 \text{ cm}}{2}\right)\left(\frac{1910}{\text{min}}\right)\left(\frac{1 \text{ min}}{60 \text{ s}}\right)$$

$$v = 2540 \text{ cm/s} = 25.4 \text{ m/s}.$$

▼
Problem-Solving Strategy

Comparing Quantities

When asked to compare two quantities, you should do so by computing the quantities and finding their ratio. In the following example we compare the acceleration of the moon to that of a body falling near the earth by forming the ratio a_{moon}/g.

▼
Example 5.4

Determine the centripetal acceleration of the moon as it circles the earth, and compare that acceleration with the acceleration of bodies falling on the earth. The period of the moon's orbit is 27.3 days.

Strategy According to Newton's first law, the moon would move with constant velocity in a straight line unless it were acted on by a force. We can infer the presence of a force from the fact that the moon moves with approximately uniform circular motion around the earth (Fig. 5.6). The acceleration toward the earth can be calculated from the period and the orbital radius. The mean center-to-center, earth-moon distance, given in a table in the end pages, is 3.84×10^8 m. The period of 27.3 days is not in SI units and must be converted.

Solution The acceleration of the moon toward the earth is

$$a_c = \frac{v^2}{r} = \frac{4\pi^2 r}{T^2} = \frac{4\pi^2(3.84 \times 10^8 \text{ m})}{(27.3 \text{ days} \times 24 \text{ h/day} \times 3600 \text{ s/h})^2}$$

$$a_c = 2.72 \times 10^{-3} \text{ m/s}^2.$$

The ratio of the moon's acceleration to that of an object falling near the earth is

$$\frac{a_c}{g} = \frac{2.72 \times 10^{-3} \text{ m/s}^2}{9.81 \text{ m/s}^2} = \frac{1}{3600}.$$

Discussion The ratio of the earth-moon distance to the earth's radius is about 60. According to Newton's law of gravitation, the ratio of the attracting forces, and thus the accelerations, is the inverse ratio of the square of the distances and is approximately $1/(60)^2 = 1/3600$. This predicted ratio and the ratio just

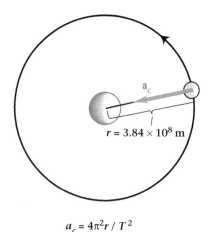

$a_c = 4\pi^2 r / T^2$
$T = 27.3$ days

Figure 5.6
Example 5.4: The moon orbiting the earth.

calculated are the same. Considerations of this kind helped convince Newton and others of his time of the inverse-square nature of the gravitational force.

··■

The position of a point in circular motion with tangential velocity v at a constant radial distance r from the center of the circle is given by the angle θ shown in Fig. 5.7. This angle in radians is given in terms of the arc length s and the radius r ($\theta = s/r$), as defined earlier. The rate of change of this angle is the **angular velocity** ω. The average angular velocity $\overline{\omega}$ is

$$\overline{\omega} \equiv \frac{\Delta\theta}{\Delta t} = \frac{\Delta s}{\Delta t} \cdot \frac{1}{r}.$$

In the limit that the time interval goes to zero, $\Delta s/\Delta t$ becomes the instantaneous speed v. Then the magnitude of the instantaneous angular velocity ω becomes

$$\boxed{\omega = \frac{v}{r}.} \tag{5.6}$$

We see from the definition of angular velocity that the dimension of ω is the reciprocal of time (that is, time^{-1}) and the units are radians per second (rad/s). Remember that, since the angle in radians was defined as a ratio of lengths, it has no dimension. The unit of radian is carried as a reminder that the angles are measured in radians and not in degrees.

When the change in time Δt is one period, the change in angle corresponds to one complete revolution, or 2π rad. Thus, we can also express the angular velocity as

$$\omega = \frac{\Delta\theta}{\Delta t} = \frac{2\pi}{T},$$

so that

$$\boxed{\omega = 2\pi f.} \tag{5.7}$$

Since ω is directly proportional to f and has the dimension of inverse time, it is often called the **angular frequency.** The two names for ω may be used interchangeably. We will use these terms again in describing rotations (Chapter 9) and oscillations (Chapter 14).

We can also express the centripetal acceleration in terms of the angular velocity by combining Eqs. (5.4) and (5.6) to get

$$a_c = \omega^2 r.$$

Uniform circular motion represents the special case of two-dimensional motion in which the acceleration is always perpendicular to the velocity. In that case, the acceleration changes only the direction of the velocity, and not its magnitude (speed). We found earlier that for projectile motion the acceleration is generally neither parallel nor perpendicular to the velocity, so that both magnitude and direction of the velocity change. Figure 5.8 depicts these two cases.

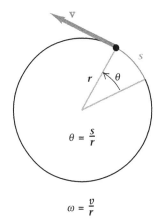

$$\theta = \frac{s}{r}$$

$$\omega = \frac{v}{r}$$

Figure 5.7
A point moving with a constant speed v along a circle of radius r is described in terms of its angular position θ. Its angular velocity (also called the angular frequency) is $\omega = v/r$.

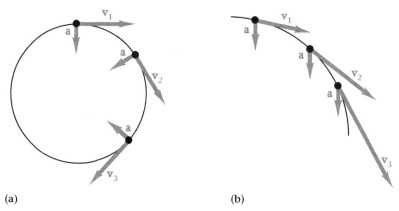

(a)   (b)

Figure 5.8
(a) In uniform circular motion, the acceleration is always perpendicular to the velocity, so that only the direction of the velocity changes. (b) In other two-dimensional motions, the acceleration is neither perpendicular nor parallel to the velocity. Then both direction and magnitude of the velocity change.

Figure 5.9
Example 5.5: The Wheelie.

Example 5.5

At Six Flags Over Georgia near Atlanta, the Wheelie carries passengers in a circular path with a radius of 7.7 m (Fig. 5.9). The ride makes a complete rotation every 4.0 s. (a) What is a passenger's angular velocity due to the circular motion? (b) What acceleration does a passenger experience?

Solution (a) The ride has a period $T = 4.0$ s. We can use it to compute the angular velocity as

$$\omega = \frac{2\pi}{T} = \frac{2\pi \, \text{rad}}{4.0 \, \text{s}} = \frac{\pi}{2.0} \, \text{rad/s} \approx 1.6 \, \text{rad/s}.$$

(b) Because the riders travel in a circle, they undergo a centripetal acceleration given by

$$a_c = \omega^2 r = \left(\frac{\pi}{2} \, \text{rad/s}\right)^2 (7.7 \, \text{m}) = 19 \, \text{m/s}^2.$$

Notice that this is almost twice the acceleration of a body in free fall.

5.2 Force Needed for Circular Motion

We have just seen that an object of mass m moving in a circular path with a uniform speed v is accelerated because the direction of its instantaneous velocity is continuously changing. For example, a toy airplane whirled in a circle by a string is accelerated. By Newton's second law, the net force acting on the object is in the same direction as the observed acceleration. This net force is called the **centripetal force** because it is directed toward the center of the circle. It is this net force that causes the motion of the object to be circular; without the centripetal force, the object would travel in a straight line and not in a circle. The magnitude of the centripetal force is obtained from Newton's second law as

$$F_c = ma_c$$

$$\boxed{F_c = \frac{mv^2}{r}.}$$ (5.8)

Substituting for v in terms of T or ω also gives a valid expression. For example, centripetal force is also given by $F_c = m\omega^2 r$.

As we have seen, circular motion requires acceleration and the acceleration is the result of a net force. Thus, any object undergoing circular motion necessarily experiences a force that causes the object to move in a circular path. It is this force that we call the centripetal force. Note that the centripetal force is not a fundamental force in the same sense that gravity is a fundamental force. It is just the name we give to the net force—whatever its origin—that causes an object to move in a circle. Computations of centripetal force are illustrated by Examples 5.6 and 5.7.

Master the Concept

Force and Circular Motion

Question: The Wave Swinger ride at the fair has two circular rows of chairs suspended by chains of equal lengths. The outer row is along the outer edge of the top of the ride and the inner row has a smaller radius. Do riders in both rows swing out at the same angle when the ride is rotating?

Answer: When the ride is in motion, the passengers in the chairs swing outward. At one particular angle the chain provides the necessary horizontal force for circular motion and the vertical force needed to balance the gravitational force. Riders in both rows move with the same angular velocity, but those in the outer row move in a larger radius and thus have a larger angular acceleration. Because of this larger angular acceleration, a larger centripetal force is needed. Thus, for riders in the outer row, the horizontal component of the chain force is larger relative to their gravitational force than it is for those on the inner row. The result is that riders in the outer row swing out to the larger angle from the vertical direction than do the riders in the inner row as you can see in Fig. 5.22 on p. 170.

Example 5.6

Approximately how much force does the earth exert on the moon?

Strategy Assume the moon's orbit to be circular about a stationary earth. The force can be found from $F = ma_c$.

$$F = ma_c = m\frac{v^2}{r} = m\frac{4\pi^2 r}{T^2}.$$

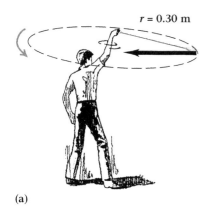

$r = 0.30$ m

(a)

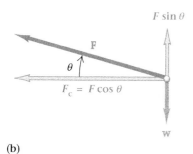

$F \sin \theta$

F

θ

$F_c = F \cos \theta$

w

(b)

Figure 5.10
Example 5.7: (a) A fishing weight is tied to a string and whirled in a horizontal circle. (b) The free-body diagram for (a). The force **F** along the string must provide both the horizontal centripetal force and the upward vertical force that opposes the gravitational force **w**.

Use the data given in Fig. 5.6 for r and T. The mass of the moon is given in the end sheets as 7.35×10^{22} kg.

Solution The numerical values can be inserted into the equation to give

$$F = \frac{(7.35 \times 10^{22} \text{ kg})4\pi^2(3.84 \times 10^8 \text{ m})}{(27.3 \text{ day} \times 8.64 \times 10^4 \text{ s/day})^2} = 2.00 \times 10^{20} \text{ N}.$$

▼

Example 5.7

A student ties a 0.060-kg lead fishing weight to the end of a piece of string and whirls it around in a horizontal circle. If the radius of the circle is 0.30 m and the object moves with a speed of 2.0 m/s, what is the horizontal component of force that directs the lead weight toward the center of the circle (Fig. 5.10a)? What is the tension in the string?

Strategy To begin, we draw the free-body diagram of Fig. 5.10(b). The tension **F** along the string provides both a horizontal and a vertical force. The centripetal acceleration is provided by the horizontal component F_c. The weight will move up or down, changing the angle θ, until the vertical component of **F** is equal and opposite to the gravitational force **w**.

Solution The horizontal force component is

$$F_c = ma_c = \frac{mv^2}{r}$$

$$F_c = \frac{(0.060 \text{ kg})(2.0 \text{ m/s})^2}{0.30 \text{ m}} = 0.80 \text{ N}.$$

The tension in the string is the vector sum of F_c and the vertical force opposing **w**. Its magnitude is

$$F = \sqrt{F_c^2 + w^2}$$
$$F = \sqrt{(0.80 \text{ N})^2 + (0.060 \text{ kg} \times 9.81 \text{ m/s}^2)^2} = 0.99 \text{ N}.$$

A car moving in a circle with constant speed must be acted on by a force in order to execute circular rather than straight-line motion. This centripetal force is provided by the friction between the tires and the road. Passengers inside the car must also be subject to a centripetal force or they will not travel in the same path as the car. They experience forces exerted by the seat or the door of the car that cause them to move along the same path. This description is in accord with what is seen by an observer at rest outside the car.

Inside the noninertial frame of the car rounding the curve, the driver may actually believe she experiences an outward force that pushes her against the car door. In reality, however, it is the car seat and door that press inward on the driver, causing her to move in a circular path (Fig. 5.11). The occupant of the car exerts a force on the car that is equal and opposite to the centripetal force. This apparent outward force, which is experienced only by the person in the car moving in a curve (a rotating reference frame), is called a centrifugal force. However, an observer at rest outside the car would say that there is no centrifugal force. The words centripetal and centrifugal were used in their present-day context in the *Principia.*

Example 5.8

Imagine a giant donut-shaped space station located so far from all heavenly bodies that the force of gravity may be neglected. To enable the occupants to live a "normal" life, the donut rotates and the inhabitants live on the part of the donut farthest from the center (Fig. 5.12). If the outside diameter of the space station is 1.5 km, what must be its period of rotation so that the passengers at the periphery will perceive an artificial gravity equal to the normal gravity at the earth's surface?

Solution   The weight of a person of mass m on the earth is a force

$$F = mg.$$

The centripetal force required to carry the person around a circle of radius r is

$$F = ma_c = \frac{m4\pi^2 r}{T^2}.$$

We may equate these two force expressions and solve for the period T:

$$mg = \frac{m4\pi^2 r}{T^2},$$

$$T = 2\pi\sqrt{\frac{r}{g}} = 2\pi\sqrt{\frac{750 \text{ m}}{9.81 \text{ m/s}^2}} = 55 \text{ s} = 0.92 \text{ min.}$$

A common laboratory tool that operates by the principle of centripetal force is the centrifuge. This device is primarily used to increase the sedimentation rate of small particles suspended in a liquid or to separate slightly dissimilar liquids. One type of centrifuge is shown in Fig. 5.13(a). When the rotor spins, the tubes swing outward until at very high speeds they are virtually horizontal. In this position the liquid is unable to exert the centripetal force required to keep the small suspended particles moving in a circle. Consequently, the particles move outward toward the end (bottom) of the tubes. At high speeds, the resulting forces on the particles may be many times greater than the gravitational force, so that the small particles collect at the bottom of the tubes more quickly than if left to settle by gravity alone. Further details will be found in the discussion of Stokes's law in Chapter 10.

Example 5.9

A centrifuge used to separate blood cells from blood plasma rotates at 55 rotations per second. What is the acceleration at the center of a centrifuge tube 8.0 cm from the axis of rotation?

Figure 5.11
Centripetal forces cause both driver and car to move together in a circular path. Friction between the tires and the road exerts an inward force on the car; the car seat and door exert an inward force on the driver. By Newton's third law, the driver at rest inside the car also exerts an outward force on the car seat, equal in magnitude and opposite in direction to the centripetal force.

Centripetal forces on the car

Vehicle's tendency to move in a straight line

Figure 5.12
Example 5.8: A rotating space station. Occupants are kept on the outer wall by an "artificial gravity" produced by the rotational motion.

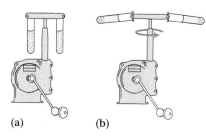

(c)

Figure 5.13

(a) A simple centrifuge. At rest the tubes hang down as shown. (b) As the shaft rotates at high speed, the tubes swing out. (c) Commercial laboratory centrifuges with a fixed tube angle commonly rotate at speeds of 3400 rpm.

Solution Since we are given a frequency of rotation, we choose the acceleration formula

$$a_c = \omega^2 r,$$

where $\omega = 2\pi f$. We then obtain

$$a_c = (2\pi f)^2 r = (2\pi \, 55/s)^2 (0.080 \text{ m})$$
$$a_c = 9.6 \times 10^3 \text{ m/s}^2.$$

We may compare this acceleration with the acceleration of gravity, $g = 9.81 \text{ m/s}^2$, to get

$$a_c = 970 \, g.$$

Discussion It is common to compare accelerations with the acceleration of gravity as we have done here. It becomes a way of gauging how much force acts on an object. An acceleration of one g corresponds to a force equal to the object's weight, $2g$ corresponds to a force twice the object's weight, and so on. Sometimes people refer to forces in terms of g. In that case they are not giving the force itself, rather they are giving the ratio of force on an object to its weight.

.... ■

As we saw earlier, on a flat curve a car is turned by the frictional force exerted on the tires by the road. If the frictional force is not large enough, the car does not travel around the proper curve, but instead skids toward the outside. For high-speed turns on highways and race tracks, it is common practice to bank the curves to compensate for the tendency of vehicles to skid outward. Banking the curves also reduces the sideways force on the passengers and thus makes them more comfortable.

Figure 5.14(a) shows the force vectors acting on a car rounding an unbanked curve. The weight of the car is shown as the downward vector $m\mathbf{g}$. The normal forces $\mathbf{F}_N$ of the road supporting the car act on each of the tires. The sum of these four normal forces just equals the weight of the car. The frictional forces $\mathbf{F}_{fr}$ acting on the tires provide the unbalanced force that gives the car its centripetal acceleration and causes it to turn.

Figure 5.14

(a) A car rounding a flat curve. The car's weight is balanced by the sum of the normal forces $\mathbf{F}_N$. Frictional forces $\mathbf{F}_{fr}$ between the tires and the road provide the centripetal acceleration. (b) On a banked road, the normal force may be resolved into a vertical component and a horizontal component directed toward the center of the curve. For each bank angle there is one particular speed for which the normal force provides the necessary centripetal force.

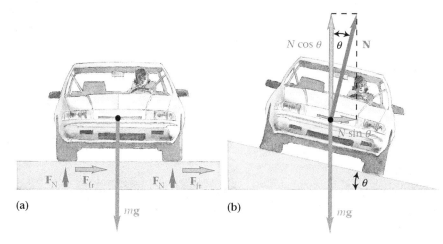

If the curved road is banked at an angle θ, the normal force has a horizontal component toward the center of the circle (Fig. 5.14b). When the car is moving, this inward component of the normal force still points to the center of the circle. At one particular speed, this force component by itself provides just the necessary force for turning the car without skidding, even if there are no sideways frictional forces between the tires and the road. At this speed the car will not skid, even on an ice-covered road.

At this nonskidding speed, all of the forces between the car and the road are perpendicular or normal to the road surface. The road exerts a normal force $\mathbf{N} = \Sigma \mathbf{F}_N$ on the car. The vertical component $N \cos \theta$ must be equal and opposite to the gravitational force mg. The horizontal component of $\mathbf{N}$ provides the centripetal force that turns the car. Thus, for the vertical component we get

$$N \cos \theta = mg,$$

and for the horizontal component we get

$$N \sin \theta = \frac{mv^2}{r}.$$

We can divide the second equation by the first to get

$$\tan \theta = \frac{v^2}{gr}. \tag{5.9}$$

This equation gives the banking angle θ for a curve of a given radius r to be negotiated at a speed v without tending to slide out or in, away from the circular path.

Example 5.10

A race track designed for average speeds of 240 km/h (66.7 m/s) is to have a turn with a radius of 975 m. To what angle must the track be banked so that cars traveling 240 km/h have no tendency to slip sideways?

Strategy If there is no tendency to slip sideways, the vertical component of the normal force must equal the weight and the horizontal component must provide the centripetal force. These conditions were used to derive Eq. (5.9), which can be applied here.

Solution We can determine θ from Eq. (5.9):

$$\tan \theta = \frac{v^2}{gr} = \frac{(66.7 \text{ m/s})^2}{(9.81 \text{ m/s}^2)(975 \text{ m})} = 0.465,$$

$$\theta = 24.9°.$$

5.3 Kepler's Laws of Planetary Motion

As we mentioned in Chapter 4, Johannes Kepler and others of his time knew that the orbits of the earth and other planets about the sun are not exactly circular. Kepler made use of Tycho Brahe's observational data to deduce that planetary

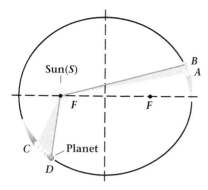

Figure 5.15
Diagram of Kepler's three laws of planetary motion. The ellipse has been exaggerated so that it has a much greater eccentricity than any actual planetary orbit. Note that in accordance with Kepler's first law, the sun is located at one of the foci, *F*. According to Kepler's second law, the time it takes a planet to move from *A* to *B* and from *C* to *D* is the same if the areas of the wedges *ABS* and *CDS* are the same. Kepler's third law says that the ratio of the orbital period *T* squared to the cube of the average radius *R* is the same for all the planets.

orbits are actually ellipses. Eventually his analysis of Tycho's data was expressed as three rules or laws describing the motion of the planets. Later, Newton relied on Kepler's results in formulating his theories about the motion of the planets. Here we state the three Kepler laws. Later, in this and other chapters, we show how Kepler's laws can be derived from Newtonian mechanics and the law of universal gravitation.

Kepler's laws of planetary motion give unambiguous predictions that are subject to verification. They are usually stated in the following way (refer to Fig. 5.15):

1. The orbit of each planet is an ellipse* and the sun is at one focus.

2. An imaginary line from the sun to a moving planet sweeps out equal areas in equal intervals of time.

3. The ratio of the square of a planet's period of revolution to the cube of its average distance from the sun is a constant.** This constant is the same for all planets. (The period of revolution is the time for one complete orbit.)

That Kepler worked out these laws without knowing their underlying cause is a remarkable example of perseverance. The cause of planetary motion did not become clear until nearly 70 years later, when Isaac Newton published the laws of gravitation and of motion.

Like all "laws" of nature, Kepler's laws represent the distillation or summation of many observations. They are not "fundamental" in the same way as some other laws that we will study later; that is, they describe observations without giving their causes. However, Kepler's laws are similar in an important way to almost all of the other laws that we will encounter: They are expressed in mathematical terms. Although these laws can be put in words alone, their most succinct and useful form is as a mathematical statement. For example, contrast the statement that "planets move faster when closer to the sun" with Kepler's second law. The second law includes not only the information conveyed by those words but also the ability to make exact predictions. Theories in the physical sciences, and physics in particular, are partly judged on their ability to predict what will occur, as well as to explain what has happened. This ability usually requires that they have a mathematical form. Likewise, compare the statement that "planetary orbits are elongated ovals" with the more precise and meaningful statement that "planetary orbits are ellipses."

Kepler's *first law* has wider applicability than given in the statement above. We now know that the orbit of the moon around the earth, the orbits of other moons around other planets, the orbits of comets, and the orbits of artificial satellites are all ellipses. Contrary to the exaggerated way in which Fig. 5.15 depicts the orbits, planetary orbits are almost circular. Table 5.1 lists the characteristics of the planetary orbits. Although we can usually approximate planetary orbits with circles, this approximation is not always valid for artificial satellites.

---

*A review of the properties of the ellipse is found on page A–2 of Appendix A.
**For Keplerian orbits, the average distance of the planet from the sun is the length of the semi-major axis of its orbit.

Table 5.1	The Orbits and Periods of the Planets	
Planet	Semimajor Axis of Orbit in AU*	Orbital Period in Years
Mercury	0.387	0.241
Venus	0.723	0.615
Earth	1.000	1.000
Mars	1.524	1.881
Jupiter	5.203	11.862
Saturn	9.516	29.458
Uranus	19.166	84.013
Neptune	30.012	164.793
Pluto	39.557	248.530

Source: The Astronomical Almanac, for the Year 1991. Washington, D.C.: U.S. Government Printing Office, 1989.

*The distances in this table are given in astronomical units, AU. One AU is a distance equal to the semimajor axis of the earth's orbit around the sun. That is, 1 AU = 1.50×10^8 km = 9.3×10^7 mi.

Kepler's *second law* can be used to predict the speed of a planet in one part of its orbit if we know its speed in another part. Assume, for example, that a planet takes one month to go from A to B (Fig. 5.15). If we draw pie-shaped sectors ASB and CSD so that each sector has the same area, then according to the second law, the planet will also take one month to go from C to D. Since the arc CD is longer than the arc AB and the times of travel are the same, the speed along CD is greater than the speed along AB.

Kepler's *third law* deals with a relationship between planets, rather than predicting the behavior of a single planet alone. Stated in symbols, it becomes

$$\frac{T^2}{R^3} = k, \tag{5.10}$$

where the period T is the time for one complete orbit, R is the average distance of the planet from the sun, and k is a constant that is the same for all planets circling the sun.

Example 5.11

Compare the prediction of Kepler's third law for the distance of Mars from the sun with the measured value of the semimajor axis of its orbit given in Table 5.1.

Solution Since the ratio T^2/R^3 is the same for all planets, we may equate the value of the ratio for Mars to that for earth, using subscripts M to denote Mars and E to denote earth:

$$\frac{T_{\mathrm{M}}^2}{R_{\mathrm{M}}^3} = \frac{T_{\mathrm{E}}^2}{R_{\mathrm{E}}^3}$$

or

$$R_M^3 = \frac{T_M^2 R_E^3}{T_E^2},$$

$$R_M = \left(\frac{T_M^2 R_E^3}{T_E^2}\right)^{\frac{1}{3}}.$$

We may use the average distance of the earth from the sun as our unit of distance. This distance is called the astronomical unit, abbreviated AU. One astronomical unit is equal to 1.50×10^{11} m. We may likewise take the year as our unit of time. From Table 5.1, the period of Mars is 1.881 years, and the period of the earth is 1.000 year. These values give

$$R_M = \left(\frac{(1.881 \text{ year})^2 (1 \text{AU})^3}{(1 \text{ year})^2}\right)^{\frac{1}{3}} = 1.524 \text{ AU}.$$

This result is in agreement with the observed value listed in Table 5.1.

5.4 The Law of Universal Gravitation

Now that we have examined uniform circular motion and Kepler's laws, let us return to the subject that prompted Newton's writing of the *Principia:* gravitation. In the *Principia,* Newton showed that the gravitational force acting on a body moving in an elliptical orbit—as a planet does—is inversely proportional to the square of the distance from the body to the center of force; that is, $F \propto 1/r^2$. We have seen in Example 5.4 why this was a reasonable conjecture, at least for a circular orbit.

The gravitational force between objects depends not only on the distance between them, but also on their masses. We have seen that the gravitational force on an object near the earth's surface is directly proportional to that object's mass. Furthermore, from Newton's third law we know that the same object exerts an equal and opposite force on the earth. From such reasoning, Newton proposed that the magnitude of the gravitational force between two objects is proportional to *both* their masses. Thus, the force between any two bodies with masses m_1 and m_2 has the form

$$F \propto \frac{m_1 m_2}{r^2},$$

where r is the distance between them. Strictly speaking, the law applies to what we call point masses, which are objects that have no size. However, for the sun, planets, and other bodies with spherical symmetry, the distance r is measured as the distance between their respective centers.

When we insert a constant of proportionality, this statement becomes

$$\boxed{F = G\frac{m_1 m_2}{r^2}.}$$
(5.11)

Back to the Future

JOHANNES KEPLER

Today, children routinely learn the names of all the planets and their order from the sun, and travel throughout the solar system does not seem impossible. It's hard to imagine a time when people didn't know about the planets and how they move through space. An early step toward understanding the solar system occurred almost 400 years ago, with Johannes Kepler's analysis of planetary orbits.

Kepler (Fig. B5.1) proposed a scheme for explaining the radii of the orbits of the five known planets that was based on the geometry of the only five regular geometrical solids. This mystical scheme, which accidentally gave fairly good agreement with what was then known (but ruled out the existence of any more planets), gained him considerable publicity and led to his association with Tycho Brahe in 1600. Upon Tycho's death 18 months later, Kepler took possession of his data.

Kepler spent almost ten years trying to fit Tycho's observations of the position of Mars to a circular orbit, or to some combination of circles. He even came to a point where the disagreement between his calculations and Tycho's observations was only 8 minutes of arc. This is the angle covered by a dime held on edge and viewed from a distance of about 22 in. (56 cm). But Tycho's measurements were at least twice this good, equivalent to moving the dime to 44 in. Kepler had so much faith in the precision of Tycho's observations that he knew his own analysis must be in error. He discarded his work and started over many times, arriving finally at what are now called Kepler's laws of planetary motion. Kepler discovered the first two of his three laws in the attempt to understand the orbit of the planet Mars. They appeared in Kepler's *Astronomia Nova* in 1609. The third law appeared in 1619 in *Harmonices Mundi* (The Harmony of the Worlds). Kepler achieved a prominence in history for believing that the world worked according to logical principles that could be discovered and understood.

Figure B5.1 Johannes Kepler (1571–1630). In his first academic position at Graz, Austria, Kepler was both astronomer and astrologer.

Incidentally, Kepler was not the only person to benefit from the great precision of Tycho's measurements. Not only was there a general improvement in the quality of observations but in 1582 the new calendar of Pope Gregory XIII, called the Gregorian calendar, was instituted, in part because of the more accurate observations. The basic principle of this calendar system has not been changed since its introduction.

Because Kepler's laws rest on more general laws of nature, including Newton's universal law of gravitation, they apply to more systems than just the planets moving about the sun. The moon in its orbit about the earth obeys Kepler's laws with an adjusted constant k. Other objects in orbit about the earth also obey the same basic laws. The orbits and periods of artificial satellites used for observations and communications can likewise be understood in terms of Kepler's laws. Figure B5.2 shows a communication satellite of the type used to distribute television programs. When boosted to the proper altitude in an equatorial orbit, these satellites remain over the same place on earth as they move in synchronism with the earth's rotation on its axis. (They are called geosynchronous satellites.) Television companies and home users can receive the signals by aiming their dish antennas at the satellite.

Figure B5.2 A communication satellite of the type used to transmit television signals around the earth.

Equation (5.11) expresses Newton's **law of universal gravitation.** It states that every particle in the universe attracts every other particle with a force that is directly proportional to the product of their masses and inversely proportional to the square of the distance between them. Note that there is an attractive force between *any* pair of objects, whether they be the sun and the earth, the earth and you, or a leaf and a grain of sand.

Newton had some difficulty in showing to his own satisfaction that the law of universal gravitation holds when applied to spherical bodies of uniform density* if *r* is measured from the center of one sphere to the center of the other (Fig. 5.16). Newton's mathematical work on this problem eventually led to his invention of calculus, with which he proved that the mass of a symmetrical object of uniform density behaves under the law of universal gravitation exactly as if it were concentrated at the point of the object's center of symmetry. Such a point is called the *center of gravity.*

During the next two centuries, astronomers showed that the law of universal gravitation accounts for the motion of the entire solar system with great precision. The one exception was the motion of Mercury, a problem solved only in the twentieth century by the introduction of Einstein's theory of general relativity. Today's astronomers view gravitation as the force shaping the structure of the universe. No other fundamental force acts over such enormous distances and is always an attractive force, never balanced by repulsive forces. We believe gravitational forces are responsible for the formation of stars from clouds of gas and the formation of galaxies from millions of stars. When huge masses like these are involved, gravitational forces can be awesome in magnitude.

The **universal gravitational constant** *G* must be determined by experiment. Its numerical value depends on the system of units in which we make the measurement. Before describing the determination of *G*, let us consider two examples that allow us to use the law of gravitation without knowing the value of *G*. The first gives a result for things here on the surface of the earth; the second makes a prediction about the solar system.

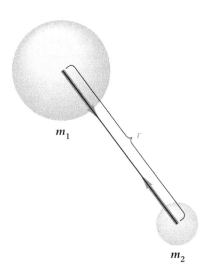

Figure 5.16

For spherical bodies of uniform density, the gravitational force between them is found from Newton's law with the distance *r* measured from the center of one to the center of the other.

Example 5.12

Consider a mass *m* falling near the earth's surface. Find its acceleration *g* in terms of the universal gravitational constant *G*, and draw some conclusions from the form of the answer.

Solution The gravitational force on the body is

$$F = \frac{GmM_E}{r^2},$$

where M_E is the mass of the earth and *r*, the distance of the mass from the center of the earth, is essentially the earth's radius (Fig. 5.17).

We have already noted that the gravitational force on a body at the earth's surface is

$$F = mg.$$

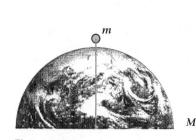

Figure 5.17

Example 5.12: A small object near the earth's surface is attracted by a gravitational force $F = GmM_E/r^2$.

---

*The **density**, ρ, of an object is defined as its mass per unit volume: $\rho = m/V$, where *m* is the mass of the object whose volume is *V*.

Setting the two expressions for the gravitational force on m equal to each other, we get

$$mg = \frac{GmM_E}{r^2},$$

or

$$g = \frac{GM_E}{r^2}.$$

Both G and M_E are constant, and r does not change significantly for small variations in height near the surface of the earth. Thus, the right-hand side of this equation does not change appreciably with position on the earth's surface. For this reason we may replace r with the average radius of the earth R_E to get

$$g = \frac{GM_E}{R_E^2}.$$

Discussion The law of gravitation predicts that the acceleration due to gravity of an object at the earth's surface is approximately constant and does not depend on the mass of the object. Experimentally we know that g does not vary appreciably from one place to another. This constancy of g is just what Galileo found (Section 2.7). Thus, the law of universal gravitation not only describes the forces that hold the planets in their orbits, but also describes the forces on objects close to the earth.

Example 5.13

Show that Kepler's third law follows from the law of universal gravitation.

Strategy We make the approximation that the orbits of the planets are circles. This approximation is essentially correct for those planets visible to the unaided eye. Because the mass of the sun is so much larger than the mass of the planet, we can assume, as Kepler did, that the sun lies at the center of the planetary orbit. It is also approximately true that the orbital speed is constant.

Solution Using the symbols in Fig. 5.18, we can say that the sun's gravitational force on any planet of mass m is

$$F = G\frac{mM}{r^2},$$

where M is the mass of the sun and r is the center-to-center distance between the planet and the sun. The circular orbit implies a centripetal force that may be expressed in terms of the orbital period as

$$F_c = \frac{4\pi^2 mr}{T^2}.$$

This net force for circular motion is provided by the gravitational force. Equating these two forces, we get

$$\frac{GmM}{r^2} = \frac{4\pi^2 mr}{T^2}.$$

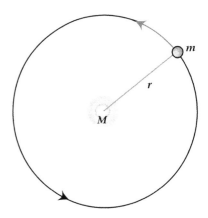

Figure 5.18
Example 5.13: A planet of mass m makes a circular orbit of radius r about the sun (mass M) with a period T. (Figure is not drawn to scale.)

Rearranging gives

$$\frac{T^2}{r^3} = \frac{4\pi^2}{GM}.$$

Discussion The right-hand side of this equation depends on the mass of the sun and on the universal gravitational constant, but not on any property of the planet. Therefore the ratio on the left-hand side is identical for all planets, just as Kepler observed. However, now we see that this result is not an independent physical law, but a consequence of a more fundamental law—the law of universal gravitation. We have derived Kepler's third law only for uniform circular motion of the planet, but the result is true for elliptical orbits if we use the average distance from the sun for r.

5.5 The Universal Gravitational Constant *G*

After publication of Newton's *Principia,* experimenters tried to make some independent test of the law of universal gravitation, despite its obvious success in explaining the main features of planetary and lunar motion. Perhaps the most satisfying type of experiment would consist of placing known masses a known distance apart and measuring the attractive force between them. Under such conditions, the validity of the law could be checked and G determined in a straightforward manner from Eq. (5.11). However, common experience tells us that the gravitational force between ordinary bodies is extremely small. To measure this slight force, a sensitive device called a torsion balance was invented independently by Charles Coulomb in France and John Michell in England in the 1770s. Coulomb used his balance to measure the force between electrical charges (see Chapter 16). Michell, a professor of geology at Cambridge, designed his balance to measure gravitational forces and so to "weigh the earth." He did not complete the work before his death, but the apparatus eventually passed into the hands of Henry Cavendish, who refined and made use of it.

In 1798, 71 years after Newton's death, Cavendish first measured the force between small masses on earth. His interest, like that of many of his contemporaries, was in finding the earth's density. Only much later were his experimental results interpreted by others to give a value for G. Thus, although Cavendish is often remembered for determining the value of G, in fact he never did so.

Since the time of Cavendish, the value of G has been determined in a number of ways. The presently accepted value is

$$G = 6.673 \times 10^{-11} \text{ N} \cdot \text{m}^2/\text{kg}^2.$$

Using this value of G, we can apply the law of universal gravitation to many different situations. Examples 5.14 and 5.15 illustrate a few of these.

Example 5.14

Use the law of universal gravitation and the measured value of the acceleration of gravity g to determine the average density of the earth.

Strategy We start with the result of Example 5.12 that

$$g = \frac{GM_E}{R_E^2},$$

where M_E is the mass of the earth, R_E is its radius, and g is the acceleration of gravity at the earth's surface. Then we substitute for M_E an expression involving ρ, the average density of the earth, defined as the ratio of the earth's mass to its volume, $\rho = M_E/V$. The result gives us ρ as a combination of numerical values.

Solution If we take the earth to be a sphere of radius R_E, then

$$\rho = \frac{M_E}{\frac{4}{3}\pi R_E^3}.$$

The equation for g can then be rewritten in terms of the density as

$$g = \frac{G\left(\frac{4}{3}\pi R_E^3 \rho\right)}{R_E^2} = \frac{4}{3} G\pi R_E \rho.$$

Upon rearranging, we find the density to be

$$\rho = \frac{3g}{4\pi R_E G}.$$

Inserting the numerical values, we get

$$\rho = \frac{3(9.81 \text{ m/s}^2)}{4\pi(6.38 \times 10^6 \text{ m})(6.67 \times 10^{-11} \text{ N} \cdot \text{m}^2\text{kg}^{-2})}$$

$$\rho = 5.50 \times 10^3 \text{ kg/m}^3.$$

This is the average density of the entire earth and is 5.5 times the density of water. Because the average density is greater than that of soil and rock, we know that the interior of the earth must be very dense compared to the material in the earth's crust. (See Henry Cavendish and the Density of the Earth, p. 167.)

Example 5.15

Estimate the period of an artificial earth-orbiting satellite that passes just above the earth's surface (Fig. 5.19).

Strategy In reality, a satellite's orbit must be high enough so that the satellite is above most of the earth's atmosphere. However, the height at which low-orbiting satellites operate is small compared to the radius of the earth (about 6.4×10^6 m). Therefore, for estimating purposes, we can approximate the radius of the orbit by saying that it's the same as the radius of the earth.

Solution We set the force required to give a circular orbit—the centripetal force—equal to the gravitational force. We let the mass of the satellite be m, the mass of the earth M_E, the radius of the orbit R_E, and the satellite's period T. Then

$$\frac{m4\pi^2 R_E}{T^2} = \frac{GmM_E}{R_E^2}, \quad \text{or} \quad T = \sqrt{\frac{4\pi^2 R_E^3}{GM_E}}.$$

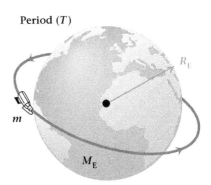

Period (T)

Figure 5.19
Example 5.15: Finding the period of an earth-orbiting satellite.

Rather than substituting the numerical values now, we use the result of Example 5.12 that $gR_E^2 = GM_E$, so that the above expression for the period becomes

$$T = \sqrt{\frac{4\pi^2 R_E^3}{gR_E^2}} = \sqrt{\frac{4\pi^2 R_E}{g}}.$$

Notice that the period depends only on the radius of the earth and the acceleration of gravity. To complete our estimate, we insert the approximate values of $\pi^2 \approx 10$, $g \approx 10 \text{ m/s}^2$, and $R_E \approx 6.4 \times 10^6$ m,

$$T \approx \sqrt{\frac{4(10)(6.4 \times 10^6 \text{ m})}{10 \text{ m/s}^2}} \approx 5100 \text{ s} \approx 85 \text{ min}.$$

This value compares favorably with the observed periods of low-orbiting satellites. For example, the space shuttle typically has an orbital period of 90 min.

*5.6 Gravitational Field Strength

We can gain additional insight into gravitation by considering gravitational forces from a different but related point of view. Recall that gravitational forces are not contact forces but instead act over distances in space. The gravitational force on an object at some point in space can be described in terms of a property of that space. We consider that a mass, such as the earth, influences the surrounding space in such a way that another mass, such as the moon, in that space will experience a force in the direction of the first mass. This property of the space is called the gravitational field. The field due to the first mass exists even when the second mass is not present.

We define the **gravitational field strength** *at any point in space to be the gravitational force per unit mass on a test mass m_0.* Thus, at a point in space where a test mass m_0 experiences a gravitational force **F**, the gravitational field strength is

$$\Gamma \equiv \frac{\mathbf{F}}{m_0}. \tag{5.12}$$

Note that the gravitational field strength is just the acceleration that a unit mass would experience at that point in space. The test mass must be small so that its gravitational field does not modify the field that is being measured.

Later, we will use the concept of a field when studying electricity and magnetism. Even though the electric field does not have the same units as the gravitational field, the concepts of field apply in both cases, allowing us to draw useful analogies between gravitation and electricity when they are considered from the standpoint of fields.

Since the gravitational force is a vector, the field must also be a vector, having both magnitude and direction. If the gravitational force arises from the attraction of the test mass by a mass M located a distance r from the test mass, then the magnitude of the field strength is

$$\Gamma = \frac{F}{m_0} = \frac{GMm_0}{r^2 m_0} = \frac{GM}{r^2}.$$

Back to the Future

HENRY CAVENDISH AND THE DENSITY OF THE EARTH

Like most eighteenth-century English scientists, Henry Cavendish (1731–1810) was influenced by the questions in Newton's *Principia* and *Optics.* This influence led him to investigate gravitational forces. Because gravitational forces between ordinary objects are so very small, Cavendish had to use a special balance to measure them (Fig. B5.3). His balance was based on a design by the Cambridge geologist John Michell (1724–1793)

Cavendish's 1798 paper, *Experiment to Determine the Density of the Earth,* contained a drawing of the torsion balance used in his experiment. In Cavendish's own words,

Figure B5.4 Details from a gravity map of South Carolina. The contour lines are spaced 5 mgal apart. The *gal,* a unit named after Galileo, is 1 cm/s². Thus, 1 mgal is approximately 10^{-6} *g*. From South Carolina Geological Survey MS 21, "Simple Bouguer Anomaly Map of South Carolina."

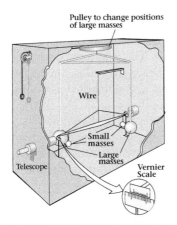

Figure B5.3 The Cavendish Balance: A torsional balance constructed of two small masses balanced on a light rod suspended by a thin fiber. Two large masses (lead spheres) are arranged symmetrically on either side of the rod so as to give it a rotational force. The restoring force is supplied by the fiber.

"The apparatus is very simple; it consists of a wooden arm, 6 feet long, made so as to unite great strength with little weight. This arm is suspended in an horizontal position, by a slender wire 40 inches long, and to each extremity is hung a leaden ball about 2 inches in diameter; and the whole is enclosed in a narrow wooden case, to defend it from the wind.

As no more force is required to make this turn round on its center, than what is necessary to twist the suspending wire, it is plain, that if the wire is sufficiently slender, the most minute force, such as the attraction of a leaden weight a few inches in diameter, will be sufficient to draw the arm sensibly aside. The weights which Mr. Michell intended to use were 8 inches in diameter. One of these was to be placed on one side of the case, opposite to one of the balls, and as near it as could conveniently be done, and the other on the other

side, opposite to the other ball, so that the attraction of both the weights would conspire in drawing the arm aside; and when its position, as affected by these weights, was ascertained, the weights were to be removed to the other side of the case, so as to draw the arm the contrary way, and the position of the arm was to be again determined; and, consequently, half the difference of these positions would show how much the arm was drawn aside by the attraction of the weights."

By improving on Michell's apparatus and by using the utmost care, Cavendish performed this delicate experiment in a series of 17 trials whose results clustered around an average value of 5.48 for the density of the earth as compared with water. (See Example 5.14.) Recall that the density of any material is the ratio of its mass to its volume. Cavendish reckoned that his measurement was correct to within about 7%. His result corresponds to a value for *G* of $(6.70 \pm 0.48) \times 10^{-11}$ N · m²/kg², which differs little from the modern value of

$$G = 6.673 \times 10^{-11} \text{ N} \cdot \text{m}^2/\text{kg}^2.$$

Cavendish's interest in the density of the earth has its counterpart today. Local variations in the density of the earth's crust can yield information about mineral and oil deposits. Consequently, geologists have developed instruments to measure the acceleration of gravity with great precision. One type of gravity meter uses a very sensitive spring scale in which a mass is pulled down more where the force of gravity (and therefore *g*) is larger. Another type uses the connection between the period of a pendulum and the acceleration of gravity, a topic discussed in Chapter 14.

These small variations from place to place can be used to map the underlying geological structure. Modern gravity meters can easily measure variations in *g* as small as 10^{-6} m/s². Figure B5.4 is a map showing the variations in the acceleration of gravity in South Carolina. The contours for constant values of *g* are spaced at intervals of 5×10^{-5} m/s². A trained geologist can use such a map to help infer information about the mineral content and seismic structure of the underlying terrain.

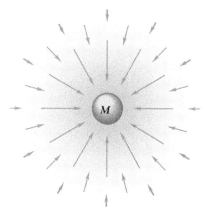

Figure 5.20

A representation of the gravitational field around a point mass M. Each arrow indicates the magnitude and direction of the field at the base of the arrow.

The field vector lies along the line from m to M and is directed toward the mass M. For example, the gravitational field at the earth's surface is a vector directed toward the center of the earth with magnitude 9.81 m/s^2.

Once the gravitational field at any point in space has been determined (either by measurement or by calculation), then we can compute the force on any other mass m placed at that point by using $\mathbf{F} = \mathbf{\Gamma}m$. In fact, we may say that the gravitational field is a property of space. Instead of focusing on the mass of an object and how the gravitational force depends on distance, we focus on the space itself and how a property of the space (the field) is affected by the presence of objects near and far. Masses can then be treated as sources of the gravitational field, and the force on some particular mass is determined by the field present at the location of that mass. We can represent this field visually with the aid of arrows representing the direction and magnitude of the field at different points in space. This representation is shown in Fig. 5.20 to illustrate the field around a point mass M. Each arrow represents the field at the base of the arrow. The lengths of the arrows are proportional to the magnitude of the field at each point. (We have shown a two-dimensional drawing, but the gravitational field itself extends outward from the source in all directions in three-dimensional space.)

Another way to help visualize the gravitational field is to diagram **lines of force,** also called **field lines.** These continuous lines are drawn in the direction of the force on a test mass (Fig. 5.21). The relative number of lines is proportional to the strength of the force and hence proportional to the field. Such a representation helps show that the field strength diminishes as the distance from the mass increases. The farther away from the source of the gravitational field, the farther apart the lines are, and the weaker the field becomes.

We will draw lines of force later, in the chapters on electricity and magnetism, as an aid in understanding the forces encountered there. The field concept was introduced by Michael Faraday (Chapter 20) in connection with his experiments on electricity and has become the contemporary way of describing the effects and interactions of the fundamental forces of nature.

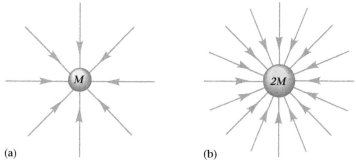

(a)   (b)

Figure 5.21

Lines of force (a) around a mass m and (b) around a mass $2M$.

▼ Summary

Useful Concepts

■ Angles can be measured in degrees or radians, where the angle in radians is given by

$$\theta = \frac{s}{r} \quad \text{and} \quad 1 \text{ radian} = 57.3°.$$

■ Uniform circular motion can be described by an angular velocity and a centripetal (center-seeking) acceleration. The centripetal acceleration always points to the center of the circular path of motion and is perpendicular to the linear velocity:

$$a_c = \frac{v^2}{r}.$$

■ The frequency of revolution is the reciprocal of the period, which is the time required for one revolution:

$$f = \frac{1}{T}.$$

■ The angular velocity (also called angular frequency) is

$$\omega = \frac{v}{r}$$

and is proportional to the rotational frequency f,

$$\omega = 2\pi f.$$

■ The centripetal acceleration used in Newton's second law gives the centripetal force,

$$F_c = \frac{mv^2}{r}.$$

The centripetal force is not a fundamental force, but describes the effect of any net force applied to a body that keeps it moving in uniform circular motion.

■ Kepler's laws of planetary motion are

1. The orbit of each planet is an ellipse with the sun at one focus.

2. An imaginary line from the sun to a moving planet sweeps out equal areas in equal intervals of time.

3. The ratio of the square of a planet's period of revolution to the cube of its average distance from the sun is a constant. This constant is the same for all planets:

$$\frac{T^2}{R^3} = k,$$

■ Newton's law of universal gravitation gives the force between *any* two point masses, no matter what their mass and no matter where they are located,

$$F = \frac{Gm_1 m_2}{r^2}.$$

■ We can visualize the gravitational field by drawing continuous lines of force (field lines) showing the direction of the gravitational force at any point.

Important Terms

You should be able to write the definition or meaning of each of the following terms:

radian	Kepler's laws of planetary
uniform circular motion	motion
centripetal acceleration	law of universal gravitation
period	density
frequency	universal gravitational constant
hertz	gravitational field strength
angular velocity	lines of force
(angular frequency)	field lines
centripetal force	

▼ Conceptual Questions

5.1 Can you think of any reasons for dividing a full circle into 360°?

5.2 Draw a diagram showing how you would measure the angle that a distant person subtends at your eye.

5.3 Describe the forces acting on a passenger riding on a Ferris wheel. Explain any difference between the situation near the top of the ride and that near the bottom.

5.4 When a fenderless bicycle is ridden along a wet street, the rider gets a wet stripe down his back from water droplets thrown off the rear wheel. Explain this observation.

5.5 Explain the action of the spin cycle in removing water from clothes in an automatic washing machine.

5.6 What complications would you encounter in playing catch with a baseball if you and your partner were standing on a rotating carousel?

5.7 How can an object in uniform circular motion be moving at a constant speed and at the same time be constantly accelerated?

5.8 Make an order-of-magnitude estimate of the linear speed of a point on the earth's equator due to the earth's rotational motion. Compare this speed with the linear speed of the earth's orbital motion.

5.9 Explain what causes the riders in the swing of Fig. 5.22 to move outward when the ride begins to rotate.

5.10 What are the restrictions on the orbit of a communications satellite if it is to remain stationary above a given location on the earth?

5.11 If the average distance between the earth and the moon were suddenly cut in half, how would the lunar period be affected?

5.12 What is universal about the law of universal gravitation?

5.13 Assume that you are inside a train moving along a level track at constant speed. All of the window shades are drawn so that you cannot see out. You have with you a sensitive spring balance with a mass hanging from it and a finely ruled protractor. How can you use these instruments to tell whether the train is traveling along a straight track or going around a curve?

Figure 5.22
Question 5.9.

Problems

Section 5.1 Uniform Circular Motion

Hints for Solving Problems

In uniform circular motion, the speed is constant and the centripetal acceleration, which is perpendicular to the velocity, points to the center of the circle. Be sure you know how to express centripetal acceleration in terms of different rotational quantities.

5.1 A protractor is made so that the edge of its scale is 7.5 cm from the center point. If the scale is marked in degrees, how far apart are the marks along the edge?

5.2 The moon subtends an angle of 9.06×10^{-3} radians and is 3.84×10^8 meters from the earth. What is the approximate diameter of the moon?

5.3 A 12-in.-diameter phonograph record rotates about its center by one-quarter turn. (a) Through how many radians has it turned? (b) How far has a point on the rim moved?

5.4 What is the centripetal acceleration of an automobile driving at 40 km/h on a circular track of radius 20 m?

5.5 The earth is 1.5×10^{11} m from the sun and has a period of about 365 days. Assume the earth's orbit to be circular and determine the magnitude and direction of its radial acceleration in m/s^2.

5.6 The centripetal acceleration at a point in a sample tube 5.60 cm away from the axis of rotation of a centrifuge is 4300 m/s^2. What is the instantaneous speed at that point?

5.7 Show that v^2/r has the dimensions of acceleration.

5.8 The centripetal acceleration at the equator is about 3.4 cm/s^2. Use that information and the length of a day to estimate the radius of the earth.

5.9 A bicycle tire is 66 cm in diameter. (a) At what frequency f does the tire rotate when the bicycle is traveling at a speed of 30 km/h? (b) What is the angular frequency ω?

5.10● What is the magnitude and direction of the centripetal acceleration due to the earth's rotation at a location near Kansas City at 38° latitude?

5.11● The period of a stone swung in a horizontal circle on a 2.00-m radius is 1.00 s. (a) What is its angular velocity in rad/s? (b) What is its linear speed in m/s? (c) What is its radial acceleration in m/s^2?

5.12● During 0.19 s, a wheel rotates through an angle of 2.36 rad as a point on the periphery of the wheel moves with a constant speed of 2.87 m/s. What is the radius of the wheel?

5.13● A 32.5-cm-radius tire on a moving car turns through 3π rad in 0.27 s. What is the speed of the car in kilometers per hour?

5.14● Jupiter's moon Europa has an average orbital radius of 6.67×10^8 m and a period of 85.2 h. Calculate the magnitude of (a) its average orbital speed, (b) the angular velocity, and (c) the centripetal acceleration of Europa.

Section 5.2 Force Needed for Circular Motion

Hints for Solving Problems

The formulas for centripetal force describe the force necessary to make an object move in a circle. In this chapter the applied force is often gravity. Remember that objects in circular motion obey Newton's three laws. Also, remember to draw and label a free-body diagram before attempting a problem.

5.15 Calculate the centripetal force on a 2000-kg automobile rounding a curve of 175 m radius at a speed of 50 km/h.

5.16 A stunt driver drives a car so fast that it leaves the ground as it tops a hill. If the hill can be approximated by a 165-m-radius vertical circle, what speed must the car exceed if it is to leave the ground?

5.17 A race track curve has a radius of 100 m and is banked at an angle of 68°. For what speed was the curve designed?

5.18 A velodrome track is banked so that a bicycle traveling at 62.3 km/h will have no tendency to slip to either side when traveling on the path that has a radius of curvature of 77.0 m. What is the banking angle?

5.19• What angle does a plumb bob line make with the vertical in a train rounding a 300-m-radius curve at 27 m/s?

5.20• A spring scale on a rotating platform indicates that the horizontal force on a 0.452 kg mass is 1.34 N when the mass is 2.37 m from the axis of rotation. How long does it take for the platform to make one revolution?

5.21• A 0.208-kg toy whistle can be whirled in a horizontal circle of 1.00 m radius at a maximum of 3.00 rev/s before the string breaks (see Fig. 5.10). What is the force needed to break the string?

5.22• A 0.237-kg block slides down the inside of a 0.213-m-radius circular track, reaching the lowest point with a speed of 1.37 m/s. If the coefficient of friction between the block and track is 0.28, what is the frictional retarding force on the block at the lowest point?

5.23• A 0.436-kg ball is suspended on a 0.452-m cord from a fixed point. The ball swings in a horizontal circular path at 0.811 revolutions per second. (a) What is the tension in the cord? (b) What is the angle θ between the cord and the vertical?

5.24• A coin placed on a turntable rotating at 33.3 rev/min will stay there if its center is placed no further than 8.5 cm from the axis of rotation. (a) Find an expression for the maximum distance the center of the coin can be placed from the axis if the turntable rotates at 45 rev/min? (b) What is the coefficient of friction between the coin and turntable?

5.25• A 0.255-kg ball tethered to a tall pole on a 1.37-m rope is thrown so that it travels in a horizontal circle with the rope making an angle $\theta = 40°$ with the vertical pole (Fig. 5.23). (a) What is the speed of the ball? (b) What is the tension in the rope?

5.26• An electron with mass 9.11×10^{-31} kg moves with a speed of 2.00×10^6 m/s in a circle of 2.85 cm radius under the influence of a magnetic field. A proton of mass 1.67×10^{-27} kg, moving in the same plane with the same speed, experiences the same centripetal force. What is the radius of the proton's orbit?

5.27• A stunt pilot in an airplane diving vertically downward at a speed of 220 km/h turns vertically upward by following an approximately semicircular path with a radius of 180 m (Fig. 5.24). (a) How many g's does the pilot experience due to his motion alone? (b) By what factor does the pilot's weight appear to increase at the bottom of the dive?

5.28•• A highway curve with a radius of 750 m is banked properly for a car traveling 120 km/h. If a 1590-kg Porsche

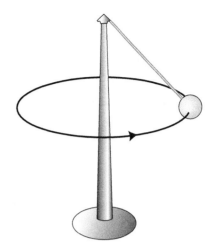

Figure 5.23
Problem 5.25.

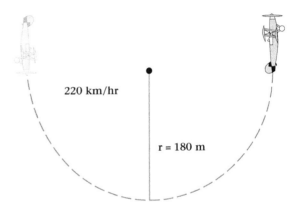

220 km/hr

r = 180 m

Figure 5.24
Problem 5.27.

928S rounds the curve at 230 km/h, how much sideways force must the tires exert against the road if the car does not skid?

5.29•• A small dog slides with constant speed down a metal sliding board at 30° to the horizontal. The dog then sits 1.3 m from the center of a rotating turntable made of the same metal as the sliding board. What is the maximum angular frequency at which the turntable may turn without the dog sliding off?

5.30•• Passengers riding in the Great Six Flags Air Racer are spun around a tall steel tower (Fig. 5.25). At top speed the planes fly at a 56° bank approximately 14 m from the tower. In this position the support chains make an angle of 56° with the vertical. Calculate the speed of the planes.

Section 5.3 Kepler's Laws of Planetary Motion

5.31 Calculate the distance from the sun to Saturn, given the information that Saturn's period of revolution about the sun is 29.46 years.

5.32 An amateur astronomer claims to see a new planet beyond the orbit of Pluto, with a calculated period of 230 years. Can this claim be true? Assume the orbit to be nearly circular.

Figure 5.25
Problem 5.30: The Air Racer.

5.33• Use the known period of $27\frac{1}{3}$ days for the motion of the moon about the earth and the distance from the earth to the moon of 3.84×10^8 m to calculate the radius of the orbit of an earth satellite that stays above the same point on the equator. (*Hint:* Use Kepler's third law.)

5.34• In *Gulliver's Travels*, the Lilliputians claim "They have likewise discovered two lesser stars, or satellites, which revolve about Mars, whereof the innermost is a distance from the centre of the primary planet exactly three of his diameters, and the outermost five; the former revolves in the space of ten hours, and the latter in twenty-one and a half; . . . " Could the claim of the Lilliputians be true, if time were measured to within the nearest one-quarter hour?

5.35• Calculate the ratio of T^2/R^3 for each planet in the solar system. Use the data from Table 5.1. What is the percentage difference between the highest and lowest values? The percentage difference is the ratio of the difference in the values to the average of the two values expressed as a percentage.

5.36•• Assuming that the orbits of the planets are circular, show that the product of the orbital radius with the square of the speed of a planet is the same for all planets. The speed is the distance traveled divided by the time required to go that distance.

Section 5.4 The Law of Universal Gravitation

5.37 What is the ratio of the acceleration of gravity on the surface of the moon to the acceleration of gravity on the surface of the earth? (The radius of the moon is 0.273 times the radius of the earth, and the mass of the moon is 0.0123 times the mass of the earth.)

5.38• Saturn's mass is 95 times that of earth, and its radius is 9.0 times that of earth. (a) Calculate the acceleration of gravity at the surface of Saturn. Express your answer in *g*'s. (b) Calculate the average density of Saturn.

5.39• At what fraction of the center-to-center distance from the earth to the moon will their opposing gravitational forces on a spaceship traveling between them be equal in magnitude? (The mass of the moon is 0.0123 times the mass of the earth.)

5.40•• You drive an automobile of mass 2.10×10^3 kg from sea level to the top of a mountain 2.05 km high. What is the automobile's change in weight? (*Hint:* You will need to use the binomial expansion given in Appendix A.)

5.41•• Assuming the earth to be an oblate spheroid, so that the distance from the center to the equator is 27 mi (43.5 km) greater than the distance from the center to the poles, calculate the approximate percentage change in a person's weight at the poles and at the equator. Take into account the fact that the earth is turning. (*Hint:* You will need to use the binomial expansion given in Appendix A.)

Section 5.5 The Universal Gravitational Constant G

5.42 An apple ($m = 0.20$ kg) falls to the earth. Determine (a) the apple's acceleration toward the earth; (b) the earth's acceleration toward the apple. (c) Discuss the appropriate reference frames in which to determine the accelerations in (a) and (b).

5.43 Calculate the mass of a lead brick of dimensions 5.0 cm × 10 cm × 30 cm given that the density of lead is 1.13×10^4 kg/m³.

5.44 Gold has a density of 1.93×10^4 kg/m³. (a) Calculate the volume of 0.500 kg of gold. (b) If this amount were shaped into a cube, what would be the length of one edge of that cube?

5.45 Suppose the earth and moon were held at rest at their present separation and then released to move under their mutual gravitational attraction. What would be the initial acceleration of each body? Be specific about your choice of coordinate frames.

5.46 Compute the gravitational force between the sun ($M = 1.99 \times 10^{30}$ kg) and the planet Uranus ($m = 14.5M_E$, orbital radius $r = 19.2$ AU).

5.47 Calculate the mass of Jupiter from the knowledge that its satellite Io (Fig. 5.26) orbits at an average distance of 4.22×10^5 km from its center with an orbital period of 42.5 h.

5.48 Calculate the orbital period of Venus from knowledge of G, the mass of the sun ($M = 1.99 \times 10^{30}$ kg), and the Venusian orbit radius of 1.08×10^{11} m.

5.49 In Henry Cavendish's famous experiment, we can determine that the force between the ball and weight in each pair was about 1.53×10^{-7} N when the torsion pendulum was in its equilibrium position. From the data given in Fig. 5.27, calculate the universal constant of gravitation.

5.50• If the earth revolved rapidly enough, the weight of objects at the equator would be zero. What would be the length of the day in that case?

Figure 5.26
Problem 5.47: Jupiter's moon Io.

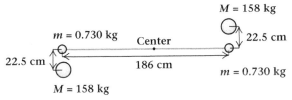

Figure 5.27
Problem 5.49: Diagram of a torsion pendulum in its equilibrium position as viewed from above.

5.51• (a) Determine the force the sun exerts on a kilogram of water on the earth's surface at a point nearest the sun and at a point farthest from the sun. (b) Do the same for the force exerted by the moon. (c) Explain why the tides are associated with the motion of the moon.

5.52• (a) Calculate the mass of the sun from the radius of the earth's orbit (1.5×10^{11} m), the earth's period in its orbit, and the gravitational constant G. (b) What is the density of the sun and how does it compare with the density of the earth? (The sun's radius is 6.96×10^8 m.)

5.53• (a) What is the radius of the orbit of a communications relay satellite that always remains above one point on the earth's surface? Such an orbit is called a geosynchronous orbit. (b) Can such a satellite be placed in geosynchronous orbit over *any* point on the earth's surface? Why?

5.54• Assume that the orbit of the moon about the earth is a perfect circle with a center-to-center distance from earth to moon of 3.84×10^8 m. (a) What is the gravitational force between the earth and the moon? (b) What is the speed of the moon in its orbit? Give your answer in meters per second.

5.55• An astronaut weighing 700 N on earth travels to the planet Mars. What does the astronaut weigh on Mars? (The mass of Mars is 0.107 of the earth's mass. The radius of Mars is 0.530 of the earth's radius.)

5.56• If an astronaut dropped a small rock near the surface of Mars, how far would the rock fall in 1.00 s? (The mass of Mars is 0.107 the mass of earth, and the radius of Mars is 0.530 the radius of the earth.)

5.57•• (a) Show that the speed of a satellite in orbit just above the surface of a planet of density ρ is proportional to the radius of the planet. (b) Imagine a small planet with the same density as the earth. What would be its radius if a sprinter capable of running 100 m in 10 s could launch herself into orbit just by running?

5.58•• Before Cavendish, Robert Hooke attempted to measure G by weighing the same object at heights differing by 300 ft (91.4 m). (a) What fractional change in weight would be predicted by the law of universal gravitation? (b) What difference in height would he have had to use to detect a change in the weight of a 1.0000-kg mass equivalent to the weight of 1.00-g mass?

*Section 5.6 Gravitational Field Strength

5.59 What is the gravitational field strength on the surface of the earth due to the earth alone? In your answer, give magnitude, direction, and proper units to agree with Eq. (5.12).

5.60 Compare the magnitude of the gravitational field at the surface of the earth due to the moon with that due to the sun. The mass of the sun is 1.99×10^{30} kg, the mass of the moon is 7.35×10^{22} kg, and the distance from the surface of the earth to the moon is 3.78×10^8 m.

5.61• Two 1.0-kg masses are located so that one is at each of two corners of an equilateral triangle with sides 1.0 m long. Determine the magnitude and direction of the gravitational field at the third corner due to these masses. Neglect the effects of all other masses, including the earth.

Additional Problems

5.62 The disk in a CD player does not rotate at a constant rate, but spins at a rate determined by a control circuit so that the linear speed of the track being read is constant. The laser beam used to read the data on the disk starts at an inner radius of 2.5 cm and continues to read until reaching an outer radius of 5.8 cm. If the disk turns at the rate of 490 rev/min at the start, what will be its rotation rate at the end?

5.63 Comets, like planets, are part of the solar system. Ericke's comet is a comet with the shortest known period, 3.3 years. What is its average distance from the sun?

5.64• A popular amusement park ride consists of a broad short cylinder arranged so that it rotates around its vertical axis (Fig. 5.28). People stand inside the cylinder with their backs to the outer wall and "feel pushed back" when the cylinder rotates. When the cylinder is rotating fast enough, it is tipped so that its axis of rotation is almost horizontal. If the radius of the cylinder is 4.5 m, how fast must it rotate so that the riders do not fall away from the walls at the topmost position? Give your answer in hertz.

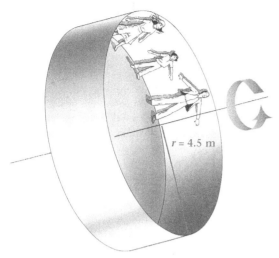

r = 4.5 m

Figure 5.28
Problem 5.64.

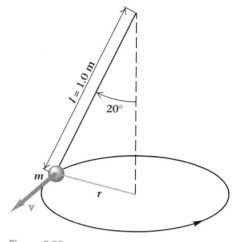

Figure 5.29
Problem 5.70.

5.65• The gravitational attraction due to a spherical mass is the same as that of a point mass of the same magnitude located at the center of the sphere. Use this fact to calculate the radius of a lead sphere that would attract you with a force 10^{-3} times your own weight if you stood right next to it. (The density of lead is 1.14×10^4 kg/m³.)

5.66• The average density of the planet Mercury is 5.61×10^3 kg/m³. The acceleration of gravity on its surface is 3.92 m/s². Calculate the average radius of Mercury.

5.67• You swing a bucket of water at constant speed in a vertical circle at arm's length (0.70 m). What is the minimum number of revolutions per second you must maintain to keep the water from spilling out of the bucket?

5.68• A strange new planet that has no atmosphere has a satellite that orbits very close to the planet's surface with a period of 1.63 h. What is the approximate density of the planet? (*Hint:* Approximate the orbital radius with the planet's radius.)

5.69• (a) Compute the mass of the earth from knowledge of the earth-moon distance (3.84×10^8 m) and of the lunar period (27.3 days). (b) Then calculate the average density of the earth. The average radius of the earth is 6.38×10^6 m.

5.70• A bob of mass m is whirled in a circular path on the end of a string 1.0 m long. If the string makes an angle of 20° with the vertical (Fig. 5.29), what is the tangential speed of the bob?

5.71• The Wheelie, described in Example 5.5 and shown in Fig. 5.9, can be tilted until its plane of rotation makes an angle of 89° with the horizontal. Show that when it is in this position, the force exerted by the wheel on the riders at the top is equivalent to only 0.94 g, while at the bottom it is 2.9 g. You may approximate by assuming the tilt angle to be 90°.

5.72•• Halley's comet has a period of about 75 years and comes relatively close to the sun. Estimate how far it is from the sun when it is at the farthest point of its elliptical orbit.

5.73•• A long string tied to an overhead support has a weight hanger attached to its lower end. The string can support a maximum weight Mg without breaking. A piece of the same string is doubled and a mass M is attached to one end of the doubled string. The mass is then swung in a vertical circle of 0.75 m radius. What is the maximum frequency of rotation that can be maintained without breaking the string?

5.74•• A coin placed on a flat stationary phonograph record just begins to slide when the record is tilted to an angle of 45° from the horizontal. The 30-cm-diameter record is placed on a horizontal turntable, and the coin is placed at the edge of the record. Will the coin slide off when the record is rotated at the rate of $33\frac{1}{3}$ rev/min?

5.75•• An automatic tumble dryer has a 0.65-m-diameter basket that rotates about a horizontal axis. As the basket turns, the clothes fall away from the basket's edge and tumble over. If the clothes fall away from the basket at a point 60° from the vertical (Fig. 5.30), what is the rate of rotation in units of revolutions per minute?

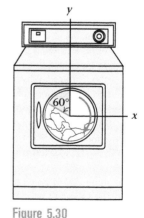

Figure 5.30
Problem 5.75.

5.76•• A newly found planet with a density of 3.90×10^3 kg/m³ has no atmosphere and is orbited by a low altitude satellite with an orbital speed of 3.55 km/s. What is the mass of the planet? (*Hint:* Approximate the orbital radius with the planet's radius.)

5.77•• What is the gravitational acceleration on a rocket ship of mass m moving along a line between the earth and the moon at distances from the earth of $\frac{1}{4}$, $\frac{1}{2}$, and $\frac{3}{4}$ the earth-moon distance. Include the gravitational effects of both the moon and the earth. The mass of the moon is 0.0123 times the mass of the earth. Express your answer in terms of the acceleration of gravity g at the earth's surface.

5.78•• A light spring with spring constant k is attached to a peg in a level, frictionless surface. A mass m is attached to the other end of the spring. The spring is free to rotate about the peg. The mass is given a push so that it moves in a circular orbit about the peg. Find an expression for the extension in the spring when the mass orbits with a period T.

chapter 6

Work and Energy

6.1 Work

6.2 Work Done by a Varying Force

6.3 Energy

6.4 Kinetic Energy

6.5 Potential Energy

6.6 Conservation of Mechanical Energy

*6.7 Energy Conservation with Nonconservative Forces

6.8 Power

Physics in Practice: Human Energy

Perhaps the most generally useful idea in all of science is the concept of energy and its conservation. Energy is a vital part of our daily lives. The food we eat gives our bodies energy for movement; electrical energy lights our homes and streets; oil and gas propel our cars and keep us warm. These are all examples of using energy. In this chapter we define work and mechanical energy and arrive at quantitative relationships between them. We will extend and apply these principles in the following chapters.

The terms *force* and *energy* were not always clearly defined. Before the midnineteenth century, they were often used interchangeably. However, progress in mechanics and in thermal physics helped clarify these ideas and the distinction between them. In 1807 the English scientist Thomas Young (1773–1829) introduced the word *energy* to denote the quantity of work that a system can do. Later, the Scottish engineer and thermal physicist W. J. M. Rankine (1820–1872) popularized this definition and coined the terms *potential energy* and *conservation of energy*. As is often the case in science, this clarification of terms and definitions led to greater insight and understanding of natural laws and their consequences.

Today the principle of conservation of energy is part of the framework of physical theory. Our faith in this principle is based on years of experience. We will encounter this idea in one form or another throughout the rest of the book and use it to derive other results. Indeed, we will see that many laws in various areas of physics are simply alternative versions of the law of conservation of energy, stated in different terms. ■

6.1   Work

The word *work* means many different things to us in our daily lives. We say that we work when we rake the yard, or buy groceries, or drive a truck. We also do work when we push a box across the floor. How much work we do depends on both how hard we push and how far we move the box. In the physical sciences, the meaning of work is more precise and restricted than in everyday usage. If we exert a constant force **F** on an object (Fig. 6.1), causing it to move a distance x parallel to **F**, then the **work** W done by the force is defined to be the product of the magnitude of the force times the distance through which it acts as the object is moved.

There are two important conditions in our definition of work. First, the force must be exerted on the object through a distance. In other words, *the force must move the object.* Consider the ancient Greek myth about Atlas, who held up the sky. Atlas is often depicted as a stooped but powerful figure, bearing the earth on his shoulders. Atlas soon tired of his terrible burden. But according to our definition, as long as he held the earth stationary, he actually did no work on it. In a similar fashion, you could push with all your might against a stationary wall until your muscles ached with the effort. Nevertheless if the wall did not move, you would not have done any work on the wall. Note, however, that work is being done within your body as muscle fibers repeatedly contract.

Second, for work to be done, the force must have a component parallel to the direction of motion. If an applied force is not along the direction of motion, we can resolve it into components parallel to and perpendicular to the displacement (Fig. 6.2). *Only the component of force that is parallel to the displacement contributes to the work.* Thus, if the force **F** makes an angle θ with the line of motion, chosen as the x direction in the figure, then the component of force that contributes to the work is $F_x = F \cos \theta$. Mathematically, the work done is defined to be

$$W \equiv F_x x = Fx \cos \theta. \qquad (6.1)$$

When **F** is along the direction of the displacement **x** (as shown in Fig. 6.1), then $\theta = 0$ and $\cos \theta = 1$. For that special case the work becomes

$$W = Fx.$$

Notice that, although the work done depends on the force, work itself is a scalar, not a vector, quantity. It has magnitude but no direction. We can add

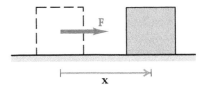

Figure 6.1

A force **F** acting in a direction parallel to the displacement **x** of an object does an amount of work $W = Fx$.

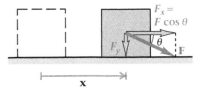

Figure 6.2

A force **F** making an angle θ with the horizontal pushes a box through the displacement **x** and does an amount of work $W = Fx \cos \theta$.

Figure 6.3
(a) A person does positive work by lifting the weight with an applied force **F** in the same direction as the displacement **x**. (b) The frictional force $\mathbf{F}_{fr}$ does negative work by acting in a direction opposite the displacement. (c) When the applied force is perpendicular to the displacement, zero work is done.

amounts of work directly, just like any other scalar quantities. When the component of the force is in the same direction as the displacement, the work done on the object is positive. When the component of the force is opposite to the displacement, the work done on the object is negative. If the force is perpendicular to the displacement, the work is zero (Fig. 6.3).

The SI unit for work is the newton-meter or kg · m²/s². This combination of units has also been given the name **joule** (J), in honor of James Prescott Joule (1818–1889), one of the great contributors to our understanding of energy (see Chapter 11):

$$1 \text{ joule (J)} = 1 \text{ N} \cdot \text{m} = 1 \text{ kg} \cdot \text{m}^2/\text{s}^2.$$

In the British system, the unit of work is the foot-pound:

$$1 \text{ ft-lb} = 1.356 \text{ J}.$$

You can get some feeling for the size of the joule by looking ahead at Table 6.2 on page 182.

Example 6.1

A child pulls a toy 2.0 m across the floor by a string, applying a force of constant magnitude 0.80 N (Fig. 6.4). During the first meter the string is parallel to the floor. During the second meter the string makes an angle of 30° with the horizontal direction. What is the total work done by the child on the toy?

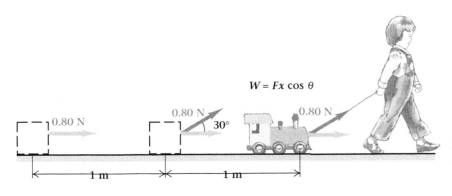

$$W = Fx \cos \theta$$

0.80 N

0.80 N 30°

0.80 N

1 m

1 m

Figure 6.4

Example 6.1: A child pulls a toy, with the string first parallel to the motion and then at an angle of 30°.

Strategy We must calculate the work separately for the first and second parts of the motion and then add them together. Since work is a scalar, we can add directly and do not need to use vector addition.

Solution For the first part, the work W_1 is

$$W_1 = F_1 x_1 \cos \theta_1, \qquad \text{where } \theta_1 = 0°$$
$$W_1 = (0.80 \text{ N})(1.0 \text{ m})(1.0) = 0.80 \text{ J}.$$

For the second part of the motion, the work W_2 is

$$W_2 = F_2 x_2 \cos \theta_2, \qquad \text{where } \theta_2 = 30°$$
$$W_2 = (0.80 \text{ N})(1.0 \text{ m})(0.87) = 0.69 \text{ J}.$$

The total work W is then

$$W = W_1 + W_2 = 0.80 \text{ J} + 0.69 \text{ J} = 1.5 \text{ J}.$$

6.2 Work Done by a Varying Force

If the force exerted on a moving object is constant, then we can calculate the work by the simple application of Eq. (6.1). In Example 6.1, the force changed after the first meter of displacement, but then remained constant for the remainder of the motion. In this case, we applied Eq. (6.1) to each part of the motion separately. However, often the force exerted on an object changes continuously. In these situations we must calculate the small amount of work ΔW for each small displacement Δx, over which the force is constant or approximately constant:

$$\Delta W = F \Delta x \cos \theta.$$

Then we can add together these amounts of work ΔW to give the total work for the entire process.

An important example of this idea is a spring that obeys what is called Hooke's law. We know that the more force we apply to a spring, the more it stretches. For a spring that obeys Hooke's law, the extension of the spring (its displacement from equilibrium) is proportional to the applied force. In Fig. 6.5, the displacement of the spring from its equilibrium position is denoted by x. The

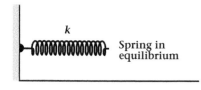

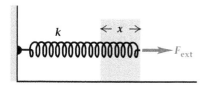

Figure 6.5

A spring that obeys Hooke's law. F_{ext} is the force applied to the spring to give an extension x.

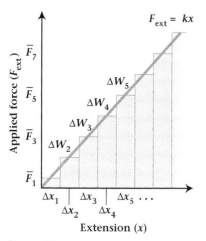

Figure 6.6

The force F_{ext} plotted against the extension of the spring of Figure 6.5. The work done in extending the spring equals the area under the force-displacement curve.

applied force F_{ext} required to extend it that far is given by

$$F_{ext} = kx, \tag{6.2}$$

where k is a constant whose value is determined for each particular spring.* Note that the SI units of k are N/m.

Let us calculate how much work is done in stretching a spring a total distance x. We use the graphical technique introduced in Section 2.4, where we found that the displacement is given by the area under the velocity-time curve. Here we find that the work is given by the area under the force-displacement curve. Figure 6.6 is a graph of the applied force plotted against the spring extension. (The extension of the spring is a displacement.) We mark off small displacements Δx along the abscissa of the graph and draw vertical lines from them up to the force-displacement curve. Then, much as we did in Chapter 2, we form a series of rectangles whose width is Δx and whose height is halfway between the applied force at the beginning and at the end of Δx. This height corresponds to the average applied force $\bar{F}$ over each displacement Δx.

We wish to calculate the small amounts of work ΔW corresponding to the small displacements Δx and then add them together:

$$W = \Delta W_1 + \Delta W_2 + \Delta W_3 + \cdots.$$

In each small displacement Δx, the work equals the product of Δx with the average force over that displacement. This is just the area of each rectangular strip in Fig. 6.6. The total work then corresponds to the total area of all the strips. As we decrease the size of each displacement Δx, thus increasing the number of strips, their total area approaches the area of the triangle with base x and altitude F_{ext}. Therefore

$$W = \tfrac{1}{2}xF_{ext} = \tfrac{1}{2}x(kx),$$

or

$$\boxed{W = \tfrac{1}{2}kx^2.} \tag{6.3}$$

The work done in stretching a spring by an amount x is given by $\tfrac{1}{2}kx^2$.

Example 6.2

(a) How much work is required to extend an exercise spring (Fig. 6.7) by 45 cm if the spring constant k has the value 310 N/m? (b) What force is required to extend the spring by 45 cm?

Strategy We are given the spring constant k and the extension x of the spring from its equilibrium position. With these two quantities we can compute the work from Eq. (6.3) and the force from Eq. (6.2).

---

*Further discussion of Hooke's law is found in Chapter 14. Usually, Hooke's law is written as $F = -kx$, where F is the force exerted *by* the spring and is in the opposite direction from the spring extension x.

Solution (a) We can calculate the work by substituting directly into the expression for the work done in stretching a spring. We find

$$W = \tfrac{1}{2}kx^2 = \tfrac{1}{2}(310 \text{ N/m})(0.45 \text{ m})^2 = 31 \text{ J}.$$

(b) The force is found from Hooke's law,

$$F_{\text{ext}} = kx = (310 \text{ N/m})(0.45 \text{ m}) = 140 \text{ N}.$$

Discussion Notice that before inserting the numerical value for the extension x we converted the units from cm to m.

Energy

Figure 6.7
Example 6.2: Force is exerted to stretch the exercise spring. Work is done as the spring stretches.

Now that we understand the concept of work, we can use it to define energy. Because energy appears in so many different forms, such as mechanical, chemical, or electrical, it is difficult to give a single, brief definition. As a start, we can define **energy** by saying: *Energy is the ability to do work.* A compressed spring has energy because it may do work in returning to its uncompressed state. A falling body has energy because it may drive a stake into the ground upon striking it. Gunpowder, which may do work on exploding, has energy. An electrical battery has energy because it can turn an electric motor that does work.

An ocean wave or a falling rock has mechanical energy (Fig. 6.8), whereas gunpowder and gasoline have chemical energy, and steam has thermal energy.

Figure 6.8
An ocean wave possesses energy associated with its motion. This is a form of mechanical energy.

Table 6.1	*The Values of Some Common Energy Units in Joules*
1 ft-lb	$= 1.356 \text{ J}$
1 Btu	$= 1.055 \times 10^3 \text{ J}$
1 kWh	$= 3.600 \times 10^6 \text{ J}$
1 calorie*	$= 4.187 \text{ J}$

*The unit ordinarily used in nutrition is the Calorie or kilocalorie, which is equal to 10^3 calories. This unit is also called a "large calorie." Note that the larger unit is distinguished from the smaller unit by being written with a capital letter.

Energy may be transformed from one form to another. Chemical energy changes to mechanical energy when an automobile engine burns gasoline; mechanical energy changes to electrical energy when water from a dam turns the turbine of an electric generator; and mechanical energy turns into thermal energy when you rub your hands together to warm them.

Energy, in all its forms, is measured in the same units as work. Other energy units in common use, in addition to the joule and the foot-pound, arise out of convenience in different situations. The British thermal unit (Btu) and calorie (cal) are often useful in discussing thermal energy, and the kilowatt-hour (kWh) is most frequently used in the case of electrical energy. These units will be discussed again and are mentioned here only to emphasize that they all measure the same thing. Their values in joules are listed in Table 6.1. Table 6.2 gives the energy values in joules of a range of phenomena.

6.4 Kinetic Energy

A body in motion possesses energy associated with its motion because it can do work upon impact with another object. This energy of motion is called **kinetic energy.**

To derive an expression for kinetic energy, let's consider a particle* subjected to a constant force **F** directed along the x direction. This force may or may not be gravitational in origin; we only require that it be constant. Under the influence of this constant force, the particle moves a distance x. The work done on

---

* By a particle we mean an idealized object so small that we can imagine it as a single point in space with no size and no internal structure. For simplicity, we will use this model to approximate the behavior of real objects.

Table 6.2	*Approximate Energy Values*	
Source		**Approximate Energy (in J)**
Total U.S. use in one year (from all sources, 1995 est.)		9.6×10^{19}
Generated by Grand Coulee Dam in one year		6.5×10^{16}
Generated by Hoover Dam in one year		2×10^{16}
Burning 1 ton of coal		30×10^9
Burning 1000 ft^3 of natural gas		1×10^9
Burning 1 gallon of gasoline		2×10^8
Kinetic energy of a car at 60 mi/h		1×10^6
Person running 10 km/h		3×10^2
Bowling ball dropped from waist		70
1 calorie		4
Penny dropped 10 cm		2.5×10^{-3}
Fission of one atom of uranium		1.8×10^{-11}
Kinetic energy of a molecule of air		6×10^{-21}

the particle is $W = Fx$. If F is the net force on the particle, then we can then use Newton's second law to replace the force by the product of mass times acceleration, obtaining

$$W = (ma)(x).$$

If the particle was initially moving in the direction of $\mathbf{F}$ with a speed v_1, then after moving through the distance x it will have a speed v_2 given by the kinematic expression from Chapter 2:

$$v_2^2 = v_1^2 + 2ax.$$

If we rearrange this last expression and multiply by $m/2$, we get

$$(ma)(x) = \tfrac{1}{2}mv_2^2 - \tfrac{1}{2}mv_1^2,$$

or

$$W = \tfrac{1}{2}mv_2^2 - \tfrac{1}{2}mv_1^2. \tag{6.4}$$

In applying a force to the particle, we performed an amount of work $W = max$. The effect of the work done on the particle has been to change its motion. The quantity $\tfrac{1}{2}mv^2$ is given the name kinetic energy (KE). More specifically, this quantity is called the **translational kinetic energy.** A particle of mass m moving with a speed v possesses a kinetic energy due to its translational motion that is given by

$$\boxed{\mathrm{KE} \equiv \tfrac{1}{2}mv^2.} \tag{6.5}$$

The SI units for kinetic energy are $\mathrm{kg \cdot m^2/s^2}$ or joules, the same as the units for work.

The concept of kinetic energy is not limited to particles only. Any object with mass m moving with velocity v has a translational kinetic energy given by Eq. (6.5), whether it is a particle or an extended body (Fig. 6.9).

Using the definition of kinetic energy, we see that the quantity on the right-hand side of Eq. (6.4) is the difference between the final and initial kinetic energies:

$$\boxed{W = \Delta \mathrm{KE} = \tfrac{1}{2}mv_2^2 - \tfrac{1}{2}mv_1^2.} \tag{6.6}$$

Figure 6.9
Even when moving at a low speed, a train has a large kinetic energy because of its large mass.

Equation (6.6) is known as the **work-energy theorem:** *the work done on a particle by the net force acting on it is equal to the change in kinetic energy of the particle.* The left-hand term represents the net work done on the particle. The right-hand side of the equation is the difference between the final and initial kinetic energies. If the work done on the particle is positive, then its kinetic energy increases. The work-energy theorem emphasizes that work, or equivalently energy, is needed to set a particle in motion. The theorem is valid even for a force that is not constant.

Master the Concept

Energy and Automobiles

Question: Why do cars get better mileage in freeway driving than in city traffic?

Answer: The fuel burned in a car engine provides the energy to propel the car. Much of this energy is expended in accelerating the car from rest or from slower speeds to higher speeds. When driving on the freeway, the speed can be held essentially constant so that the energy required is primarily used to overcome friction and air drag. However, in the stop-and-go driving of city traffic much more energy is needed to repeatedly accelerate the car up to speed. Consequently, city driving requires more fuel per mile than does freeway driving.

Example 6.3

A baseball player throws a 0.17-kg baseball at a speed of 36 m/s. Find the ball's translational kinetic energy.

Solution From the definition of kinetic energy we have

$$KE = \tfrac{1}{2}mv^2,$$

$$KE = \tfrac{1}{2}(0.17 \text{ kg})(36 \text{ m/s})^2 = 110 \text{ J}.$$

Discussion Remember that if you put the mass and the velocity in SI units of kg and m/s, the kinetic energy will be given in the SI unit of joules.

Example 6.4

Sometimes we can measure the kinetic energy of a particle emitted during radioactive decay by determining how far it travels in matter before stopping. Using this technique, a physicist determines that an alpha particle had an initial kinetic energy of 8.0×10^{-14} J. The mass of an alpha particle is known to be 6.65×10^{-27} kg. What was the initial speed of the alpha particle in m/s? What was the speed when expressed as a fraction of the speed of light ($c = 3.00 \times 10^8$ m/s)?

Strategy Because we are given the kinetic energy and the mass, we can calculate the particle's speed from our definition of kinetic energy even if we don't know what an alpha particle is. (We will describe it later, in Chapter 26.)

Solution From our definition of kinetic energy we have

$$KE = \tfrac{1}{2}mv^2,$$

which we can solve for v to give

$$v = \sqrt{\frac{2KE}{m}}.$$

Inserting the numerical values gives

$$v = \sqrt{\frac{2(8.0 \times 10^{-14}\,\text{J})}{6.65 \times 10^{-27}\,\text{kg}}} = 4.9 \times 10^6\,\text{m/s}.$$

Comparing the speed of the alpha particle to the speed of light c gives

$$\frac{v}{c} = \frac{4.9 \times 10^6\,\text{m/s}}{3.00 \times 10^8\,\text{m/s}} = 0.016,$$

or

$$v = 0.016c.$$

Example 6.5

(a) How much work is done to move a 1840-kg Jaguar XJ6 automobile from rest to 27.0 m/s (60 mi/h) on a level road? (b) If this takes place over a distance of 117 m, what is the average net force?

Solution (a) We can use the work-energy theorem to find the work,

$$W = \tfrac{1}{2}mv_2^2 - \tfrac{1}{2}mv_1^2.$$

We set v_1 equal to zero, $v_2 = 27.0$ m/s, and $m = 1840$ kg. Then the work is

$$W = \tfrac{1}{2}(1840\,\text{kg})(27\,\text{m/s})^2 = 6.71 \times 10^5\,\text{J}.$$

(b) The average net force can be found from

$$W = Fx,$$

$$F = \frac{W}{x} = \frac{6.71 \times 10^5\,\text{J}}{117\,\text{m}} = 5.74 \times 10^3\,\text{N}.$$

Discussion Note that we could have computed the car's average acceleration and then used Newton's second law to find the force. However, the present method of solution uses only scalar quantities, rather than vectors, and for more complicated situations is the easier method to use.

6.5 Potential Energy

We have seen that an object in motion has kinetic energy. Objects may also have energy in other forms. When a spring is stretched, it acquires energy called *potential energy*. For example, when you do work to wind the spring of a toy car, you give the spring potential energy; it has the ability to move the car when it unwinds and therefore to do work. Other examples include a jack-in-the-box and the compressed gas in an aerosol spray can. A mass lifted from the ground also gains potential energy. If it is dropped, it loses potential energy and gains kinetic energy. If it strikes a stake on the ground, the mass can do work by driving the stake farther into the ground.

In all of these examples, work must be done to increase an object's potential energy, and in all cases the object acquires the capability of doing work when released. We can think of **potential energy** as stored energy. These examples illustrate mechanical potential energy; other forms of potential energy include chemical and electrical potential energy, which we will discuss in later chapters.

The term *potential energy* does not mean that the energy is not real energy. Rather, it means that the energy is stored and is available to be converted into work or some other form of energy.

Gravitational Potential Energy

Gravitational potential energy is one of the most familiar forms of potential energy. Figure 6.10 shows a log of mass m initially at rest on the ground. It is then lifted slowly at a uniform velocity with a constant upward force just strong enough to equal the downward force of gravity mg. If the log is raised from the ground to a height h, the work done on the log is the net lifting force times the distance traveled, or

$$W = Fh = mgh.$$

If the log is released, it will fall. As it falls it accelerates, gaining velocity and kinetic energy, and thereby the ability to do work. Because the log at height h is capable of doing work if it is released, we say it has potential energy due to its position. More specifically, we say in this case that it has **gravitational potential energy.** The change in the log's gravitational potential energy is equal to the work required to raise the log to that height.

Thus, near the earth's surface an object's gravitational potential energy with respect to some reference level is

$$PE = mgh, \qquad (6.7)$$

where h is the height above the reference level. Again, the units are joules. Note specifically that the gravitational potential energy depends on the position of the body and is not a property of the body alone.

Gravitational potential energy must always be referred to a specific reference level. For instance, in Fig. 6.11, the potential energy of the vase with respect to the floor is greater than its potential energy with respect to the table. Yet there is only one physical situation, not two. This example does not imply any ambiguity in the concept of potential energy; it only points out that the reference level is arbitrary. However, once you have chosen the reference level from which to measure potential energy in a given physical situation, you must keep that same reference throughout your analysis and calculation of that situation. Remember, *the physically important quantity is the difference in potential energy between two levels.*

Figure 6.12 shows several different paths by which a stack of boards can be lifted from point A to point B. Though some pathways are longer than others, *the same amount of work is done in each case.* Remember that only the component of the displacement in the direction of the force contributes to the work done on an object. In this case the direction of the gravitational force is vertical and the net vertical displacement is the same for each pathway. Thus, we conclude that the gravitational potential energy depends only on the difference between the heights of A and B. We will discuss this further in Section 6.6.

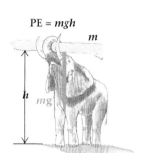

PE = mgh

Figure 6.10
The gravitational potential energy of a log of mass m raised to a height h above the earth's surface is given by mgh.

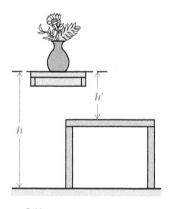

Figure 6.11
The potential energy of a vase with respect to the table (mgh') is less than its potential energy with respect to the floor (mgh).

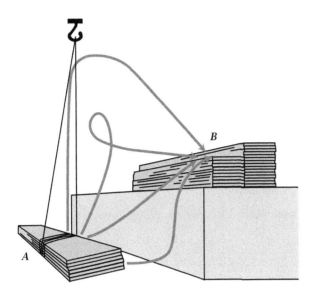

Figure 6.12
The work done in lifting a load between two heights in a uniform gravitational field is independent of the path traveled by the load.

▼

Problem-Solving Strategy

Gravitational Potential Energy

In working problems with gravitational potential energy, you must choose a reference coordinate system and stick with it throughout the problem. The particular choice is arbitrary, but a clever choice will simplify your efforts. The important quantity is the change in vertical position.

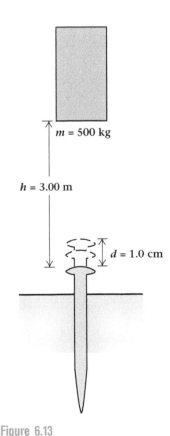

$m = 500$ kg

$h = 3.00$ m

$d = 1.0$ cm

▼

Example 6.6

How much potential energy does a 7.5-kg ceiling fan have with respect to the floor when it is 3.0 m above it?

Strategy   We are looking for the potential energy with respect to the floor, so it is natural to choose the floor as the zero level of PE.

Solution   If we let h be the height above the floor, we find

$$PE = mgh$$
$$PE = (7.5 \text{ kg})(9.81 \text{ m/s}^2)(3.0 \text{ m}) = 220 \text{ J}.$$

▼

Example 6.7

In Fig. 6.13, the 500-kg mass of a pile driver is dropped from a height of 3.00 m onto a piling in the ground. The impact drives the piling 1.0 cm deeper into the ground. If all the original potential energy of the mass is converted

Figure 6.13
Example 6.7: A pile driver drops a 500-kg mass onto a piling, driving it deeper into the ground.

into work in driving the piling into the ground, what is the frictional force acting on the piling? Assume the frictional force to be constant over the 1.0-cm travel.

Strategy We can solve this problem by using the concept of energy. This method has the advantage that we do not need to know the exact nature of the interaction, only that all of the energy is converted into work. We know that the driver falls through a distance h, striking the piling and driving it into the ground. We assume all of the potential energy goes into causing this motion. In driving the piling, the driver must overcome the frictional force between the ground and the piling. The frictional force will be opposite in direction to the force exerted by the driver.

Solution The work needed to drive the piling through a distance d is

$$W = Fd,$$

where F is the force needed to overcome friction. The initial potential energy relative to the final position is

$$PE = mgh.$$

The final potential energy is 0. We equate the work done and the change in potential energy to give

$$Fd = mgh - 0,$$

$$F = \frac{mgh}{d}$$

$$F = \frac{(500 \text{ kg})(9.81 \text{ m/s})(3.00 \text{ m})}{0.010 \text{ m}} = 1.5 \times 10^6 \text{ N}.$$

Discussion In reality, some of the original potential energy will go into radiated sound and into heating of the point of impact. Most of the original potential energy goes into moving the stake against the frictional force, energy that is eventually dissipated as heat. (We will discuss this in more detail in Chapter 11.) Also note that, because the height is large compared with the displacement of the piling, we approximate the distance through which the heavy mass moves as simply h.

Elastic Potential Energy

Just as we can store energy by raising a mass in a gravitational field, we can store energy in a spring by stretching or compressing it. We have seen in Section 6.2 that the work required to stretch a spring a distance x from its equilibrium position is $\frac{1}{2}kx^2$. When the external force is removed, the spring returns to its original length converting its stored energy into kinetic energy. Thus, in the same way that we defined gravitational potential energy, we can define a potential energy of the spring that we call **elastic potential energy,** PE_s, given by

$$PE_s = \tfrac{1}{2}kx^2. \tag{6.8}$$

Notice that when the spring is compressed corresponding to a negative value of x, the elastic potential energy is positive just as it is when the spring is stretched.

In either case, extension or compression, the spring exerts a force in a direction that would move the spring back to its equilibrium length.

Example 6.8

A 1550-kg Pontiac Gran Prix is supported by four coil springs, each with a spring constant of 7.00×10^4 N/m. (a) By how much are the springs compressed beyond their normal length? (b) How much energy is stored in the springs?

Strategy For simplicity we assume that the four springs support an equal portion of the car's weight. The amount of compression of each spring can then be found from the force on the spring and the spring constant. Finally, from the compression of the spring we can compute the stored energy from the definition of elastic potential energy given in Eq. (6.8).

Solution (a) Assuming the weight of the car is equally distributed, the force on each spring is one-fourth the weight of the car. The compression of each spring may be computed from the Hooke's law relationship $F_{ext} = kx$.

$$x = \frac{F_{ext}}{k} = \frac{mg/4}{k} = \frac{(1550 \text{ kg})(9.81 \text{ m/s}^2)/4}{7.00 \times 10^4 \text{ N/m}} = 5.43 \times 10^{-2} \text{ m}.$$

(b) The energy stored in one spring is given by $PE_s = \frac{1}{2}kx^2$. The total energy stored is four times the energy stored in one spring.

$$PE_{s \text{ tot}} = 4\left(\frac{1}{2}kx^2\right) = (2)(7.00 \times 10^4 \text{N/m})(5.43 \times 10^{-2} \text{ m})^2 = 413 \text{ J}.$$

6.6 Conservation of Mechanical Energy

When you apply a force to a spring and stretch it, the spring returns to its original length when released. On the other hand, if you apply a force to a book and push it across a table against the frictional force, the book does not return to its original position when you release it. In both cases you do work against a resisting force, but the nature of the forces is different. The spring force represents what is called a conservative force; friction is a dissipative, or nonconservative, force.

If the work done by a force on an object depends only on the initial and final positions of the object, then that force is a **conservative force.** The work is independent of the path taken. If you move an object against a conservative force and return it to the starting place, the total work done is zero. For example, if you do an amount of work to lift a barbell from the floor, the same amount of work is done on you if you lower the barbell to its initial location (Fig. 6.14). The total work you've done on the barbell is zero. (This does not mean that a weightlifter does no work in lifting and lowering a barbell. Energy losses occur within the body.)

As we saw earlier, the gravitational force is a conservative force. The expression for the work given in Eq. (6.7) depends on the difference in initial and final positions (see Fig. 6.12), not on the path taken between them. A spring with a restoring force proportional to its extension is another example of a

Figure 6.14
The work done in raising a barbell is equal to the work done on the weightlifter by the barbell if it is lowered to its initial position.

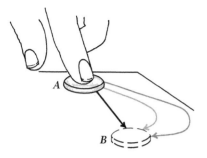

Figure 6.15
The work done to push a coin from A to B depends on the path taken.

conservative force. We conclude, from the requirement that the work done be independent of the path taken, that conservative forces must be forces that depend on position, rather than forces that may vary with time, speed of the object, path taken, or some other parameter.

The work done against a frictional force depends on the path. If you push a coin from A to B (Fig. 6.15) with constant speed, the work done is different for different paths. Thus, friction is a nonconservative force. The resistance of air or water to the motion of a body through it is another example of a nonconservative force.

An important distinction between conservative and nonconservative forces is that we can write an expression for the potential energy for conservative forces. You have seen this for gravitation. You have seen also that the energy needed to compress a spring that obeys Hooke's law is the stored, or potential, energy. No such expression is possible for frictional forces. The term *conservative force* is appropriate because a conservative force corresponds to the conservation, or constancy, of the sum of the kinetic energy and the potential energy.

Let's return to the case of a body that is raised to a small height h above the ground (Fig. 6.16). Over this distance the earth's gravitational field is essentially constant. The gravitational potential energy of the body is PE = mgh. If the rope breaks, the body is released from rest and falls. As it falls it gains speed as a result of the acceleration of gravity, and at any instant it has a kinetic energy corresponding to its instantaneous speed, given by

$$\text{KE} = \tfrac{1}{2}mv^2.$$

If the speed at height h_1 is v_1, then we can determine the speed v_2 at height h_2 by using the kinematic expression from Chapter 2,

$$v_2^2 = v_1^2 + 2a(x_2 - x_1).$$

Figure 6.16
A body is released from height h above the ground. It falls to height h_1, where its speed is v_1, and to height h_2, where it has a new speed v_2. Its total kinetic and potential energy stays the same.

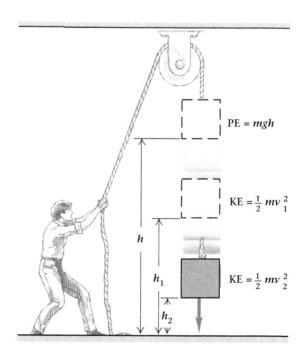

If we choose a coordinate system in which up is positive and down is negative, then the acceleration a is $-g$ and $x_2 - x_1$ becomes $h_2 - h_1$. The kinetic energy at h_2 is then

$$\tfrac{1}{2}mv_2^2 = \tfrac{1}{2}mv_1^2 - mg(h_2 - h_1).$$

This equation may be rearranged to give

$$\tfrac{1}{2}mv_2^2 + mgh_2 = \tfrac{1}{2}mv_1^2 + mgh_1. \qquad (6.9)$$

The sum of the body's kinetic energy and potential energy is its total **mechanical energy.** According to Eq. (6.9), the mechanical energy at height h_2 is equal to the mechanical energy at height h_1. Thus, an object's total mechanical energy is constant for motion in a constant gravitational field provided that no other forces are introduced. For this special case we say that the mechanical energy is *conserved*. The total energy is the same at the top (h) as it is at any other height. The total mechanical energy E can be written in the form

$$E = KE + PE. \qquad (6.10)$$

The value of the potential energy (PE) and kinetic energy (KE) may change, but their sum, the total energy (E), is a constant and does not change.

Equations (6.9) and (6.10), along with additional observations and experiments, leads to the generalization that *if the forces are all conservative, the sum of the kinetic and potential energies is a constant*. This statement is the **law of conservation of mechanical energy,** which can be written as

$$\boxed{KE_2 + PE_2 = KE_1 + PE_1.} \qquad (6.11)$$

Alternatively, we can rearrange Eq. (6.11) to write it in the form

$$\Delta KE + \Delta PE = 0. \qquad (6.12)$$

Sometimes this last equation is a useful way to state the law of conservation of mechanical energy.

We can combine Eq. (6.12) with the work-energy theorem Eq. (6.6) to get

$$W_c = \Delta KE = -\Delta PE \qquad (6.13)$$

or

$$W_c = PE_i - PE_f,$$

where we have used W_c to represent the work done by conservative forces. Thus, the work done on an object by a conservative force is equal to the object's initial potential energy minus its final potential energy.

The principle of conservation of energy is extremely useful in a wide variety of cases. Often the effects of friction are small enough that we can ignore them and use the law of conservation of mechanical energy. In later chapters we will study other forms of energy, such as thermal energy and electrical energy. We will find that energy can be transformed from one form to another and that we can extend the principle of conservation of energy to include those other forms. Example 6.9, which follows, demonstrates an application of conservation of mechanical energy.

Significance of Conservation Laws

Those laws of nature that state that some quantity is the same before and after an event or interaction are called **conservation laws.** They reflect one of our most basic ways of describing nature. The law of conservation of mechanical energy is, in some sense, a more fundamental principle than Newton's mechanics, which we used to derive it here. Because conservation laws allow us to consider quantities, such as energy, that do not change during an event, we do not need to know the details of the interaction. We simply deal with the value of the conserved quantity before and after the interaction. Moreover, the fact that some quantities are conserved, and some are not, tells us something about nature itself.

In all of physics there are only a relatively small number of conservation laws. We will introduce the conservation of momentum in Chapter 7 and only a few more conservation laws in the remainder of the text. It can be argued that conservation laws represent the most powerful and, at the same time, simplest view of nature. They allow us not only to understand how much electrical energy it takes to keep our house warm or cool, but also to discover new particles and new behavior on the atomic and subatomic scale.

Example 6.9

A student accidentally knocks a plant off a window sill, where it falls from rest to the ground 5.27 m below (Fig. 6.17). Use the principle of conservation of energy to determine its speed just before it strikes the ground.

Strategy The total mechanical energy E of the plant is a constant. It consists of two parts: kinetic energy KE and potential energy PE, which are not individually constant, but whose sum is constant:

$$E = KE + PE.$$

By expressing these energies in terms of the height h and the final velocity v, we can determine v in terms of h.

Solution Use subscripts T for top and 0 for ground, we equate the total energy at the top of the fall to the total energy at the bottom,

$$E_T = E_0$$
$$KE_T + PE_T = KE_0 + PE_0.$$

But $KE_T = 0$ because the initial speed is zero, and $PE_0 = 0$ because $h = 0$. Thus we have

$$PE_T = KE_0,$$

or

$$mgh = \tfrac{1}{2}mv^2.$$

Upon solving for v, we get

$$v = \sqrt{2gh}$$
$$v = \sqrt{2(9.81 \text{ m/s}^2)(5.27 \text{ m})} = 10.2 \text{ m/s.}$$

PE = mgh, KE = 0

5.27 m

PE = 0, KE = ½ mv^2

Figure 6.17
Example 6.9: A plant falls from a height of 5.27 m above ground.

Discussion Note that we could have obtained the same result using the methods described in Chapter 2. However, the principle of energy conservation is important because it can be applied in much more complicated situations where the methods of Chapter 2 are impractical.

Potential Energy Diagrams

Let us consider what happens to a roller coaster as it moves along a track (Fig. 6.18a). The height of the track above some reference level determines the potential energy at that point. In part (a) a car of mass m leaves point A with no initial velocity ($v_A = 0$). We can determine its speed at any other location B using the principle of conservation of energy:

$$KE_A + PE_A = KE_B + PE_B.$$

At A the kinetic energy of the coaster is zero because its speed is zero. Thus the equation for conservation of mechanical energy becomes

$$0 + mgh_A = \tfrac{1}{2}mv_B^2 + mgh_B$$
$$\tfrac{1}{2}mv_B^2 = mgh_A - mgh_B.$$

We rearrange to find the speed

$$v_B = \sqrt{2g(h_A - h_B)}.$$

This result suggests a diagrammatic way of viewing a situation in which energy is conserved. In Fig. 6.18(b) we have plotted the potential energy of the car as a function of its horizontal displacement x. Since the potential energy is

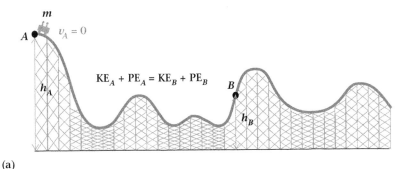

(a)

(b)

Figure 6.18

(a) A roller coaster on a track. The total mechanical energy $E = KE + PE$ is conserved. (b) The potential-energy diagram for the roller coaster on the track. We choose the zero energy level to be ground level. The kinetic energy is the difference between total energy E_1 and the potential energy.

directly proportional to the height h, the potential energy curve has the same shape as the track itself. Such a graph of potential energy against displacement is called a **potential-energy diagram.** The total energy is represented here by E_1 and is constant. In this case, since $KE_A = 0$, E_1 is equal to the initial potential energy PE_A. On the diagram you can see that the kinetic energy is given by the distance between the total-energy curve and the potential-energy curve. Thus, the kinetic energy at point B is

$$KE_B = E_1 - PE_B.$$

When these energies are expressed in terms of position and speed, we get

$$\tfrac{1}{2}mv_B^2 = E_1 - mgh_B,$$

or

$$v_B = \sqrt{2\left(\frac{E_1}{m} - gh_B\right)}.$$

However, since for this case the total energy E_1 is equal to the initial potential energy mgh_A, this expression becomes

$$v_B = \sqrt{2g(h_A - h_B)}.$$

This result is the same as our earlier finding.

If the roller coaster in part (a) had been moving at point A, it would have had an initial kinetic energy, as well as an initial potential energy. Then the total energy would have been greater than E_1, as shown by the dotted line E_2 in part (b). In this case the speed at any point B would be

$$v_B = \sqrt{2\left(\frac{E_2}{m} - gh_B\right)}.$$

This is just the same as the previous expression, with E_1 replaced by E_2. In either case the value of the total energy would be known from the initial conditions.

We emphasize that the roller coaster's kinetic energy, and therefore its speed, is determined by the difference between the total-energy line and the potential-energy curve. As indicated by the potential-energy diagram, at a point where the potential energy is smaller, the kinetic energy, and therefore the speed, is larger. From such a diagram you can determine the speed if you know the position.

Example 6.10

A block of mass m is released from rest and slides down a frictionless track of height h (Fig. 6.19) At the bottom of the track the block slides freely along a horizontal surface until it hits a spring of spring constant k attached to a heavy, immovable wall. How far is the spring compressed at the maximum point of compression?

Strategy At the beginning of the problem, the mass is at rest at a height h above the horizontal surface. If we choose the horizontal surface as our origin for measuring gravitational potential energy, then the mass m has an initial potential energy of mgh and zero kinetic energy. As the mass slides down the track it loses potential energy and gains kinetic energy until at the bottom all

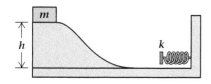

Figure 6.19

Example 6.10: A mass moves down a frictionless ramp until it strikes a spring.

of its energy is kinetic. Finally, the mass hits the spring and begins to compress it, exchanging kinetic energy for spring potential energy until it stops and all of the energy is potential energy.

Solution We can equate the initial mechanical energy to the final mechanical energy to get

$$KE_i + PE_{gi} + PE_{si} = KE_f + PE_{gf} + PE_{sf},$$

where we have used the g and s to denote gravitational and spring energies and i and f to denote initial and final energies. Inserting the values gives

$$0 + mgh + 0 = 0 + 0 + \tfrac{1}{2}kx^2.$$

Solving for x, the maximum amount that the spring is compressed, we find

$$x = \sqrt{\frac{2mgh}{k}}.$$

Discussion At the instant that the spring is compressed a maximum amount, the speed of the mass is zero. However, this is not a stable condition, for the spring is pushing outward with a force $F = kx$, which begins to accelerate the mass until all of the spring potential energy is converted into kinetic energy of the mass. Then, if there are no losses of energy, the mass will make its way back up the track to its starting point.

▼

Example 6.11

Students from a physics class visit an amusement park to test their understanding of Newton's laws. They ride a roller coaster (Fig. 6.20) that is pulled up to the top of a 48-m-tall hill. The coaster then moves over the crest at an average

Figure 6.20
Example 6.11: A roller coaster.

speed of 0.50 m/s before it plunges to a low point 3 m above the ground. From there it climbs over a smaller hill only 16 m high. One of the students on the roller coaster records the trip with a 1.5-kg video camera. (a) What is the coaster's speed as it goes over the top of the 16-m hill? (b) What force (magnitude and direction) must the student exert on the camera to hold it steady as the car passes through the crest of the 16-m hill? The path of the track over the hill is approximately circular with a radius of 20 m. Assume that the student holds the camera 1.0 m above the track and that friction is small enough to be ignored.

Strategy The speed of the coaster at any point along the track depends on its height. We may determine the speed by using the law of conservation of mechanical energy. Once we know the speed we can find the centripetal force required to move the camera along with the coaster. The centripetal force is the net force exerted on the camera. It is the vector sum of the force exerted by the student and the gravitational force.

Solution (a) We find the speed of the coaster from the conservation of mechanical energy.

$$KE_{top} + PE_{top} = KE_B + PE_B,$$

where the subscript B represents any point along the track. In this case we let point B be the crest of the 16-m hill. Then the equation becomes

$$\tfrac{1}{2}mv_{top}^2 + mgh_{top} = \tfrac{1}{2}mv_B^2 + mgh_B.$$

After dividing out the common factor m, we get

$$\tfrac{1}{2}v_{top}^2 + gh_{top} = \tfrac{1}{2}v_B^2 + gh_B.$$

Rearrange and solve for v_B.

$$v_B^2 = v_{top}^2 + 2g(h_{top} - h_B),$$
$$v_B = \sqrt{v_{top}^2 + 2g(h_{top} - h_B)}.$$

We then insert the numerical values to find v_B.

$$v_B = \sqrt{(0.50 \text{ m/s})^2 + 2(9.81 \text{ m/s}^2)(48 \text{ m} - 16 \text{ m})} = 25.06 \text{ m/s} \approx 25 \text{ m/s}.$$

(b) Next we find $\mathbf{F}_s$ the force that the student exerts on the camera. The force of gravity $\mathbf{F}_g$ also acts on the camera. The vector sum of these forces provides the centripetal force that carries the camera around the curved path of the track. Thus the centripetal force is

$$\mathbf{F}_c = \mathbf{F}_g + \mathbf{F}_s.$$

We know that the magnitude F_g is mg and that it is directed vertically downward.

$$F_g = mg = (1.5 \text{ kg})(9.81 \text{ m/s}^2) = 14.72 \text{ N}.$$

We can compute the magnitude of the centripetal force from the speed and the radius of the path of the camera. Because the coaster is going over a hill, the centripetal force at the top must also be downward.

$$F_c = \frac{mv^2}{r} = \frac{(1.5 \text{ kg})(25.06 \text{ m/s})^2}{21 \text{ m}} = 44.86 \text{ N}.$$

The force provided by the student is

$$\mathbf{F}_s = \mathbf{F}_c - \mathbf{F}_g.$$

If we let up be positive and down negative, then the force becomes

$$F_s = -F_c - (-F_g)$$
$$F_s = -44.86\,\text{N} + 14.72\,\text{N} = -30.14\,\text{N} \approx -30\,\text{N}.$$

The student must pull down on the camera with a force of 30 N to keep the camera in the coaster.

Discussion Notice that the force of 30 N exerted on the camera by the student is about twice the normal weight of the camera. To the student riding in the coaster, the camera seems to be flying upward with a force twice its weight.

What would be the direction of the required force when the coaster passes through the lowest point of the track? The track curves upward at the lowest point so the center of the effective curve is above the track. The resulting centripetal force must be upward. Thus the rider would have to exert an upward force to overcome the gravitational force and provide the neccessary centripetal force. In that case the camera would seem heavier than normal.

*6.7 Energy Conservation with Nonconservative Forces

We know that friction plays a role in most real situations. For example, a box sliding down a ramp is slowed by the retarding force of friction. Consequently, we expect that its mechanical energy when it reaches the bottom of the ramp will be less than it was at the top. Thus, in the presence of a frictional (or other nonconservative) force, mechanical energy is not conserved. Even so, we can still account for the effects of nonconservative forces.

Let us express the work in the work-energy theorem of Eq. (6.6) in two parts, the work W_c due to conservative forces and the work W_{nc} due to the nonconservative forces:

$$W_c + W_{nc} = \Delta\text{KE}. \qquad (6.14)$$

If we substitute Eq. (6.13) for the work done by conservative forces, we find upon rearranging that

$$W_{nc} = \Delta\text{KE} + \Delta\text{PE} = \Delta E,$$

or

$$W_{nc} = E_{\text{final}} - E_{\text{initial}}. \qquad (6.15)$$

As before, E is the total mechanical energy, so Eq. (6.15) means that the work done by the nonconservative forces equals the change in total mechanical energy. That is, it is equal to the change in kinetic energy plus the change in potential energy.

Friction is a nonconservative force. The direction of the frictional force acts to retard the motion. Therefore the work done by friction is negative. In that case, the final mechanical energy is less than the initial mechanical energy. Then we can write Eq. (6.15) as

$$E_{final} - E_{initial} = W_{friction}, \tag{6.16}$$

where $W_{friction}$ is the product of the frictional force F_{fr} with the distance d through which it acts. In order to make it clear that the final energy is less than the initial energy, we rewrite Eq. (6.16) as

$$E_{final} - E_{initial} = -|W_{friction}|,$$

or

$$\boxed{E_{initial} = E_{final} + |W_{friction}|.} \tag{6.17}$$

The effect of a frictional force is to decrease the final mechanical energy of the system. For this reason frictional forces are known as **dissipative forces.** When dissipative forces are present, they act to remove mechanical energy from the system. This energy is not lost, however, but is transformed into a different form. As we will see in Chapter 11, during the nineteenth century careful observers found that the mechanical energy lost to friction is transformed into thermal energy.

▼

Example 6.12

A 55-kg carton of bananas with an initial speed of 0.45 m/s slides down a ramp inclined at an angle of 23° with the horizontal. If the coefficient of friction between the carton and the ramp is 0.24, how fast will the carton be moving after it has traveled a distance of 2.1 m down the ramp?

Strategy The carton is acted upon by the conservative force of gravity drawing it down the ramp and by the nonconservative force of friction retarding its motion, as shown in Fig. 6.21. We can find the speed of the carton by applying the law of conservation of energy in the form of Eq. (6.17):

$$E_{initial} = E_{final} + |W_{friction}|$$

$$\tfrac{1}{2}mv_i^2 + mgh_i = \tfrac{1}{2}mv_f^2 + mgh_f + F_{fr}d,$$

where d is the distance traveled down the ramp.

Solution The distance traveled by the carton is $d = 2.1$ m. The difference in height from the initial position to the final position is $h_i - h_f = d \sin 23°$, and the frictional force is $\mu mg \cos 23°$. Inserting these values into the last equation we get

$$\tfrac{1}{2}mv_f^2 = \tfrac{1}{2}mv_i^2 + mg(h_i - h_f) - F_{fr}d$$

$$\tfrac{1}{2}mv_f^2 = \tfrac{1}{2}mv_i^2 + mgd \sin 23° - \mu mgd \cos 23°.$$

We can multiply each term by $2/m$ to get

$$v_f^2 = v_i^2 + 2gd(\sin 23° - \mu \cos 23°),$$

$$v_f = \sqrt{v_i^2 + 2gd(\sin 23° - \mu \cos 23°)}.$$

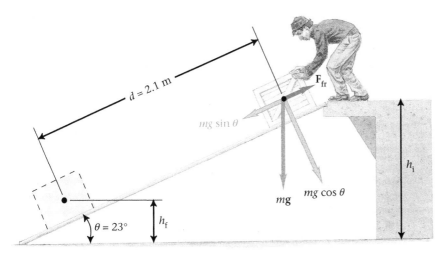

Figure 6.21
Example 6.12: A carton slides down a ramp.

Now we can insert the numerical values for v_i, g, d, and μ to get

$$v_f = \sqrt{(0.45 \text{ m/s})^2 + 2(9.81 \text{ m/s}^2)(2.1 \text{ m})(\sin 23° - 0.24 \cos 23°)}$$

$$v_f = 2.7 \text{ m/s}.$$

6.8   Power

In many cases it is useful to know not just the total amount of work being done, but how rapidly work is being done. For instance, if you have a motor that can provide only a certain amount of work in one day and you wish to accomplish twice that much work, then you must either take two days for the job or get an additional motor. We define **power** as the time rate of doing work; that is,

$$P \equiv \frac{\Delta W}{\Delta t}, \qquad (6.18)$$

where ΔW is the amount of work done in the time interval Δt. In SI units, work is measured in joules and time in seconds. The unit of power is the joule/second, a combination that has been given the name **watt** (abbreviated W):

$$1 \text{ joule/second} = 1 \text{ watt}.$$

The measurement of power grew out of the need of early steam-engine builders to specify the properties of their engines. James Watt (1736–1819), the most inventive of these engine builders, developed the steam engine into an efficient, versatile engine that could be used to drive machinery. As part of his efforts to measure the power of his steam engine, Watt made systematic measurements on the work a horse could perform in a given time. From these measurements he defined a horsepower as 550 foot-pounds per second. The relationship between the watt and the horsepower (hp) is

$$1 \text{ hp} = 746 \text{ W} = 0.746 \text{ kW}.$$

Table 6.3	Approximate Power Production and Consumption
Device	**Approximate Power (in W)**
Hoover Dam	1.92×10^9
Jumbo jet aircraft	1.3×10^8
Automobile use of chemical energy at 60 mph	1.1×10^5
Electric stove	1.2×10^4
Clothes dryer	5.6×10^3
Average per capita use of electricity (U.S.)	1.5×10^3
Available solar power per square meter (average U.S. over 24-h day)	180
Solid-state color TV	120
Two-cell flashlight, halogen lamp	1.5
Pocket calculator (LCD display)	7.5×10^{-4}

Table 6.3 gives the approximate power produced or consumed in a number of situations.

Example 6.13: A jogger expends energy when running on a treadmill.

Example 6.13

Using a calibrated treadmill, a jogger measures her energy output as 4.8×10^5 J for an hour's run. What average output power did she develop?

Solution From the definition of power as the rate of doing work, we have

$$P = \frac{\Delta W}{\Delta t} = \frac{4.8 \times 10^5 \text{ J}}{3600 \text{ s}}$$
$$P = 1.33 \times 10^2 \text{ W} \approx 130 \text{ W}.$$

Discussion Compare this with the power consumption of a household electric lamp. Note that this is the output power—that is, the power expended to move the jogger along. The total power expended, some of which goes into work against the internal friction in the jogger's body, is greater than the output power.

Example 6.14

A 70-kg person runs up a staircase 3.0 m high in 3.5 s. How much power does he develop in climbing the steps?

Solution If we assume that the work is done at a constant rate, then the definition of Eq. (6.18) becomes

$$P = \frac{W}{t}.$$

In this case, the work done is the change in gravitational potential energy, mgh, so the power is

$$P = \frac{mgh}{t} = \frac{(70 \text{ kg})(9.81 \text{ m/s})(3.0 \text{ m})}{3.5 \text{ s}} = 590 \text{ W}.$$

Discussion Note that we have actually computed the average power, which is the total work done divided by the total time. The power may also be given in units of horsepower as

$$P = 590 \text{ W}\left(\frac{1 \text{ hp}}{746 \text{ W}}\right) = 0.79 \text{ hp}.$$

This result is consistent with the general observation that humans are capable of power outputs in the range of 0.5 to 1 hp for 30 s. For longer periods of time, human power output is much decreased. For steady work over 8 h, human power is of the order of 0.1 to 0.2 hp.

Our definition of power in Eq. (6.18) applies to all types of work, whether mechanical, electrical, or thermal. However, we can rewrite the definition in a special way for mechanical work by simply rearranging terms. When a force acts on an object so that it moves with a speed v, we can calculate the power from the force and the speed. If we consider the force to be constant, the change in work is $\Delta W = F \Delta x$. Then power becomes

$$P = F\frac{\Delta x}{\Delta t},$$

or

$$P = Fv. \tag{6.19}$$

It can be shown that Eq. (6.19) is true for instantaneous power even when the force is not constant.

Example 6.15

The heart may be regarded as an intermittent pump that forces about 70 cm^3 of blood into the 1.0-cm-radius aorta about 75 times a minute (Fig. 6.22). Measurements show that the average force with which the blood is pushed into the aorta is about 5.0 N. What is the approximate power used in moving the blood to the aorta?

Strategy Because we know the force, we can use Eq. (6.19) to determine the power if we can find the speed of the blood. The average speed can be computed from the volume of blood that is pumped and the pumping rate. Assume the aorta to be a cylinder and that a length s of it is filled with blood each time the heart beats. We start with the definition of speed and modify it by multiplying the numerator and denominator of the fraction by the cross-sectional area of the aorta, to give

$$v = \frac{s}{t} = \frac{s\pi r^2}{t\pi r^2} = \frac{\text{volume}}{t\pi r^2}.$$

Here r is the radius of the aorta and t is the time for one heartbeat.

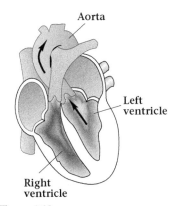

Figure 6.22
Example 6.15: The human heart.

HUMAN ENERGY

Does energy conservation apply to your body? The answer is yes. The food you eat is the fuel that provides your body with energy to maintain its functions and to do external work. Catalytic agents, called enzymes, allow this fuel to burn at body temperatures, converting chemical energy into thermal and other energy. If you take in too much fuel, some of the energy is stored in the form of body mass and your weight increases. If you take in too little energy, you lose weight. Thus, if you want to maintain your weight, the energy you take in must be equal to the energy your body uses. This equilibrium energy is sometimes called the sustaining energy.

The exact value of the sustaining energy intake depends on body mass and activity level. Figure B6.1 shows the approximate range of sustaining energy intake per day as a function of body mass. The lower boundary of the shaded area corresponds to inactive people; the upper boundary corresponds to very active people. In the United States, most people take in between 2000 and 3000 Calories (8400 – 12600 kJ) per day.

Most food energy goes into just running your body and keeping it warm. When you first wake up in the morning and are lying quietly in bed, your body is using energy at the lowest rate for the day. The average energy use in that condition, called the basal metabolic rate, is about 1400 Calories per day for women and about 1600 Calories per day for men. This rate of use corresponds to an average power output of about 75 watts. Most of this energy goes into repairing cells. The waste energy shows up as heat to maintain your body temperature.

As you increase your activities during the day, your energy needs increase also. For example, Fig. B6.2 shows how the rate of energy use increases with increasing walking speed. The increased rate for faster walking implies that when you move your legs or arms, some energy is needed to overcome the internal friction in your body. Furthermore, your muscles are inefficient at converting chemical energy into mechanical motion. Only about one fifth of the chemical energy used by your muscles is converted into mechanical work; the remainder is dissipated as heat, explaining in part why you get hotter when you run than when you walk. The average daily expenditure of energy for inactive men is about 2800 Calories; for inactive women it is about 2000 Calories. People who engage in very strenuous work have much higher energy needs. For example, athletes in training for the triathlon need as much as 8000 Calories per day.

How much energy do you use in sports and other activities? Table B6.1 gives you some typical values for a 150-lb person. To get a value for your own weight, multiply the value in the table by your weight in pounds and divide the result by 150. The values in the table correspond to sustained activity. When you jump, throw, or bat, your peak effort is expended over a shorter time and the rate of energy use can be larger than for sustained activity. In short bursts of a second or so duration, 0.60 Calories *per second* have been measured in golf, weight lifting, and high jumping. An expenditure of 0.60 Calories per second is approximately two-and-one half times as great as the rate of energy use when running an 8-min mile.

Table B6.1	Calories used by a 150-lb Person in 10 Minutes	
Activity	**Energy Used (Calories)**	**(Joules)**
Volleyball	34	142,000
Walking (3 mph)	40	167,000
Walking (4 mph)	58	242,000
Jogging (11 min-mile)	91	380,000
Running (8 min-mile)	141	590,000
Bicycling (5.5 mph)	47	197,000
Bicycling (10 mph)	81	339,000
Swimming (breaststroke)	72	301,000
Swimming (crawl)	87	364,000
Calisthenics	49	205,000
Tennis	68	285,000
Handball or racquetball	95	398,000
Skiing (downhill)	95	398,000
Skiing (cross country)	108	452,000
Skating (moderate)	54	226,000
Canoeing (4 mph)	70	293,000
Mountain climbing	100	420,000
Golf	54	226,000

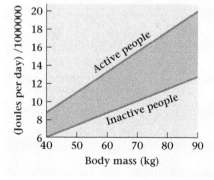

Figure B6.1 Sustaining energy versus body mass.

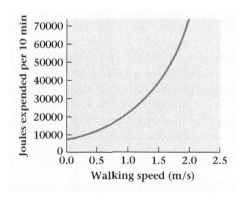

Figure B6.2 Rate of energy use as a function of walking speed.

Figure B6.3 Aerobic exercise burns quite a few Calories. This energy comes from the food you eat and store as fat in your body.

Solution We know from the statement of the problem that the volume per unit time is 70 cm^3 per 0.80 s (75 beats per minute is 0.80 second per beat). Using the expression just found for the speed, we may rewrite Eq. (6.19) as

$$P = Fv = F \frac{\text{volume}}{t\pi r^2}.$$

Substituting the numerical values gives

$$P = 5.0 \text{ N} \frac{(70 \text{ cm}^3)(10^{-6} \text{ m}^3/\text{cm}^3)}{(0.80 \text{ s})\pi(0.010 \text{ m})^2} = 1.4 \text{ N} \cdot \text{m/s}$$

$$P = 1.4 \text{ W}.$$

▼
Summary

Useful Concepts

■ The work done on an object by a force F acting over a distance x at an angle θ to the displacement is

$$W = Fx \cos \theta.$$

■ The work required to stretch a spring a distance x, and the energy stored in it, is

$$W = \tfrac{1}{2}kx^2.$$

■ Energy is the ability to do work.

■ An object's kinetic energy of translation is

$$\text{KE} = \tfrac{1}{2}mv^2.$$

■ According to the work-energy theorem, the work done on a particle by the net force acting on it is equal to the change in kinetic energy of the particle.

$$W = \Delta \text{KE} = \tfrac{1}{2}mv_2^2 - \tfrac{1}{2}mv_1^2.$$

■ The level from which you choose to measure an object's gravitational potential energy is arbitrary, but you must not change it while working a problem. The gravitational potential energy of a mass m at a height h near the earth's surface is given by

$$\text{PE} = mgh.$$

■ The potential energy stored in a spring (the elastic potential energy) is given by

$$\text{PE}_s = \tfrac{1}{2}kx^2,$$

where x is the displacement of the spring from its equilibrium position and k is the spring constant.

■ The work done by a conservative force acting on an object depends only on the initial and final positions of the object, not on the path taken. The sum of kinetic energy and potential energy is a constant if the forces are conservative. This is the law of conservation of mechanical energy.

$$\text{KE}_2 + \text{PE}_2 = \text{KE}_1 + \text{PE}_1$$

■ In the presence of frictional forces, the final mechanical energy is less than the initial mechanical energy. They differ by the work lost to friction:

$$E_{\text{initial}} = E_{\text{final}} + |W_{\text{friction}}|.$$

■ Power is defined as the rate of doing work:

$$P \equiv \frac{\Delta W}{\Delta t}.$$

Important Terms

You should be able to write the definition or meaning of each of the following terms:

work
joule
energy
kinetic energy
translational kinetic energy
work-energy theorem
potential energy
gravitational potential energy
elastic potential energy

conservative force
mechanical energy
conservation of
    mechanical energy
conservation laws
potential-energy diagram
dissipative forces
power
watt

Conceptual Questions

6.1 Why is no work done on an object when a force acting on the object does not move it?

6.2 Does the sun do work on the earth as it moves in its orbit?

6.3 A student rows upstream just fast enough to stay at rest with respect to the bank. Does the rower do work?

6.4 A car moves along the highway at a constant velocity, leading us to conclude that the net force on the car is zero. Discuss where, if anywhere, work is done.

6.5 What happens to the work done in stretching a spring?

6.6 A baseball and a Ping-Pong ball are thrown with the same velocity. Which one has the greater kinetic energy? Why?

6.7 Explain how a pile driver works.

6.8 Do you do the same work to lift a 1-kg weight through a vertical height of 1 m everywhere on the face of the earth?

6.9 Explain the basic ideas that govern the design and operation of a roller coaster. Under what conditions can successive hills be as high as or higher than the initial one?

6.10 Time yourself to see how long it takes you to do 10 deep knee bends. Then estimate how much work you do in lifting yourself back up each time. From these numbers, estimate the rate at which you were doing work.

6.11 Why do you shift to a lower gear to pedal a multispeed bicycle uphill? Do you save any energy in doing so?

6.12 Explain the observation that smaller cars generally get better fuel mileage than larger cars.

Problems

Sections 6.1 and 6.2 Work and Work Done by a Varying Force

Hints for Solving Problems

Be careful about signs: Work done on an object is positive, work done by the object is negative. A force in the direction of displacement does positive work; a force opposite to the direction of displacement does negative work; a force perpendicular to the displacement does zero work.

6.1 How much work does a 52-kg woman do against gravity when climbing from the bottom to the top of a 2.8-m-high staircase?

6.2 A gardener pushes a box of tools across a driveway by applying a 32.5-N force that pushes downward at an angle of 22.4° with respect to the horizontal. How much work is done if the box moves 2.25 m in the horizontal direction?

6.3 A 50-kg sled is pulled 20 m over the ice at a constant speed. The coefficient of friction between sled and ice is 0.13. (a) What is the frictional force? (b) How much work is done in pulling the sled the 20 m?

6.4 Two forces parallel to the x axis do 14.7 J of work on a small tray while moving it 20.7 m in the x direction across a gym floor. One of the forces has a value of $+3.89$ N in the x direction. What is the other force?

6.5 A worker does 300 J of work against a frictional retarding force of 15 N in pushing a power sweeper across a floor in 3.0 s. If the sweeper moves with constant speed, how fast is it going?

6.6 A person finds that he can stretch a spring exercise device 1.25 times as far as a friend can. (a) What is the ratio of the forces they can apply? (b) What is the ratio of the work they each do in stretching the spring?

6.7• A boy uses 75 J in pushing a sled a distance of 3.0 m across the snow, applying the force in a horizontal direction. (a) How much force is needed to push the same sled through the same distance if the force is applied in a downward direction of 45° with respect to the horizontal? (b) How much force is required if it is applied in an upward direction of 45°? Assume that the work required in parts (a) and (b) is the same as that required when the force is applied horizontally.

6.8• A spring requires 46.1 J of work to extend it 12.0 cm and 278 J of work to extend it 27.0 cm. Does the spring obey Hooke's law?

6.9• A constant horizontal force of 2.29 N is applied to a 1.82-kg block initially at rest on a friction-free surface. How much work is done on the block in the first 1.35 s after the force is applied?

6.10• (a) How much work is needed to push a 132-kg packing crate a distance of 2.65 m up a frictionless inclined plane that makes an angle of 20.0° with the horizontal? (b) How much work would be required to move the crate the same distance if the coefficient of friction were 0.20?

6.11• How much work is done to move the 8.0-kg block 10 cm to the right if the spring is initially relaxed (Fig. 6.23)? The spring constant is 20 N/m, and the coefficient of friction between the block and the floor is 0.50.

6.12•• (a) A 50-kg gymnast stretches a vertical spring by 0.50 m when she hangs from it. How much energy is stored in the spring? (b) The spring is cut into two equal lengths, and the gymnast hangs from one section. In this case the spring stretches by 0.25 m. How much energy is stored in the spring this time?

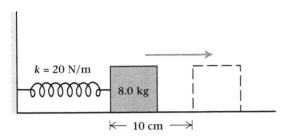

Figure 6.23
Problem 6.11.

6.13•• A net force acting on a large dictionary does 46.3 J of work in moving it a distance of 13.3 m along a frictionless surface that makes an angle of 36° with the horizontal x axis. The x component of the force is twice as large as the y (vertical) component. What are the magnitude and direction of the force vector?

Section 6.3 Energy

6.14 How many electricity-generating plants the size of Hoover Dam would be required to supply the total energy consumption of the United States? (Use the data in Table 6.2, p. 182.)

6.15 How many gallons of gasoline would it take to produce the electrical energy equal to that generated by Hoover Dam in one year? Assume that one third of the energy of the gasoline is converted to electrical energy and two thirds is lost.

6.16 (a) Approximately how many kilowatt-hours of electrical energy does one ton of coal produce if one third of the energy available is converted to electrical energy? (b) How many gallons of gasoline would be required to produce the same electrical energy? Again assume only one third of the available energy is converted to electrical energy. (Refer to the data in Table 6.2.)

6.17• The area of the United States (excluding Alaska and Hawaii) is approximately 3.5×10^6 mi². (a) Use the data in Table 6.3 to estimate the total solar power falling on this part of the United States. (b) Assuming a population of approximately 2.7×10^8 people, what area would have to be devoted to solar collectors with a 10% conversion efficiency in order to get all of the needed power from solar power? (c) What percentage of the area of the United States would be covered with solar collectors? (d) How does the answer to (b) compare with the area of the state in which you live?

Section 6.4 Kinetic Energy

6.18 (a) What is the kinetic energy of an 1800-kg car moving at 25 m/s? (b) At 120 km/h?

6.19 A 2.5-g Ping-Pong ball at rest is set in motion by the use of 1.8 J of energy. If all of the energy goes into the motion of the ball, what is the ball's maximum speed?

6.20 A 0.324-kg air-track glider moves linearly with an initial speed of 1.37 m/s. In order to increase the speed of the mass, 7.31 J of work are done. What is the final speed of the glider?

6.21 Sam can throw a baseball twice as fast as can his little brother, Bill. How many times as much kinetic energy can Sam give the baseball as Bill can?

6.22• How far does a 1.58-kg stone with a kinetic energy of 3.11 J go in 1.86 s if it is moving in a straight line?

6.23• (a) How much work is required to increase the speed of a 1200-kg automobile from 10 km/h to 30 km/h? (b) How much work is required to further increase the speed by the same amount, this time from 30 km/h to 50 km/h? Neglect the effects of friction.

6.24• A 1.03-kg hammer moving at 1.25 m/s drives a nail 0.752 cm into a board. What is the average resisting force?

6.25• Show for a satellite moving in a circular orbit about a center of gravitational attraction, such as the sun or earth, that the product of the orbital radius and the satellite's translational kinetic energy is a constant.

Section 6.5 Potential Energy

Hints for Solving Problems

Once you choose a reference level for gravitational potential energy, do not change it while solving the problem.

6.26 Two blocks of 6.00 kg and 2.00 kg are hung over a pulley on a rope, with the 6.00-kg block resting on the floor. What is the change in the potential energy of the system if the 6.00-kg block is raised 0.800 m?

6.27 How much potential energy with respect to ground level does a 10.0-kg lead weight have when it is 2.00 m above the surface of the ground?

6.28 A 0.302-kg coffee mug rests on a table top 0.740 m above the floor. (a) What is the potential energy of the mug with respect to the floor? (b) What is its potential energy with respect to a counter top 1.100 m above the floor?

6.29 A spring compressed by 0.080 m stores 150 J as elastic potential energy. What is the value of the spring constant k?

6.30 A spring hangs vertically from the ceiling. The spring extends an amount Δx when a mass m is hung from the spring's free end. Find an expression for the energy stored in the spring in terms of m, the acceleration of gravity g, and Δx.

6.31 A 750-g air-track glider slides along at a speed of 0.85 m/s until it hits a spring attached to the end of the very heavy track. The spring is compressed by 1.35 cm at the maximum compression. What is the value of the spring constant k?

6.32• By calculating the work done along each part of the path and adding the amounts (taking account of the signs), show that the work done in moving a 1.00-kg mass to a point 1.00 m over from and 1.00 m above its initial point is the same for all four paths shown in Fig. 6.24.

6.33• A constant force of 15.3 N acts upward on a iron block that weighs 11.7 N. (a) If the block is initially at rest, what is its kinetic energy 6.53 s after the force is applied? (b) What is the increase in the potential energy of the body 6.53 s after the force is applied?

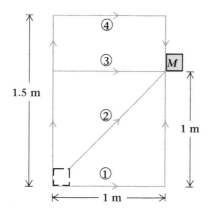

Figure 6.24
Problem 6.32.

6.34• A spring is extended by 2.35 cm when a mass of 0.250 kg is suspended from it. A second spring is extended twice as much (4.70 cm) when a mass M is suspended from it. If the energy stored in the two springs is the same (a) what is the value of the mass M and (b) how much energy is stored in each spring?

Section 6.6 Conservation of Mechanical Energy

Hints for Solving Problems

You should be careful to distinguish the initial and final states of a situation involving energy. Determine the potential energy and kinetic energy for each state. Then equate the initial mechanical energy to the final mechanical energy. Use energy conservation rather than kinematic methods to solve these problems.

6.35 A carpenter drops a hammer off the roof of a house. If the hammer falls a distance of 6.46 m, what is its speed just before striking the ground? Neglect air friction.
6.36 An ice cube slides from rest without friction down a long inclined ramp that makes an angle of 37.5° with the horizontal. What is the speed of the cube after it slides 1.27 m down the plane?
6.37 A block slides on a semicircular frictionless track (Fig. 6.25). If it starts from rest at position A, what is its speed at the point marked B?

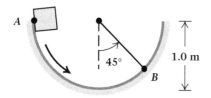

Figure 6.25
Problem 6.37.

6.38 An egg falls from a nest at a height of 3.08 m. What speed will it have when it is 0.50 m from the ground? Neglect air friction.
6.39 A baseball is thrown almost straight up at a speed of 12.3 m/s and falls back on the roof of a building 5.42 m above the height from which the ball was thrown. What is the speed of the ball just before it reaches the roof?
6.40 A block of mass m = 750 g is released from rest and slides down a frictionless track of height h = 55.2 cm. At the bottom of the track the block slides freely along a horizontal table until it hits a spring attached to a heavy, immovable wall (Fig. 6.26). The spring compressed by 2.64 cm at the maximum compression. What is the value of the spring constant k?

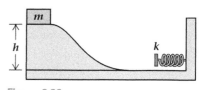

Figure 6.26
Problem 6.40.

6.41• Suppose the roller coaster car in Fig. 6.27 starts from rest at point A and moves without friction. (a) How fast is it going at points B, C, and D? (b) What constant deceleration must be applied at D to have it stop at E?

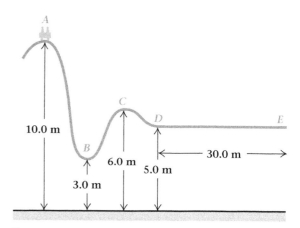

Figure 6.27
Problem 6.41.

6.42• A box of mass M is pushed at a constant speed for a distance s up an incline by a force parallel to the incline. The incline makes an angle θ above the horizontal and the coefficient of friction between the box and the surface is μ.
(a) Draw a diagram of the situation. (b) Draw a free-body diagram. (c) Derive the equation for the work done.
6.43• A classroom demonstration is performed with an Atwood machine. The masses are m_1 = 1.00 kg and m_2 = 1.10 kg (Fig. 6.28). If the larger mass descends a distance of

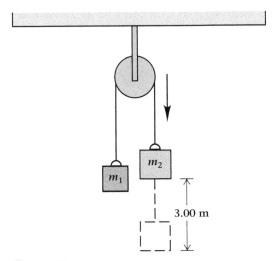

Figure 6.28
Problem 6.43.

3.00 m to the floor, what is the speed of the mass just before it hits?

6.44• From what height must a car be dropped to give it the same kinetic energy just before impact that it has when traveling at 60 km/h?

6.45• A 500-kg roller coaster starts from rest at point *A* (Fig. 6.29) and rolls freely (no friction) to point *B* where the brakes are applied and it slides along horizontally with a frictional force of 440 N. How far does the coaster slide past point *B* before coming to rest?

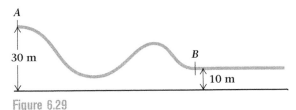

Figure 6.29
Problem 6.45.

6.46• A hammer dropped from rest by an astronaut from a height of 1.47 m above the surface of a planet has a speed of 4.1 m/s when it reaches a height of 0.32 m. Is the planet earth?

6.47• A block slides on a semicircular frictionless track (Fig. 6.30). (a) If it starts from rest at point *A*, what is its speed when it reaches the bottom of the track at point *B*? (b) Draw a free-body diagram of the block at the instant it is at point *B*. (c) What force does the track exert on the block when it passes through point *B* if the block's mass is 1.00 kg?

6.48•• Two low-friction carts of equal mass are joined by a spring. When suspended vertically the spring is extended 6.25 cm beyond its normal length (Fig. 6.31). The carts are then placed on a track and pulled together by a string until the spring is compressed by 6.25 cm from its normal length.

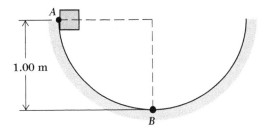

Figure 6.30
Problem 6.47.

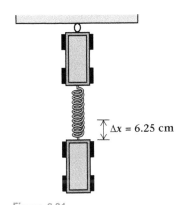

Figure 6.31
Problem 6.48.

When the string is cut, the carts move off in opposite directions. What are the speeds of the carts when the distance between them is equal to the unextended length of the spring? Ignore the mass of the spring and the friction in the carts.

6.49•• The block on the loop-the-loop in Fig. 6.32 slides without friction. From what height must it start at *A* so that it presses against the track at *B* with a net upward force equal to its own weight? Give your answer in terms of *R*.

6.50•• A small mass slides without friction down the loop-the-loop track shown in Fig. 6.32. (a) Show that the speed at

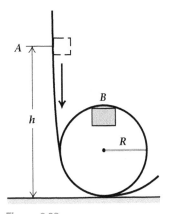

Figure 6.32
Problems 6.49 and 6.50.

point B must be at least as large as $\sqrt{gR}$ if the mass does not fall away from the track. (b) What must be the height h required to achieve the speed found in part (a)? Give your answers in terms of R.

*Section 6.7 Energy Conservation with Nonconservative Forces

6.51 A 30-kg suitcase falls from a hot-air balloon at a height of 1000 m. (a) If it loses 90% of its initial potential energy through friction with the air, what kinetic energy does it have just before it strikes the ground? (b) What speed does it have just before it strikes the ground?

6.52• A 4.20-kg box of books is pulled up a 4.06-m-long inclined plank to a height of 1.50 m. A force of 21.6 N parallel to the incline is needed to pull the box up the plank. (a) How much work is done by the 21.6-N force and (b) what percentage of that is lost to friction?

6.53• A 5.00-kg object slides down an inclined board from a height of 2.05 m to the ground, losing 10.0% of its energy to friction. What is its speed when it reaches the ground?

6.54• Assume that the force of friction between a shuffleboard puck and the playing surface is constant. Use the principle of energy conservation to show that a puck with an initial speed v will go a distance d before coming to a stop, where

$$d = \frac{v^2}{2\mu g}$$

and μ is the coefficient of friction.

6.55•• A wooden block placed at the end of a flat wooden board of length L begins to slide down the board when it is tilted to an angle of 34° from the horizontal. The block slides at a constant speed all the way to the other end of the board. (a) What is the change in potential energy of the block when it goes from the high end to the low end? (b) What is the work done against the force of friction? (c) Explain why your answers to (a) and (b) are the same or different. What assumptions have you made in working the problem?

Section 6.8 Power

6.56 (a) What is the engine power in kilowatts of a 108-hp Honda Civic CRX? (b) Of a 210-hp Ford Thunderbird SC? (c) Of Kyle Petty's 640-hp Winston Cup Pontiac race car?

6.57 About how many storage batteries would an electric car need in order to develop 80 hp? (Assume conventional electric batteries can deliver energy on a continuous basis at a rate of about 300 W.)

6.58 The 4.21-kg weight that drives the time mechanism of a grandfather clock descends 17.0 cm in exactly 24 hours. What power is delivered to the mechanism?

6.59 An astronaut with space suit has a mass of 110 kg. Climbing up a hill 7.3 m high in 7.2 s requires the astronaut to expend a power of 200 W. Is the astronaut on the earth?

6.60 An electric motor that can develop 1.0 hp is used to lift a mass of 25 kg through a distance of 10 m. What is the minimum time in which it can do this?

6.61 If electricity costs $0.083 per kilowatt-hour, how much does it cost to use a 250-W light bulb for 12 h?

6.62 An automobile engine develops 30 hp in moving the automobile at a constant speed of 50 mi/h. What is the average retarding force due to such things as wind resistance, internal friction, and tire friction?

6.63• Niagara Falls is about 53 m high. An estimated 6.0×10^6 kg of water pass over the falls every second. If all this energy were usefully employed, what power could be produced?

6.64• The force needed to pull the tape through an audio cassette player is 0.98 N. In operation the tape travels at a constant speed of $1\frac{7}{8}$ in./s. The motor consumes a power of 1.8 W. What percentage of the power input to the motor is required to pull the tape at its operating speed?

6.65• A 2150-kg loaded elevator moving with a constant speed rises 28 m in 15 s. The frictional force with the guide rails is a constant 1534 N. What power is required?

6.66•• A force of 125 N is needed to keep a small boat moving at 2.14 m/s. (a) What is the power required to keep the boat moving at the steady speed? (b) If the resistive force of the water increases with the square of the speed, what power is required if the speed is increased by 50%?

6.67•• A 73-kg person expends 400 W when walking on a level treadmill at a speed of 7.2 km/h. When the treadmill is inclined without changing the speed, the person's expended power increases to 600 W. Estimate the angle of incline of the treadmill by assuming that all of the increased output power goes into overcoming the force of gravity.

6.68•• Show that the height h to which an animal of mass m can jump is given approximately by

$$h = \frac{1}{2g}\left(\frac{4sP}{m}\right)^{\frac{2}{3}},$$

where P is the power expended and s is the distance over which the animal accelerates.

Additional Problems

6.69 A force of 24.3 N is needed to hold a spring extended 5.66 cm from its equilibrium position. How much work is done in extending the spring?

6.70 How many horsepower are developed when a 2.25-kg book is lifted 0.520 m in 2.00 s?

6.71• A 30-cm-long crank is attached to a simple machine that lifts a 210-kg load. The efficiency of a machine is the ratio of the output work to the input work, and its mechanical advantage is defined to be the ratio of the output force to the input force. When the crank turns through 400 complete revolutions by the application of a 12-N force perpendicular to the crank arm, the load is raised by 4.0 m. (a) What is the efficiency of the machine? (b) What is the mechanical advantage of the machine?

6.72• Simple machines such as levers, wedges, and pulleys allow a small force moved through a large distance to be transformed into a large force that acts through a small distance. The efficiency of a machine is the ratio of the output work to the input work, and its mechanical advantage is defined to be the ratio of the output force to the input force. Calculate the mechanical advantage of a crowbar used as a 100% efficient lever if the lifting end is 3.0 cm from the pivot and the input force is applied 50 cm from the pivot.

6.73• A stone thrown downward with a speed of 15.7 m/s from a height of 12.7 m above the ground has a kinetic energy of 293 J when it is 1.29 m above the ground. What is the mass of the stone?

6.74• A 40-kg child sits in a swing suspended with 2.5-m-long ropes. The swing is held aside so that the ropes make an angle of 15° with the vertical. Use conservation of energy to determine the speed the child will have at the bottom of the arc when she is let go.

6.75•• A force is given by $F = kx^2$, where x is in meters and $k = 10$ N/m^2. What is the work done by this force when it acts from $x = 0$ to $x = 0.1$ m? (Try using a graphical technique.)

6.76•• A 0.039-kg ball swings on the end of a 1.27-m-long string. On one swing the tension in the string is 0.435 N at the lowest point. By the second swing the ball has lost 3.1% of its energy. What is the ball's speed at the lowest point on the second swing?

6.77•• A 0.437-kg croquet ball depresses the pan of a spring balance 10.0 mm when resting upon it. If the croquet ball is then dropped from a height of 20.0 cm above the empty pan, how far will the pan be depressed if all the energy of the croquet ball goes into compressing the spring? (The energy in a compressed or stretched spring is the same for the same displacement.)

6.78•• The block in Fig. 6.33 is initially at rest on an inclined plane at the equilibrium position that it would have if there were no friction between the block and the plane. How much work is required to move the block 10 cm down the plane (a) if the frictional coefficient is $\mu = 0$ and (b) if the frictional coefficient is $\mu = 0.17$?

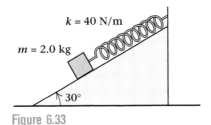

Figure 6.33
Problem 6.78.

6.79•• The 5.0-kg mass in Fig. 6.34 is released from rest 1.0 m above the floor. If the coefficient of friction between the

2.0-kg mass and the table is 0.28, what is the speed of the 5.0-kg mass just before it strikes the floor?

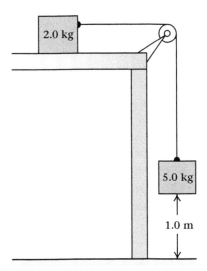

Figure 6.34
Problem 6.79.

6.80•• A 1300-kg car uses 15% more horsepower to travel 20 km/hr up a 5% grade than to travel at the same speed on a level surface? What is the average resisting force due to friction?

6.81•• Two masses are joined by a light cord that passes over frictionless pulleys as shown in Fig. 6.35. The 0.50-kg mass is pulled aside so that the cord makes an angle θ with the vertical and then it is released. What must be the angle θ for the 1.00 kg mass to just be lifted from its resting place by the motion of the smaller mass?

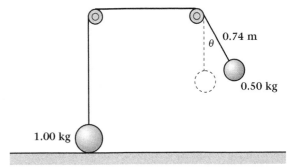

Figure 6.35
Problem 6.81.

7

7.1 Linear Momentum
7.2 Impulse
7.3 Newton's Laws and the Conservation of Momentum
7.4 Conservation of Momentum in One-Dimensional Collisions
7.5 Conservation of Momentum in Two- and Three-Dimensional Collisions
***7.6** Changing Mass

Linear Momentum

Nearly two decades before Newton's *Principia* was published, the Royal Society of London called for experimental studies of the behavior of colliding objects. Responses were received from several of Newton's contemporaries, including Sir Christopher Wren and Christiaan Huygens (1629–1695). Their observations led to the discovery of laws governing the exchange of momentum and energy between two colliding objects. These ideas were known to Newton and influenced his work. Their most important result was the law of conservation of linear momentum. According to this law, the total momentum after a collision is the same as the total momentum before the collision. This law made a key contribution to the growing understanding of mechanics.

Momentum, as stated in Newton's second law, is often called linear momentum to distinguish it from the angular momentum associated with rotational motion, which we will discuss in Chapter 9. The independent laws concerning the conservation of energy and of linear momentum are among the most basic laws in contemporary physics. Although we will derive these laws from Newton's laws of motion, in some respects they are even more fundamental and far-reaching than Newton's laws. For example, even in situations where Newton's laws do not apply, such as speeds approaching the speed of light or dimensions on atomic scales, these conservation laws are still valid. The use of conservation laws is one of the most fundamental ways of describing nature.

For simplicity, we focus on one conservation law at a time. Here we want to emphasize the conservation of momentum. However, in some cases we will first apply conservation of momentum and then use conservation of mechanical energy. In the next chapter we will examine collisions in which the laws of conservation of momentum and of conservation of kinetic energy are applied simultaneously. ■

7.1 Linear Momentum

The concept of momentum, which we first introduced in Chapter 4, Section 4.4, is extremely important in physics. Whenever we examine a moving object, we must consider both its mass and its velocity. The **linear momentum** of a body with mass m, traveling with velocity $\mathbf{v}$, is defined to be the product of the mass and the velocity. Since mass is a scalar quantity and velocity is a vector quantity, their product, momentum (which we designate with the letter $\mathbf{p}$) is a vector quantity:

$$\mathbf{p} \equiv m\mathbf{v}. \tag{7.1}$$

The word *momentum* (pl. *momenta*) is Latin and means "movement" or "moving power."

Most of us are intuitively aware of the importance of momentum in understanding the behavior of moving objects. For example, consider the difference between being hit by a bicycle traveling at 10 m/s (22 mi/h) and being hit by a locomotive traveling at the same velocity. We see that the mass of an object is an important consideration! Velocity is also important; just think of the difference between being hit by a baseball thrown by a child and being hit by a baseball thrown by a major league pitcher.

7.2 Impulse

When a baseball hits a bat (Fig. 7.1) or when two billiard balls collide, they exert forces on each other over a very short time interval. Forces of this type, which exist only over a very short time, are often called impulsive forces. Let's examine such forces to see how they are related to momentum.

In Chapter 4, we introduced Newton's second law in the form

$$\mathbf{F} = \frac{\Delta(m\mathbf{v})}{\Delta t} = \frac{\Delta \mathbf{p}}{\Delta t},$$

where $\mathbf{F}$ is the net force applied to an object and $\Delta \mathbf{p}$ is its change in momentum during a time Δt. If we multiply both sides of this equation by the time interval Δt, we get

$$\mathbf{F}\Delta t = \Delta \mathbf{p}. \tag{7.2}$$

Figure 7.1

A bat striking a baseball. The interaction takes place over a very small time interval.

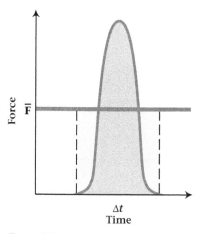

Figure 7.2

Average and instantaneous force during a typical brief collision between two moving bodies. The area under the curve of force versus time is equal to the impulse. Since the area of the rectangle whose height is the average force equals the area under the curve, we can replace the instantaneous force by the average force to obtain the impulse.

The quantity on the left, $\mathbf{F}\Delta t$, is called the **impulse.** It is the product of the force $\mathbf{F}$ and the time interval Δt over which the force acts. Even though the force occurs very briefly, the force is not usually constant over the time interval (Fig. 7.2). Nevertheless, the impulse is equal to the area under the force-time curve. Even if we don't know the exact shape of the force curve, we can replace the force in Eq. (7.2) with the average force $\overline{\mathbf{F}}$ over the time of interaction Δt:

$$\overline{\mathbf{F}}\Delta t = \Delta \mathbf{p}. \tag{7.3}$$

The usefulness of the impulse concept is illustrated in the two following examples.

Example 7.1

Using the following data, determine the average force on a baseball hit by a bat. The baseball has a mass of 0.14 kg and an initial speed of 30 m/s. It rebounds from the bat with a speed of 40 m/s in the opposite direction and is in contact with the bat for 0.0020 s. (High-speed photographs can be used to determine the contact time.)

Solution Since the mass of the ball is constant, we can rewrite Eq. (7.3) as

$$\overline{F} = \frac{\Delta p}{\Delta t} = \frac{\Delta(mv)}{\Delta t} = \frac{m\,\Delta v}{\Delta t}$$

$$\overline{F} = \frac{m(v_{\text{final}} - v_{\text{initial}})}{\Delta t}.$$

We choose the direction of v_{final} as positive; then v_{initial} must be negative. The change in momentum becomes

$$m\,\Delta v = m(v_{\text{final}} - v_{\text{initial}}) = 0.14 \text{ kg}[40 \text{ m/s} - (-30 \text{ m/s})]$$
$$= (0.14 \text{ kg})(70 \text{ m/s}).$$

The average force is then

$$\overline{F} = \frac{(0.14 \text{ kg})(70 \text{ m/s})}{0.0020 \text{ s}} = 4900 \text{ kg} \cdot \text{m/s}^2 = 4900 \text{ N}.$$

Typically, the maximum force is much greater than the average force, as shown in Fig. 7.2.

Example 7.2

A 51-kg teenager jumps to the ground from a chair 0.34 m high (Fig. 7.3). If she bends her knees slightly on landing, lowering herself by only 8.0 cm, what is the average force with which her feet hit the ground?

Strategy First, if we know the girl's momentum just before striking the ground, we can compute her change in momentum and thus the impulse involved. To determine her momentum, we need to know her speed just before she hits the ground. We obtain it from the kinematic relation in Eq. (2.9),

$$v^2 = v_0^2 + 2gh,$$

where g is the gravitational acceleration, h is the height of the chair, v is the speed just before striking the ground, and v_0 is her initial vertical speed. If we take $v_0 = 0$, the speed v becomes $v = \sqrt{2gh}$.

Second, if we know the time interval during which the impulse acts, we can determine the average force. The force of landing acts over the time during which the girl bends her knees to absorb the shock. If we assume the deceleration to be constant, then the slowing-down distance d is given by the product of the average speed and the time:

$$d = \frac{(v_i + v_f)}{2} \Delta t.$$

Here the initial speed when her feet contact the ground is $v_i = v$ and the final speed v_f is zero, so $d = (v/2)\Delta t$. The time over which the slowing-down, or knee-bending, process takes place is $\Delta t = 2d/v$. Because we can determine both the time interval and the change in momentum, we can compute the average force.

Solution The girl's momentum changes from its initial value at the moment her feet strike the ground to a value of zero at the end of the knee flexing. So we may write the change of momentum as

$$\Delta p = p_{\text{final}} - p_{\text{initial}} = 0 - mv = -mv.$$

The average impulsive force is

$$\overline{F} = \frac{\Delta p}{\Delta t}.$$

Upon substituting $-mv$ for Δp and $2d/v$ for Δt, we get

$$\overline{F} = \frac{-mv}{2d/v} = \frac{-mv^2}{2d}.$$

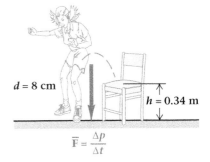

$$\mathbf{F} = \frac{\Delta p}{\Delta t}$$

Figure 7.3
Example 7.2: A person jumping from a chair to the ground bends her knees to absorb the shock.

Using $v = \sqrt{2gh}$, we find

$$\overline{F} = \frac{-m(\sqrt{2gh})^2}{2d} = -\frac{mgh}{d}.$$

Now insert the numerical values, including $g = 9.81$ m/s^2, to get

$$\overline{F} = \frac{-(51 \text{ kg})(9.81 \text{ m/s}^2)(0.34 \text{ m})}{0.080 \text{ m}} = -2100 \text{ N (about 480 lb)}.$$

Discussion We see from the expression $\overline{F} = mgh/d$ that the impulsive force is inversely proportional to the knee-bending distance d. A greater amount of bending reduces the average force, whereas a smaller amount increases the force. If the girl had landed with her knees locked, the force would have been so large that she might have suffered one or more broken bones. The force we have just calculated is the impulsive force that changes her momentum. In addition, there is a contribution due to her weight (even when she is standing still), but we have neglected it in this calculation.

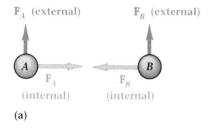

(a)

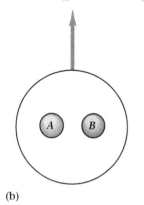

(b)

Figure 7.4
A system of two interacting bodies.
(a) Considered individually, each body is subject to a net force composed of two forces: one external and one internal due to the other body.
(b) Considered as a system, the net force on the two bodies is just the sum of the external forces.

7.3 Newton's Laws and the Conservation of Momentum

You already know that the velocity of a single particle or object does not change unless there is a net force acting on it. If there is no force acting on the object, its momentum is constant with time. We express this fact by saying that the object's momentum is conserved. In this section we first consider the motion of a single particle or object. Then we examine the motion of a system of interacting objects.

If a single object of mass m is subject to zero net force, Newton's second law states that the rate of change of momentum with time is zero. This is equivalent to saying that *the object's momentum remains constant when the net force acting on it is zero.* That is, if

$$\frac{\Delta \mathbf{p}}{\Delta t} = \mathbf{F} = 0,$$

then

$$\mathbf{p} = m\mathbf{v} = \text{constant}.$$

Most interesting physical systems consist of two or more objects interacting with one another. For such systems we can apply Newton's laws to each individual object. In doing so we find that while the momenta of the individual objects may change, *the total momentum of the system is constant whenever the net external force on the system is zero.* The effect of the internal forces of interaction among the objects is to exchange momentum among them in such a way that the total momentum is conserved.

To see how this result arises, consider the behavior of the two interacting bodies in Fig. 7.4. We are free to consider each of them independently (part a) or to regard them together as a system (part b). We can write the total force on one body as the sum of the forces exerted from outside the system (the external force) plus the force exerted on it by the other body inside the system (the internal force). Thus the total force on one body, say body A, is

$$\mathbf{F}_A \text{ (total)} = \mathbf{F}_A \text{ (internal)} + \mathbf{F}_A \text{ (external)}.$$

The force on the other body is

$$\mathbf{F}_B \text{ (total)} = \mathbf{F}_B \text{ (internal)} + \mathbf{F}_B \text{ (external)}.$$

The internal forces make up an action-reaction pair and, by Newton's third law, are equal in magnitude but opposite in direction. As a result, the sum of the internal forces is zero. Consequently, if we add up these two equations, we find that the net force on the system is just the sum of the external forces on the two bodies:

$$\mathbf{F} \text{ (total)} = \mathbf{F}_A \text{ (external)} + \mathbf{F}_B \text{ (external)}$$

The total rate of change of the system's momentum is equal to the sum of the external forces and is independent of the internal forces. We can express this result as

$$\mathbf{F}_{\text{net}} = \frac{\Delta \mathbf{p}}{\Delta t}, \tag{7.4}$$

where $\mathbf{F}_{\text{net}}$ is the net external force and $\mathbf{p}$ is the total momentum of the system. Equation (7.4) is the extension of Newton's second law to a system of two

---

Master the Concept

Momentum Conservation

Question: When a basketball player leaps high for the ball, he suddenly gets an upward momentum. How do you reconcile this observation with the law of conservation of momentum?

Answer: In order to jump, the player must push against the floor. In doing so the earth recoils as the player moves up. The momentum imparted to the earth has the same magnitude but opposite direction as that of the player. However, because the mass of the earth is so very much larger than the mass of the player, the earth's recoil velocity is too small to be noticed. Nevertheless, the total momentum is conserved.

Question: At the top of the leap the player's momentum changes direction. How do you reconcile this observation with the law of conservation of momentum?

Answer: The force of gravity acts on the player throughout the jump. It is this force that alters the player's momentum during the jump. If we only consider the motion of the player, then the gravitational force is an external force and the law of momentum conservation is not appropriate. However, let us consider the system that includes both the player and the earth. Gravity acts on each as equal-but-opposite internal forces in accord with Newton's third law. The combined momentum of the player and the earth remains constant as expected from the law of conservation of momentum: the total momentum of a system is constant when the net external force on the system is zero.

bodies. By similar reasoning we can extend it to include systems of three, four, or any number of bodies. In all cases, **when the net external force on a system is zero, the total momentum of that system is constant.** This is a statement of the law of **conservation of linear momentum.**

As we said earlier, conservation of linear momentum is one of the most useful laws in physics, enabling us to determine the momentum of a system after an interaction without needing to know all the details of the interaction. We will illustrate the application of momentum conservation with examples in the next few sections.

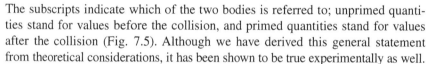

7.4 Conservation of Momentum in One-Dimensional Collisions

Christiaan Huygens and others knew of momentum conservation even before Newton published the *Principia.* The results of Huygens's investigations of collisions independently led to the following statement of the law of conservation of linear momentum: *Provided there are no external forces acting on a system, the total momentum before collision equals the total momentum after collision.* For a collision involving two bodies, the conservation law can be expressed symbolically as

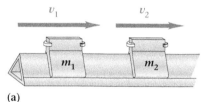

(a)

$$m_1\mathbf{v}_1 + m_2\mathbf{v}_2 = m_1\mathbf{v}'_1 + m_2\mathbf{v}'_2. \tag{7.5}$$

The subscripts indicate which of the two bodies is referred to; unprimed quantities stand for values before the collision, and primed quantities stand for values after the collision (Fig. 7.5). Although we have derived this general statement from theoretical considerations, it has been shown to be true experimentally as well.

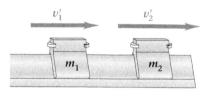

(b)

Figure 7.5
A one-dimensional collision of two gliders on an air track. (a) Before collision. (b) After collision.

Equation (7.5) is a statement of conservation of linear momentum that follows directly from Eq. (7.4). We will find it an especially useful version in problems involving collisions. Note that we do not need to know anything about the details of the collision mechanism itself. The rule holds for collisions between hard elastic bodies, such as billiard balls, as well as for collisions between soft bodies that do not "bounce" upon colliding, such as blobs of putty. In fact, in the absence of external forces, the law of conservation of momentum is observed to hold for any kind of collision on any scale, from subatomic to galactic.

Even though momentum is always conserved in collisions, kinetic energy may or may not be conserved. For this reason, we usually classify collisions according to whether kinetic energy is conserved or not. If kinetic energy is conserved during a collision, we call it an **elastic collision,** a situation approximated by the collisions between pool balls or glass marbles (Fig. 7.6). At the other extreme are collisions in which two objects stick together after impact. These collisions are known as **perfectly inelastic collisions.** A collision between two railroad cars that couple together upon impact is an example of a perfectly inelastic collision. In between are the **inelastic collisions** that are neither elastic nor perfectly inelastic. Because we can analyze perfectly inelastic collisions using only the law of conservation of momentum, we will consider them now. In the next chapter we will examine the somewhat more complicated case of elastic collisions in which both momentum and kinetic energy are conserved simultaneously.

Figure 7.6
Collisions between pool balls are approximately elastic.

First, let's simplify our discussion to just head-on, or one-dimensional, collisions. Suppose, for example, that we consider the *perfectly inelastic collision* of two gliders on a linear air track (Fig. 7.7). The air track allows us to control the gliders' motions so that they move only in one direction. This means that the vector equation for momentum conservation (Eq. 7.5) reduces to a single one-dimensional algebraic equation:

$$m_1 v_1 + m_2 v_2 = m_1 v_1' + m_2 v_2'.$$

If the collision is perfectly inelastic, the two bodies stick together and move off with the same velocity, $v_1' = v_2'$. We can immediately determine the final velocity in terms of the masses and the initial velocities.

Suppose that the glider of mass m_1 has an initial velocity v_1 and that glider m_2 has an initial velocity v_2 in the same direction. If $v_1 > v_2$, a collision occurs when glider m_1 overtakes glider m_2. If the gliders stick together after the collision, the final velocities m, are identical, so $v_1' = v_2' = v'$. Then the momentum equation becomes

$$m_1 v_1 + m_2 v_2 = (m_1 + m_2) v'.$$

Solving for the final velocity v', we get

$$v' = \frac{m_1 v_1 + m_2 v_2}{m_1 + m_2}$$

$$v' = \frac{m_1}{m_1 + m_2} v_1 + \frac{m_2}{m_1 + m_2} v_2.$$

This last equation reveals the significance of the restriction to perfectly inelastic collisions. If we know the masses and initial velocities, we can compute the final velocity readily from momentum considerations alone. If the collision is not perfectly inelastic, so that the two bodies do not stick together and therefore have different velocities after collision, then the more general equation (Eq. 7.5) applies. For collisions that are not perfectly inelastic, knowing the masses and initial velocities is not enough to determine the final velocities—we need more information. We consider this point again in Chapter 8.

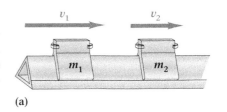

(a)

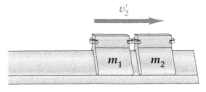

(b)

Figure 7.7
A one-dimensional collision of two gliders on an air track. (a) Before collision. (b) If putty or sticky tape is attached to their bumpers, the two gliders stick together. The resulting collision is perfectly inelastic.

▼

Problem-Solving Strategy

Conservation of Linear Momentum in One Dimension

Linear momentum is always conserved in any collision or event that is free from external forces. When applying the law of conservation of momentum the following steps are helpful.

1. Define a coordinate system and identify the velocities both in magnitude and direction.
2. Make a sketch of the situation including both "before" and "after" the collision.
3. Write the equation for the total momentum before and after the collision.
4. If the collision is perfectly inelastic, remember there is only one final velocity.

Example 7.3

In a safety test of automobile equipment, two cars of unequal mass undergo a head-on collision in which they stick together after the collision (Fig. 7.8). A Buick Park Avenue with a mass of 1660 kg and an initial velocity of 8.0 km/h strikes a 830-kg Geo Metro with a velocity of 10.0 km/h toward the first car. (a) What is the velocity of the combination immediately after collision? (b) How do the accelerations of the two cars during collision compare?

Strategy (a) We first choose a coordinate system. Let's take the direction of the Buick as the positive direction, and call its velocity v_1. Then $v_1 = 8.0$ km/h. Because the cars are traveling in opposite directions, the direction of the Geo is negative, $v_2 = -10.0$ km/h. The mass of the Buick is twice the mass of the Geo, so we can use m for the mass of the small car and $2m$ for the mass of the larger car. After impact, the cars stick together and thus move off with the same velocity. So, we can use the law of momentum conservation to find that single final velocity.

Solution (a) Because the collision is perfectly inelastic, the equation of momentum conservation becomes

$$m_1 v_1 + m_2 v_2 = (m_1 + m_2)v'.$$

If we set $m_1 = 2m$ and $m_2 = m$, the equation becomes

$$2m v_1 + m v_2 = (2m + m)v' = 3mv'.$$

The common factor of m can be eliminated to give

$$2v_1 + v_2 = 3v',$$

or

$$v' = \frac{2v_1 + v_2}{3}$$

$$v' = \frac{2(+8.0 \text{ km/h}) - 10.0 \text{ km/h}}{3} = +2.0 \text{ km/h}.$$

Figure 7.8
Example 7.3: A head-on collision between two cars of unequal mass.

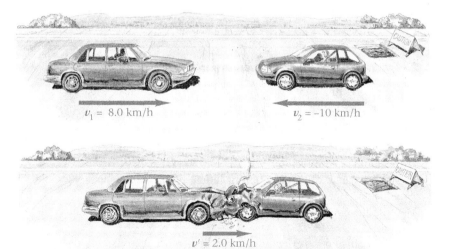

$v_1 = 8.0$ km/h $v_2 = -10$ km/h

$v' = 2.0$ km/h

The positive sign indicates that the final motion is in the same direction as the initial motion of the larger car.

(b) The change in velocity of the Buick is

$$\Delta v_{\text{large car}} = v_{\text{final}} - v_{\text{initial}} = +2.0 \text{ km/h} - 8.0 \text{ km/h} = -6.0 \text{ km/h}.$$

The change in velocity of the small car is

$$\Delta v_{\text{small car}} = v_{\text{final}} - v_{\text{initial}} = +2.0 \text{ km/h} - (-10.0 \text{ km/h}) = +12.0 \text{ km/h}.$$

The accelerations are given by $\Delta v/\Delta t$, where the collision time Δt is the same for both. Thus, the ratio of the accelerations is the ratio of the change in velocities. From our results we see that the magnitude of the small car's average acceleration is twice as great as the magnitude of the large car's acceleration.

Discussion Because total momentum is conserved, the change in momentum of the two cars is equal in magnitude but opposite in direction. The forces on the two cars must also be equal and opposite. What about the forces on the occupants of the cars? Are they the same? No, they are not. The force on a passenger is $\mathbf{F} = m\mathbf{a}$, where m is the mass of the passenger. The acceleration is proportional to the change in velocities. Thus, the occupants of the smaller car, who undergo an acceleration that is twice as great as that of the passengers of the larger car, experience greater forces. Consequently, the occupants of the smaller car are much more likely to experience serious injuries than are the occupants of the larger car.

▼

Example 7.4

A 60-kg ice skater is standing at rest on a frozen lake. The friction between his skates and the surface of the ice is negligible. If he throws a 2.0-kg block of ice horizontally with a velocity of 12 m/s, what is his recoil velocity?

Strategy This situation is essentially that of a perfectly inelastic collision run in reverse; that is, a system separates into two bodies with no net force acting on the system as a whole. (We can neglect the force of gravity because it acts along a direction perpendicular to the direction of separation.) Therefore, we can apply the law of conservation of momentum to find the skater's recoil velocity.

Solution The total momentum before the interaction is zero. Therefore, the total momentum afterward must also be zero. Writing the equation for momentum conservation, we get

$$0 = m_1 v_1' + m_2 v_2'.$$

If $m_1 v_1'$ is the momentum of the block of ice, then the skater recoils with a velocity

$$v_2' = -\frac{m_1 v_1'}{m_2}$$

$$v_2' = -\frac{(2.0 \text{ kg} \times 12 \text{ m/s})}{60 \text{ kg}} = -0.40 \text{ m/s}.$$

The negative sign indicates that the skater's motion is in the direction opposite to that in which the block of ice was thrown.

Example 7.5

A booster rocket and its payload are traveling at a speed of 900 m/s. An explosion separates the booster from the payload with a relative speed of 100 m/s, and the payload is thrown forward along the initial direction of motion. Find the velocity of the payload and of the booster immediately after they separate. Assume that the mass of the booster is four times that of the payload and that the effects of gravity are negligible.

Strategy We first draw a sketch of the rocket before and after the explosion (Fig. 7.9). If the mass of the payload is m, the mass of the booster is $4m$. Before the explosion, both pieces are attached and travel with the same velocity $v_i = 900$ m/s. After the explosion, the payload is thrown forward, so momentum transfer to the booster must be in the backward direction. Since the explosion provides internal forces, but not external force on the system of payload and booster together, we can solve this problem by applying the principle of momentum conservation.

Solution The initial momentum is

$$\text{momentum before} = (m + 4m)v_i = (5m)v_i.$$

After the separation, the momentum is

$$\text{momentum after} = mv_p + (4m)v_b,$$

where v_p = payload velocity and v_b = booster velocity. Conservation of momentum tells us that

$$\text{momentum before} = \text{momentum after},$$

or

$$(5m)v_i = mv_p + 4mv_b.$$

We have two unknown quantities, v_b and v_p, so we need another equation relating them. This is the statement of relative speed after the explosion:

$$\text{relative speed} = 100 \text{ m/s} = v_p - v_b.$$

Solving for v_p and inserting the result into the equation of momentum conservation, we get

$$5mv_i = m(v_b + 100 \text{ m/s}) + 4mv_b$$
$$= 5mv_b + m(100 \text{ m/s}),$$

which may be solved for the booster velocity:

$$v_b = v_i - 20 \text{ m/s} = 880 \text{ m/s}.$$

The payload velocity is 100 m/s faster, or

$$v_p = 980 \text{ m/s}.$$

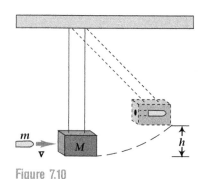

Figure 7.9
Example 7.5: A booster rocket separates from its payload.

v_i

v_b

$4\,m$

v_p

m

$v_p - v_b = 100$ m/s

Figure 7.10
Example 7.6: A ballistic pendulum. The height to which the block rises may be used to find the speed of a bullet fired into the block.

m

M

v

h

Example 7.6

Figure 7.10 shows a *ballistic pendulum,* a device invented by Benjamin Robins in 1742 to measure the speed of a bullet. The bullet is fired into a block of wood (or other material) suspended from two light strings or wires. The bullet is stopped by the block, making a perfectly inelastic collision. The block containing the bullet then swings until it reaches a height h. Show that the initial velocity of the bullet can be determined from a knowledge of the mass of the bullet, the mass of the block, and the height of the swing.

Strategy We can analyze this situation in two parts; the first is the inelastic collision of the bullet with the block, and the second is the swinging of the block on its strings. First we use the law of conservation of momentum to analyze the collision. Then we use the law of conservation of mechanical energy to examine the swing. Combining these analyses will allow us to determine the initial speed of the bullet.

Solution Initially the bullet of mass m has a velocity v while the block of mass M is at rest. If the collision time is short, the bullet comes to rest with respect to the block before the block moves appreciably. Thus, there are no external forces, so momentum is conserved. If we let V represent the velocity of the block and bullet immediately after the collision, we get

$$mv = (m + M)V.$$

After the collision, the block and bullet have a kinetic energy given by

$$KE = \tfrac{1}{2}(m + M)V^2.$$

The pendulum swings out, rising as it goes. As it does so, it exchanges kinetic energy for gravitational potential energy. When it reaches the maximum height h, it will have a potential energy $(m + M)gh$ that just equals the kinetic energy it had immediately after the collision. By equating this potential energy with the kinetic energy, we can evaluate V and in turn find the bullet velocity v:

$$\tfrac{1}{2}(m + M)V^2 = (m + M)gh,$$

so

$$V = \sqrt{2gh}.$$

When we put this expression for V in the equation for momentum conservation and solve for the bullet velocity v, we get

$$v = \frac{m + M}{m}\sqrt{2gh}.$$

Discussion Looking back over the solution, you can see that we applied separate conservation laws to separate parts of the problem. In the first part (the collision), momentum was conserved, but mechanical energy was not. In the second part (the swinging of the pendulum), mechanical energy was conserved. Nevertheless, when we combine the two parts we have enough information to uniquely determine the initial velocity of the bullet.

| 7.5 | **Conservation of Momentum in Two- and Three-Dimensional Collisions** |

In the previous examples, we limited ourselves to one-dimensional situations. However, in many common situations, such as collisions between billiard balls or air molecules, the objects move in different directions after the collision and it is necessary to consider two or three dimensions. Then the vector aspect of momentum becomes important. We first write out the general equations, simplify to two dimensions, and then consider a specific example. As before, provided that the net external force on the system is zero, we write the conservation rule as: *The momentum before collision equals the momentum after collision.*

In the general case, we could resolve each velocity vector in Eq. (7.5) into three mutually perpendicular components (v_x, v_y, v_z). For the vector equation to be true, the component equations must also be satisfied separately. As a consequence, the vector equation contains three independent statements, corresponding to its three components:

$$x \text{ component:} \quad m_1 v_{1x} + m_2 v_{2x} = m_1 v'_{1x} + m_2 v'_{2x}, \qquad (7.6a)$$

$$y \text{ component:} \quad m_1 v_{1y} + m_2 v_{2y} = m_1 v'_{1y} + m_2 v'_{2y}, \qquad (7.6b)$$

$$z \text{ component:} \quad m_1 v_{1z} + m_2 v_{2z} = m_1 v'_{1z} + m_2 v'_{2z}. \qquad (7.6c)$$

We have used two subscripts on each velocity component. The first subscript indicates whether the velocity is for mass 1 or mass 2, and the second subscript indicates which component (x, y, or z) of velocity is being considered. An example follows of a two-dimensional collision in which the x and y components are analyzed separately.

Example 7.7

Two cars approaching each other along streets that meet at a right angle collide at the intersection. After the crash, they stick together. If one car has a mass of 1450 kg and an initial speed of 11.5 m/s and the other has a mass of 1750 kg and an initial speed of 15.5 m/s, what will be their speed and direction immediately after impact?

Strategy The collision is perfectly inelastic. We can use the law of conservation of momentum to find the speed just after impact. We must choose a coordinate system. Call the lighter car number 1 with velocity $\mathbf{v}_1$ in the x direction, and let car number 2 have velocity $\mathbf{v}_2$ in the y direction (Fig. 7.11). Then we can find the final velocity $\mathbf{v}$ in terms of the initial velocities and masses.

Solution From conservation of momentum we get

$$m_1 \mathbf{v}_1 + m_2 \mathbf{v}_2 = (m_1 + m_2)\mathbf{v}.$$

If we separate this vector equation into components, we get

$$x \text{ component:} \quad m_1 v_1 = (m_1 + m_2)v_x,$$

$$v_x = \frac{m_1 v_1}{m_1 + m_2} = \frac{1450 \text{ kg} \times 11.5 \text{ m/s}}{(1450 + 1750) \text{ kg}} = 5.21 \text{ m/s},$$

and

$$y \text{ component:} \quad m_2 v_2 = (m_1 + m_2)v_y,$$

$$v_y = \frac{m_2 v_2}{m_1 + m_2} = \frac{1750 \text{ kg} \times 15.5 \text{ m/s}}{(1450 + 1750) \text{ kg}} = 8.48 \text{ m/s}.$$

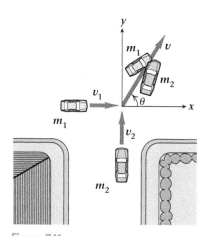

Figure 7.11
Example 7.7: A perfectly inelastic collision in two dimensions. The two cars stick together after impact.

The magnitude of the final velocity is

$$v = \sqrt{v_x^2 + v_y^2} = 9.95 \text{ m/s}.$$

The velocity **v** makes an angle with the x direction given by

$$\theta = \tan^{-1} \frac{v_y}{v_x} = 58.4°.$$

Thus, the two cars move off with a speed of 9.95 m/s at an angle of 58.4° from the initial direction of travel of the 1450-kg car.

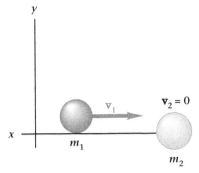

(a)

Consider the situation shown in Fig. 7.12, in which two objects collide but do not stick together after impact. The object m_1 with an initial velocity $\mathbf{v}_1$ strikes object m_2, initially at rest. These objects could be billiard balls, subatomic particles, whatever you like, and the two need not have the same mass. After the collision, we observe that object 1, which was initially in motion along the x direction, is now traveling with a velocity $\mathbf{v}_1'$ at an angle θ_1 with respect to the x direction. Can we determine the speed and direction of the second object?

The directions of the velocity vectors $\mathbf{v}_1$ and $\mathbf{v}_1'$ define a plane, which we may choose as the xy plane. There is no initial momentum in the z direction and $\mathbf{v}_1'$ has no z component, so there can be no z component of velocity associated with $\mathbf{v}_2'$. Thus $\mathbf{v}_2'$ must also lie in the xy plane. Because all the motion is in the xy plane—that is, over a flat surface—the problem is two-dimensional only. If we choose the x direction as the initial direction of $\mathbf{v}_1$, then the equations of momentum conservation reduce to

$$(p_x) \qquad m_1 v_{1x} = m_1 v_{1x}' + m_2 v_{2x}' \qquad (7.7a)$$

and

$$(p_y) \qquad 0 = m_1 v_{1y}' + m_2 v_{2y}'. \qquad (7.7b)$$

From these two equations we see that if we know the masses of the two objects, the velocity of the incident object, and the velocity components of one of the outgoing objects, then we can find the velocity components of the other object. Thus, we can indeed determine the speed and direction of the second object. An application of these equations is illustrated in the following example.

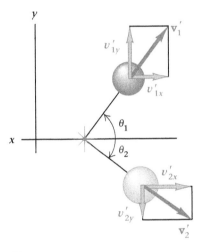

(b)

Figure 7.12

A collision in two dimensions. (a) Object m_1 moving in the x direction, object m_2 at rest. (b) Velocities after collision. Momentum is conserved in both the x and y directions.

▼

Problem-Solving Strategy

Conservation of Linear Momentum in Two Dimensions

The strategy that applies to momentum conservation in one dimension also applies in two dimensions. However, in two dimensions the velocities of each object must be resolved into x and y components. Then the equations for momentum conservation are applied separately for each direction.

Example 7.8

A billiard ball moving at 10.0 m/s along the positive x axis collides with a second billiard ball at rest. The balls have identical masses. After the collision, the incoming (or incident) ball moves on with a speed of 7.7 m/s at an angle of 40° from the x axis. What are the speed and direction of motion of the struck ball?

Solution We first determine the individual components of the final velocity of the second body, then calculate its direction of motion. In this example, $m_1 = m_2$, so the mass may be eliminated in Eq. (7.7). Referring to the diagram in Fig. 7.12(b), we see that the x component of velocity of the incident ball after collision is

$$v'_{1x} = v'_1 \cos \theta_1.$$

Substituting this equation into Eq. (7.7a), we obtain the x component of velocity of the struck ball,

$$v'_{2x} = (v_1 - v'_1 \cos \theta_1).$$

The y component of motion of the second ball is determined in a like manner. First, from the diagram we have

$$v'_{1y} = v'_1 \sin \theta_1,$$

which gives, upon substitution into Eq. (7.7b),

$$v'_{2y} = -v'_1 \sin \theta_1.$$

The minus sign indicates that the motion is in the negative y direction. The final speed and direction of the second body are now

$$v'_2 = \sqrt{(v'_{2x})^2 + (v'_{2y})^2} = \sqrt{(v_1 - v'_1 \cos \theta_1)^2 + (-v'_1 \sin \theta_1)^2},$$

$$\tan \theta_2 = \frac{v'_{2y}}{v'_{2x}} = \frac{-v'_1 \sin \theta_1}{v_1 - v'_1 \cos \theta_1}.$$

We can evaluate the speed and direction of mass 2 when the values for v_1, v'_1, and θ_1 are inserted into these equations. They give $v'_2 = 6.4$ m/s at $\theta_2 = 50°$ below the x axis. Note that we cannot determine the final velocities and angles from a knowledge of the initial conditions only, although it can be done in some special cases, as we will show in Chapter 8.

For a situation involving more than two bodies, we still have the same general principles. Figure 7.13 shows one such case, which is two-dimensional and involves the movement of three bodies. Two occupants of an ice sled simultaneously throw objects horizontally from the sled in different directions. The accompanying vector diagram shows the final momenta of the objects and the sled. To analyze the situation, we would write x and y components for the momenta, as before. Only now we would have three bodies in the equations, which would be extensions of Eq. (7.6).

(a)

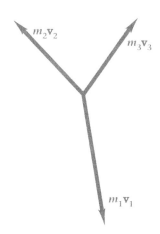

(b)

Figure 7.13

(a) Two occupants of a stationary ice sled simultaneously throw objects from the sled in different directions. The view is from directly overhead. (b) Momentum diagram for the situation of (a) after the objects have been thrown.

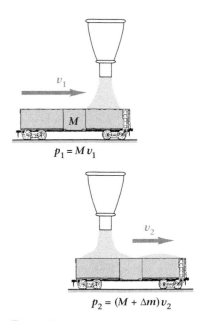

*7.6 Changing Mass

In Chapter 4 we considered the dynamics of bodies with constant mass. Because the mass was constant, it was relatively easy, when given the force, to find the acceleration and then the subsequent motion of the body. However, in many practical cases the mass is not constant.

An example of a system with changing mass is the railroad car of Fig. 7.14. The car is in motion while taking on sand at a constant rate. For simplicity, we assume that the car has some initial velocity, v_1, and rolls freely without any friction. It is not connected to a locomotive.

The initial momentum p_1 is the product of the mass of the car M and its initial velocity v_1,

$$p_1 = Mv_1.$$

Although the falling sand has zero initial speed in the horizontal direction, it is accelerated horizontally when it hits the moving car. The resulting action-reaction pair speeds up the sand while slowing down the car. After a time Δt, an amount of sand Δm has been added and the system (car plus sand) has a new velocity v_2. The corresponding momentum of the system is then

$$p_2 = (M + \Delta m)\, v_2.$$

The change in momentum is

$$p_2 - p_1 = Mv_2 + \Delta mv_2 - Mv_1 = M(v_2 - v_1) + \Delta mv_2,$$

which can be written as

$$\Delta p = M\Delta v + v_2 \Delta m.$$

If we divide through by Δt, we find the system's change in momentum per unit time is

$$\frac{\Delta p}{\Delta t} = M\frac{\Delta v}{\Delta t} + v_2 \frac{\Delta m}{\Delta t}.$$

But the change in momentum per unit time is equal to the net external force applied. Since there is no external force along the direction of motion, $\Delta p/\Delta t = 0$ and

$$M\frac{\Delta v}{\Delta t} = -v_2 \frac{\Delta m}{\Delta t}.$$

We see that $\Delta v/\Delta t$ is negative, as expected; the car is slowing down. If we wanted to keep the car moving with constant speed so that $v_1 = v_2$, then we would have to supply an external force $F = v_1 \Delta m/\Delta t$.

A second example of motion with changing mass is that of a rocket, whose mass diminishes as it consumes its fuel. Figure 7.15 represents the basic principle of rocket propulsion. Gases are expelled at high velocity from the rear of the rocket. Conservation of momentum for the rocket-gas system then requires a forward velocity of the rocket.

Figure 7.14

A railroad car in motion takes on sand from a stationary hopper. Momentum in the horizontal direction is conserved despite the system's changing mass.

Figure 7.15

The basic principle of rocket propulsion: Gas expelled from the rear of the rocket causes it to move forward, because of the conservation of momentum.

Because the force of gravity acts on an earthbound rocket, we cannot properly apply the principle of conservation of momentum without considering the earth-rocket system. For simplicity, let us imagine a rocket so far from the earth that we can neglect external forces. The rocket engine ejects gases at the rate of $\Delta m/\Delta t$ (where m is the mass of the fuel) at a velocity v_r with respect to the rocket. The velocity v_r is taken to be constant here. Thus, the magnitude of the reaction force on the rocket is

$$F_R = v_r \frac{\Delta m}{\Delta t}. \tag{7.8}$$

This force is called the *thrust* of the rocket motor. The direction of $\mathbf{F}_R$ is opposite to the direction in which the gases are expelled.

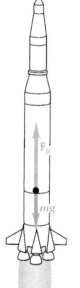

Figure 7.16
Example 7.9: The acceleration of a rocket depends on the net force acting on it.

Example 7.9

A fully fueled rocket with a total mass of 5000 kg is set to be fired vertically. If the rocket engine ejects its exhaust gases at a speed of 3.0×10^3 m/s and burns fuel at the rate of 50 kg/s, what is the rocket's initial upward acceleration?

Strategy   There are two forces that act on the rocket, the thrust of the engines that pushes upward and the gravitational attraction that pulls the rocket down (Fig. 7.16). The acceleration is a result of the net force that acts on the rocket.

Solution   The thrust F_R generated by the rocket engine is the burn rate times the exhaust velocity:

$$F_R = v_r \frac{\Delta m}{\Delta t} = (3.0 \times 10^3 \text{ m/s})(50 \text{ kg/s}) = 1.5 \times 10^5 \text{ N}.$$

If we call the upward direction positive, then the force, $\mathbf{F}_R$, of the rocket engine is positive and the force, mg, due to gravity is negative. The initial acceleration of the rocket is given by the net force divided by the initial mass:

$$a = \frac{F_{\text{net}}}{m} = \frac{F_R - mg}{m} = \frac{F_R}{m} - g = \frac{1.5 \times 10^5 \text{ N}}{5 \times 10^3 \text{ kg}} - 9.81 \text{ m/s}^2$$

$$a = 20 \text{ m/s}^2 \text{ upward.}$$

Summary

Useful Concepts

This chapter introduces a fundamental conservation law of physics.

■ *Conservation of linear momentum:* The total linear momentum of a system is constant whenever the net external force on the system is zero.

■ Linear momentum is given by

$$\mathbf{p} = m\mathbf{v}.$$

■ An impulsive force is related to the change in momentum by

$$\bar{\mathbf{F}}\Delta t = \Delta \mathbf{p}.$$

■ For two bodies in collision, the statement of conservation of momentum is

$$m_1\mathbf{v}_1 + m_2\mathbf{v}_2 = m_1\mathbf{v}_1' + m_2\mathbf{v}_2'.$$

■ In the case of a rocket engine with a changing mass m of burning fuel, the thrust is

$$F_R = v_r \frac{\Delta m}{\Delta t}.$$

This is a form of Newton's second law with variable mass, $F = \Delta(mv)/\Delta t$.

Important Terms

You should be able to write the definition or meaning of each of the following terms:

linear momentum
impulse
conservation of linear
  momentum

elastic collision
perfectly inelastic collision
inelastic collision

▼
Conceptual Questions

7.1 Discuss the usage of the word *momentum* in everyday conversation and compare it with the physical definition of momentum.

7.2 Explain the conservation of momentum that occurs when a fast-moving baseball is struck by a bat.

7.3 A golf club strikes a stationary golf ball and sends it flying. Which has the greater momentum change? Why?

7.4 You are in a cart loaded with bricks rolling without friction along a smooth straight track. What happens when you throw bricks (a) to the rear, (b) to the side, (c) or straight ahead?

7.5 A golf ball is thrown hard at a brick wall. A lump of soft clay with the same mass as the golf ball is thrown against the wall with the same initial velocity. Which of these events delivers the greater impulse to the wall?

7.6 What is the function of seat belts and air bags in automobiles? How do they reduce injuries?

7.7 When a balloon is blown up and released, it flies about as the air escapes. What makes it go?

7.8 The velocity of a bullet fired from a rifle held against the shooter's shoulder is measured very carefully. The rifle is then clamped to a massive bench so that it has no measurable recoil. How does that affect the velocity of the bullet?

7.9 Suppose you are holding the far end of a long garden hose of uniform diameter that extends straight from a faucet. Do you feel any force when the water is turned on? Would it make any difference if you bent the end of the hose through a 90° angle?

7.10 Why are the passengers in a bus less likely to be injured than passengers in a car in a collision of a bus with a car?

7.11 Sometimes when extinguishing a fire on a burning ship, a fireboat will have some of its nozzles pointing away from the fire. Why?

7.12 If the momentum of a system can only be changed by forces external to the system, how is it possible that a "Mexican jumping bean" can sometimes jump up from a table top?

7.13 Is it possible for two objects to simultaneously have identical kinetic energies and identical momenta? Explain your answer.

▼
Problems

Section 7.1 Linear Momentum

Hints for Solving Problems

Momentum is the product of mass and velocity. Although SI units are usually preferred, many of the problems in this section can be solved using mixed units such as kg · km/h.

7.1 What is the momentum of a 1500-kg Mercedes-Benz 300E traveling at 115.0 km/h?

7.2 (a) What is the momentum of a 109-kg football player running at a top speed of 9.86 m/s? (b) What is the momentum of a 9.72-g rifle bullet traveling at 728 m/s?

7.3 Which is greater, the momentum of a 1645-kg Cadillac DeVille traveling at 32 km/h or a 1061-kg Mazda Miata traveling at 47 km/h?

7.4 An 1.73-kg physics book flies through the air with a momentum of 18.8 kg · m/s. What is its speed?

7.5 (a) What is the ratio of the momentum of a 2.3×10^5-kg jet passenger airplane flying at 960 km/hr to that of a 1.1-kg pitching horseshoe moving at 11.3 m/s? (b) What is the ratio of their kinetic energies?

7.6 The momentum of an object traveling at 5.3 m/s is determined to be 350 kg · m/s. Could the moving object be an automobile?

7.7 A detector of subatomic particles measures the momentum of a particle directly, without the mass being known. In one experiment, the particle's momentum was determined to be 1.82×10^{-26} kg · m/s. (a) What was the particle's speed if it was an electron? (b) What was its speed if it was a proton? The masses can be found in the end sheets.

7.8 Show that the expression for kinetic energy can be written in terms of the momentum as

$$\text{KE} = \frac{p^2}{2m}.$$

7.9• What is the momentum of a 46.0-g golf ball just before it hits the ground when it is dropped from a height of 1.36 m?

7.10• A stone of mass m is dropped from rest at a height of 1.84 m. From what height would a stone of mass $m/2$ have to be dropped to have the same momentum upon striking the ground?

7.11• A 0.145-kg baseball is thrown horizontally at 3.38 m/s from a height of 3.67 m above level ground. (a) What is the ball's momentum immediately after it is thrown? (b) What is the ball's momentum just before it strikes the ground?

7.12•• A 0.500-kg stone is thrown upward in a parabolic path. The magnitude of the stone's momentum at the top of the path is one-half its initial value. (a) At what angle with respect to the horizontal direction is the stone thrown? (b) If the stone reaches a maximum height of 3.60 m above the point from which it started, what is the initial momentum?

7.13•• A 0.564-kg block and a 1.54-kg block are held 2.38 m above the ground. The 1.54-kg block is allowed to fall from rest. (a) With what downward speed must the 0.564-kg block be thrown so that just before it strikes the ground it has the same momentum as the heavier block just as it strikes the ground? (b) With what upward speed must the 0.564-kg block be thrown so that it will have the same momentum as does the heavier block just before it strikes the ground in part (a)?

Section 7.2 Impulse

Hints for Solving Problems

When calculating a change in momentum, be sure to be consistent in choice of signs and directions before and after the interaction.

7.14 A croquet mallet delivers an impulse of 8.83 N · s to a 0.44-kg croquet ball initially at rest. What is the speed of the ball immediately after being struck?

7.15 The engine of a model rocket is rated with a total impulse of 5.00 N · s and a thrust duration of 1.20 s. What is the average force exerted by the engine?

7.16 A 0.145-kg baseball traveling 35.2 m/s is stopped in 0.163 s by a catcher's mitt. (a) What is the average accelera-

tion of the ball? (b) What is the average force on the catcher's mitt?

7.17 A 68-kg soccer player kicks a stationary 0.425-kg ball giving it a speed of 13.7 m/s. The player's foot is in contact with the ball for 0.097 s. (a) What is the average force on the ball? (b) What is the average force on the player's foot?

7.18 A 0.14-kg baseball with an initial speed of 28 m/s rebounds with a speed of 34 m/s after being struck with a bat. If the duration of contact between ball and bat was 2.1 ms, what was the average force between ball and bat?

7.19 By expressing each quantity in terms of SI base units, show that the product of force and time has the same dimensions as momentum. (*Hint:* You may want to refer to Section 1.3, Unit Conversions.)

7.20• A person about to jump from a 1.60-m-high platform wants to limit the average stopping force on landing to 12 times her weight. By how much will it be necessary to lower herself by flexing her knees as she lands? (By stopping force we mean the force in excess of her weight.)

7.21• How much work did the girl in Example 7.2 (p. 213) do in stopping by bending her knees? Give an algebraic rather than a numeric answer. Compare that work with the original potential energy she had before she jumped.

7.22• A 1.2-kg hammer hits a nail at a speed of 20 m/s and rebounds at 80% of that speed. The resisting force of the nail is 8000 N. Approximately how long is the hammer in contact with the head of the nail?

7.23• A 0.437-kg croquet ball rolls without friction on a smooth surface with a speed of 1.39 m/s toward a mallet-wielding player. (a) What impulse is required to just stop the ball? (b) What impulse is required to send it in the opposite direction with the same speed? (c) What is the average force in each of the previous parts if the mallet and ball are in contact for 2.00 ms?

7.24• When a 0.64-kg ball is dropped on your hand from 0.73 m above it, your hand recoils 2.4 cm before stopping. What is the average total force on your hand while stopping the ball?

7.25•• A machine gun fires 12 bullets/s into a target. The speed of the 0.014-kg bullets is 731 m/s. What is the average force necessary to hold the gun still?

7.26•• A 0.140-kg block on a wooden table is given a sharp blow with a hammer. The block then slides across the table to a stop. The coefficient of friction between the block and table is 0.32. The hammer's force on the block as a function of time is well approximated by an isosceles triangle with its base on the horizontal time axis. The length of the base is 0.0072 s and the maximum force is 35.7 N. How far does the block go? Use a graphical technique.

7.27•• A plastic ball dropped onto a hard surface from a height of 1.4 m rebounds to 60% of its original height. Measurements of the average force during the time the ball is in contact with the surface show the total average force to be 10 times the weight of the ball. How long was the ball in contact with the surface?

Section 7.4 Conservation of Momentum in One-Dimensional Collisions

Hints for Solving Problems

Collisions can be treated in terms of the final and initial states. When there is no net force, the final momentum equals the initial momentum.

7.28 A 78-kg ice hockey player standing on a frictionless sheet of ice throws a 6.0-kg bowling ball horizontally with a speed of 3.0 m/s. With what speed does the hockey player recoil?

7.29 A 3.51-kg rifle fires a 9.72-g bullet with a velocity of 891 m/s. What is the recoil velocity of the rifle?

7.30 A child playing marbles shoots a marble directly at another marble at rest. The first marble stops, and the second marble continues in a straight line with the same speed that the first marble had initially. What is the ratio of the masses of the two marbles?

7.31 A 0.20-kg model railroad car moving with a speed of 0.24 m/s is struck from behind by an 0.42-kg model locomotive moving along the same line with a speed of 0.52 m/s. If they stick together after the collision, what is their velocity?

7.32• A light spring-gun projectile launcher is mounted on an 0.443 kg air-track glider. The gun points upward at an angle of 28° with the horizontal track. With the glider at rest, a 74.3-g projectile is fired from the gun with a speed of 2.96 m/s. What is the speed of the air-track glider after the gun is fired?

7.33• A projectile launcher mounted horizontally on a stationary air-track glider with total mass of 235 g fires a 54.8-g projectile that hits and sticks to an adjacent 347-g glider initially at rest? The speed of the projectile is 96.4 cm/s. What are the final speeds of both gliders?

7.34• A perfectly inelastic collision takes place between two objects, one of which is initially at rest. Does the ratio of the final total kinetic energy to the initial total kinetic energy depend on the speed of the initially moving object?

7.35• The 3.56-g bullet from a 22-250 rifle is fired into the 1.174-kg block of a ballistic pendulum (Fig. 7.10). The bullet sticks within the block, which swings back, rising 0.595 m. What was the speed of the bullet just before impact?

7.36• A ballistic pendulum is used to measure the speed of a 9.72-g rifle bullet. The 2.27-kg block of the pendulum is measured to rise 14 cm. However, because of the difficulty of determining the position of the block, there is an uncertainty of ±0.5 cm in the measurement of the height. What range of bullet velocity is consistent with these measurements?

7.37• A 3000-kg rocket and its 500-kg payload are traveling at a speed of 2000 m/s. The payload is thrown forward by an explosion that separates it from the rocket with a relative velocity of 140 m/s. (a) What is the velocity of the payload after separation? (b) What is the velocity of the rocket?

7.38• Two toy locomotives approach each other along the same line, and upon collision both stop dead still. If one locomotive has three times the speed of the other and the sum of their masses is 2.88 kg, what is the mass of each locomotive?

7.39•• A 25-g dart is thrown with a speed of 32 m/s at a 1.60-kg target mounted on a spring as shown in Fig. 7.17. The target recoils 2.4 cm. Assume the spring obeys Hooke's law and determine the spring constant.

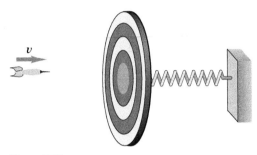

Figure 7.17
Problem 7.39.

7.40•• A 7.45-g bullet from a 9-mm pistol has a velocity of 353 m/s. It strikes the 0.725-kg block of a ballistic pendulum and passes completely through the block. If the block rises through a distance $h = 12.1$ cm, what was the velocity of the bullet as it emerged from the block?

7.41•• Two equal masses m are hung over a frictionless pulley as shown in Fig. 7.18. Another mass m is dropped onto one of the suspended masses from a height h above it. With what initial speed do the masses move immediately after the collision?

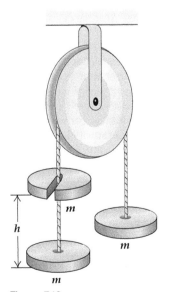

Figure 7.18
Problem 7.41.

7.42•• A ball of mass m is fired with velocity v_0 into the barrel of a spring gun of mass M initially at rest on a frictionless surface (Fig. 7.19). The ball sticks in the barrel at the point of maximum compression of the spring. No energy is lost to friction. What fraction of the ball's initial kinetic energy is stored in the spring?

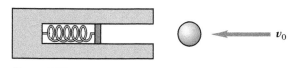

Figure 7.19
Problem 7.42.

Section 7.5 Conservation of Momentum in Two- and Three-Dimensional Collisions

Hints for Solving Problems

Treat conservation of momentum in the x direction independently from that in the y direction.

7.43 Two cars approach each other along streets that meet at a right angle. They collide at the intersection. After the collision they stick together. If one car has a mass of 1300 kg and an initial speed of 2.25 m/s and the other has a mass of 1800 kg and an initial speed of 4.50 m/s, what will be their speed and direction immediately after impact?

7.44 An Escort and a Camaro traveling at right angles collide and stick together. The Escort has a mass of 1200 kg and a speed of 30 km/h in the positive x direction before the collision. The Camaro has a mass of 1500 kg and was traveling in the positive y direction. After the collision, the two move off at an angle of 64° to the x axis. What was the speed of the Camaro?

7.45• A railroad track lies alongside a frozen lake. A railroad train moves along the track with a constant speed of 7.0 m/s. A boy on a frictionless ice sled is initially moving parallel to the train track with the same speed as the train and 10 m away from it. The boy and sled together weigh 100 kg, and the boy carries a 5.0-kg bag of sugar with him. At some time the boy tosses the sugar to a girl on the train with a velocity of 2.0 m/s perpendicular to the direction of his motion. The girl on the train catches the bag of sugar and immediately throws it back to the boy, who catches it. The girl on the train throws the bag of sugar perpendicular to her motion with the same speed at which she caught it. What are the final direction and speed of the boy and sled?

7.46• Two pendulums are hung adjacent to each other as shown in Fig. 7.20. Bob 1 has a mass m, and bob 2 has a mass $2m$. Bob 1 is pulled aside until the support string makes an angle of 45° with the vertical direction and then released. When the bobs collide, they stick together. What is the maxi-

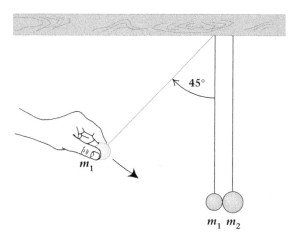

Figure 7.20
Problem 7.46.

mum angle made by the support strings with respect to the vertical after the collision?

7.47• A station wagon and a small car approaching each other at an angle, collide, and stick together after the collision. The station wagon has a mass 1820 kg and a speed of 30 km/h in the positive x direction. The car has a mass of 1060 kg and a speed of 25 km/h in a direction 135° from the x axis. With what velocity do they move off after the collision?

7.48• The ice sled in Fig. 7.13 is initially at rest. The two children on the sled each throw stones horizontally at the same time. The left-hand child throws a 0.87-kg stone with a speed of 2.1 m/s and the right-hand child throws her 0.23-kg stone with a speed of 5.4 m/s. The angle between the stones' paths is 75°. In what direction with respect to the 0.23-kg stone's path does the sled move? Assume that the sled moves without friction on the ice. (*Hint:* Choose a coordinate system with x along the direction of motion of the 0.23-kg stone.)

7.49•• A 7.2-kg bowling ball moving at 2.74 m/s strikes an identical ball that is originally at rest. After the collision the path of the initially moving ball makes an angle of 27° with respect to its original path. The path of the second ball makes an angle of −53° with respect to the same direction. What is the speed of each ball immediately after the collision?

7.50•• A 1000-kg car collides with a 1200-kg car that was initially at rest at the origin of an x-y coordinate system (Fig. 7.21). After the collision, the lighter car moves at 20 km/h in a direction of 30° with respect to the positive x axis. The heavier car moves at 12 km/h at −44° with respect to the positive x axis. What were the initial speed and direction of the lighter car?

*Section 7.6 Changing Mass

7.51 The initial mass of a rocket is 2.6×10^6 kg. A fuel-burning rate of 1.0×10^4 kg/s gives an initial acceleration of 1.5 m/s^2. What is the velocity of the exhaust gases? Assume the rocket is in free space.

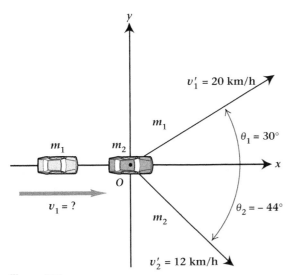

Figure 7.21
Problem 7.50.

7.52 What is the thrust of a rocket that burns fuel at a rate of 1.3×10^4 kg/s if the exhaust gases have a velocity of 2.5×10^3 m/s with respect to the rocket?

7.53 A 24-ton freight car rolls along a straight track with a speed of 10 mi/h. A 2.0-ton automobile falls vertically and lands on it from above and then falls off after a few moments. What is the final speed of the railroad car?

7.54 A 28,000-kg railroad car with an open top rolls along a straight track with a speed of 4.61 km/h. It passes under a waterfall that pours water straight into the car at a rate of 500 kg/s. How much force is necessary to keep the car traveling at constant speed? Assume that friction can be neglected.

7.55• A rocket with initial mass of 8.0×10^3 kg is fired vertically. Its exhaust gases have a relative velocity of 2.5×10^3 m/s and are ejected at a rate of 40 kg/s. (a) What is the initial acceleration of the rocket? (b) What is its acceleration after 20 s have elapsed?

7.56• A rocket with initial mass of 8.0×10^3 kg is fired in the vertical direction. Its exhaust gases are ejected at the rate of 45 kg/s with a relative velocity of 2.4×10^3 m/s. (a) What is the initial acceleration of the rocket? (b) What is the acceleration after 25 s have elapsed?

Additional Problems

7.57 A 0.14-kg baseball thrown with a speed of 25 m/s was hit with an average force of 4500 N. Afterward it had a velocity of 32 m/s in the opposite direction. How long was it in contact with the bat?

7.58 A proton with a speed of 2.36×10^6 m/s makes a signal in a modern particle detector that depends only on the proton's momentum. A subatomic particle called a D^+ meson is observed to leave the same momentum-dependent signal.

What is the speed of the D^+ meson? (You need only know the ratio of the masses. See Table 32.1, p. 1010.)

7.59 A 2.0-kg mass with a speed of 0.50 m/s collides head-on with a 1.5-kg mass moving with a speed of 0.30 m/s toward the first mass. After the collision, the 2.0-kg mass stops. What is the speed of the second mass after the collision?

7.60 In a crash test of automobiles, two cars of equal mass undergo a head-on collision in which they stick together after the collision. If the initial velocity of one car was 5.0 km/h and that of the second car was 8.0 km/h toward the first, what is the velocity of the combination immediately after collision?

7.61 A 0.46 kg golf ball dropped from rest at a height of 1.27 m rebounds to a height of 0.87 m. What is the change of the golf ball's momentum upon rebounding?

7.62• A baseball, thrown against a target that is free to move, rebounds from it with a speed 0.80 of its initial speed. The mass of the target is 20 times that of the baseball. If the baseball had an initial speed of 28 m/s, how far will the target move in 0.1 s?

7.63• A 9.72-g bullet is fired from a 30-30 rifle at a speed of 728 m/s into the 1.250-kg block of a ballistic pendulum suspended by strings 3.9 m long. (a) Through what vertical distance does the block rise? (b) How far does it swing horizontally?

7.64• A 0.046-kg golf ball was hit with an impulsive force that averaged 8000 N. If the ball was in contact with the club head for 5.0×10^{-4} s, what was the speed of the ball immediately after impact?

7.65• A bowling ball with initial velocity of v_0 strikes a stationary bowling ball a glancing blow. The first ball goes off in a direction $30°$ from the initial direction with a speed of 4.0 m/s. The second ball recoils in a direction $-45°$ from the initial direction with a speed of 3.0 m/s (Fig. 7.22). What is the ratio of the mass of the struck ball to that of the incident ball?

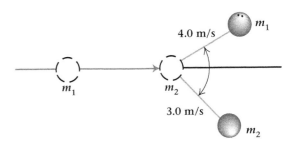

Figure 7.22
Problem 7.65.

7.66• A 900-kg car collides with a 1400-kg car that was initially at rest at the origin of an x-y coordinate system. After the collision, the lighter car moves at 20 km/h in a direction $40°$ with respect to the positive x axis. The heavier car moves at 10 km/h along the positive x axis. What were the initial speed and direction of the lighter car?

7.67• A bowling ball collides head-on with another bowling ball initially at rest. The first ball rebounds with a speed one-twentieth its original speed. The second ball moves off in the direction of the first ball's initial motion with a speed that is 95% of the original speed of the first ball. What is the ratio of the masses of the balls?

7.68•• A 1.0-kg toy car moves freely along a model railroad track with a speed of 0.50 m/s. An additional 0.20-kg mass is carried on the car in a device that projects the mass horizontally away from the car with a speed of 0.20 m/s relative to the initial motion of the car. Calculate the final velocity of the car along the track when the 0.20-kg mass is projected (a) in the same direction as the car's motion, (b) in the opposite direction from the car's motion, and (c) at right angles to the car's motion.

7.69•• In an introductory laboratory experiment, a 56.7-g steel ball is shot from a spring gun into the 203-g pendulum of a ballistic pendulum. The pendulum swings aside and is kept at its maximum height by mechanical means (Fig. 7.23). The change in height is measured to be 13.1 cm. (a) What is the velocity of the steel ball when fired from the spring gun? (b) The pendulum is then swung aside, and the gun is placed on a table so that it can be aimed horizontally to fire the ball into the room. If the ball leaves the gun at a height of 1.12 m from the floor, how far does it travel horizontally before hitting the floor?

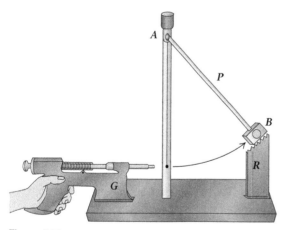

Figure 7.23
Problem 7.69: A ballistic pendulum consisting of a spring gun (*G*), a projectile (*B*), a pendulum (*P*) that pivots about axis (*A*), and a rack (*R*).

7.70•• A 15.2-g bullet hits a 0.463-kg block from below (Fig. 7.24). The initial speed of the bullet is 624 m/s and it emerges from the block at 131 m/s. (a) How high does the block rise? (b) If the block is 2.34-cm thick, estimate the average force on the block. Assume that the bullet passes completely through before the block moves appreciably.

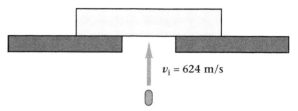

Figure 7.24
Problem 7.70.

7.71•• Hans Brinker, with a mass of 59 kg, is standing in the middle of a frozen lake of frictionless ice. He wants to reach the shore in the shortest possible time without skating. Hans has two 3.0-kg snowballs. He can throw snowballs with a relative speed of 10 m/s, regardless of their mass. Determine whether Hans should throw both masses at one time or throw one mass and then throw the other mass one second later. (If this is not a realistic question, state what is wrong with the assumptions made.)

7.72•• A 0.70-kg piece of modeling clay is held lightly in the extended fingers of the right hand 1.00 m above the floor. An identical piece of clay is dropped from the left hand held 0.80 m directly above the right hand. The falling piece hits and sticks to the other, and they continue together to the floor. (a) How long does it take for them to reach the floor? Call time zero the moment when the left-hand piece is released. (b) Is this more or less time than it would take the left-hand piece to fall straight to the floor if it had not struck the right-hand piece?

7.73•• A 0.350-kg air-track glider is set in motion by an electromechanical "pusher" doing 1.47 J of work on it. The moving glider then strikes another glider of the same mass that was at rest and sticks to it. (a) With what velocity does the pair of gliders move off? (b) What is the kinetic energy of the system after the collision? (c) Discuss your answer to part (b) and compare it with the original 1.47 J.

7.74•• Two cars approaching each other collide and stick together after the collision. One car has a mass 1820 kg and a speed of 30 km/h in the positive *x* direction. The second car has a mass of 1060 kg. After the collision they both move off with a speed of 18 km/h in a direction +37° from the *x* axis. What was the initial velocity of the second car?

7.75•• A 0.43-kg soccer ball resting on the ground is kicked so that it travels the maximum distance for the kicker's effort. It lands 42 m away from its initial position. If the kicker's shoe is in contact with the ball for 0.038 s, estimate the average force of the kick.

7.76•• A rocket with initial mass of 5.0×10^3 kg is fired vertically. Its exhaust gases are ejected at the rate of 30 kg/s with a relative velocity of 3.0×10^3 m/s. (a) Find the initial acceleration of the rocket. (b) How high does the rocket climb in 10 s? (*Hint:* Ignore the change in mass to perform this calculation.) (c) How would the answer to (b) change if you included the change in mass of the rocket?

7.77•• A model rocket handbook gives an approximate formula for the velocity v of a rocket at the time t at which the fuel burns out:

$$v = \left(\frac{F_R}{w_{ave}} - 1 \right) gt,$$

where F_R is the thrust of the rocket motor and w_{ave} is the average weight of the rocket. Verify the formula and state the assumptions made in the derivation.

7.78•• A 0.74-kg apple is tossed straight up from 1.3 m above the ground with an initial speed of 7.3 m/s. When it has traveled 1.5 m upward it is struck by a 0.15-kg arrow, which stays in the apple. Just before impact the arrow was traveling at a speed of 30 m/s at an upward angle of 57° from the horizontal. (a) What speed did the apple have just before the arrow struck it? (b) What were the speed and direction of the apple-arrow combination immediately after impact? (c) How far from a spot directly below the apple's initial location does the apple-arrow combination hit the ground? (You may wish to refer to Chapter 3, Section 3.7.)

8.1 Definition of Elastic Collisions

8.2 Elastic Collisions in One Dimension

*8.3 Elastic Collisions in Two Dimensions

*8.4 General Form of Gravitational Potential Energy

Physics in Practice: Symmetry and Conservation Laws

*8.5 Motion in a Gravitational Potential

*8.6 Escape Speed

Applying the Conservation Laws

We have emphasized several times in the past two chapters that the application of conservation laws can solve an immense range of physical problems. Indeed, their importance becomes evident as you see how many different situations from all areas of natural science are governed by the same conservation laws. The collision of two subatomic particles and the orbiting of the sun by a comet obey the same conservation rules for energy and momentum, even though the important force is different in the two cases. The transformation of energy between living cells and the transformation of the chemical energy of fuel to warm your home obey similar principles, though we will have to extend our ideas of energy to understand thermal processes (Chapters 11 and 13).

In this chapter we analyze in some detail several different physical situations. The common threads that bind these analyses together are the principles of conservation of energy and conservation of momentum. Because we frequently apply these principles simultaneously, we often have to solve simultaneous equations and manipulate these equations algebraically. However, we never go beyond routine algebra and elementary trigonometry. The mathematics may sometimes become

tedious, but there are no principles that you have not already used. Even so, simple collisions between billiard balls can give rise to a great deal of algebraic manipulation. For this reason, you should be particularly careful to study and fill in all the mathematical steps in the examples. In that way you will be able to handle the assigned problems.

The type of analysis we show here is similar in some respects to how physicists approach a new problem. The starting point is a simplified model of the physical situation (with assumptions and restrictions stated). Conserved quantities, such as energy or momentum, are carefully noted. The conservation laws are then used to get a solution. In fact, this type of analysis from conservation laws has led to the discovery of new subatomic particles, as we will see in Chapters 29 and 32. ■

8.1 Definition of Elastic Collisions

We have already encountered examples of momentum conservation in Chapter 7. There, for simplicity, we mainly considered perfectly inelastic collisions, in which two colliding objects stick together after impact. We now wish to broaden our understanding to include collisions in which the colliding objects rebound from each other.

Consider a ball of mass m dropped straight down onto a hard surface so that it rebounds straight up. Figure 8.1 shows the path of the ball slightly offset from vertical for clarity. Let us label the initial height from which the ball was dropped as h, and the height to which it rebounds as h'. We will show that the ratio of the magnitude of the ball's velocity just after impact to its magnitude immediately before impact can be expressed solely in terms of h' and h.

If the ball is dropped from rest, its total energy immediately before impact with the surface is equal to the total energy it had at the top, provided that we can neglect air resistance:

$$\text{PE}_{\text{bottom}} + \text{KE}_{\text{bottom}} = \text{PE}_{\text{top}} + \text{KE}_{\text{top}}.$$

The kinetic energy at the top is zero because the ball starts from rest. The kinetic energy at the bottom is then equal to the difference in potential energy between the top and the bottom:

$$\text{KE}_{\text{bottom}} = \text{PE}_{\text{top}} - \text{PE}_{\text{bottom}}.$$

If we choose the hard surface to be the zero level of potential energy, then the potential energy at the bottom is zero and the potential energy at the point of release—that is, at the height h—is mgh. The kinetic energy at the bottom thus becomes

$$\tfrac{1}{2}mv^2 = mgh.$$

Rearranging this equation, we obtain

$$v = \sqrt{2gh}.$$

The speed v is the speed immediately before impact.

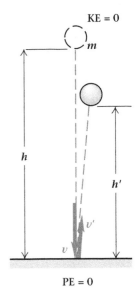

Figure 8.1
A ball of mass m dropped onto a hard surface from a height h rebounds to a height h'. If $h' = h$, the collision is elastic and kinetic energy is conserved.

Similar analysis for the upward path gives the speed v' immediately after impact in terms of the maximum rebound height h' as

$$v' = \sqrt{2gh'}.$$

The ratio of the speed immediately after impact to the speed just before impact is

$$\frac{v'}{v} = \sqrt{\frac{h'}{h}}.$$

If the ball were to rebound to its initial height (that is, to $h' = h$), then we would say that the collision was elastic. In this case v' would be the same as v and the kinetic energy immediately after the collision would be the same as the kinetic energy immediately before the collision. We call a collision **elastic** when the kinetic energy is conserved. If the ball does not rebound to its initial height, then kinetic energy is not conserved and the collision is called **inelastic.*** Note that inelastic collisions do not have to be perfectly inelastic. The colliding objects may have some recoil and loss of kinetic energy at the same time, as is often the case when two cars collide. In inelastic collisions, the total energy is still conserved, but some of the initial kinetic energy is converted into other forms, such as thermal energy.

When we studied momentum conservation in Chapter 7, we primarily considered perfectly inelastic collisions in which the colliding objects did not rebound at all, but stuck together after the collisions. Momentum was conserved in these inelastic collisions, but kinetic energy was not. At the other extreme are the elastic collisions, in which *both* kinetic energy and momentum are conserved simultaneously. Most collisions are neither elastic nor perfectly inelastic. Bouncing balls are prime examples of such collisions (Fig. 8.2). However, many situations can be approximated as either elastic or perfectly inelastic. *The collisions of hard spheres, such as billiard balls, are nearly elastic. A blob of modeling clay thrown against the wall is an example of a perfectly inelastic collision.*

The laws of conservation of energy and momentum have been validated countless times over the years. Today they have become such a fundamental part of our belief about nature that they are used as analytical tools in experiments, rather than being the subjects of experiments to test their validity. However, conservation of kinetic energy alone is not always sufficient. Kinetic energy may be exchanged for potential energy, for thermal energy, or, as we shall see in Chapter 25, for mass. The rule for the conservation of total energy includes energy in all its forms. Because we believe that energy and momentum are conserved, we can often obtain information about a collision or other interaction without observing it directly. Instead, we measure the energy and momentum of objects before and after the interaction and determine facts about the nature of the interaction itself.

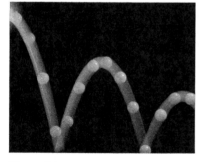

Figure 8.2
Successive bounces of a ball on a hard surface, showing the loss of energy with each bounce.

▼

8.2   Elastic Collisions in One Dimension

We begin our analysis of elastic collisions by considering a collision in one dimension and applying the laws of conservation of momentum and conservation of kinetic energy to this situation. We will expand our analysis to two dimensions in the next section.

---

*Remember that in the absence of external forces, momentum is conserved whether or not kinetic energy is conserved.

Figure 8.3 shows two objects constrained to move along the x axis only. The first object, of mass m_1, is traveling in such a way that it collides head-on with the second object, of mass m_2, which may or may not be at rest. We choose the positive x direction to be the direction of travel of the first object. Since there are no external forces acting in this direction on the system of the two objects, we can use the law of conservation of momentum as given in Eq. (7.5), p. 216,

$$m_1 v_1 + m_2 v_2 = m_1 v'_1 + m_2 v'_2. \tag{8.1}$$

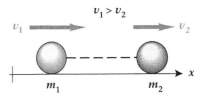

Figure 8.3
An object of mass m_1 travels with velocity v_1 prior to a head-on collision with an object of mass m_2 and velocity $v_2 < v_1$.

Here v_1 and v_2 are the initial velocities of the first and second objects, respectively, and v'_1 and v'_2 are their velocities immediately after the collision. If the collision is elastic, we can also use conservation of kinetic energy to get

$$KE_1 + KE_2 = KE'_1 + KE'_2. \tag{8.2}$$

Expressing the kinetic energy in terms of mass and velocity, we get

$$\tfrac{1}{2}m_1 v_1^2 + \tfrac{1}{2}m_2 v_2^2 = \tfrac{1}{2}m_1 v'^2_1 + \tfrac{1}{2}m_2 v'^2_2 \tag{8.3}$$

We can then use Eqs. (8.1) and (8.3) to predict the results of any straight-line, elastic collision between two bodies.

Identical Masses, One Object at Rest

A case of special interest, and one well known to billiard players, is the one-dimensional elastic collision between objects of equal mass in which one object (m_2) is at rest before the collision (Fig. 8.4). Because collisions between billiard balls are very nearly elastic, we describe them by assuming elastic conditions. For simplicity, we also neglect the effects of rotations. For the situation $m_1 = m_2$ and $v_2 = 0$, the momentum conservation equation simplifies to

$$v_1 = v'_1 + v'_2 \tag{8.4}$$

and the kinetic energy equation becomes

$$v_1^2 = v'^2_1 + v'^2_2. \tag{8.5}$$

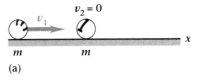

(a)

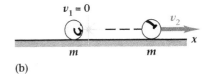

(b)

Figure 8.4
A head-on collision of two billiard balls. (a) Before impact. (b) After impact.

We can solve these two equations simultaneously by substitution, giving the final velocities v'_1 and v'_2 in terms of the initial velocity. You should show for yourself that one result is

$$v'_1 = 0,$$
$$v'_2 = v_1.$$

This result says that the first ball stops and the second ball moves with the same velocity that the first ball had initially. Equations (8.4) and (8.5) are also satisfied by the values $v'_1 = v_1$ and $v'_2 = 0$. These values are not useful, however, because they are the same as the initial conditions and do not correspond to a collision.

Unequal Masses, Both Moving

Now that we have seen the application of the conservation laws to the special case of a collision between a moving object with a stationary object of equal mass, let's consider the general situation in which both objects may be moving and their masses are unequal. If we know the masses and initial velocities of the two objects, then we have two unknown quantities, the final velocities after the collision. To find them we must solve the two Eqs. (8.1) and (8.3) simultaneously.

We begin by rewriting the equation for momentum conservation as

$$m_1(v_1 - v_1') = -m_2(v_2 - v_2'). \tag{8.6}$$

Next we remove the common factor of $\frac{1}{2}$ from the kinetic energy equation, which we then rearrange and factor into

$$m_1(v_1 - v_1')(v_1 + v_1') = -m_2(v_2 - v_2')(v_2 + v_2'). \tag{8.7}$$

Upon dividing Eq. (8.7) by Eq. (8.6), we get

$$v_1 - v_2 = -(v_1' - v_2'). \tag{8.8}$$

This last equation shows that the magnitude of the relative velocity before the collision is equal to the magnitude of the relative velocity after the collision. In other words, the relative speed of approach of object 1 to object 2 before the collision is the same as their relative speed of separation after the collision. Notice that this relation is independent of the masses. It does not matter if the objects have the same mass or not and if they are different it does not matter which is more massive.

We can combine Eq. (8.8) with Eq. (8.6) to eliminate v_2' and get the final velocity of object 1 in terms of the two initial velocities:

$$v_1' = \frac{m_1 - m_2}{m_1 + m_2} v_1 + \frac{2m_2}{m_1 + m_2} v_2. \tag{8.9}$$

Similarly, we can solve for v_2', finding

$$v_2' = \frac{2m_1}{m_1 + m_2} v_1 - \frac{m_1 - m_2}{m_1 + m_2} v_2. \tag{8.10}$$

Unequal Masses, One Object at Rest

Now that we have the two general solutions for the final velocities, let's examine them in the special case in which object 2 is initially at rest. Then, since $v_2 = 0$, the second term on the right of the equal sign vanishes in the equations for v_1' and v_2'. The outcomes are

$$v_1' = \frac{m_1 - m_2}{m_1 + m_2} v_1 \tag{8.11}$$

and

$$v_2' = \frac{2m_1}{m_1 + m_2} v_1. \tag{8.12}$$

These results can be evaluated in terms of the relative sizes of the masses. There are three possibilities: $m_1 < m_2$, $m_1 = m_2$, and $m_1 > m_2$.

1. Suppose m_1 is less than m_2, then v_1' is negative indicating that object m_1 recoils in the direction from which it came (Fig. 8.5). Object m_2 moves off in the original direction of m_1, but with a velocity smaller than v_1.

2. When the two masses are equal, we see that $v_1' = 0$ and $v_2' = v_1$. This is the same result that we obtained previously by direct computation.

3. Finally, suppose that m_1 is greater than m_2. Then v_1' and v_2' are both in the original direction of m_1, but v_1' is smaller than v_1 and v_2' is greater than v_1 (Fig. 8.6).

It is important to understand that these results depend on the simultaneous application of the law of conservation of momentum (Eq. 8.1) and the law of conservation of kinetic energy in elastic collisions (Eq. 8.3). From knowledge of the masses and the initial velocities, we have calculated both final velocities. Neither law alone is sufficient to predict the results for both velocities. (Because there are two unknowns, we must have two equations to solve for them.) The following examples illustrate the application of these conservation laws.

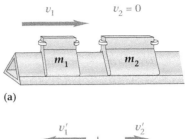

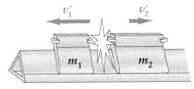

(a)

(b)

Figure 8.5
Head-on collision of two air-track gliders. The heavier glider is initially at rest. (a) Before impact. (b) After impact.

▼

Problem-Solving Strategy

One-Dimensional Elastic Collisions

Remember that in elastic collisions both momentum and kinetic energy are conserved. For a one-dimensional collision between two objects, there are two separate equations that must be satisfied simultaneously. These equations contain six separate quantities: two masses, two initial velocities, and two final velocities. If any four of the quantities are known, the other two are uniquely determined by the equations. The following steps are helpful in applying the conservation laws to elastic collisions.

1. Define a coordinate system and identify the masses and velocities. Determine which quantities are given and which need to be determined.
2. Make sketches of the situations for both "before" and "after" the collision.
3. Write the equation for the total momentum before and after the collision.
4. Write the equation for the kinetic energy before and after the collision.
5. Solve the equations simultaneously.

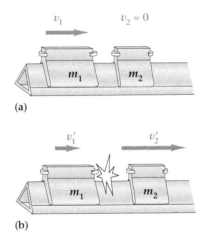

(a)

(b)

Figure 8.6
Head-on collision of two air-track gliders. The lighter glider is initially at rest. (a) Before impact. (b) After impact.

Example 8.1

Two railroad boxcars are initially in motion to the right along the same straight track, which we denote as the x axis with the positive direction to the right (Fig. 8.7). The ratio of the masses of the two cars is $m_1/m_2 = 1/2$. The rearmost boxcar, m_1, has a velocity twice as great as the forward boxcar, m_2. The faster-moving car, m_1, overtakes the other car and collides with it. After the collision, what is the velocity of each boxcar if the collision is elastic?

Strategy Although we could compute the answers from the general solutions given by Eqs. (8.9) and (8.10), we will start at the beginning by applying the laws of conservation of energy and momentum. This example illustrates a common situation. We will get two sets of answers that satisfy our mathematical formulation of the conservation laws. We must then take a careful look at the physical meaning of the solutions in order to select the answer that corresponds to reality. You should fill in the missing algebraic steps for yourself.

Solution If the initial velocity of the second boxcar, m_2, is v, then the initial velocity of the first boxcar, m_1, is $2v$. If we write $m_1 = m$ and $m_2 = 2m$, the law of conservation of momentum becomes

$$(m)(2v) + (2m)(v) = mv_1' + (2m)v_2'.$$

This equation may be simplified as

$$4v = v_1' + 2v_2'.$$

Conservation of kinetic energy gives

$$\tfrac{1}{2}(m)(2v)^2 + \tfrac{1}{2}(2m)(v)^2 = \tfrac{1}{2}mv_1'^2 + \tfrac{1}{2}(2m)v_2'^2,$$

or

$$6v^2 = v_1'^2 + 2v_2'^2.$$

We can rearrange the momentum equation to give v_1' in terms of the other velocities. Then we substitute v_1' into the energy equation to give

$$3v_2'^2 - 8vv_2' + 5v^2 = 0.$$

Figure 8.7

Example 8.1: Elastic collision between two boxcars of unequal mass.

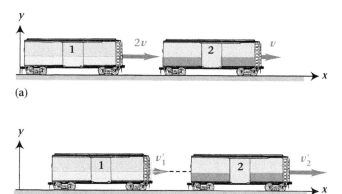

(a)

(b)

We now have a quadratic equation in v_2'. (The initial velocity v is a constant.) Upon substitution into the quadratic formula,* we find

$$v_2' = \frac{+8v \pm \sqrt{(-8v)^2 - 4(3)(5v^2)}}{2(3)} = \frac{8v \pm 2v}{6}.$$

Both solutions must be considered. If we choose the plus sign, we find

$$v_2' = \tfrac{5}{3}v.$$

If we choose the minus sign, we find

$$v_2' = v.$$

Both of these values cannot represent the physical situation, since only one event actually happens. However, we must keep both until we can eliminate one of them by physical considerations. Upon substituting $v_2' = v$ into the momentum equation, we get

$$v_1' = 2v.$$

Upon substitution of $v_2' = \tfrac{5}{3}v$ into the momentum equation, we get

$$v_1' = \tfrac{2}{3}v.$$

Thus, from the purely algebraic standpoint we have two pairs of possible answers:

$$\{v_1' = \tfrac{2}{3}v \quad \text{and} \quad v_2' = \tfrac{5}{3}v\} \quad \text{or} \quad \{v_1' = 2v \quad \text{and} \quad v_2' = v\},$$

both of which satisfy the conservation equations.

The resolution of the problem comes from a careful look at what the answers mean. Remember that this is a straight-line collision and that boxcar 1 is the rearmost car. It must always remain the rearmost car because it cannot pass through the other car. This means that after the collision, its velocity in its initial direction must be less than the velocity of car 2. Therefore the correct answer is $v_1' = \tfrac{2}{3}v$ and $v_2' = \tfrac{5}{3}v$. Note that the other answer—corresponding to the case in which both cars maintain their initial velocities, but with boxcar 1 passing through boxcar 2 without collision—is not physically possible. Because the equation for conservation of kinetic energy is quadratic, we always obtain two sets of answers; however, one set corresponds to the initial conditions and can be discarded.

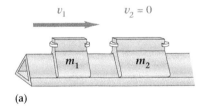

(a)

Example 8.2

In an experiment on a linear air track, a glider of mass $m_1 = m$ moving with initial speed v_1 to the right collides in an elastic collision with a glider of mass $m_2 = 2m$ initially at rest (Fig. 8.8). What are the final velocities of the two gliders?

Strategy We can obtain the final velocities by the simultaneous application of conservation of momentum and energy. Again we obtain two sets of solutions.

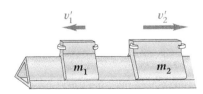

(b)

Figure 8.8
Example 8.2: A glider of mass m collides with a glider of mass $2m$ initially at rest.

---

*You may want to refer to the appendix for Chapter 2, Solving Quadratic Equations.

You should sketch a diagram for yourself before proceeding to help sort out which of the two solutions is physically meaningful.

Solution We apply conservation of momentum to get

$$mv_1 = mv_1' + 2mv_2',$$

where v_1' is the final velocity of the light glider and v_2' is the final velocity of the heavy glider. Conservation of energy gives

$$\tfrac{1}{2}(m)v_1^2 = \tfrac{1}{2}(m)v_1'^2 + \tfrac{1}{2}(2m)v_2'^2.$$

We may eliminate the common factors of $\tfrac{1}{2}m$ to get two equations that must be solved simultaneously for the two unknown velocities:

$$v_1 - v_1' = 2v_2', \qquad \text{(momentum)}$$
$$v_1^2 - v_1'^2 = 2v_2'^2. \qquad \text{(energy)}$$

The momentum equation may be squared to get

$$(v_1^2 - 2v_1v_1' + v_1'^2) = 4v_2'^2.$$

Now we multiply the energy equation by 2 and subtract the above equation from it, obtaining

$$v_1^2 + 2v_1v_1' - 3v_1'^2 = 0.$$

This equation may be factored, giving us

$$(v_1 - v_1')(v_1 + 3v_1') = 0.$$

As before, we have two solutions,

$$v_1' = v_1 \quad \text{or} \quad v_1' = -\tfrac{1}{3}v_1.$$

The solution $v_1' = v_1$ indicates that the body of mass m has the same velocity after the collision that it had before the collision; that is, it implies that there was no collision. We choose instead the physically meaningful solution of $v_1' = -\tfrac{1}{3}v_1$. The negative sign indicates that the light glider recoils in the direction opposite to its initial motion.

If we insert $v_1' = -\tfrac{1}{3}v_1$ into the momentum equation, we obtain

$$v_2' = \tfrac{2}{3}v_1.$$

You may wish to insert these values into the energy equation to verify their correctness.

Discussion We could have obtained the final velocities by direct substitution into Eqs. (8.11) and (8.12), which were derived for this situation, in which one mass is initially at rest. You should compute the values from those equations for yourself to check.

▼

*8.3 Elastic Collisions in Two Dimensions

When two billiard balls collide on the surface of a billiard table, the general result is that they move off in different directions. Since all velocities lie in the plane of the surface, the collision is two-dimensional. We can analyze elastic collisions in two dimensions by using the fact that momentum is a vector quantity.

There are two equations for conservation of momentum—one for the x components and one for the y components of momentum—and one equation for conservation of energy. (Remember that energy is a scalar quantity.) However, *four* quantities must be determined to specify completely the final outcome of a two-dimensional collision: the two velocity components of each body, or equivalently, the magnitudes and directions of the two vector velocities. These four quantities cannot be determined from three simultaneous equations, even if we know all of the initial velocity components. However, if one of these quantities can be specified, either from observation or from some physical consideration, then the other three quantities can be uniquely determined.

Figure 8.9 depicts an elastic collision between two spheres of mass m_1 and m_2. One of the spheres, m_2, is initially at rest. To simplify our work, we choose a coordinate system in which the initial velocity is along the x axis. This choice guarantees that there is no initial momentum in the y direction. Using the law of conservation of momentum, we obtain an equation for the x component of momentum:

$$m_1 v_{1x} = m_1 v'_{1x} + m_2 v'_{2x}. \quad \text{(momentum along } x) \quad (8.13)$$

Conservation of the y component of momentum gives

$$0 = m_1 v'_{1y} + m_2 v'_{2y}. \quad \text{(momentum along } y) \quad (8.14)$$

Conservation of energy gives

$$\tfrac{1}{2} m_1 v_1^2 = \tfrac{1}{2} m_1 v_1'^2 + \tfrac{1}{2} m_2 v_2'^2. \quad \text{(kinetic energy)} \quad (8.15)$$

Simultaneous solution of these three equations is necessary to determine the subsequent motion of the spheres. However, we still require prior knowledge of one postcollision velocity component or angle before we can find the other quantities. The following example illustrates the use of conservation laws in two dimensions.

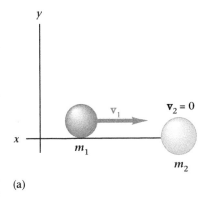
(a)

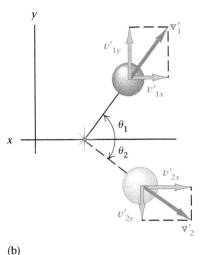
(b)

Figure 8.9
A glancing collision in two dimensions, viewed from above. (a) Before the collision. (b) After the collision, the two spheres move off in different directions.

Example 8.3

Consider two billiard balls of equal mass that collide elastically. One of them has an initial speed v_1, and the other is at rest. After the collision, the ball that was initially in motion is deflected at an observed angle θ_1 with respect to its original direction. Find the final speed of each ball and the direction in which the other ball is moving.

Solution Referring to Fig. 8.9, we can rewrite the equation for the x component of momentum (Eq. 8.13) in terms of the angles θ_1 and θ_2,

$$v_1 = v'_1 \cos \theta_1 + v'_2 \cos \theta_2, \quad (x \text{ momentum})$$

where θ_1 and θ_2 are both defined as positive in the diagram. Notice that since both balls have the same mass, m is a common factor to all terms and has been eliminated from the equation. Similarly, the equation for conservation of the y component of momentum (Eq. 8.14) may be expressed as

$$v'_1 \sin \theta_1 = v'_2 \sin \theta_2, \quad (y \text{ momentum})$$

and the kinetic energy conservation equation (Eq. 8.15) becomes

$$v_1^2 = v_1'^2 + v_2'^2. \quad \text{(kinetic energy)}$$

The x-component momentum equation may be rearranged and squared to give

$$v_1^2 - 2v_1v_1' \cos \theta_1 + v_1'^2 \cos^2 \theta_1 = v_2'^2 \cos^2 \theta_2.$$

The y momentum equation may also be squared to give

$$v_1'^2 \sin^2 \theta_1 = v_2'^2 \sin^2 \theta_2.$$

When these two equations are added, we have

$$v_1^2 - 2v_1v_1' \cos \theta_1 + v_1'^2 = v_2'^2,$$

where we have made use of the trigonometric identity $\cos^2 \theta + \sin^2 \theta = 1$.

At this point we can combine the kinetic energy equation and the last equation to eliminate v_2'. The result expresses v_1' in terms of the initial speed v_1 and the angle θ_1:

$$v_1^2 - 2v_1v_1' \cos \theta_1 + v_1'^2 = v_1^2 - v_1'^2,$$
$$v_1'^2 = 2v_1v_1' \cos \theta_1 - v_1'^2$$
$$v_1'^2 = v_1v_1' \cos \theta_1.$$

The solution is

$$v_1' = v_1 \cos \theta_1,$$

corresponding to ball 1 emerging at angle θ_1. This value of v_1' may, in turn, be inserted into the kinetic energy equation to yield v_2':

$$v_2' = v_1 \sin \theta_1.$$

To get this result, you need to use the trigonometric identity

$$\cos^2 \theta + \sin^2 \theta = 1.$$

Finally, the recoil angle of the second ball can be obtained from the y momentum equation as

$$\sin \theta_2 = \frac{v_1'}{v_2'} \sin \theta_1 = \frac{v_1'}{v_1}.$$

Discussion We see that knowledge of the initial speed v_1 and the recoil angle θ_1 is sufficient to determine the magnitude of the other speeds v_1' and v_2' as well as the angle θ_2. This example is similar to Example 7.8. In both examples we were asked to find the speed and direction of the struck ball. In the earlier example we were given the speed and direction of the outgoing incident ball. Here we are given only the direction. Since we have three equations (x momentum, y momentum, and kinetic energy), we can solve for three unknowns. Thus, when kinetic energy is conserved we can make predictions about the results of collisions that cannot be made from momentum conservation alone.

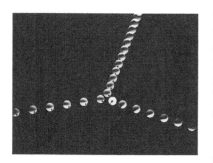

Figure 8.10
Example 8.4: A multiflash photograph of an elastic collision between two balls of equal mass. After the collision, the two balls move off at a right angle to each other.

Example 8.4

A ball of mass m moving with a speed of 2.00 m/s collides with a stationary ball of the same mass in an elastic collision (Fig. 8.10). The incident ball is scattered at an angle of 58° from its original direction. Find the final speed of each ball and the direction of recoil of the struck ball.

Strategy This problem is a numerical example of the collision described in Example 8.3. We are given that $v_1 = 2.00$ m/s and $\theta_1 = 58°$. We may use the equation developed in Example 8.3 to find the speed v_1' of the scattered ball, and conservation of kinetic energy to find the speed v_2' of the struck ball.

Solution The speed v_1' is

$$v_1' = v_1 \cos \theta_1 = (2.00 \text{ m/s}) \cos 58° = 1.06 \text{ m/s}.$$

We obtain the speed of the struck ball from the kinetic energy equation as

$$v_2' = \sqrt{v_1^2 - v_1'^2} = \sqrt{2.00^2 - 1.06^2} = 1.70 \text{ m/s}.$$

Finally, the recoil angle of the second ball is obtained from

$$\sin \theta_2 = \frac{v_1'}{v_1} = 0.530,$$

$$\theta_2 = 32°.$$

Discussion Notice that θ_1 and θ_2 add to 90°. The two objects move off at right angles to each other's motion. This behavior is characteristic of elastic collisions between two objects of equal mass; the struck object always moves off at a right angle to the recoil direction of the incident object.

*8.4 General Form of Gravitational Potential Energy

In Chapter 6 we considered gravitational potential energy near the surface of the earth. If we wish to determine the potential energy of an object that is far removed from the earth's surface, then the equation we found,

$$\text{PE} = mgh, \tag{8.16}$$

is inadequate. We derived this result under the assumption that the gravitational force on an object is constant, an assumption that is approximately correct for bodies near the earth's surface, but fails as the distances involved get larger. We can't expect Eq. (8.16) to be appropriate for describing the potential energy of the earth-moon system or even of an artificial satellite orbiting the earth.

Suppose we wish to calculate the potential energy difference between points A and B, where A is at a distance r_A from the earth's center and B is at a distance r_B from the earth's center (Fig. 8.11). We can determine this energy difference by computing the work required to move an object of mass m from A to B. First we move the object along the path of constant radius from point A to a point C. Remember, work is done only when we exert a force through a distance to overcome the gravitational force. Since the direction of the gravitational force is radial, no work is done in going from point A to point C because the motion is perpendicular to the force. To move from C to B, we must apply a force to move the mass outward against the gravitational force. The total work expended in going from A to B is then just the work done against the gravitational force in going from C to B.

This work W_{AB} equals the change in potential energy ΔPE_{AB} when the mass m is moved from A to B. We would like to express this as the difference between the potential energy at B and the potential energy at A,

$$\Delta\text{PE}_{AB} = \text{PE}_B - \text{PE}_A.$$

SYMMETRY AND CONSERVATION LAWS

What is symmetry? We see symmetry all around us: A butterfly is symmetric because the right side is a reflection of the left side (Fig. B8.1). We say that the butterfly has a mirror symmetry through it midline. Snowflakes have even more symmetry. In addition to mirror symmetries, they have rotational symmetry. A snowflake rotated through any multiple of 60° looks the same as before it was rotated (Fig. B8.2). Our technical definition of symmetry is much the same as our ordinary understanding: something is symmetric if the way it looks is unchanged by a reflection, rotation, or translation. Furthermore, any operation or procedure

Figure B8.1 A butterfly has a mirror symmetry through its midline.

has symmetry if performing the operation leaves an object unchanged. For example, if we examine one region of a honeycomb and then move over a few cells to a new region, that new region of the honeycomb looks the same as the first region (Fig. B8.3). We say the honeycomb has symmetry of translation. If we rotate the honeycomb by 60°, it still looks the same. The honeycomb has symmetry of rotation by 60°, 120°, or 180°, but not symmetry of rotation through 30°, 45°, or 90°. In this case, as in the case of the snowflake, the symmetry is discrete or discontinuous. Just as the butterfly and snowflake have mirror symmetries, so too does the honeycomb. These symmetries are all discontinuous; there is only a finite number of mirror axes.

Early in the history of science, crystals were classified according to the symmetry of their external shape. Eventually, it was discovered that these external shapes were due to the actual arrangement of the atoms and molecules that make up the crystals. These atomic alignments themselves are symmetric. After the discovery of x rays, crystallographers switched their attention from the shapes of crystals to their atomic structures. More recently, the invention of the scanning tunneling microscope has allowed us to visualize the atoms in the surfaces of materials and to see their symmetry (Fig. B8.4).

Other symmetries are continuous. For example, a uniform sphere such as a white billiard ball (cue ball) looks the same after rotation through any angle about any axis passing through its center. We say that the cue ball is invariant under rotation about any central axis. In contrast, a baseball or soccer ball has rotational symmetry about only a few axes, and the symmetries are discrete about those axes.

Symmetry is often seen in the work of architects, designers, and artists in addition to appearing in nature. Much of what we perceive as beauty in bridges and buildings is related to the symmetries they possess. The symmetrical shape of the Gateway Arch in St. Louis is important not only for its beauty but also for its strength (Fig. B8.5).

Is symmetry limited to geometry? No! There is much more. The mathematician Amalie "Emmy" Noether (1882–1935) recognized the physical significance of the

Figure B8.2 (a), (b) Snowflakes have mirror symmetries as well as (c)

Figure B8.3 A honeycomb has translational symmetry of as well as rotational symmetry

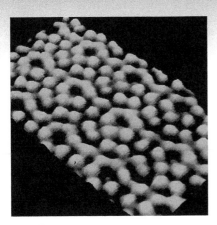

Figure B8.4 Atomic surface of a crystal.

invariances associated with symmetries. Noether's Principle states that *for every continuous symmetry there is a corresponding conservation law and vice versa.* Both the law of conservation of momentum and the law of conservation of energy are consequences of symmetries. That the results of a mechanics experiment are independent of the location of the origin of the coordinate system indicates that space is symmetric (or uniform) under translation. The law of conservation of momentum corresponds to the translational symmetry of space. Conservation of angular momentum, charge, and other more abstract quantities also result from observed symmetries in nature.

Figure B8.5 The Gateway Arch in St. Louis has a mirror symmetry along a vertical line through its center.

Symmetries associated with the more abstract parameters found in condensed matter physics and particle physics are important to their understanding. A good example of how symmetry can lead to new ideas is found in the discovery of the Ω^- particle. The basic constituents of matter, such as protons, neutrons, electrons, and other less well known particles

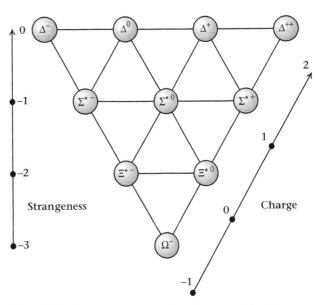

Figure B8.6 Geometric representation of the properties of elementary particles.

were—at one time—called elementary particles. In 1962, the American physicist Murray Gell-Mann (1929–) and the Israeli physicist Yuval Ne'eman (1925–) independently used a property of particles previously developed in 1953 by Gell-Mann and Nisijima (1926–) to sort elementary particles into groups that display symmetry. Even though the properties are not spatial quantities and have no geometric meaning, these groups can be represented geometrically (Fig. B8.6). The test of the idea came when it was noted that one of the groupings contained a place for a particle yet unknown. A search was begun for a particle with the properties predicted by the theory. After careful experiments, the particle known as Ω^- was found in less than two years. The measured mass of the newly discovered particle was within 0.2% of the value predicted by the theory. Never before had the properties of a yet-unseen particle been so closely predicted. The prediction of this new particle was based on considerations of symmetry and its discovery confirms the fundamental correctness of the use of symmetry.

247

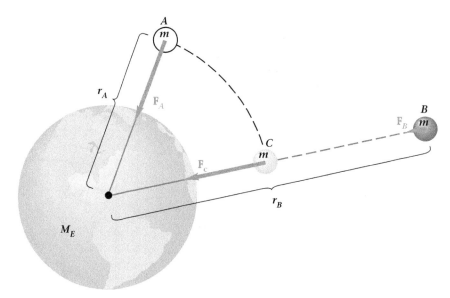

Figure 8.11
The gravitational potential energy of a body at point A is less than it is at point B, since work must be done to move the body from A to B. No work is done on moving from A to C because the motion is perpendicular to the direction of the force. $\mathbf{F}_A$, $\mathbf{F}_B$, and $\mathbf{F}_C$ are the gravitational forces acting on the body at points A, B, and C.

Since the gravitational force is not constant and varies as $1/r^2$, the work needs to be evaluated using the methods of calculus. The result for the work to move a mass m from A to B—that is, the difference in potential energy—is

$$\Delta \text{PE}_{AB} = \frac{-GM_{\text{E}}m}{r_B} - \frac{-GM_{\text{E}}m}{r_A}, \tag{8.17}$$

where M_{E} is the mass of the earth, and the potential energies at r_A and r_B are given by

$$\text{PE}_A = \frac{-GM_{\text{E}}m}{r_A} \quad \text{and} \quad \text{PE}_B = \frac{-GM_{\text{E}}m}{r_B}.$$

When we considered potential energy in Section 6.5, it was necessary to choose a reference, or zero. The choice of reference was based on convenience, the important physical quantity being the difference in potential energy between two positions. When the difference in gravitational potential energy is given by Eq. (8.17), we can again choose a reference on the basis of convenience. We will choose $r = \infty$ (infinity) to be the zero reference. This choice has the advantage of making the potential energy at the reference distance equal to zero. Then the potential energy at any distance is

$$\boxed{\text{PE} = -G\frac{M_{\text{E}}m}{r}.} \tag{8.18}$$

Equation (8.18) gives the potential energy at a distance r from the earth's center and is in agreement with our previous observation that objects have more potential energy as they are moved farther away from the earth. According to Eq. (8.18), a body's potential energy is negative near the earth's surface and becomes less negative (i.e., greater) as it moves away from the earth. The maximum potential energy is zero, the value obtained at an infinite distance from the

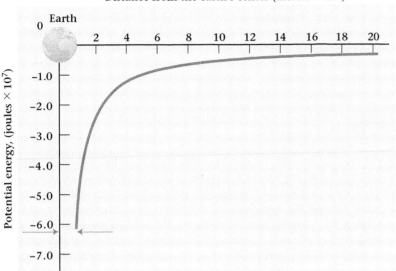

Figure 8.12
The potential energy of a 1-kg mass as a function of distance from the earth's center. The graph starts at the earth's surface.

earth's center. Figure 8.12 shows a graph of the potential energy of a 1-kg mass as a function of distance from the center of the earth.

It might seem as if we have two different expressions for the change in potential energy of a body lifted from the earth's surface. Certainly, Eqs. (8.16) and (8.18) do not appear to be the same. We can show, however, that they give essentially the same answer for small changes in distance from the earth's surface. Let us imagine that a mass m is initially at rest on the surface of the earth. We then lift it to a height h. What is its change in potential energy? If R_E is the radius of the earth, then Eq. (8.17) gives

$$\Delta PE = \frac{-GM_Em}{R_E + h} - \frac{-GM_Em}{R_E}$$

$$\Delta PE = GM_Em\left(\frac{1}{R_E} - \frac{1}{R_E + h}\right)$$

$$\Delta PE = GM_Em\left(\frac{h}{R_E(R_E + h)}\right).$$

If R_E is much greater than h, then the quantity in the brackets becomes approximately h/R_E^2 and the change in potential energy is given by*

$$\Delta PE = \frac{GM_Emh}{R_E^2}.$$

In Chapter 5 we found that the acceleration of gravity g is given by $g = GM_E/R_E^2$, so that the above equation can be written as

$$\Delta PE = mgh.$$

---

*If h is 1 km above the earth's surface, the approximation of $h/R_E(R_E + h)$ by h/R_E^2 gives an error of only 0.015%.

This equation is the same as Eq. (8.16). Thus, for changes in position near the earth's surface, Eqs. (8.16) and (8.18) both give the same answer. For motion over distances that are not small compared with the earth's radius, you must use Eq. (8.18). In all cases remember that it is the *change* in potential energy that is important.

*8.5 Motion in a Gravitational Potential

Figure 8.13
Booster rockets are used to launch the space shuttle into orbit around the earth.

In this and the next section, we discuss some aspects of the motion of objects, such as spacecraft, that are projected from the earth and orbit around it (Fig. 8.13). These topics are included here because they demonstrate the power of conservation laws and because the mathematical techniques are similar to those we have already used in this chapter. Here we use only the laws of universal gravitation and of conservation of energy. Although a complete treatment of satellite and spacecraft motion also requires the law of conservation of angular momentum, which we will discuss in Chapter 9, we have chosen to restrict ourselves here to situations where angular momentum is zero and need not be included.

An object thrown straight up reaches a maximum height h that depends on its initial upward velocity v_0. We can determine the relation between h and v_0 from the principle of energy conservation by equating the potential energy at height h to the kinetic energy at height 0 (see Example 6.9). The result is $v_0 = \sqrt{2gh}$, where g is the gravitational acceleration. In arriving at this relationship, we assumed that the distance h is small enough to allow us to consider the gravitational force to be constant. If we consider objects such as rockets and satellites, which are projected to great distances above the earth's surface, the assumption of a uniform gravitational force is no longer acceptable. It is possible, though tedious, to derive the correct relationship between speed and distance from a consideration of the actual forces involved. However, it is much easier to analyze such problems from the standpoint of energy. This approach has the additional advantage of introducing some important techniques that are of general usefulness.

The gravitational potential energy of an object of mass m at a distance r from the center of the earth was given in the last section. For the case in which the potential energy is set equal to zero at $r = \infty$, it is

$$PE = -G\frac{M_E m}{r},$$

where G is the universal gravitational constant and M_E is the earth's mass. The potential-energy diagram for this case is the curve in Fig. 8.14, which plots potential energy against radial distance from the center of the earth. Because of our choice of reference level, the potential energy of the object is negative for any finite distance r.

Let the object be projected straight upward with a total energy E_0. As it rises it loses kinetic energy and gains potential energy. Its total energy remains constant as it moves in the earth's gravitational field if we neglect air resistance. The kinetic and potential energies at any point P are related by

$$KE_P + PE_P = E_0.$$

If the total energy E_0 is known, then the kinetic energy at any point is the difference between the total energy and the potential energy. The total energy E_0 is indicated in Fig. 8.14 for a particular case in which E_0 is negative. For any radial distance $r < A$, where A depends on the total energy E_0, the object has a positive kinetic energy, as indicated at P. As the object moves away from the earth toward A, its kinetic energy decreases and its potential energy increases. When it reaches A, its kinetic energy becomes zero. At this point, the object stops and falls back toward the earth. When it passes the point P on its way back to the earth's surface, it has the same kinetic energy that it had at that same point on the way up. In other words, the object is moving with the same speed but now headed down instead of up.

A simple way to visualize the object's motion is to imagine it represented by a bead sliding without friction along a wire bent into the shape of the potential-energy curve. An upward push sends the bead along the wire from r_e to a, where it stops and slides back down to r_e. The bead loses speed as it goes from r_e to a, and regains speed as it returns. This analogy can be quite useful, but you must remember that the actual motion of the object is along a straight line directed radially away from the earth.

Let us return to the question of finding the relationship between the object's initial upward speed v_0 and the maximum height h to which it can ascend. We take the initial location to correspond to the earth's surface at $r = R_E$. Applying the rule of conservation of energy gives

$$\text{KE}(R_E) + \text{PE}(R_E) = \text{KE}(r) + \text{PE}(r).$$

At maximum height h ($r = R_E + h$), the kinetic energy of the object is zero and the energy equation becomes

$$\tfrac{1}{2}mv_0^2 - \frac{GM_Em}{R_E} = 0 - \frac{GM_Em}{r}.$$

We can rearrange this to give

$$v_0 = \sqrt{2GM_E\left(\frac{1}{R_E} - \frac{1}{r}\right)}.$$

This equation gives the initial upward speed required for an object at the earth's surface if it is to rise to a distance r from the center of the earth.

Compare this equation for v_0 with the simpler form given earlier for a uniform gravitational field, $v_0 = \sqrt{2gh}$. To make the comparison easier, we express the gravitational constant G in terms of the acceleration g (see Example 5.12):

$$GM_E = gR_E^2.$$

The result of inserting this expression into the above equation for speed is

$$v_0 = \sqrt{2gR_E^2\left(\frac{1}{R_E} - \frac{1}{r}\right)}.$$

We may also replace r by $R_E + h$ to get

$$v_0 = \sqrt{\frac{2ghR_E}{R_E + h}}. \tag{8.19}$$

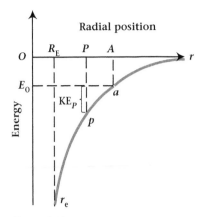

Figure 8.14
Potential-energy diagram of an object projected straight up. Energy is shown along the vertical axis and radial position from the center of the earth along the horizontal axis.

If h is small, so that $R_E + h \approx R_E$, then Eq. (8.19) reverts to the simpler form of the case for constant gravitational force. However, Eq. (8.19) is correct for all heights. The value of g remains the value measured at the earth's surface.

Example 8.5

A rocket is projected upward from the earth's surface (Fig. 8.15) to a height of $0.0100\,R_E$, where R_E is the mean radius of the earth. (a) What initial speed is necessary? For simplicity, assume that the rocket reaches its initial speed over a very short interval and that effects of air resistance can be ignored. (b) What fractional error would occur if the calculation were made under the assumption that the earth's gravitational field were uniform at all heights?

Solution (a) For the correct answer we use

$$
\begin{aligned}
v_0 &= \sqrt{\frac{2ghR_E}{R_E + h}} \\
&= \sqrt{\frac{2g(0.0100\,R_E)(R_E)}{R_E + 0.0100\,R_E}} = \sqrt{2gR_E(0.00990)} \\
&= \sqrt{2(9.81\text{ m/s}^2)(6.38 \times 10^6\text{m})(0.00990)} \\
&= 1113\text{ m/s} \approx 2490\text{ mi/h}.
\end{aligned}
$$

Figure 8.15
A rocket is projected straight up from the earth's surface.

(b) Let us take the ratio of the correct to the approximate expressions for the initial speed:

$$
\frac{v_0\text{ (correct)}}{v_0\text{ (approximate)}} = \frac{\sqrt{\dfrac{2ghR_E}{R_E + h}}}{\sqrt{2gh}} = \sqrt{\frac{R_E}{R_E + h}} = \sqrt{\frac{1}{1 + 0.01}}
$$

$$
\frac{v_0\text{ (correct)}}{v_0\text{ (approximate)}} = 0.995.
$$

Discussion As we expect, since the strength of the gravitational field decreases rather than remains constant with increasing height, the correct initial speed is less than the one calculated from the approximation. Nevertheless, for a distance of nearly 600 km, the difference in the calculations is only 0.5%.

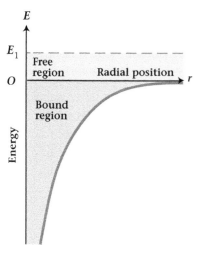

Figure 8.16
Potential-energy diagram for a mass attracted to the earth. Objects with total energy E less than 0 are bound to the earth. Those with E greater than zero are free to escape from it. Particles with $E = 0$ are just barely free and approach $r = \infty$ with zero velocity.

*8.6 Escape Speed

Look at the potential-energy diagram of an object projected straight up (Fig. 8.14) and remember the analogy of the bead on the wire. We see that for a projectile to escape the earth—that is, for the bead not to slide back down again—its initial energy must be enough to move the point a to infinity. Thus, the total initial energy must be at least zero ($E_0 \geq 0$). For zero total energy, the projectile will "reach infinity" with zero speed. Rockets (or other objects) with total energy less than zero cannot escape the earth. Bodies with total energy greater than zero, as E_1 in Fig. 8.16, are unbound. For a projectile that is just able to escape from the earth's gravitational field, the total energy is zero.

A rocket that is fired for only a short time behaves essentially like a projectile that is given an initial upward speed. The minimum initial upward speed necessary for the rocket not to fall back to earth again is called the **escape speed,** v_{esc}, and is found by setting the projectile's total energy equal to zero:

$$\frac{1}{2}mv_{esc}^2 - \frac{GM_Em}{R_E} = 0.$$

We can rearrange to find that

$$v_{esc} = \sqrt{\frac{2GM_E}{R_E}}. \tag{8.20}$$

Note that the escape speed does not depend on the mass of the rocket. The value of the escape speed for any object on the earth can be calculated to be 11.2 km/s. It is interesting to note that the speed needed to completely escape from the earth's gravitational field is only $\sqrt{2}$ times as much as the speed of an object in orbit just above the earth's surface. (See Problem 8.51.)

Example 8.6

What is the escape speed for a rocket on the surface of Mars?

Solution We can obtain the escape speed from the surface of Mars from the law of conservation of energy in the same way that we obtained Eq. (8.20):

$$\frac{1}{2}mv_{esc}^2 - \frac{GM_Mm}{R_M} = 0.$$

The escape speed is then

$$v_{esc} = \sqrt{\frac{2GM_M}{R_M}}.$$

When the mass of Mars, 6.58×10^{23} kg, and its radius, 3.38×10^6 m, are inserted into the equation for v_{esc}, we get

$$v_{esc} = \sqrt{\frac{2(6.67 \times 10^{-11} \text{ N} \cdot \text{m}^2/\text{kg})(6.58 \times 10^{23} \text{ kg})}{3.38 \times 10^6 \text{ m}}},$$

$$v_{esc} = 5.10 \times 10^3 \text{ m/s}.$$

The escape speed from the surface of Mars is less than one-half the escape speed from the earth's surface.

Example 8.7

Calculate the minimum initial speed needed to project a rocket from the earth to the moon. For simplicity, use a model in which the positions of the earth and the moon are fixed and that ignores the effects of air friction in the earth's atmosphere.

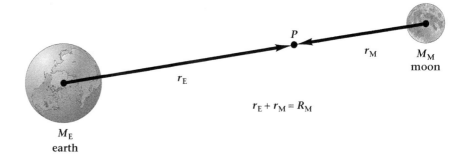

Figure 8.17
Example 8.7: Point P along a line from the earth to the moon is a distance r_E from the earth and a distance r_M from the moon.

Strategy The gravitational potential energy of the rocket due to both the earth and the moon has a maximum somewhere between the earth and the moon. We use a stationary model with a radial rocket velocity. The minimum initial speed needed corresponds to the minimum kinetic energy to get the rocket over this maximum potential energy.

Solution Consider points along a line between the earth and the moon (Fig. 8.17). Then the distance to the earth r_E plus the distance to the moon r_M equals R_M the center-to-center distance from earth to moon: $r_E + r_M = R_M$. The potential energy of the rocket is

$$\text{PE} = -G\frac{M_E m}{r_E} - G\frac{M_M m}{R_M - r_E},$$

where M_E is the mass of the earth, M_M is the mass of the moon, and m is the mass of the rocket.

This potential energy is shown in Fig. 8.18. Point A located a distance r_A from the earth is the position of the maximum potential energy along the path. It is the point at which the gravitational force on the rocket due to the earth is equal and opposite to the force on the rocket due to the moon:

$$\frac{G M_E m}{r_A^2} = \frac{G M_M m}{(R_M - r_A)^2}.$$

The rocket must have a total energy of at least E_A if it is to get "over the hump" at A and reach the moon along the direct path. A rocket leaving the earth with initial energy slightly greater than E_A will slow as it approaches A, where its velocity will be nearly zero. Past the point A, the rocket speeds up as it approaches the moon.

Upon solving the force equation for r_A we find

$$r_A = \frac{R_M}{1 + \sqrt{\dfrac{M_M}{M_E}}} = 0.90\, R_M.$$

The potential energy PE_A of the rocket at point A can be found in terms of the earth-moon distance by inserting $r_A = 0.90\, R_M$ for r_E in the potential energy equation. The result is:

$$\text{PE}_A = -\frac{1.234 G M_E m}{R_M}.$$

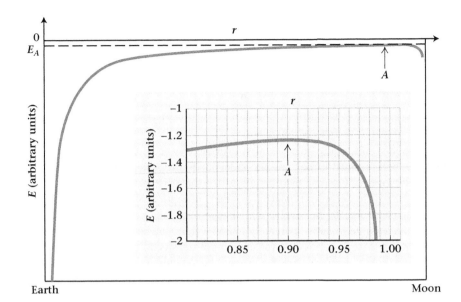

Figure 8.18
Example 8.7: Gravitational potential energy for a mass along a straight line between the earth and the moon.

To reach the moon along the direct path, a rocket must have an initial total energy KE + PE of at least PE_A. At the earth's surface, the rocket's total energy is

$$\text{KE} + \text{PE} = \tfrac{1}{2}mv_0^2 - \frac{GM_E m}{R_E} - \frac{GM_M m}{R_M - R_E} = \text{PE}_A.$$

Because the mass of the moon is $0.0123\, M_E$ and $R_M \approx 60 R_E$, the potential energy due to the moon at the earth's surface is only 1/6000 as big as that due to the earth. Thus, to a good approximation we may drop the term due to the moon, insert the value for PE_A, and solve to find the initial speed v_0.

$$v_0 = \sqrt{2GM_E\left(\frac{1}{R_E} - \frac{1.234}{R_M}\right)} = 11.1 \text{ km/s}.$$

The minimum initial speed required at the earth's surface is $v_0 = 11.1$ km/s or nearly 40,000 km/h.

Discussion It is interesting to note that the minimum initial upward speed to just project a rocket to the moon is only about 1% smaller than the speed needed to completely escape from the earth's gravitational field. Since travelers to the moon need to cross the potential hump in a reasonable time, they must necessarily have speeds greater than that found here. Consequently, great care is needed in steering the spacecraft to ensure that it reaches the moon and is not lost in space. Actual lunar voyages are not made along a straight line joining the earth and moon and the spacecraft are not simply fired from a giant gun. However, it is still necessary to give the spacecraft sufficient total energy to overcome the potential barrier between earth and moon.

The expression for the escape speed in the previous example leads to an interesting consequence that is outside the realm of Newtonian mechanics. Astronomical objects with greater mass to radius ratio than the earth (that is to say, denser objects) have greater escape speeds. For stars, the escape speed is quite high. If a star is dense enough, the escape speed approaches the speed of light c, the limiting speed for all motion. When

$$\sqrt{\frac{2GM}{R}} = c,$$

nothing, not even light itself, can escape. Because no light can escape from such a dense object, it is called a *black hole*.

The idea of a black hole was first proposed by P. S. Laplace (1749–1827) in 1796, before much of our present understanding of the nature of light or the stars was known. Current theories allow for the existence of black holes, although very different from Laplace's original conception. We know that stars are not permanent objects, but evolve and change over long periods of time. At the end of the lifetime of some extremely massive stars, the core can undergo a collapse; in this case it is possible for the central density to become large enough for a black hole to form. Although a proper understanding of black holes requires astronomy, general relativity, and quantum mechanics, the numerical result is the same as Laplace obtained.

We can obtain the radius of a black hole of mass M from the last equation. This radius, called the *Schwarzschild radius*, is given by

$$R_{\mathrm{s}} = \frac{2GM}{c^2}. \tag{8.21}$$

The Schwarzschild radius indicates the size that an object of mass M must have if it is to have the enormous density of a black hole. For a black hole with the mass of the sun, the Schwarzschild radius is only about 3 km.

Even though black holes give off no light from within, they can be detected by their gravitational effects. For example, a black hole can combine with a cloud of gas, a star, or a galaxy of stars to form an orbiting system, whose

Figure 8.19
An image from the Wide Field and Planetary Camera II on NASA's Hubble Space Telescope shows a spiral-shaped disk of hot gas in the core of the galaxy M87. Measurements by the telescope reveal that disk rotates so rapidly that it contains a black hole at its hub.

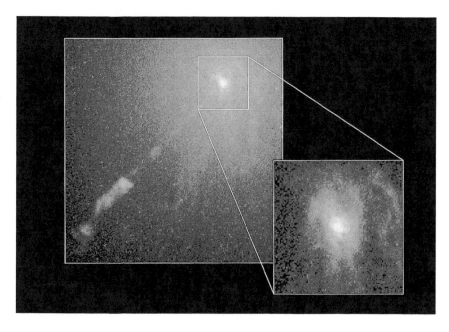

combined motions conform approximately to Kepler's laws. If we can infer the motion of the stars from astronomical observations, then we can detect the presence and mass of the black hole. One of the many observed objects thought to be a black hole is found in the core of the galaxy M87 located about 50 million light-years away in the constellation Virgo. Measurements from the Hubble Space Telescope reveal a spiral-shaped disk of hot gas rotating about a central hub (Fig. 8.19). Calculations show that the object at the hub has a mass three billion times the mass of the sun, yet it occupies a space no larger than our solar system. It must be a black hole.

Summary

Useful Concepts

In this chapter we applied the laws of conservation of energy and momentum to analyze elastic collisions, and motion in a gravitational field. These examples indicate the wide variety of problems solvable by conservation laws.

■ In one dimension the law of conservation of momentum for collision of two objects is

$$m_1 v_1 + m_2 v_2 = m_1 v_1' + m_2 v_2'.$$

■ In an elastic collision, kinetic energy is conserved, leading to the equation

$$\tfrac{1}{2} m_1 v_1^2 + \tfrac{1}{2} m_2 v_2^2 = \tfrac{1}{2} m_1 v_1'^2 + \tfrac{1}{2} m_2 v_2'^2$$

■ For collisions in two dimensions, we take account of the vector nature of momentum, determining separate conservation equations in the x and y directions.

■ The gravitational potential energy of an object of mass m at a distance r from the center of the earth and above the earth's surface is

$$\text{PE} = -G \frac{M_E m}{r}.$$

■ We can use the general form of the gravitational potential energy and the conservation of energy to determine the escape speed from the earth,

$$v_{\text{esc}} = \sqrt{\frac{2 G M_E}{R_E}}.$$

Important Terms

You should be able to write the definition or meaning of each of the following terms:

elastic collision   escape speed
inelastic collision

Conceptual Questions

8.1 A stationary firecracker is hung by a thread from a tree limb and then explodes into three pieces. Do the paths of the three pieces lie in a plane? Explain your answer with care.

8.2 Give some examples of elastic, inelastic, and perfectly inelastic collisions.

8.3 Two bodies collide elastically in midair. The only restriction on their initial motions is that they must collide. Explain how this situation can be viewed as only a two-dimensional problem.

8.4 Can an object have, at the same time, more kinetic energy but less momentum than another object?

8.5 Are there any combinations of masses and initial velocities in a one-dimensional elastic collision so that the velocity of one of the bodies is unchanged by the collision? Are there

any conditions under which the speed is the same after the collision as it was before? In either case, explain your answer.

8.6 What would be the effect on the game of billiards if the cue ball were twice as massive as the other balls?

8.7 The Newtonian Demonstrator (Fig. 8.20) is a popular item in novelty shops as well as physics departments. When one ball is pulled aside, released, and allowed to strike the others, one ball pops out from the opposite side. When two balls are pulled aside and released, two balls pop out on the other side as a result of the ensuing collision. Explain why this is so.

8.8 A cosmonaut wishes to dock his spacecraft with another craft several hundred meters ahead of him in the same orbit. The two spacecraft are moving with the same speed at the same radius in the same circular orbit. The cosmonaut can use

Figure 8.20
Question 8.7: A Newtonian demonstrator.

thruster rockets directed fore, aft, up, or down. Which should he use and in what order? Describe the subsequent motion of his craft.

8.9 A projectile fired from the earth's surface needs to be given an upward speed equal to the escape speed v_{esc} in order to escape from the earth. Would a rocket fired from the earth need that same speed in order to escape? Why?

8.10 Why is gravitational potential energy (Eq. 8.18) negative?

8.11 What happens to a spacecraft that leaves the earth with a speed greater than the escape speed?

Problems

Section 8.1 Definition of Elastic Collisions

Hints for Solving Problems

Remember that for elastic collisions, both kinetic energy and momentum are conserved. You will find it helpful to draw two diagrams of a collision, one before and one after impact.

8.1 A steel ball is dropped from a height of 2.37 m onto a flat stone slab. On rebounding, the speed of the ball is 3.94 m/s when it is 1.52 m above the stone slab. Is the collision elastic?

8.2 A glass marble is dropped onto a steel slab from a height of 2.0 m. If the marble rebounds to a height of 1.6 m, what fraction of its initial energy was lost? Where has the energy gone?

8.3 A ball bearing is dropped from a height of 2.0 m onto a steel slab. If the ball bounces to a height of 1.4 m, what is its upward speed as it passes the 1.0-m mark?

8.4 A ball tossed upward with a speed of 4.27 m/s from 1.52 m above the floor falls to the floor and bounces to a height of 2.38 m. Is the collision with the floor elastic?

8.5 A ball thrown downward at 2.32 m/s from a height of 1.07 m above the floor bounces up to a height of 1.34 m. Is the collision with the floor elastic?

8.6• A tennis ball dropped from a height of 3.00 m loses 50% of its mechanical energy at each bounce. To what height does it rise after the third bounce?

8.7• A marble dropped from 1.37 m onto a flat surface bounces to a height of 1.27 m on its first bounce. If the marble loses the same fraction of mechanical energy on each bounce, how high does it rise after the fourth bounce?

Section 8.2 Elastic Collisions in One Dimension

8.8 A 0.400-kg toy truck moving at an initial speed of 0.100 m/s collides head-on with a 0.300-kg toy car at rest. The collision is elastic. Find their final speeds and directions.

8.9 Two billiard balls travel toward each other along a straight line with the same speed. What are their speeds and directions after an elastic collision?

8.10 Two air-track gliders of equal mass are initially moving in the same direction along a straight line. The rearmost glider has an initial speed of 3.0 m/s and the forward glider has a speed of 2.0 m/s. If the collision is elastic, what are the speeds and directions of the gliders after the collision?

8.11 An air-track glider with an initial speed of 4.0 m/s has a head-on collision with another glider at rest that is three times as massive. What are the final speeds and directions of the gliders if the collision is elastic?

8.12• Two glass marbles moving along a straight line toward each other undergo an elastic collision. The speed of one marble is $2v$ and its mass is m; the speed of the other marble is v and its mass is $2m$. What are the speeds and directions of the marbles after the collision?

8.13• A 1200-kg car traveling 27 m/s crashes into the rear of a 9000-kg truck moving in the same direction at 22 m/s. Immediately after the collision the car is moving at 20 m/s. (a) How fast was the truck moving immediately after the collision? (b) Is kinetic energy conserved in the collision?

8.14• A 326-g stationary air-track glider is attached to the end of an air track by a compressible spring with spring constant $k = 5.32$ N/m (Fig. 8.21). A 163-g glider moving at 1.27 m/s collides elastically with the stationary glider. How

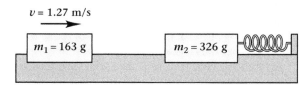

Figure 8.21
Problem 8.14.

far does the spring compress? Assume that the air track is very much heavier than the gliders.

8.15● Is it possible for a moving air-track glider to collide elastically with a stationary glider in such a way that both of them move in the same direction with the same speed after the collision? Use the conservation laws to explain your answer.

8.16● After an elastic collision between two pool balls of equal mass, one is observed to have a speed of 3.0 m/s along the positive *x* axis and the other has a speed of 2.0 m/s along the negative *x* axis. What were the original speeds and directions of the two balls?

8.17● A 1000-kg automobile going 10 m/s collides head-on with a 1200-kg automobile traveling in the opposite direction at 4.0 m/s. (a) What is the maximum kinetic energy that can be dissipated in damaging the two cars? (b) What limits this amount of energy?

8.18●● A 283-g air-track glider moving at 0.69 m/s on a 2.4-m long air track collides elastically with a 467-g glider at rest in the middle of the horizontal track. The end of the track over which the struck glider moves is not frictionless, and the glider moves with a coefficient of friction $\mu = 0.02$ with respect to the track. Will the glider reach the end of the track? Neglect the length of the gliders.

8.19●● A ball of mass 2 *m* is projected upward with speed v_0 from the floor (Fig. 8.22). Another ball of mass *m* is hung from the ceiling by a light string at a height *h* directly above the first ball, so that the projected ball collides with it. Derive an expression for the height above the floor to which the second ball will rise as a function of v_0, *h*, and *g*, assuming that the collision is elastic.

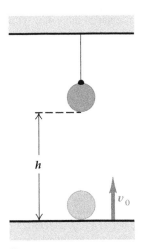

Figure 8.22
Problem 8.19.

8.20●● A 237-g air-track glider moving at 0.80 m/s on a 2.4-m long air track collides elastically with a 513-g glider at rest in the middle of the track. The end of the track over which the struck glider moves is not level, but slants upward at an an-

gle of 0.70° with respect to the horizontal. Will the glider reach the end of the track? Neglect the length of the gliders.

8.21●● Show that for a one-dimensional elastic collision between mass m_1 moving with initial velocity v_1 and mass m_2 with initial velocity v_2, the final velocities are

$$v'_1 = \frac{m_1 - m_2}{m_1 + m_2}v_1 + \frac{2 m_2}{m_1 + m_2}v_2 \quad \text{and}$$

$$v'_2 = \frac{2 m_1}{m_1 + m_2}v_1 - \frac{m_1 - m_2}{m_1 + m_2}v_2$$

8.22●● Blocks of mass *m* and 2 *m* are positioned on a semi-circular frictionless track at a height of *R*/4 above the lowest point (Fig. 8.23). The blocks are released simultaneously and collide elastically. How high does each block rise after the collision?

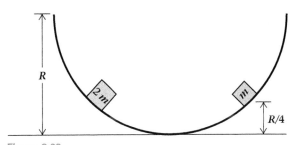

Figure 8.23
Problem 8.22.

*Section 8.3 Elastic Collisions in Two Dimensions

Hints for Solving Problems

In two dimensions, conservation of momentum provides independent equations in the *x* and *y* directions. A third equation comes from conservation of energy. For two objects in collision, if we know their masses and initial velocities, there will be four quantities in a typical two-dimensional collision that are required to define the final state. They might be the final velocity components v_{1x}, v_{1y}, v_{2x}, and v_{2y}. Since you can only determine three unknown quantities from three equations, you need one other quantity from the given information in order to uniquely determine the other three quantities. In elastic collisions between a moving object and a stationary object of the same mass, the angle between the two outgoing objects is 90°.

8.23 Use the results of Example 8.3 and the trigonometric relationship $\cos \theta = \sin(90° - \theta)$ to show that for a two-dimensional elastic collision between two balls of identical mass the relationship between the two outgoing angles is $\theta_1 + \theta_2 = 90°$.

8.24 A proton traveling with speed v_1 collides elastically with another proton initially at rest. After the collision the protons move off, making angles of $+45°$ and $-45°$ with respect to the direction of motion of the incident proton. What are the final speeds of the protons after the collision in terms of the initial speed v_1?

8.25• A ball of mass m moving with a speed v_1 collides elastically with a stationary ball of the same mass. The incident ball is scattered at an angle of $60°$ from its incident direction. What fraction of the initial kinetic energy is imparted to the struck ball?

8.26• An elastic collision occurs between two air hockey pucks in which one puck is at rest and the other is moving with a speed of 0.50 m/s. After the collision, the puck initially in motion makes an angle of $20°$ with its original direction, and the struck puck moves at an angle of $70°$ on the other side of the original direction. What is the final speed of each puck?

8.27• A deuteron collides elastically with another deuteron initially at rest. After the collision, one deuteron is observed to have half of the original kinetic energy. In what direction must it be moving? What is the direction of motion of the struck deuteron?

8.28•• A tennis ball collides with an identical ball at rest. The collision occurs in such a way that one-fourth the initial kinetic energy is lost in deformation of the balls. The outgoing balls leave the impact point, making equal angles with respect to the direction of the original ball. Determine the angle θ between the direction of one of the balls and the initial direction of the first ball.

8.29•• A billiard ball traveling at speed v_0 scatters elastically from an identical ball making an angle of $27°$ with respect to its original direction. The incident ball subsequently scatters from another identical ball so that the path of the incoming ball becomes parallel to its original direction. What is the speed of the incident ball after being scattered twice?

*Section 8.4 General Form of Gravitational Potential Energy

8.30 What is the value of the gravitational potential energy of a 1.00-kg mass on the surface of the earth if the zero of potential energy is taken at $r = \infty$?

8.31 What is the gravitational potential energy of the moon with respect to the earth if the zero of potential energy is taken at $r = \infty$?

8.32 What is the change in gravitational potential energy of a 1.00-kg mass that is carried from the surface of the earth to a distance of one earth radius above the surface?

8.33 What is the change in the gravitational potential energy of a 5.00-kg mass that is carried from the earth's surface to a height of $\frac{1}{4}$ the earth's radius above the earth?

8.34• A metal slug is dropped from a height of $1/20$ r_M above the moon's surface. Find the speed with which the slug strikes the moon's surface.

8.35•• How high from the surface of the earth must an object be raised so that the increase in potential energy as given by

PE $= mgh$ and by PE $= -GM_Em/r$ will differ by 2%? Express this distance as a multiple of the earth's radius.

8.36•• (a) What is the increase in potential energy of a mass m moved from the surface of the earth (R_E) to a distance of $2R_E$ from the center of the earth? (b) Is this the same value obtained by using ΔPE $= mg'\Delta R$ where g' is the simple average acceleration of gravity, $g' = (g_{RE} + g_{2RE})/2$? (c) If the average in (b) is not correct, determine the correct average g' by setting the actual change in potential energy equal to $mg'\Delta R$ and solving for g'.

*Section 8.5 Motion in a Gravitational Potential

> **Hints for Solving Problems**
>
> In a gravitational field, the potential energy is always negative if the reference level is zero at infinity.

8.37 With what minimum upward speed must a rocket be projected vertically to reach a height above the earth equal to the earth's radius? Ignore air friction.

8.38 How fast must you project an object for it to reach a height equal to the moon's distance from the earth? Ignore the gravitational attraction of the moon.

8.39 A rocket is projected upward from the earth's surface ($r = R_E$) with an initial speed v_0 that carries it to a distance $r = 4R_E$ from the center of the earth. What is the launch speed v_0? Assume that air friction can be ignored and give your answer in terms of G, R_E, and the earth's mass M_E.

8.40 A rocket is projected upward from the earth's surface ($r = R_E$) with an initial speed v_0 that carries it to a distance $r = 1.5R_E$ from the center of the earth. What is the launch speed v_0? Assume that air friction can be ignored and give your answer in terms of g and R_E.

8.41 What is the potential energy of a 1.0-kg mass at a distance three-quarters of the way from the earth to the moon? Ignore the effects of the sun, but not of the moon.

8.42• A spaceship lies along a line from the sun to Jupiter. At what distance from Jupiter (1.90×10^{27} kg) is the gravitational attraction of the spaceship to the planet equal to the attraction of the spaceship to the sun (1.99×10^{30} kg)? Give your answer as a fraction of the distance between the sun and Jupiter.

8.43• A meteor headed straight toward the earth has an approach speed of 8.0×10^3 m/s at a distance of $4R_E$ from the center of the earth, where R_E is the earth's radius. How far from the center of the earth will it be when its speed increases to 1.2×10^4 m/s? Express your answer in terms of R_E.

8.44• Imagine that a meteor headed straight toward the earth has an approach speed of 8.0×10^3 m/s at a distance of $3R_E$ from the center of the earth, where R_E is the earth's radius. What will its speed be when it reaches the atmosphere at $R \approx R_E$?

*Section 8.6 Escape Speed

8.45 Compute the escape speed from the surface of Mars, which has a radius of 3.37×10^6 m and a mass of 6.42×10^{23} kg.

8.46 A distant planet has a mass of $0.82\ M_E$ and a radius of $0.95\ R_E$. What is the ratio of the escape speed from this planet to the escape speed from the earth?

8.47• The radius of Uranus is approximately 3.69 times the radius of the earth. If the escape speed from Uranus is 22 km/s, what is the ratio of the acceleration of gravity on Uranus to its value on earth?

8.48• The escape speed from a distant planet is 35 km/s. If the acceleration of gravity on the planet surface is 11.1 m/s², what is the radius of the planet?

8.49• (a) What is the Schwarzschild radius of a body with the mass of the earth? (b) What would be the average density of that body if its radius were the same as its Schwarzschild radius?

8.50•• Calculate the minimum initial speed needed to project a rocket from the moon to the earth. For simplicity, assume a straight line path as in Example 8.7.

8.51•• Show that the escape speed from the earth is $\sqrt{2}$ times as large as the orbital speed of an object in orbit just above the earth's surface.

Additional Problems

8.52 A 0.400-kg toy truck moving at an initial speed of 0.100 m/s collides head-on with a 0.300-kg toy car at rest. The collision is perfectly inelastic, so the two toys stick together. (a) Find their final speed and (b) calculate how much kinetic energy is lost in the collision.

8.53 Show that the escape speed from earth can be expressed as $v_{esc} = \sqrt{2gR_E}$, where g is the gravitational acceleration at the earth's surface and R_E is the earth's radius.

8.54 A 30-caliber rifle with a mass of 3.14 kg fires a 7.13-g bullet with a speed of 606 m/s with respect to the ground. What kinetic energy is released by the explosion of the gunpowder that fires the bullet?

8.55• A 58-kg girl skis down a slope from a height of 9.0 m above the bottom of a hill. At the bottom she plows into a snowdrift that stops her in 2.0 s. What average force does she exert on the snow? How far does she go into the snowdrift?

8.56• A 1200-kg spacecraft is separated from its 4800-kg booster stage by an explosion (Fig. 8.24). The two parts move away from each other with a relative speed of 100 m/s. Calculate the energy imparted to the two masses by the explosion.

8.57• A rocket moving at 1000 m/s consists of a 1200-kg space capsule and a 6000-kg booster stage. An explosion that separates them throws the capsule forward so that it has a speed of 1100 m/s. How much energy was released in the explosion?

8.58• A pendulum with a bob of mass $3\ m$ is lifted to a height h above its lowest point and allowed to fall so that it

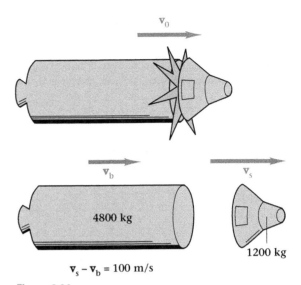

$$\mathbf{v}_s - \mathbf{v}_b = 100\ \text{m/s}$$

Figure 8.24
Problem 8.56.

collides elastically with a block of mass $2\ m$ that rests on a frictionless horizontal surface (Fig. 8.25). The struck mass then travels a distance s and collides elastically with another block of mass m. Find an expression for the speed of the block with mass m as a function of the height h to which the pendulum was raised.

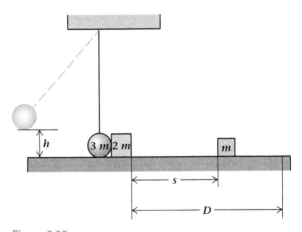

Figure 8.25
Problem 8.58.

8.59• Two air-track gliders of mass $m_1 = 234$ and $m_2 = 543$ g are tied together with thread, with a coil spring compressed between them. The gliders are at rest on an air track. The spring, with spring constant $k = 200$ N/m, is compressed by 4.70 cm from its equilibrium length. The thread is burned in two, and the gliders move apart. What is the speed of each glider?

8.60• A 2.5-kg block collides with a horizontal spring of negligible mass and spring constant $k = 320$ N/m. The block compresses the spring by 8.5 cm from its rest position (Fig. 8.26). How fast was the block going when it hit the spring if the frictional coefficient between the block and the horizontal surface is 0.40?

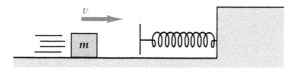

Figure 8.26
Problem 8.60.

8.61•• (a) Graph the potential energy for a 1-kg mass at positions along a straight line from the earth to the moon. Include the gravitational effects of the earth and the moon, but not of the sun. (b) Find the point along a straight line from the earth to the moon where the potential energy is a maximum by equating the force on the mass due to the earth with the force on it due to the moon.

8.62•• A puck collides elastically with identical stationary puck. The coefficient of friction between the pucks and the surface they slide on is μ. (a) Is the angle between the two outgoing pucks 90°? (b) If the angle is not 90°, is it always either greater than 90° or less than 90°?

8.63•• A ball is thrown upward with a speed v from a height h at $t = 0$. If it rebounds from the floor elastically, find an expression for the time t between bounces.

8.64•• A 36-g bullet with a speed of 350 m/s strikes a 8-cm-thick fence post. The bullet is retarded by an average force of 3.6×10^3 N while traveling all the way through the board. (a) What speed does the bullet have when it emerges? (b) How many such boards could the bullet penetrate?

8.65•• An air-track glider with an initial speed of 4.0 m/s collides head-on with another glider of equal mass initially at rest. The struck glider has a ball of wax on its bumper that deforms during the collision. What fraction of the initial energy is used in deforming the wax if the final speed of the struck glider is 3.0 m/s?

8.66•• A glass marble is dropped down an elevator shaft and hits a thick glass plate on top of an elevator that is descending at a speed of 2.0 m/s. The marble hits the glass plate 3.0 m below the point from which it was dropped. If the collision is

elastic, how high will the marble rise, relative to the point from which it was dropped?

8.67•• After colliding elastically with a stationary puck of the same mass, an air hockey puck is observed to have a momentum whose magnitude is only half the magnitude of its original momentum. What angle does it make with its original direction?

8.68•• Two cars hit head-on in an inelastic collision in which they lose 40% of their kinetic energy. One car has a mass of 1230 kg and an initial speed of 37.3 km/h in the positive x direction. The second car has a mass of 1734 kg and an initial speed of 26.5 km/h in the negative x direction. (a) What happens after the collision? Do the cars separate or stick together? (b) What are the velocities of the two cars immediately after the collision? (*Hint:* Compare the net momentum with the momenta of the individual cars.)

8.69•• Two identical bumper cars collide elastically at right angles, with one going twice as fast as the other. If the faster car is deflected 45° away from its original direction of travel, by how much is the slower car deflected away from its original direction of travel?

8.70•• Two cars collide at right angles and stick together as they skid to a stop. Car 1 has a mass of 1280 kg and a speed of 25 km/h to the east; car 2 has a mass of 950 kg and a speed of 37 km/h to the north. The average coefficient of friction between the tires and the road is 0.65. How far from the collision point, and in what direction, do the cars stop?

8.71•• A 5.00-g glass marble moving at 1.2 m/s collides head-on with an identical stationary marble. After the collision, both marbles then move in the direction of the oncoming marble. The struck marble moves with a speed 100/99 of the initial speed of the oncoming marble. After the collision, a small piece of the struck marble is found directly below the point of impact. What is the mass of the small piece? (This problem is a one-dimensional classical mechanics example of a technique used in nuclear and elementary particle physics—determining the mass of an unobserved particle by measuring the initial and final kinematic quantities and then using the conservation laws to find the missing mass. Assume in this case that momentum and kinetic energy are conserved.)

8.72•• An object is shot directly upward from the earth's surface with an initial speed v_0 sufficient for it to reach a height of 50 km. (a) Do not assume the earth's gravitational field to be constant and show that the initial speed is given approximately by $v_0 \approx \sqrt{2gh}$. (b) Calculate the initial speed v_0 and express your answer as a fraction of the escape speed from earth.

9.1   Angular Velocity and Angular
      Acceleration

9.2   Rotational Kinematics

9.3   Torque

9.4   Static Equilibrium

*9.5   Elasticity: Stress and Strain

Physics in Practice: Bridges

9.6   Torque and Moment of Inertia

9.7   Angular Momentum

9.8   Conservation of Angular Momentum

9.9   Rotational Kinetic Energy

9.10   Conservation of Energy: Translations
      and Rotations

*Physics in Practice: The Earth, the Moon,
and the Tides*

Rigid Bodies and Rotational Motion

O ur study of mechanics has included the revolution of the planets around the sun and the circular motion of an object as you swing it about your head on a string. A slightly different kind of angular motion is the daily turning of the earth on its axis or the spinning of a baseball when thrown. This latter type of motion is called rotational motion, and is defined more precisely in this chapter. Although we will primarily consider the motion of solid objects turning about a fixed axis, we will also examine moving objects that combine translational and rotational motion, as does a rolling wheel. In contrast with Chapter 5, we will not restrict ourselves to uniform circular motion, but will also include angular accelerations.

The material in this chapter is based on ideas with which you are already familiar. Topics will be developed in essentially the same order in which they were introduced for translational motion. For instance, we will begin by introducing kinematic equations to describe rotational motion, then go on to get an expression analogous to Newton's second law that will tell us what causes changes in rotational motion.

Almost all of the ideas of rotational motion can be developed in analogy with translational motion. Along the way, we will find a conservation law that is the rotational analog of the law of conservation of linear momentum, and we will find an additional expression for the kinetic energy of a rotating object. ■

9.1 Angular Velocity and Angular Acceleration

So far we have studied the translational motion of objects in one and two dimensions, including circular motion. Now we want to broaden our understanding of mechanics to include rotational motion. Any real object that has a definite shape can be made to rotate. If the object rotates with no deformation, so that all parts of the object remain at constant distances from every other part, we call the object a **rigid body.** The complex motion of a rigid body can be separated into a purely translational motion and a purely rotational motion.

In addition to the concepts of displacement, velocity, and acceleration that we use to describe linear motion, we need the corresponding quantities for angular motion. These quantities are angular displacement, angular velocity, and angular acceleration. With them we can describe the motion of a thrown, spinning ball or the start up of a merry-go-round.

Let's begin by thinking about a rigid body that rotates about a fixed axis, like the wheel of a bicycle turned upside down (Fig. 9.1). The angle θ describes the rotational position of a point on the wheel. In Section 5.1 we introduced

Figure 9.1
The wheel of an upturned bicycle spins freely about a fixed axis. When the angular velocity of the wheel changes, we say the wheel has angular acceleration.

angular measure in radians by defining an angle θ to be the ratio of the arc length s to the radius r:

$$\theta = \frac{s}{r}. \tag{9.1}$$

When the angle changes with time, the wheel has an *angular velocity*. We introduced angular velocity earlier when discussing uniform circular motion in Chapter 5. There we defined the average angular velocity $\overline{\omega}$ as the ratio of the change in angle to the change in time,

$$\overline{\omega} = \frac{\Delta\theta}{\Delta t}. $$

The instantaneous angular velocity ω is the limit of that ratio as the time interval goes to zero:

$$\omega = \lim_{\Delta t \to 0} \frac{\Delta\theta}{\Delta t}. \tag{9.2}$$

For a rigid body in rotation, all points on the body rotate with the same angular velocity ω (Fig. 9.2). Recall that the units of angular velocity are $\text{rad} \cdot \text{s}^{-1}$. (We could just use s^{-1} since the radian is dimensionless, but it is helpful to carry along the unit of radian as a reminder that the angles are measured in radians and not degrees.)

When the angular velocity of the rigid body changes, it has an angular acceleration. We define the **average angular acceleration** $\overline{\alpha}$ as the ratio of the change in angular velocity to the change in time,

$$\overline{\alpha} \equiv \frac{\omega_2 - \omega_1}{t_2 - t_1} = \frac{\Delta\omega}{\Delta t}. \tag{9.3}$$

The **instantaneous angular acceleration** α is the limit of the ratio $\Delta\omega/\Delta t$ as Δt approaches zero:

$$\alpha \equiv \lim_{\Delta t \to 0} \frac{\Delta\omega}{\Delta t}. \tag{9.4}$$

Since ω is the same for all points on a rotating rigid body, the angular acceleration will also be the same for all points on the body. The units of angular acceleration are $\text{rad} \cdot \text{s}^{-2}$.

As we saw in Chapter 5, the instantaneous tangential speed of a point on the rotating body depends on its radial distance r from the axis of rotation and on the angular velocity,

$$v = r\omega. \tag{9.5}$$

Similarly, there is a connection between the instantaneous tangential acceleration (linear motion) and the angular acceleration (rotational motion). The tangential acceleration associated with the motion of a point moving in a circular path of radius r is related to the instantaneous angular acceleration through

$$a_t = \alpha r. \tag{9.6}$$

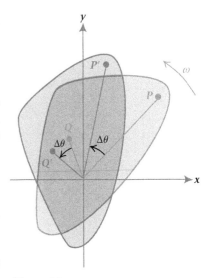

Figure 9.2
Points P and Q on the rigid body rotate with the same angular velocity, because they move through the same angle $\Delta\theta$ in the same time Δt.

In addition, for a point moving in a circular path with instantaneous angular velocity ω, we have seen that there is a centripetal acceleration a_c directed toward the rotation axis. The value of a_c is

$$a_c = \omega^2 r. \tag{9.7}$$

Because the centripetal acceleration is along the radial line from the point to the rotation axis, it is a radial acceleration. The tangential acceleration is perpendicular to the line from the point to the axis (Fig. 9.3). Thus these two accelerations are at right angles to each other.

It is important to remember that the equations we have developed here are appropriate only for circular motion of a particle moving at a constant radius about an axis or for a rigid body in rotation about an axis. If the radial distance is allowed to change, there will be additional terms required for the description of both the tangential acceleration and the radial acceleration.

Be sure that you clearly understand the difference between angular acceleration, which we have just defined in Eq. (9.6), and centripetal acceleration given in Eq. (9.7). Centripetal acceleration occurs whenever an object moves in a curved path, even if it moves with constant speed. The centripetal acceleration acts radially toward the center of rotation. Angular acceleration occurs when there is a change in the angular speed of the object. When you swing a stone in a circle around your head at a constant rate, there is no angular acceleration, but there is a centripetal acceleration. On the other hand, when you increase or decrease the angular velocity, there is an angular acceleration as well as a centripetal acceleration. For rotational motion, there is *always* a centripetal acceleration, but there is angular acceleration *only* when the angular velocity is changing. When both accelerations are present, the instantaneous acceleration of a point on the rotating object is given by the vector sum of the two accelerations (Fig. 9.3).

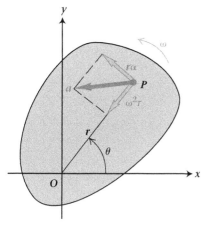

Figure 9.3

The acceleration **a** of a point P located a distance r from the axis of an object rotating with angular acceleration is the vector sum of a tangential component $a_t = r\alpha$ and a radial component $a_c = \omega^2 r$.

Figure 9.4

Example 9.1: An athlete swings the hammer in a circle to give it large velocity before letting it go.

Example 9.1

In the hammer throw, a 7.25-kg shot is swung in a circle five times and then released (Fig. 9.4). The shot moves with an average radius of 2.1 m and an average angular acceleration of 2.3 rad/s^2 reaching a maximum tangential speed of 25 m/s. (a) What is the average tangential force and (b) what is the maximum centripetal force exerted on the hammer?

Strategy (a) The average tangential force is given by the product of the average tangential acceleration with the mass of the hammer. The tangential acceleration is found from the relationship between angular acceleration and tangential acceleration given in Eq. (9.6). (b) The centripetal force is found from the product of centripetal acceleration with the mass.

Solution (a) The tangential acceleration is given by $a_t = \alpha r$. The tangential force is

$$F_t = ma_t = m\alpha r = (7.25 \text{ kg})(2.3 \text{ rad/s}^2)(2.1 \text{ m}) = 35 \text{ N}.$$

(b) The centripetal force is

$$F_c = m\omega^2 r = \frac{mv^2}{r} = \frac{(7.25 \text{ kg})(25 \text{ m/s})^2}{2.1 \text{ m}} = 2.2 \times 10^3 \text{ N}.$$

Discussion The tangential force is modest; approximately equivalent to the weight of a 3.6-kg object (the weight of two large textbooks). However, the centripetal force is quite large; nearly double the weight of a large athlete.

9.2 Rotational Kinematics

We now have three angular kinematic quantities θ, ω, and α, which are completely analogous to the linear kinematic quantities x, v, and a. If we restrict ourselves to cases in which the angular acceleration is constant, then we can find relationships between the angular kinematic variables just as we did for the translational kinematic variables. The definitions of angular displacement, angular velocity, and angular acceleration all differ from the related linear quantities by a factor of r. Because these corresponding quantities are analogous, we can simply write down the rotational kinematic equations from our knowledge of the translational ones. For example, starting with Eq. (2.8) for position,

$$x = x_0 + v_0 t + \tfrac{1}{2}at^2,$$

we can replace all the linear variables with the analogous angular variables to get

$$\theta = \theta_0 + \omega_0 t + \tfrac{1}{2}\alpha t^2. \tag{9.8}$$

In the same manner we could take Eq. (2.9),

$$v^2 = v_0^2 + 2a(x - x_0),$$

and by replacing the linear variables with the corresponding angular variables get

$$\omega^2 = \omega_0^2 + 2\alpha(\theta - \theta_0). \tag{9.9}$$

Table 9.1 lists the principal kinematic equations for constant acceleration for translational and rotational motion.

Table 9.1	Summary of the Linear and Rotational Kinematic Equations		
Linear		**Rotational**	
$\bar{v} = \Delta x/\Delta t$	(Ch. 2)	$\omega = \Delta\theta/\Delta t$	(Ch. 5)
$\bar{a} = \Delta v/\Delta t$	(Ch. 2)	$\bar{\alpha} = \Delta\omega/\Delta t$	(Ch. 9)
$v^2 = v_0^2 + 2a(x - x_0)$	(Ch. 2)	$\omega^2 = \omega_0^2 + 2\alpha(\theta - \theta_0)$	(Ch. 9)
$v = v_0 + at$	(Ch. 2)	$\omega = \omega_0 + \alpha t$	
$x = x_0 + \tfrac{1}{2}(v_0 + v)t$	(Ch. 2)	$\theta = \theta_0 + \tfrac{1}{2}(\omega + \omega_0)t$	
$x = x_0 + v_0 t + \tfrac{1}{2}at^2$	(Ch. 2)	$\theta = \theta_0 + \omega_0 t + \tfrac{1}{2}\alpha t^2$	(Ch. 9)

This table contains analogous linear (translational) and rotational equations. They were first introduced in the chapters indicated. Some expressions that were not derived in the text have been included because you may find them useful in other applications.

Example 9.2

The wheel on a moving car slows uniformly from 70 rad/s to 42 rad/s in 4.2 s (Fig. 9.5). (a) What is the angular acceleration of the wheel? (b) What angle does the wheel turn through in the 4.2 s? (c) How far does the car go if the radius of the wheel is 0.32 m?

Solution (a) To find the acceleration, we substitute directly into the definition Eq. (9.3):

$$\alpha = \frac{\Delta\omega}{\Delta t} = \frac{42 \text{ rad/s} - 70 \text{ rad/s}}{4.2 \text{ s}}$$

$$\alpha = -6.67 \text{ rad/s}^2 \approx -6.7 \text{ rad/s}^2.$$

The negative sign corresponds to the decreasing angular speed.
(b) The wheel will turn through an angle given by Eq. (9.8). Because we are only interested in the rotation starting at the beginning of the 4.2 s, we set $\theta_0 = 0$.

$$\theta = \omega_0 t + \tfrac{1}{2}\alpha t^2$$
$$\theta = (70 \text{ rad/s})(4.2 \text{ s}) + \tfrac{1}{2}(-6.67 \text{ rad/s}^2)(4.2 \text{ s})^2$$
$$\theta = 294.0 \text{ rad} - 58.8 \text{ rad}$$
$$\theta = 235.2 \text{ rad} \approx 240 \text{ rad}.$$

Note that, because there are 2π rad in a full revolution, 240 rad is equivalent to $240/2\pi \approx 38$ revolutions of the wheel.
(c) The distance traveled by the car (Fig. 9.5) is the same as the path length of a point on the edge of the wheel as it turns through the angle θ calculated above. We can find this distance from Eq. (9.1), the definition of an angle in radians:

$$\theta = \frac{s}{r}.$$

Upon rearranging, we find the distance s to be

$$s = r\theta$$
$$s = (0.32 \text{ m})(235 \text{ rad})$$
$$s = 75 \text{ m}.$$

Figure 9.5
Example 9.2: When the car's wheels turn through an angle θ, the car travels a distance $s = r\theta$, where r is the radius of the wheels.

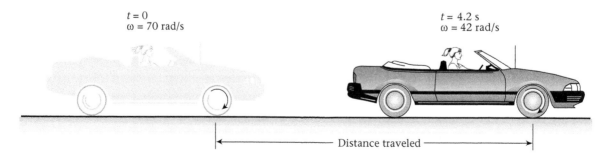

$t = 0$
$\omega = 70$ rad/s

$t = 4.2$ s
$\omega = 42$ rad/s

Distance traveled

Example 9.3

A bicycle tire turning at 0.21 rad/s is brought to rest by the brakes in exactly two revolutions. What is the angular acceleration of the wheel?

Solution Equation (9.9) may be solved to give the angular acceleration:

$$\alpha = \frac{\omega^2 - \omega_0^2}{2(\theta - \theta_0)}.$$

The initial conditions are $\theta_0 = 0$ and $\omega_0 = 0.21$ rad/s. Two revolutions is 2 times 2π radians, so the final conditions are $\theta = 4\pi$ and $\omega = 0$. Substituting these into the equation for α gives

$$\alpha = \frac{0^2 - (0.21 \text{ rad/s})^2}{2(4\pi - 0)}$$

$$\alpha = -1.8 \times 10^{-3} \text{ rad/s}^2.$$

9.3 Torque

So far, we have seen that an object at rest, such as a book on a table, remain motionless when two equal but oppositely directed forces are applied to it. That is always true if the object is a point mass. It is even true for an extended object like the book when the two forces are applied in opposite directions along the same line. However, when the forces are not along the same line, the book may turn or rotate. This motion occurs even though the net force is zero. The manner in which the book turns depends on its size and shape, as well as on its mass. What causes the book to rotate? The answer to this question is found in this and later sections of this chapter.

We begin by considering a familiar rotating object, a door hinged at one edge. We can pull on it in several ways (Fig. 9.6). However, the most effective way to open the door is to grab the edge of the door farthest from the hinges and pull at right angles to the door. Intuitively, we realize that the distance from the hinge to the point of application of the force as well as the magnitude and direction of the force are important factors affecting the tendency of the door to rotate.

The quantity measuring how effectively a force causes rotation is called **torque.** The greater the distance from the axis of rotation (door hinges) to the point where we apply the force (door handle), the greater the torque. Also, maximum torque occurs when the direction of the applied force is perpendicular to a line drawn between the axis and the point where the force is applied. By contrast, when the line and the force are in the same direction, so that the force acts directly toward or away from the axis of rotation, there is no torque.

Figure 9.7 illustrates the application of a force causing a door to rotate about an axis at point O, looking down from above the door. The torque τ about point O is defined as

$$\tau \equiv rF \sin \theta, \tag{9.10}$$

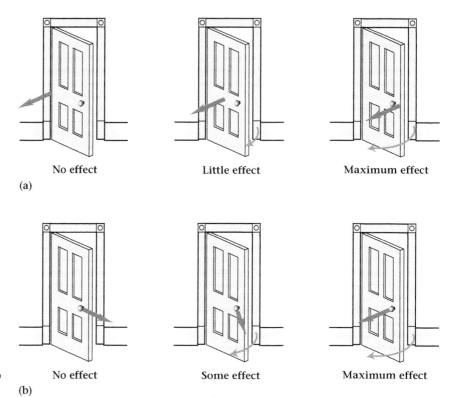

No effect   Little effect   Maximum effect

(a)

No effect   Some effect   Maximum effect

(b)

Figure 9.6
A door free to rotate about its hinges.
(a) The force applied farthest from the hinges produces the greatest torque.
(b) The force applied at right angles to the door produces the greatest effect.

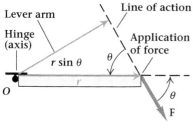

Figure 9.7
A force **F** applied at a distance r causes a torque $\tau = rF \sin \theta$ about the point O. The effective lever arm is $r \sin \theta$.

where r is the magnitude of the displacement from the axis to the point of application of the force **F** and θ is the angle between the direction of **r** and the direction of the force. The maximum torque occurs when θ is 90°—that is, when **r** and **F** are perpendicular. When **r** and **F** are in the same direction, θ becomes zero and there is no torque.

We see from the figure that applying a torque is equivalent to applying a force perpendicular to a lever. The lever arm, or moment arm, is defined as the perpendicular distance from the axis of rotation to the line of action of the force. From the geometry, we see that the lever arm is $r \sin \theta$. Therefore, saying that the torque is the product of force times the lever arm ($r \sin \theta$) is consistent with Eq. (9.10). Thinking of torque as the product of a force and a lever arm often makes a problem easier to analyze.

Figure 9.8 shows two forces generating torques. In both cases the forces are at right angles to **r**. Although the resulting torques have the same magnitude, they

Figure 9.8
(a) Force **F**₁ produces a torque causing a counterclockwise rotation about O.
(b) Force **F**₂ produces a clockwise rotation about O.

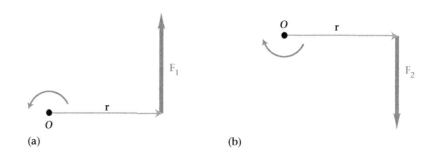

(a)   (b)

tend to cause rotations in opposite directions. In this book, we adopt the sign convention that a torque tending to produce a counterclockwise motion is positive; a torque tending to produce a clockwise motion is negative.

Torque is really a vector quantity, with both magnitude and direction. The magnitude is given by Eq. (9.10), and the direction is along the axis of rotation. This direction is perpendicular to the plane containing both the line of action of the force and the line from the axis to the point of application (Fig. 9.9a). The direction of the torque points along the direction a right-handed screw will move if **r** is rotated by **F**. Figure 9.9(b) shows an alternative way of establishing this direction.

The units of torque are the units of force multiplied by the units of length. Thus, the SI unit for torque is the newton-meter (N · m). In the British system, the unit for torque is the foot-pound (ft-lb). The units of torque are the same as those for work and energy; however, torque and work represent very different physical quantities. Moreover, remember that torque is a vector, whereas work is a scalar.

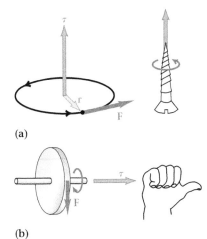

(a)

(b)

Figure 9.9
Direction of the torque vector. (a) In the direction of advance of a right-hand screw rotated by the force. (b) The right-hand rule: The curled fingers point in the direction of the force. The thumb then points in the direction of the torque.

Example 9.4

The instructions for replacing the head gasket on an automobile engine say that the bolts should be "torqued down" to 90 N · m. If you use a wrench that is 45 cm long, how much force must you apply in a direction perpendicular to the wrench handle to accomplish this? (Too much torque will pinch the gasket so that it will not seal properly.)

Solution The physical situation is shown in Fig. 9.10. We are told that the angle between the direction of the force and the line from the axis to the point of application is 90°. Thus, Eq. (9.10) becomes

$$\tau = rF,$$

and

$$F = \frac{\tau}{r}$$

$$F = \frac{90 \text{ N} \cdot \text{m}}{45 \text{ cm}} \left(\frac{100 \text{ cm}}{1 \text{ m}} \right) = 200 \text{ N}.$$

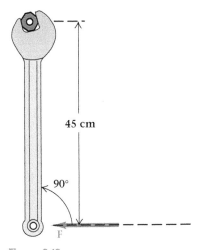

Figure 9.10
Example 9.4: Using a wrench to tighten the nut on a bolt. A force **F** is applied near the end of the handle.

Example 9.5

The crank arm of a bicycle pedal is 16.5 cm long. If a 52.0-kg woman puts all her weight on one pedal, how much torque is developed (a) when the crank is horizontal and (b) when the pedal is 15° from the top?

Solution (a) For the case where the crank arm is horizontal (Fig. 9.11a), the angle between the downward force of the woman's weight and the crank arm is 90°. The lever arm is the full extent of the crank arm, and the torque is

$$\tau = rF = r(mg) = (16.5 \text{ cm})(52.0 \text{ kg})(9.81 \text{ m/s}^2)(10^{-2} \text{ m/cm})$$
$$\tau = 84.2 \text{ N} \cdot \text{m}.$$

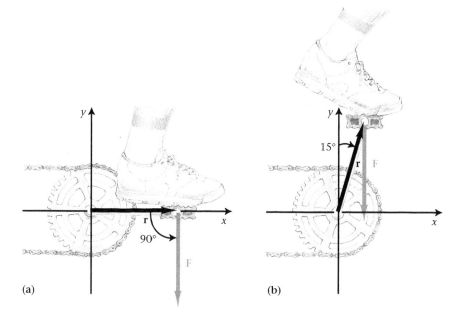

Figure 9.11
Example 9.5: Torque applied to a bicycle pedal. (a) The crank is horizontal. (b) The crank makes an angle of 15° with the vertical.

(b) For the case where the pedal is 15° from the top (Fig. 9.11b), the angle between the direction of the force and the direction of the crank arm is 165°, so the lever arm is (16.5 cm)(sin 165°) = 4.27 cm = 0.0427 m. The resulting torque is

$$\tau = (\text{lever arm})(\text{force})$$
$$\tau = (0.0427 \text{ m})(52.0 \text{ kg})(9.81 \text{ m/s}^2) = 21.8 \text{ N} \cdot \text{m}.$$

Have you ever noticed this difference when pedaling a bicycle up a hill?

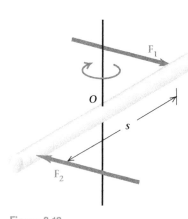

Figure 9.12
A couple. Two forces of equal magnitude act opposite and parallel to each other, but not along the same line. The rod is in translational equilibrium, but can still rotate.

| 9.4 | **Static Equilibrium** |

We saw in Section 4.9 that an object acted on by two forces, equal in magnitude but opposite in direction, has no linear acceleration. We say that the object is in translational equilibrium. The first condition for equilibrium (given in Section 4.9) was that the vector sum of the forces on a body be equal to zero:

$$\sum_{i=1}^{N} \mathbf{F}_i = 0, \tag{9.11}$$

where there are N individual forces $\mathbf{F}_i$. This condition ensures that there is no translational acceleration.

However, an object in translational equilibrium may still rotate. For example, the wheel of a stationary exercise bicycle does not move relative to the floor, but it turns when you apply a torque to it. A pair of forces, such as $\mathbf{F}_1$ and $\mathbf{F}_2$ of Fig. 9.12, that are equal in magnitude but opposite in direction *and not lying along the same line* is called a **couple.** The couple applies a torque about O equal to the sum of the torques due to the individual forces. Note that although the forces are in opposite directions, each tends to rotate the body in the same direction about O. If the distance between the lines of action of the forces is s, then each force has a lever arm $s/2$, and the torque produced by the two equal forces is

$$\tau = \frac{s}{2}F_1 + \frac{s}{2}F_2.$$

However, since $F_1 = F_2 = F$, we may write

$$\tau = sF.$$

If we want to keep the object from rotating, we must subject it to another torque of the same magnitude but in the opposite direction. We conclude that for a body to be in **rotational equilibrium,** the sum of the torques must be zero, or

$$\sum_{i=1}^{N} \tau_i = 0, \qquad (9.12)$$

where there are N individual torques τ_i.

The idea expressed in Eq. (9.12) is sometimes called the *second condition for equilibrium.* The second condition ensures that there is no rotational, or angular, acceleration. An object satisfying both conditions of equilibrium is said to be in *equilibrium.* If such an object is stationary, it is in *static equilibrium;* if it is moving with neither translational nor rotational acceleration, it is in *dynamic equilibrium.*

Figure 9.13(a) shows a uniform rod, such as a meterstick, placed on a fulcrum. It balances at its midpoint. A nonuniform rod, like a baseball bat (Fig. 9.13b), will also balance at some point, though not at its midpoint. In each case the upward force due to the fulcrum is equal to the entire weight of the object, as required by the first condition for equilibrium. In addition, the sum of the torques about the fulcrum due to gravity equals zero if the rod is in rotational equilibrium. In other words, the object behaves as if its mass were concentrated at a point lying directly above the fulcrum. This point is called the **center of mass** of the body.*

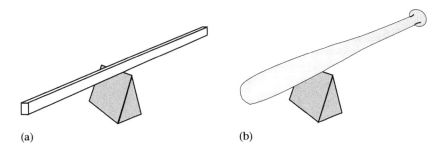

(a) (b)

Figure 9.13
(a) A uniform rod balanced at its center of mass. (b) A nonuniform rod balanced at its center of mass.

---

*Strictly speaking, the *center of gravity* is the point at which the force of gravity can be considered to act. For spherical bodies, like the planets, that point is their geometric center. Frequently the center of gravity and the center of mass are the same. They are different only when the external gravitational field is not uniform over the body.

(a)

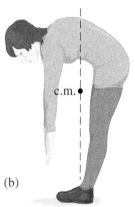

(b)

Figure 9.14
(a) The center of mass (c.m.) of a person standing erect lies above her feet. (b) When the person bends over, her hips move backward to keep her center of mass over her feet so that she does not fall over.

An object is in stable equilibrium if a small displacement causes a restoring torque to return it to its original position. If the resulting torque moves the object away from its original position, the equilibrium is unstable. We often refer to these conditions as being balanced or unbalanced. A person standing on a level floor will be balanced (stable equilibrium) if her center of mass is located over the area of support defined by the position of her feet (Fig. 9.14a). If she leans over, her legs and hips must move back as her torso moves forward so that her center of mass remains over her feet (Fig. 9.14b). Otherwise her center of mass would move out beyond her feet and she would topple over.

If a body is in static equilibrium, not only does it not rotate about some particular axis, but it does not rotate about any axis at all. We are free, therefore, to choose any possible rotation axis for the purpose of computing torques. Proper choice of the rotation axis can usually simplify the computations, since any force acting through the axis of rotation produces zero torque. Examples 9.6 and 9.7 illustrate this point.

▼
Problem-Solving Strategy

Statics Problems

1. Start by drawing a diagram of the system.
2. Isolate the object to be analyzed and make a free-body diagram showing the forces acting *on* the object. Be careful to show the point where each force acts.
3. Choose coordinate axes and specify the positive sense of rotation. Then resolve the forces into components along the axes.
4. Write the equilibrium equations, $\Sigma F_x = 0$, $\Sigma F_y = 0$, and $\Sigma \tau = 0$.
5. Choose a convenient origin for the point to compute torques. Remember that if a force acts along a line passing through the point, the torque due to that force is zero. A clever choice of origin can often simplify a problem.
6. Solve the equilibrium equations simultaneously. Remember that you will need as many equations as you have unknowns to solve for.

▼
Example 9.6

A 5.0-kg mass (m_2) and an unknown mass (m_3) hang from a 1.0-m rod of 2.0-kg mass (m_1), as shown in Fig. 9.15. The rod is supported on a knife-edge fulcrum at a distance 35 cm from one end. How large is the mass m_3 if the rod and masses are to balance on the knife edge?

Strategy We may consider all the weight of the rod to act downward at its center of mass, which in this case is at 50 cm. We then proceed as if a single mass m_1 equal to 2.0 kg (the mass of the rod) were hung from the rod at that point. Forces act at four points along the bar: the downward forces m_1g, m_2g, and m_3g at the points indicated and an upward force F at the fulcrum. The

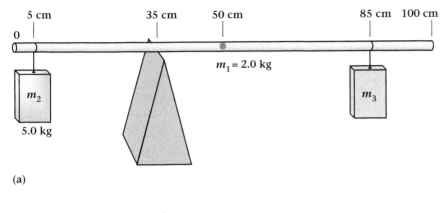

(a)

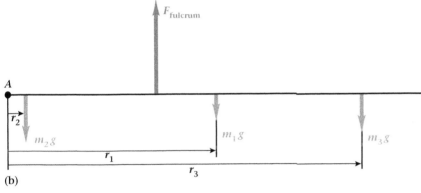

(b)

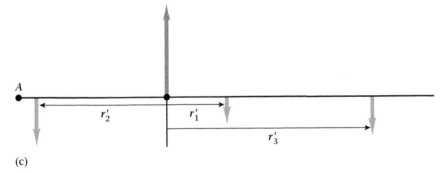

(c)

Figure 9.15
Examples 9.6 and 9.7: A rod and three masses in static equilibrium. (a) Physical situation. (b) Free-body diagram for the rod indicating radii from point of rotation A. (c) Free-body diagram for indicating radii from the fulcrum.

upward force must equal the total downward force in order to have translational equilibrium:

$$F_{\text{fulcrum}} = m_1 g + m_2 g + m_3 g.$$

We have two unknowns in this equation, so we consider the second condition of equilibrium, setting the sum of the torques equal to zero to obtain a second equation. As we said above, if the rod is in static equilibrium, not only does it not rotate about some particular axis, but it does not rotate about any axis at all. We are free to pick any point for the axis to go through. For this example, we pick the left-hand end of the rod (point A on Fig. 9.15b) and calculate torques about this point.

Solution We can use Eq. (9.12) by calling torques that tend to rotate things in a counterclockwise direction positive and those that tend to rotate things in a clockwise direction negative. We have $m_1 = 2.0$ kg, $m_2 = 5.0$ kg, and m_3 is unknown. The distances from point A to the point where the weights act are $r_1 = 0.50$ m, $r_2 = 0.05$ m, and $r_3 = 0.85$ m. The distance from A to the fulcrum is $r_F = 0.35$ cm. According to Eq. (9.12),

$$\Sigma \tau = \sum_i r_i F_i = 0.$$

Therefore, the sum of the torques about point A is as follows:

$$-r_2 m_2 g + r_F F_{\text{fulcrum}} - r_1 m_1 g - r_3 m_3 g = 0,$$
$$-r_2 m_2 g + r_F (m_1 g + m_2 g + m_3 g) - r_1 m_1 g - r_3 m_3 g = 0.$$

Since g is a common factor, it can be divided out to give

$$-r_2 m_2 + r_F (m_1 + m_2 + m_3) - r_1 m_1 - r_3 m_3 = 0.$$

Next we insert the appropriate numerical values to get

$$-(0.05 \text{ m})(5.0 \text{ kg}) + (0.35 \text{ m})(5.0 \text{ kg} + 2.0 \text{ kg} + m_3)$$
$$-(0.50 \text{ m})(2.0 \text{ kg}) - (0.85 \text{ kg})(m_3) = 0,$$
$$-0.25 \text{ m} \cdot \text{kg} + 2.45 \text{ m} \cdot \text{kg} + (0.35 \text{ m})(m_3) - 1.0 \text{ m} \cdot \text{kg} - (0.85 \text{ m})(m_3) = 0.$$

Gathering terms, we get

$$(0.50 \text{ m})(m_3) - 1.20 \text{ m} \cdot \text{kg} = 0,$$
$$m_3 = 2.4 \text{ kg}.$$

Example 9.7

Calculate the mass m_3 for Example 9.6 by computing torques about the fulcrum.

Strategy If we choose the axis of rotation to be about the fulcrum, then we have only three torques to consider: the counterclockwise torque due to m_2 and the clockwise torques due to m_1 and m_3. The torque due to the fulcrum force becomes zero because the moment arm is now zero.

Solution The sum of the torques becomes

$$+r_2' m_2 g - r_1' m_1 g - r_3' m_3 g = 0,$$

where we have used primes to indicate that the distance values are not the same as in Example 9.6. Upon rearranging, we find

$$m_3 = \frac{r_2' m_2 - r_1' m_1}{r_3'}.$$

From Fig. 9.15(c) we see that $r_2' = 30$ cm, $r_1' = 15$ cm, and $r_3' = 50$ cm. When the numerical values are inserted into the equation for m_3, we get

$$m_3 = \frac{(30 \text{ cm} \times 5.0 \text{ kg}) - (15 \text{ cm} \times 2.0 \text{ kg})}{50 \text{ cm}}$$

$$m_3 = 2.4 \text{ kg}.$$

Discussion As expected, we get the same answer here as in Example 9.6. This time the equation was simpler and the computation reduced because we only had to consider three torques. The force acting through the point of rotation produced no torque and did not have to be considered.

Example 9.8

A sign weighing 400 N is suspended at the end of a 350-N uniform rod (Fig. 9.16a). (a) What is the tension in the support cable if it makes an angle $\theta = 35°$ with the rod? (b) What would be the tension if the upper end of the cable were moved so that $\theta = 55°$?

Strategy Again we have a static equilibrium problem. We can represent the forces on the rod by a diagram like Fig. 9.16(b). The tension in the cable is resolved into components along and perpendicular to the rod. The force of the wall on the rod is eliminated from the analysis by taking the point where the rod touches the wall to be the axis of rotation for computing the torques. Then we can apply the second condition for equilibrium (Eq. 9.12) to determine the component of the tension perpendicular to the rod.

Solution (a) Choose counterclockwise torques positive and clockwise torques negative. Let L be the length of the rod, w its weight, W the weight of the sign, and T the tension in the cable. Since the rod is uniform, the weight w acts at its center of mass, a distance $L/2$ from the wall. The sum of the torques becomes

$$(T \sin \theta)L - w(\tfrac{1}{2} L) - WL = 0.$$

We can remove the common factor of L and rearrange this equation to get the tension T as

$$T = \frac{\tfrac{1}{2}w + W}{\sin \theta}.$$

When we substitute the numerical values, we get

$$T = \frac{\tfrac{1}{2}(350 \text{ N}) + 400 \text{ N}}{\sin 35°} = 1000 \text{ N}.$$

(b) If the cable is moved so that the angle it makes with the rod is 55°, the analysis in part (a) doesn't change. However, when we substitute the new numerical value for the angle, the tension becomes

$$T = \frac{\tfrac{1}{2}(350 \text{ N}) + 400 \text{ N}}{\sin 55°} = 700 \text{ N}.$$

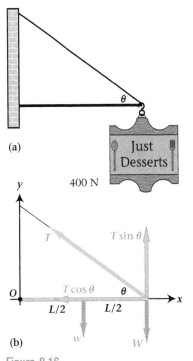

(a)

(b)

Figure 9.16
Example 9.8: (a) A 400-N sign is hung from the end of a long rod. (b) Force diagram for the sign and rod.

Example 9.9

The average mass of a woman's arm is approximately 5% of her whole body mass. When the arm is lifted as shown in Fig. 9.17, the distance between the center of mass of the arm and the center of rotation of the shoulder is

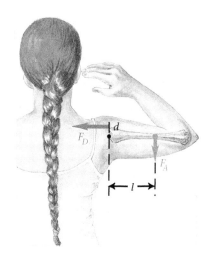

Figure 9.17
Example 9.9: The deltoid muscle supplies the force needed to hold the arm in equilibrium.

approximately 0.15 m. In a simplified model, we consider the deltoid muscle to pull horizontally with a lever arm of about 3 cm. With what force, in terms of the woman's body weight, must the deltoid muscle pull in order to hold the arm in equilibrium in the position shown in Fig. 9.17?

Strategy When the woman holds the arm steady, it is in a condition of static equilibrium for both translation and rotation. We can use the second condition for equilibrium to calculate torques about the center of rotation of the shoulder. Although we do not know a numerical value for the downward force on the arm, we can express it as a percentage of the woman's total weight $w = mg$.

Solution Remembering our sign convention for torques, we can apply Eq. (9.12) directly. Using the symbols shown in Fig. 9.17, we get

$$\sum_{i=1}^{N} \tau_i = F_D d - l F_A = 0,$$

where $F_A = 0.05w$. Upon rearranging, we find

$$F_D = \frac{l F_A}{d} = \frac{(0.15 \text{ m})(0.05w)}{0.03 \text{ m}} = 0.25w.$$

Discussion According to our model, the deltoid muscle must pull with a force of about one quarter of the woman's weight in order to hold the arm in the position shown. Although the model has oversimplified the structure of the shoulder, it does allow us to gain insight into the large forces that our muscles exert under the most ordinary conditions. If the woman extended her entire arm horizontally and held it outstretched, the center of mass would then be about 30 cm from the center of rotation. Then the force provided by the deltoid would be approximately half her body weight.

▼ *9.5   Elasticity: Stress and Strain

In the previous section, we analyzed the forces on objects in static equilibrium. In doing so we assumed that the objects were completely rigid and did not deform under the applied forces. Yet a seemingly rigid solid object such as a steel bar will deform when large forces are applied to it. When more modest forces are applied, the bar will still deform, but the amount of the deformation may be quite small.

Suppose that we pull on the ends of a bar with a force F, as shown in Fig. 9.18. We say that the bar is in tension. The internal forces in the bar resist the tension forces and hold the bar together. Even so, the bar deforms and the equilibrium length of the bar will be greater when the external forces are applied than without them. If the bar is in equilibrium with the applied forces, then every cross section of the bar must be subject to the same internal forces that resist stretching. We define the **tensile stress** as the ratio of the magnitude of the applied force F to the cross-sectional area A:

$$\text{stress} \equiv \frac{\text{force}}{\text{area}} = \frac{F}{A}.$$

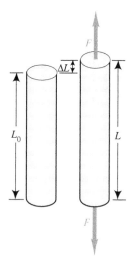

Figure 9.18
A bar with initial length L_0 is stretched by an amount ΔL when a force F is applied to its ends.

The **tensile strain** is defined as the ratio of the change in length ΔL to the initial length L_0 before the force was applied:

$$\text{strain} \equiv \frac{\text{change in length}}{\text{initial length}} = \frac{\Delta L}{L_0}.$$

The strain is the fractional change in length. As such, it is dimensionless. The bar would deform also if it were under compressive force, but this time it would be compressed rather than stretched. The **compressive strain** is defined just like the tensile strain; it is the ratio of the decrease in length to the initial length.

The amount of strain an object undergoes depends on the amount of stress applied to it. If the stress is not too great, the strain is observed to be proportional to the stress. The ratio of a stress to the corresponding strain is called an *elastic modulus*. For the tensile (or compressive) stress and strain that we have been describing, this ratio is called **Young's modulus,** denoted by Y:

$$Y = \frac{\text{stress}}{\text{strain}} = \frac{F/A}{\Delta L/L_0}. \qquad (9.13)$$

Young's modulus has the same units as does stress, N/m^2. Some typical values are found in Table 9.2. Notice also that Eq. (9.13) is equivalent to Hooke's law, which we saw in Chapter 6. For a given initial length, cross-sectional area, and Young's modulus, we get $F = kx$, where $k = YA/L_0$.

What happens when the stress on an object gets very large? You know the answer already: the object breaks. If we plot a graph of tensile stress versus strain, we find a curve with the general shape seen in Fig. 9.19. When the stress is small, the relationship is linear and the material is characterized by a unique Young's modulus. This region, shown as Oa on the graph, is known as the *elastic* region. Between the points labeled a and b, stress and strain are no longer proportional, but if the stress is removed, the material returns to its original length. For strains less than that at b, the deformation is reversible. The stress at point b is known as the *elastic limit* (or yield point) because

Table 9.2		*Elastic Moduli* ▼
Material		Young's Modulus (GPa)
Aluminum		70
Brass		91
Bone (compression)		7
Bone (tension)		18
Cast iron		120
Crown glass		60
Gold		80
Granite		46
Lead		16
Nylon		5
Steel		200
Tungsten		360

These are approximate values. The elastic behavior of a particular specimen depends on its past history and treatment.

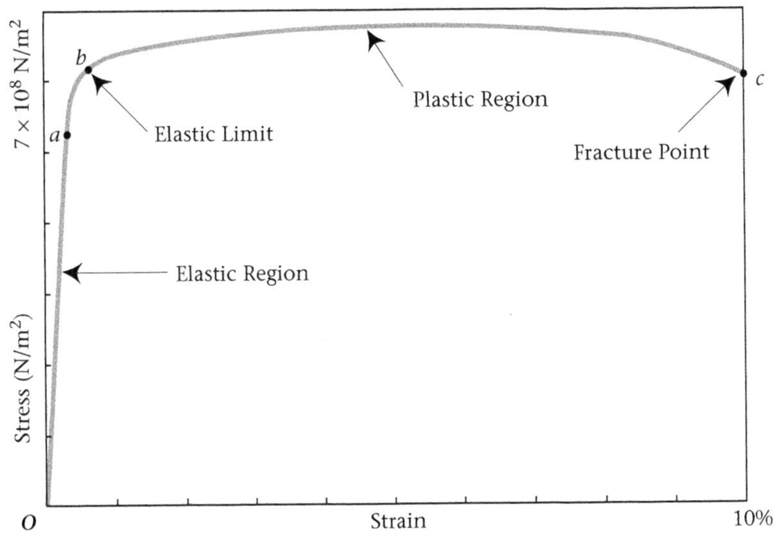

Figure 9.19

Stress-strain curve for an elastic solid, cold finished steel.

BRIDGES

How do you cross a river? Probably the first answer that comes to mind is to build a bridge. People have been building bridges for centuries, and continue today to design and construct longer and more elegant bridges.

The earliest bridges were tree trunks or stone slabs supported at both ends. The distance spanned by such beams was relatively short and depended on the strength and weight of the material used. The development of the truss, a combination of beams joined so that each piece shares part of the bridge's weight, increased the ratio of strength to weight. The members of the truss are straight pieces joined together to form a series of triangles. The resulting structure is lighter and more rigid than the equivalent simple beam and can support an external load over a much greater distance. In modern terms, the truss design required a knowledge of the strength of materials.

The earliest truss bridges were made of wood. Later trusses were reinforced with iron or even made entirely from iron. By the late 1800s, the common material for building truss bridges had become steel. Most of the railroad and highway bridges built in North America from 1890 to the middle of the twentieth century were steel truss bridges, especially for spans of 200 to 400 m.

Longer spans can be reached with arch bridges whose basic design was perfected centuries ago by the Romans. The secret of the arch is that the forces of its own weight and any added load are compressional forces, which allow the use of stone as a building material. Some of the stone bridges built by the Romans are still standing. The design of the arch results in a force that is downward and outward at the base of the arch. When the base is properly anchored, the arch bridge can span hundreds of meters. For example, the steel arch bridge over Sydney harbor spans 503 m and the New River Gorge Bridge in West Virginia spans 518 m. Both of these steel bridges utilize truss reinforcement of the basic arch. A maximum distance for steel arch bridges has been estimated at about 900 m.

The longest spans are achieved with suspension bridges that hang on steel cables stretched between tall towers. The ends of the cables are held in place on opposite shores by massive concrete anchorages. Because of the large strength-to-weight ratio of steel-wire cables, suspension bridges can be much longer than other types of bridges. The Akashi-Kaikyo Bridge in Japan is the longest span in the world, measuring 1990 m between the towers.

The modern suspension bridges of today owe much to the designers of the Brooklyn Bridge, John Roebling and his son Washington Roebling. In 1866 the elder Roebling, who

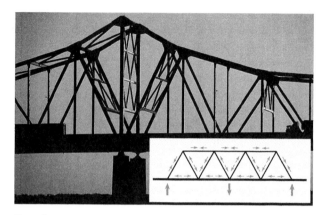

Figure B9.1   A truss bridge transmits its load to its end supports by a combination of compression (force vectors point toward each other) and tension (force vectors point away from each other).

Figure B9.2   A multiple arch bridge supports its load by transmitting compressive forces along the arch to the end supports.

had already pioneered a method of spinning wires from one anchorage to the other through the top of the supporting towers, took on the task of designing and building a bridge to connect Brooklyn to Manhattan. Three years later, the design complete, John Roebling died from a tetanus infection as a result of an accident at the site. His son then took over as chief engineer for the bridge and supervised the construction. He adapted the use of water-tight working chambers, called caissons, to the high pressures at the depths of the bridge's foundations. While working in a caisson, Washington Roebling was struck with the bends caused by a sudden decompression. He became paralyzed and supervised the remainder of the construction from his bedroom window, with his wife Emily carrying out his instructions and dealing with the workers. When the bridge opened in May of 1883, it was the longest suspension span in the world with a main span of 486 m.

Figure B9.3 A suspension bridge supports its load by transmitting tension forces along the suspension cable to the main towers. The towers transmit compressive forces to the ground.

beyond *b* the distortion is not reversible and the object does not return to its original shape. If the stress is increased still more, the maximum elongation is reached and the material fractures. The region between the elastic limit and the fracture point (or breaking point) is known as the *plastic region*. The stress required to cause fracture of the material is known as the *breaking stress,* or ultimate strength.

Example 9.10

A weightlifter raises a weight of 600 N over her head. Assuming that each of her legs supports the same weight and that the legs are parallel and vertical, determine the amount by which each femur (thighbone) compresses. Each femur has an affective cross-sectional area of 7.5×10^{-4} m^2 and a length of 0.52 m.

Strategy We are given the force on the bone and its cross-sectional area and we want to find the resulting compression ΔL. We can use Young's modulus for bone (Table 9.2) to relate the strain ($\Delta L/L$) to the stress (F/A). Because the legs are vertical and share the load, the additional force on each femur is half the 600 N.

Solution We rearrange the defining equation for Young's modulus (Eq. 9.13) to get the compression as

$$\Delta L = \frac{FL_0}{YA} = \frac{(300 \text{ N})(0.52 \text{ m})}{(7 \times 10^9 \text{ N/m}^2)(7.5 \times 10^{-4} \text{ m}^2)} = 3 \times 10^{-5} \text{ m}.$$

Each femur compresses a small amount, 0.03 mm.

Example 9.10: A weightlifter's load puts additional stress on her legs.

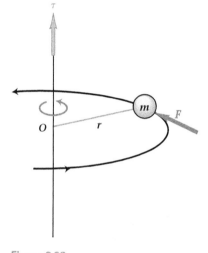

Figure 9.20
A mass constrained to move about a fixed point O at a distance r is subjected to a force **F**. The resulting torque τ changes the angular velocity of the mass.

▼

| 9.6 | **Torque and Moment of Inertia** |

Suppose you have a wheel mounted on an axle on which it is free to turn. To set the wheel turning, you need to apply a torque to it about its axle to overcome the wheel's inertia. Once the wheel is set in motion, it continues to rotate at constant angular velocity until another torque is applied. (We neglect the retarding effects of a torque due to friction.) In both cases, a torque causes the angular velocity to change. This situation is analogous to the application of a force to an object to change its linear velocity. We will find that the object undergoes an angular acceleration and that the connection between torque and angular acceleration is much like the connection between force and translational acceleration in Newton's second law. For simplicity we will introduce the ideas using only a single point mass, but the concepts apply to extended solid objects also. We start by applying a force to an object at a distance from its axis of revolution—that is, applying a torque—and then calculate the body's motion using Newton's laws.

Consider a single particle of mass m that is free to move in a plane at a fixed distance about the origin O (Fig. 9.20). This model might represent the physical situation of a ball bearing glued to one end of a soda straw of negligible mass. A force F applied to the ball bearing in a direction perpendicular to the straw causes the bearing to accelerate. The tangential acceleration a can be determined from Newton's second law written as

$$F = ma.$$

Multiplying both sides of this equation by r gives

$$Fr = mar.$$

The left-hand side of this equation is just the torque τ. The right-hand side may be rewritten in terms of the angular acceleration about O, $\alpha = a/r$. The result is

$$\tau = (mr^2)\alpha.$$

The quantity in parentheses is called the **moment of inertia, I,** and is a property of the mass and the radius r. In this instance, the value of I was fixed when we picked the mass and the length of the straw. However, the acceleration is the result of the torque acting on the system. Therefore, we write

$$\boxed{\tau = I\alpha.} \tag{9.14}$$

We have just computed the relationship between torque and angular acceleration for a single point of mass m moving in a circle of radius r. However, it can be shown that Eq. (9.14) is more general and may be used to find the angular acceleration produced by a net torque on any extended rigid body, provided we use the proper moment of inertia I. The moment of inertia plays the same role in the formulas for rotational motion that mass does in the equations for linear motion. However, the moment of inertia depends both on the mass and on the geometry, or shape, of the body, as well as on our choice of axis of rotation.

We can calculate the moment of inertia of an extended body by summing the moments of inertia of each small element of the body, obtaining the moment of inertia of the whole. The equation that expresses this idea is the definition of the moment of inertia:

$$I = \Sigma m_i r_i^2. \qquad (9.15)$$

Except for a few simple cases, the techniques of calculus are needed to perform the indicated summation. Table 9.3 gives the moments of inertia, for several bodies about specific axes. Inserting these expressions into Eq. (9.14), we can readily compute the angular acceleration when we know the torque.

In order to better understand the meaning of the moment of inertia, you can do the following experiment. Find two identical long rods (perhaps two meter-sticks) and hold one in each hand. Grasp the one in your left hand at the center and the other in your right hand at its end, a situation corresponding to two of the entries in Table 9.3. Now try to twist the rods so that they both have the same rotational motion—that is, the same angular acceleration. You will quickly find that the torques you must apply are not the same for both rods. Instead, a no-ticeably larger torque is required to move the rod held by its end. This is not surprising because the distribution of mass relative to your hand is different, even though the rods have identical shape and mass. The mass is farther away from the axis of rotation for the rod held at the end, thus it has a larger moment of inertia. As you can see from Table 9.3, its moment of inertia is four times as great as for the rod held at its center.

Equation (9.14) is the rotational analog of Newton's second law. Notice the similarity between it and the relation $F = ma$. Equation (9.14) may be expressed in words as follows: *An object's angular acceleration is proportional to the applied torque, and the proportionality constant is the moment of inertia of the object.* The torque corresponds to the force in Newton's law, the angular acceleration corresponds to the linear acceleration, and the moment of inertia plays the same role as the mass.

Example 9.11

A cylindrical winch of radius R and moment of inertia I is free to rotate without friction about an axis (Fig 9.21a). A cord of negligible mass is wrapped about the shaft and attached to a bucket of mass m. When the bucket is released, it accelerates downward as a result of gravitational attraction. Find the acceleration of the bucket.

Strategy We first examine the forces on the bucket, shown as a free-body diagram in Fig. 9.21(b). The downward gravitational force is mg, and the upward force T is the tension in the cord. If we choose the downward direction for the positive acceleration, then by Newton's second law

$$ma = mg - T,$$

and a is positive when mg exceeds T.

Table 9.3	Moments of Inertia for Some Regular Objects of Mass m

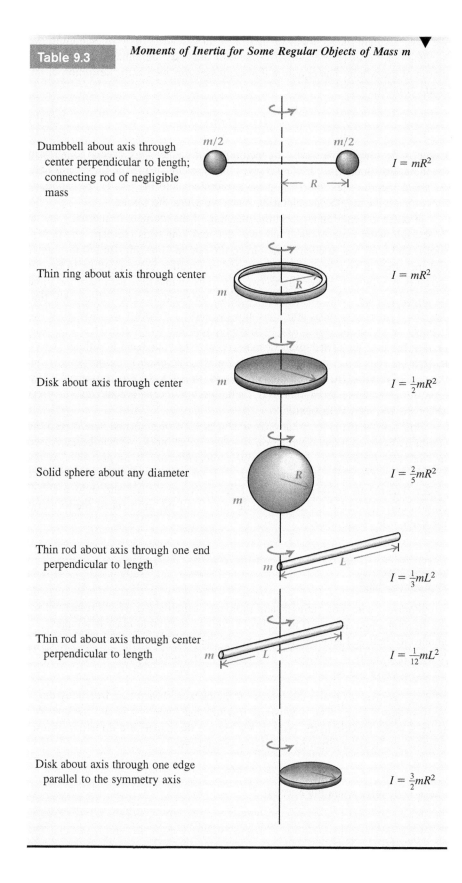

Dumbbell about axis through center perpendicular to length; connecting rod of negligible mass

$$I = mR^2$$

Thin ring about axis through center

$$I = mR^2$$

Disk about axis through center

$$I = \tfrac{1}{2}mR^2$$

Solid sphere about any diameter

$$I = \tfrac{2}{5}mR^2$$

Thin rod about axis through one end perpendicular to length

$$I = \tfrac{1}{3}mL^2$$

Thin rod about axis through center perpendicular to length

$$I = \tfrac{1}{12}mL^2$$

Disk about axis through one edge parallel to the symmetry axis

$$I = \tfrac{3}{2}mR^2$$

Next we observe that the cylinder is subject to a torque about its axis, given by RT (Fig. 9.21c). Its angular acceleration is given by

$$\tau = RT = I\alpha.$$

When the bucket moves down a distance s, a point on the circumference of the cylinder must also move through a distance s. Similarly, if the bucket accelerates an amount a, so does a point on the edge of the cylinder. The tangential acceleration a of a point on the circumference of the cylinder and the angular acceleration of the cylinder are related in the same way as the tangential velocity and the angular velocity are related. That is,

$$a = R\alpha.$$

From these equations we can determine the acceleration a.

Solution We may use the relationship for a to eliminate α in the torque equation:

$$RT = \frac{Ia}{R},$$

or

$$T = \frac{Ia}{R^2}.$$

This last expression may be inserted into the equation for the acceleration of the bucket:

$$ma = mg - \frac{Ia}{R^2}.$$

Figure 9.21
Example 9.11: (a) A cylinder rotates about its symmetry axis. A cord is wound around the cylinder, and a bucket is suspended from the end of the cord. (b) Free-body diagram for the bucket of mass m. (c) Free-body diagram for the torque about the axis of the cylinder.

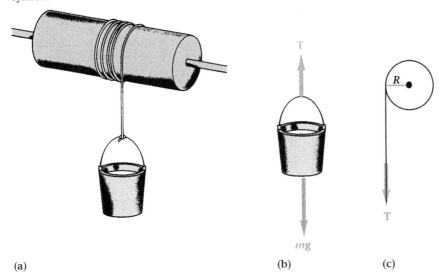

(a) (b) (c)

Upon rearranging we get

$$\left(m + \frac{I}{R^2}\right)a = mg,$$

or

$$a = \frac{mg}{m + \dfrac{I}{R^2}} = \left(\frac{1}{1 + \dfrac{I}{mR^2}}\right)g.$$

This last equation gives the acceleration of the bucket.

Discussion When the moment of inertia I becomes very large, a becomes very small. When I becomes small, a approaches g. The acceleration reverts to that for free fall in the limit that the inertia of the cylinder approaches zero. From this we see that the effect of the cylinder's inertia is to reduce the acceleration of the bucket.

▼

9.7   Angular Momentum

Suppose you have a wheel mounted on an axle on which it is free to turn. To set the wheel turning, you need to apply a torque to it about its axle to overcome the wheel's inertia. Once the wheel is set in motion, it continues to rotate at constant angular velocity until another torque is applied. (We neglect the retarding effects of a torque due to friction.) In both cases, a torque causes the angular velocity to change. This situation is analogous to the application of a force to a body to change its linear velocity. In this section we develop this analogy further.

Consider a single particle of mass m that is free to move in a plane at a fixed distance r about the origin O, as shown in Fig. 9.22. A force F applied to the mass in a direction tangent to its path produces a torque that causes the mass to accelerate. The torque may be expressed as

$$\tau = rF = r\left(\frac{\Delta p}{\Delta t}\right) = rm\frac{\Delta v}{\Delta t}.$$

However, because r and m are constant, we can write this equation as

$$\tau = \frac{\Delta(rmv)}{\Delta t}.$$

Thus, the application of a torque causes a rate of change of the quantity rmv.

We can rewrite the equation for the torque as the rate of change of a new quantity called the angular momentum L:

$$\boxed{\tau = \frac{\Delta L}{\Delta t}.} \tag{9.16}$$

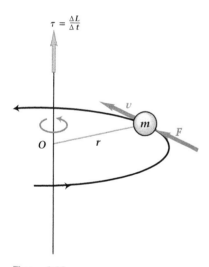

$$\tau = \frac{\Delta L}{\Delta t}$$

Figure 9.22
A mass constrained to move about a fixed point O at a distance r is subjected to a force **F**. The torque τ due to the force **F** causes a change in the angular momentum of the mass moving at a distance r about a fixed point O.

The **angular momentum** is the product of the linear momentum mv and the radius r:

$$L \equiv rmv. \qquad (9.17)$$

The quantity $L = rmv$ is the magnitude of the angular momentum vector **L**. Its direction is defined in a manner similar to the way in which we defined the direction of the torque in Fig. 9.9. That is, the angular momentum vector is at right angles to the plane containing **r** and **v**. The direction of the angular momentum is given by the right-hand rule and is directed to the right for the wheel in Fig. 9.23.

We may use the definition of angular velocity, $\omega = v/r$, to write the magnitude of the angular momentum in terms of the angular velocity ω:

$$\boxed{L = mr^2\omega.} \qquad (9.18)$$

Then we can separate the angular momentum into two parts: one term that depends on the properties of the body—that is, its moment of inertia—and another term that is the angular velocity. For a single point mass m at a fixed distance r from the axis of rotation, we can write

$$\boxed{L = I\omega,} \qquad (9.19)$$

where $I = mr^2$. For more general objects, Eq. (9.19) still holds with the appropriate moment of inertia $I = \Sigma m_i r_i^2$ (Table 9.3). Thus, we see that angular momentum is the product of moment of inertia and angular velocity in the same way that linear momentum is the product of mass and linear velocity.

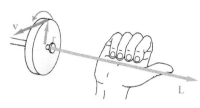

Figure 9.23
A wheel rotating on an axle. The direction of the angular momentum **L** is found from the right-hand rule. The fingers are curled so that they point along the direction of rotation; then the thumb points along the direction of the angular momentum.

Conservation of Angular Momentum

9.8

If the torque applied to a body is zero, the change in its angular momentum with respect to time is also zero. Thus, the angular momentum is constant. This situation is analogous to the conservation of linear momentum. That is, if

$$\tau = \frac{\Delta L}{\Delta t} = 0,$$

then

$$\Delta L = 0$$

and

$$L = I_i\omega_i = I_f\omega_f = \text{constant},$$

where the subscripts i and f stand for initial and final values, respectively.

When the net applied torque on an object is zero, its angular momentum is conserved. This statement of the law of **conservation of angular**

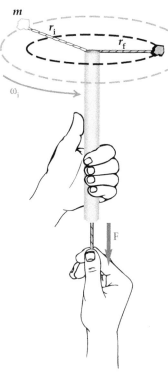

Figure 9.24
Example 9.12: A person whirls a stone around in a horizontal plane.

momentum, like that of the conservation of linear momentum, expresses an extremely important physical principle. It applies not only to large-scale phenomena, but also to atomic and nuclear phenomena. It applies to objects moving in a curved path or simply spinning about an axis.

If an object rotates with a large angular momentum, its axis of rotation remains relatively stationary in space unless a large torque is applied transverse to the initial rotation axis. The upright stability of a spinning top is a consequence of the fact that the torque due to gravity about the support point produces a changing angular momentum at right angles to the initial angular momentum. The vector sum of these two momenta causes the vertical axis of the top to move in a nearly circular path. As the top slows down, its angular momentum becomes smaller and the torque causes it to fall over.

Example 9.12

A stone attached to a string is whirled around in a horizontal circle (Fig. 9.24). If the stone is originally moving at a rate of 0.5 rad/s, what will its rate of revolution (i.e., its angular velocity) become if the radius of the circle is halved?

Strategy When the string is pulled in, the force acts through the axis of rotation. Thus, there is no torque applied to the stone and the angular momentum is unchanged.

Solution The equation for conservation of angular momentum, with subscripts i and f standing for initial and final values, respectively, becomes

$$m r_i^2 \omega_i = m r_f^2 \omega_f,$$

or

$$\omega_f = \frac{r_i^2}{r_f^2} \omega_i.$$

Substituting the initial angular velocity of 0.5 rad/s and the final radius $\frac{1}{2} r_i$ into the equation gives

$$\omega_f = \left(\frac{r_i}{0.5 r_i} \right)^2 (0.5 \text{ rad/s})$$

$$\omega_f = 2 \text{ rad/s}.$$

Note that when angular momentum is constant, decreasing the radius increases the angular velocity.

In many situations, an object's moment of inertia I may change. This is especially true in some sports activities. For example, in the case of a high diver, the only external force is due to gravity, which acts on the diver's center of mass. Thus, there is no external torque acting on the diver and angular momentum is conserved. Since the product $I\omega$ remains constant, if I is made smaller, ω must increase. From the definition of I as $I = \Sigma m_i r_i^2$ we can see that the moment of inertia decreases when an object's mass is brought closer to the axis of rotation (smaller r). The diver does this by "tucking in" (Fig. 9.25). The diver's change in moment of inertia is accompanied by a corresponding increase in angular speed, allowing him to flip rapidly. The diver comes out of the tucked position to slow down his angular speed and enter the water vertically.

The motion of the diver combines rotational motion with translational motion. Careful observation shows that the diver's center of mass travels in a parabolic arc. This is the same path it would follow if it were a point mass. This is so because the net force (due to gravity in this case) acting on the diver can be considered to act on his center of mass. The motion of the diver about the center of mass is further complicated because location of the body's center of mass is affected by the positions of the limbs. This effect can be seen in Fig. 9.25(b), where the center of mass is represented by the dot.

(a)

Master the Concept

Conservation of Angular Momentum

Question: A diver goes off the high board and tucks into a flip. She then straightens out and enters the water vertically. What happened to her angular momentum just before entering the water?

Answer: There are no external torques acting on the diver after she leaves the board, so her angular momentum must be constant. When she straightens out, her moment of inertia is so much greater than when she was tucked that for a brief moment just before striking the water she appears to rotate no longer. However, careful attention to her motion reveals that she does not stop rotating, only that her angular velocity is very small. Her angular momentum is still the same as it was during the tuck.

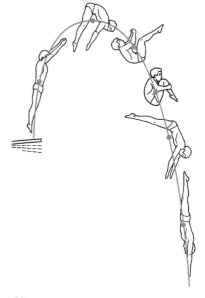

(b)

Figure 9.25
Motion of a diver. (a) In the tucked position, a diver has a smaller moment of inertia and thus a greater angular velocity than at any other point in the dive. (b) The center of mass of the diver follows a parabolic path, even though the location of the center of mass relative to the body changes as the positions of the arms and legs change.

Example 9.13

An ice skater starts spinning at a rate of 1.5 rev/s with arms extended. He then pulls his arms in close to his body, resulting in a decrease of his moment of inertia to three-quarters of the initial value (Fig. 9.26). What is the skater's final angular velocity?

Solution The skater's inward arm motion produces no external torque. Therefore, if we use the subscript i to denote initial values and f to denote final values, we have, from conservation of angular momentum,

$$I_i \omega_i = I_f \omega_f,$$

or

$$\omega_f = \frac{I_i}{I_f} \omega_i.$$

(a)   (b)

Figure 9.26
Example 9.13: An ice skater changes his angular velocity by changing his moment of inertia.

We are told that $I_f = \frac{3}{4}I_i$ and that the skater's initial frequency is $f = 1.5$ rev/s. Since the angular velocity is $\omega = 2\pi f$, we have

$$\omega_f = \frac{I_i}{\frac{3}{4}I_i\omega_i} = \frac{4}{3}2\pi f_i = \frac{4}{3}(2\pi \text{ rad/rev})(1.5 \text{ rev/s})$$

$$\omega_f = 4\pi \text{ rad/s},$$

which corresponds to a rotational rate of two rotations per second.

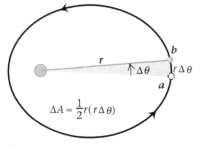

Figure 9.27
Example 9.14: A portion of the orbit of a planet moving about the sun. During a time Δt the planet moves, making an angle $\Delta\theta$ with the sun.

Example 9.14

Show that Kepler's law of equal areas is equivalent to the law of conservation of angular momentum. (This result was, in fact, obtained by Newton in the early part of the *Principia*.)

Solution Figure 9.27 shows a planet of mass m in an orbit about the sun. We do not need to know anything about the force on this planet other than that it is directed along the line joining the planet and the sun, as required by the law of universal gravitation. As the planet moves from point a to point b in a time Δt, it sweeps out an area ΔA, which is approximately triangular. The area A of a triangle is given by

$$A = \tfrac{1}{2}(\text{base})(\text{altitude}).$$

For the triangle of Fig. 9.27 we have

$$\Delta A \approx \tfrac{1}{2}(r)(r\Delta\theta),$$

or

$$\Delta A \approx \tfrac{1}{2}r^2\Delta\theta.$$

The rate at which the area is swept out, $\Delta A/\Delta t$, is then given by

$$\frac{\Delta A}{\Delta t} \approx \tfrac{1}{2}r^2\frac{\Delta\theta}{\Delta t},$$

which becomes an equality in the limit of small Δt. In this limit, the quantity $\Delta\theta/\Delta t$ becomes the angular velocity ω. Thus

$$\frac{\Delta A}{\Delta t} = \tfrac{1}{2}r^2\omega,$$

which may be rewritten in the form

$$\frac{\Delta A}{\Delta t} = \frac{mr^2\omega}{2m}.$$

Since $mr^2\omega = L$, the angular momentum, we have

$$\frac{\Delta A}{\Delta t} = \frac{L}{2m}.$$

The rate at which area is swept out is constant because the angular momentum L is constant.

Discussion The dominant force on each planet is the gravitational attraction of the sun, which is a radially directed force that produces no torque. Forces between the planets are very much smaller. Thus, the torque on the planets in their orbits is essentially zero, and the angular momentum L of any planet is constant. Our result predicts that for a given planet, $\Delta A/\Delta t$ is a constant: that is, the rate at which the planet sweeps out an area is constant. We have just derived Kepler's second law (equal areas in equal time) from the law of conservation of angular momentum.

An additional observation may be made. The conservation of angular momentum means not only that the magnitude of the angular momentum is constant, but also that its direction in space is constant. The constancy of direction leads to the conclusion that the plane of a planet's orbit is constant.

Rotational Kinetic Energy

9.9

An important part of a moving object's total kinetic energy is its energy due to rotation. Sometimes an object's rotational kinetic energy even exceeds its translational kinetic energy. In order to present a more complete picture of conservation of energy, we discuss rotational kinetic energy here.

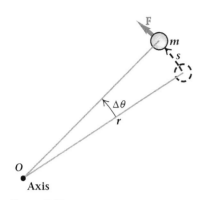

Figure 9.28
If a mass moving at a set distance r about a fixed axis is subjected to a force parallel to the direction of its motion, an increase in its kinetic energy results. This rotational kinetic energy is $\frac{1}{2}mr^2\omega^2$.

When an applied torque sets an object in rotation, it does work on the object. For example, you do work when you start a top or gyroscope spinning. The rotating body has kinetic energy due to its rotary motion, and this kinetic energy equals the work done in causing the rotation. How do we write an expression for the kinetic energy of rotation? You would be correct if you used the analogies we have developed in this chapter and guessed that the **rotational kinetic energy** is

$$\boxed{KE_{rot} = \tfrac{1}{2}I\omega^2,} \qquad (9.20)$$

where I is the moment of inertia and ω is the angular velocity. Even though it is easy to guess correctly in this case, we will briefly present a discussion to support this definition.

We start with Eq. (9.9)—the kinematic expression for the relationship between angular speed, acceleration, and displacement. Multiply the equation by $\frac{1}{2}I$, where I is the moment of inertia. The result is

$$\tfrac{1}{2}I\omega_2^2 - \tfrac{1}{2}I\omega_1^2 = I\alpha\theta,$$

where we set the initial angular displacement θ_0 to zero. Recall that $I\alpha$ is the torque τ and that the angle $\theta = s/r$ (Fig. 9.28). Rearranging to put the torque on the left-hand side, we have

$$\tau\frac{s}{r} = \tfrac{1}{2}I\omega_2^2 - \tfrac{1}{2}I\omega_1^2.$$

But the torque divided by r is the force, and force times the distance through which it acts is work. So we have

$$W = \tfrac{1}{2}I\omega_2^2 - \tfrac{1}{2}I\omega_1^2. \qquad (9.21)$$

This expression has the form of the work-energy theorem introduced in Chapter 6, except that now we have only rotational motion. Just as we did for translational motion, we identify the terms on the right-hand side as the rotational kinetic energies of a body with moment of inertia I.

▼

Example 9.15

How much energy is required to set a 12-in. phonograph record into rotation at $33\frac{1}{3}$ revolutions per minute? The record has a mass of 0.115 kg.

Solution From Table 9.3, the moment of inertia of a disk of mass m and radius R rotating about an axis through its center is $I = \frac{1}{2}mR^2$. Substituting this value for the moment of inertia I into the equation for rotational kinetic energy, we get

$$KE_{rot} = \tfrac{1}{2}I\omega^2 = \tfrac{1}{2}(\tfrac{1}{2}mR^2)\omega^2 = \tfrac{1}{4}mR^2\omega^2.$$

We now insert the numerical values, noting that

$$R = 6 \text{ in.} = (6 \text{ in.})(0.0254 \text{ m/in.}) = 0.152 \text{ m}$$

and

$$\omega = 2\pi f = 2\pi(33\tfrac{1}{3}/\text{min})(1 \text{ min}/60 \text{ s}) = 3.49 \text{ rad/s}.$$

Thus

$$KE_{rot} = \tfrac{1}{4}(0.115 \text{ kg})(0.152 \text{ m})^2(3.49 \text{ rad/s})^2$$
$$KE_{rot} = 8.09 \times 10^{-3} \text{ J}.$$

9.10 Conservation of Energy: Translations and Rotations

In the previous section, we introduced rotational kinetic energy, but for the sake of keeping the mathematics simple, we did not discuss any examples that included both translational and rotational kinetic energy. Now we extend the law of conservation of mechanical energy to include, at the same time, translational and rotational kinetic energy. Both considerations need to be taken into account when dealing with such things as rolling tires and hoops. They are even important when describing the motion of molecules in a gas.

Figure 9.29 shows a disk of mass m and radius r at the top of an inclined plane. The axis of the disk is parallel to the top edge of the plane so that the disk, when released, rolls straight down the plane. If the frictional force is great enough, there is no sliding and the disk rolls without slipping. The thickness of the disk is not important here, except that for a given material and radius, the total mass of the disk depends upon its thickness.

At the top of the plane the disk has a potential energy mgh relative to its position at the bottom. Here h is the vertical distance through which the center of mass moves from the top to the bottom of the plane. If the disk rolls down to the bottom of the plane without slipping, then all of the initial potential energy is completely transformed into kinetic energies of rotation and translation at the bottom. Because the disk rolls without slipping, we can neglect energy loss due to friction. Then we may extend the idea of conservation of mechanical energy to include rotational as well as translational kinetic energy. Consequently,

$$\Delta PE + \Delta KE_{trans} + \Delta KE_{rot} = 0,$$

or

$$-\Delta PE = \Delta KE_{trans} + \Delta KE_{rot}.$$

Here KE_{trans} is the kinetic energy due to translation of the center of mass of the disk and KE_{rot} is the kinetic energy of rotation about its center of mass. The sum of these two terms is the total kinetic energy of the rolling disk:

$$KE_{tot} = KE_{trans} + KE_{rot} = \tfrac{1}{2}mv^2 + \tfrac{1}{2}I\omega^2. \tag{9.22}$$

We see that the magnitude of the decrease in potential energy is equal to the gain in total kinetic energy, or

$$mgh = \tfrac{1}{2}mv^2 + \tfrac{1}{2}I\omega^2, \tag{9.23}$$

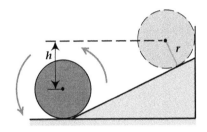

Figure 9.29
A disk rolling down an inclined plane. Its potential energy at the top is transformed into translational and rotational kinetic energy at the bottom.

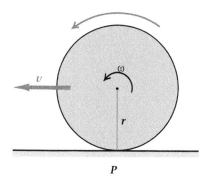

Figure 9.30
A disk rolling with speed v rotates with an angular velocity $\omega = v/r$.

where v and ω are the linear and angular speeds of the disk when it reaches the bottom of the plane and I is the moment of inertia of the disk about its center of mass. Table 9.3 lists moments of inertia for several objects of different shapes. Equation (9.23) is valid for any round object, whether it be a disk, a hoop, or a wheel. However, you must use the correct moment of inertia for the case at hand.

Because the disk rolls without slipping, there is a direct relationship between its linear and angular motions. If the disk is rolling with a speed v, then the instantaneous motion of the center of mass about the point of contact P (Fig. 9.30) is a rotation with angular velocity $\omega = v/r$. Since the center of mass is moving steadily in a straight line, a point on the rim must be in rotation about it at the same angular velocity. Thus, the angular velocity and the linear speed are related through $v = r\omega$. Then we can express Eq. (9.23) solely in terms of either v or ω. Let's choose to eliminate ω, obtaining

$$mgh = \tfrac{1}{2}mv^2 + \tfrac{1}{2}I\frac{v^2}{r^2}.$$

We can determine the speed of the disk at the bottom of the incline by solving this equation for v. The result is that after the body has rolled through a vertical height h, its speed is

$$v = \sqrt{\frac{2gh}{1 + \dfrac{I}{mr^2}}}. \tag{9.24}$$

We see that the body's speed at the bottom of the plane depends on the height of the plane and on the moment of inertia of the disk or other round object. Since the moment of inertia always depends linearly on the mass, the term I/mr^2 is independent of m and depends only on the geometry of the body. The following example illustrates a consequence of that point.

Example 9.16

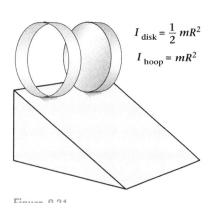

$$I_{\text{disk}} = \frac{1}{2}mR^2$$

$$I_{\text{hoop}} = mR^2$$

Figure 9.31
Example 9.16: A solid disk and a hoop of the same mass and radius on an inclined plane. Which one rolls to the bottom faster?

A uniform solid disk of radius R and mass m and a hoop of the same radius and mass are released from rest from the top of an incline (Fig. 9.31). Which object is moving more rapidly at the bottom?

Solution From Table 9.3 we find the moment of inertia of the disk to be

$$I_{\text{disk}} = \tfrac{1}{2}mR^2.$$

The moment of inertia of the hoop is

$$I_{\text{hoop}} = mR^2.$$

Inserting these values for the moment of inertia into Eq. (9.24), we get

$$v_{\text{disk}} = \sqrt{\frac{2gh}{1 + \frac{1}{2}}} = \sqrt{\frac{4gh}{3}}$$

and

$$v_{\text{hoop}} = \sqrt{\frac{2gh}{1 + 1}} = \sqrt{gh}.$$

Discussion The disk, because of its smaller moment of inertia, has a greater speed than the hoop at any point along the inclined plane, including the bottom. Consequently, if they are released simultaneously, the disk reaches the bottom first. Notice that this result is independent of the mass of each object.

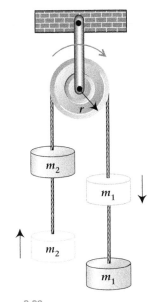

Figure 9.32
Example 9.17: Two masses on an Atwood's machine with a massive pulley.

Example 9.17

The Atwood's machine of Fig. 9.32 consists of a 0.400-kg pulley, having a diameter of 6.0 cm, and masses $m_1 = 1.20$ kg and $m_2 = 1.00$ kg. When released from rest, what is the speed of the mass m_1 after it has fallen a distance of 1.25 m? Assume that friction may be neglected.

Strategy We can solve this problem by use of the law of conservation of mechanical energy. This problem differs from those done earlier, because we now include the effects of the pulley's inertia.

Solution If we call the initial potential energy of masses m_1 and m_2 zero, then for the system at rest with zero kinetic energy, the total mechanical energy is 0. After the mass m_1 falls a distance of $h = 1.25$ m, the potential energy of the two masses is

$$PE = -m_1gh + m_2gh.$$

The kinetic energy of the masses and the pulley is

$$KE = \tfrac{1}{2}m_1v^2 + \tfrac{1}{2}m_2v^2 + \tfrac{1}{2}I\omega^2,$$

where I is the moment of inertia of the pulley, $I = \tfrac{1}{2}mr^2$, r is the pulley's radius, and m is its mass. Notice that both hanging masses move with the same speed v and that the angular velocity of the pulley is related to v through $\omega = v/r$. Thus, the total mechanical energy is

$$E = PE + KE = -m_1gh + m_2gh + \tfrac{1}{2}m_1v^2 + \tfrac{1}{2}m_2v^2 + \tfrac{1}{2}I\omega^2 = 0.$$

If we substitute for I and ω, we get

$$\tfrac{1}{2}m_1v^2 + \tfrac{1}{2}m_2v^2 + \tfrac{1}{2}(\tfrac{1}{2}mr^2)\left(\frac{v}{r}\right)^2 = m_1gh - m_2gh,$$

$$\tfrac{1}{2}(m_1 + m_2 + \tfrac{1}{2}m)v^2 = (m_1 - m_2)gh.$$

Solving for v, we get

$$v = \sqrt{\frac{2(m_1 - m_2)gh}{(m_1 + m_2 + \tfrac{1}{2}m)}}.$$

Substituting the numerical values and units, we find

$$v = \sqrt{\frac{[2(1.20 - 1.00)\text{kg}](9.81 \text{ m/s}^2)(1.25 \text{ m})}{[1.20 + 1.00 + \tfrac{1}{2}(0.400)]\text{kg}}} = 1.43 \text{ m/s}.$$

THE EARTH, THE MOON, AND THE TIDES

The periodic rise and fall of the ocean on the beach—the tides—are familiar to everyone who has spent time at the seashore (Fig. B9.4). In the open ocean the tides are approximately a half meter high. As the tides approach the shore, the geographic features of the shoreline often channel the water so that typical shore tides are about two meters. These tides vary from place to place. In some areas they are smaller, while in a few locations they are much greater. In Canada's Bay of Fundy, the tidal level varies by as much as 15 m.

People have often dreamed of harnessing the motion of the tides to produce electricity. However, the possibility of doing so is restricted to those few places where the tidal variations are sufficiently large and where a dam can be constructed across the channel. At the present time, the expense of building such facilities has rendered them impractical in comparison with other means of generating electric power.

The tides are primarily caused by the gravitational pull of the moon.* In addition to the ocean tides, the moon also causes tides in the solid body of the earth, but these earth tides are harder to observe. As the moon moves in its orbit, the earth also moves, because each moves about the center of mass of the earth-moon system. Due to the inverse-square nature of the gravitational force, the water on the side of the earth near the moon is pulled toward the moon with a greater-than-average force, while the water on the far side is pulled with a less-than-average force. Moreover, the motion of the earth about the center of mass also helps raise a tidal bulge on the side away from the moon. As a result, two bulges appear in the water, on opposite sides of the earth.

Because the rotation of the earth about its axis is faster than the motion of the moon about the earth, and because of the frictional forces between the ocean currents and the sea floor, the earth drags the tidal bulges ahead of the position they would otherwise have (Fig. B9.5). This asymmetrical position of the bulges relative to the line joining the centers of the earth and the moon produces a net torque on the moon. This torque acts to increase the moon's angular momentum. By Newton's third law, a torque of equal magnitude acts to slow the rotation of the earth.

Although the total angular momentum of the earth-moon system is conserved, angular momentum is transferred from the earth to the moon. The total mechanical energy decreases as a result of the frictional losses of the tides. Consequently, the length of the day steadily increases as the earth's rate of rotation slows, and the length of the month decreases as the

*The sun also produces a tidal effect, but it is less than half that of the moon.

296

Figure B9.4 Ocean tides. (a) Low tide and (b) high tide.

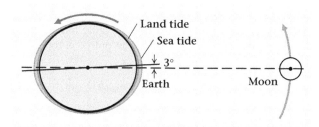

Figure B9.5 Tidal bulges occur 3° ahead of the line between the centers of the earth and the moon because of the earth's rotation. The view is from above the polar axis. (The sizes of the tides are greatly exaggerated for the sake of clarity.)

moon speeds up. Because of this increase in speed, and therefore energy, the distance of the moon from the earth also increases. These effects have been measured; the length of the day is gradually increasing at a rate of about 20 μs per year. (Thus, 200 million years ago in the Jurassic period, the length of a day was approximately 23 hours.) In addition, the moon is slowly moving away at approximately 3 cm per year. Calculations show that the moon will continue to move away from the earth until it reaches a distance of about 75 earth radii. Then the length of the day will equal the length of the month and the motion of the earth and moon will be synchronized. The earth will then keep the same face toward the moon, just as the moon now keeps the same face toward the earth.

▼

Summary

Useful Concepts

■ Angles, measured in radians, are defined to be the ratio of the arc length s to the radius r:

$$\theta = \frac{s}{r}.$$

■ The instantaneous angular velocity is given by

$$\omega = \lim_{\Delta t \to 0} \frac{\Delta \theta}{\Delta t}.$$

■ The instantaneous angular acceleration is given by

$$\alpha \equiv \lim_{\Delta t \to 0} \frac{\Delta \omega}{\Delta t}.$$

■ The tangential acceleration of a point moving in a circle is related to the angular acceleration through

$$a_t = \alpha r.$$

The moving point also has a centripetal acceleration

$$a_c = \omega^2 r.$$

■ For motion with constant angular acceleration, two frequently used kinematic equations are

$$\theta = \theta_0 + \omega_0 t + \tfrac{1}{2}\alpha t^2 \quad \text{and} \quad \omega^2 = \omega_0^2 + 2\alpha(\theta - \theta_0).$$

■ The torque about a point is

$$\tau = rF \sin \theta.$$

Counterclockwise torques are positive; clockwise torques are negative.

■ The conditions for equilibrium are

1. The vector sum of all the external forces must be zero:

$$\sum_{i=1}^{N} \mathbf{F}_i = 0.$$

2. The vector sum of all the external torques must be zero:

$$\sum_{i=1}^{N} \tau_i = 0.$$

■ An object at rest, neither translating nor rotating, is in static equilibrium. An object in motion, but not accelerating linearly or rotationally, is in dynamic equilibrium.

■ A stress on an object causes a strain. The ratio of tensile stress to tensile strain is called Young's modulus:

$$Y = \frac{\text{stress}}{\text{strain}} = \frac{F/A}{\Delta L/L_0}.$$

■ For rotation about a fixed axis of a body with a constant moment of inertia, the torque is related to the angular acceleration by

$$\tau = I\alpha,$$

where I is the moment of inertia. For an extended body the moment of inertia is $I = \Sigma m_i r_i^2$.

■ A torque produces a change in an object's angular momentum L,

$$\tau = \frac{\Delta L}{\Delta t}.$$

■ The angular momentum of a point mass m moving in a circle of radius r with angular velocity ω is

$$L = mr^2\omega.$$

■ For an extended body, the angular momentum is

$$L = I\omega,$$

where I is the moment of inertia.

■ This chapter introduces a fundamental conservation law of physics, *conservation of angular momentum:* The total angular momentum of a system is constant whenever the net external torque on the system is zero.

■ The rotational kinetic energy of an object with moment of inertia I rotating with angular velocity ω is

$$\mathrm{KE_{rot}} \equiv \tfrac{1}{2}I\omega^2.$$

■ The total kinetic energy of a rolling body separates into the translational kinetic energy of the center of mass and rotational kinetic energy about the center of mass,

$$\Delta \mathrm{KE_{tot}} = \mathrm{KE_{trans}} + \mathrm{KE_{rot}} = \tfrac{1}{2}mv^2 + \tfrac{1}{2}I\omega^2.$$

Important Terms

You should be able to write the definition or meaning of each of the following:

rigid body
average angular acceleration
instantaneous angular
  acceleration
torque
couple
rotational equilibrium
center of mass
tensile stress

tensile strain
compressive strain
Young's modulus
moment of inertia
angular momentum
conservation of angular
  momentum
rotational kinetic energy

Conceptual Questions

9.1 Carefully distinguish between force and torque. Give examples of forces without torques and forces that produce torques.

9.2 Explain how a yo-yo works.

9.3 Why do car owners go to the trouble to balance automobile tires? What happens when car wheels are unbalanced? Why is it better to balance the wheel on a rotating machine rather than by a static method?

9.4 Can a diver pull into a tuck and rotate while diving if he leaves the diving board with no angular velocity? Why?

9.5 What would happen to the planets if the gravitational force had a tangential component as well as a radial component?

9.6 A cat held upside down and dropped can right itself before it hits the floor (Fig. 9.33). Explain how the cat does so, since there are no external torques present. (*Hint:* Study the figure.)

9.7 Explain how ice skaters can quickly go from a slow to a fast spin and vice versa. What happens to their angular velocity and their moment of inertia? Is an external torque required?

9.8 How does a balancing pole help a tight-rope walker?

9.9 A passenger in the gondola of a hot-air balloon carries a motor-driven flywheel with its axis of rotation perpendicular to the earth's surface. Before lifting off, the wheel is at rest with respect to the gondola. After lifting off, the wheel is set into motion by an electric motor. A few minutes later the passenger inverts the wheel, then the wheel is allowed to come to rest. What would a person on the ground observe while all this was happening?

9.10 A ball rolls across the floor. Is it possible for its translational and rotational kinetic energies to be the same?

9.11 The large wheels in Fig. 9.34 have the same radius and mass, and they turn without friction. Initially θ_1 and θ_2 are equal, and the weight W, which is suspended by cords wrapped around the wheels, is allowed to fall from rest. Which angle will decrease more rapidly, θ_1 or θ_2?

9.12 An engineer desires to store energy in a rotating flywheel of a given mass and radius. Should he select a flywheel in the shape of a uniform solid disk or one with most of the mass on the rim? What is the ratio of the energies that can be stored in these two cases if both wheels rotate with the same angular frequency ω?

9.13 Two spheres of equal mass are released from rest at the top of an inclined plane. One sphere is solid and of uniform density. The other sphere is a shell of uniform density.
(a) Which sphere reaches the bottom of the plane first?
(b) Which sphere will have the greatest translational kinetic energy at the bottom?

9.14 How do the performers turn the Wheel of Death (Fig. 9.35)? When they are on the wheel, they are part of the rotating system. There is no motor to apply a torque to the axle.

9.15 An advertisement in a golfing magazine claims a "putter with the highest moment of inertia." How do you interpret such a claim and why is it an advantage?

Figure 9.33
Question 9.6.

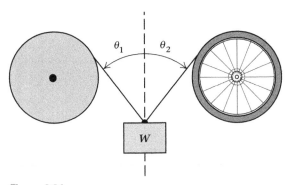

Figure 9.34
Question 9.11.

Figure 9.35
Question 9.14: The Wheel of Death.

9.16 The rolling motion of ocean liners is sometimes reduced by the use of a large flywheel within the ship. Explain how a flywheel spinning on a horizontal axis perpendicular to the length of the ship helps reduce the motion of waves striking the ship broadside.

9.17 A handbook says that to make a delicate balance you should (1) make the arms of the balance beam long, (2) make the beam as light as possible, (3) bring the center of mass of the beam very close under the point of support. What does each of these procedures do to make a balance delicate?

9.18 When the supporting stick S is jerked out from the apparatus shown in Fig. 9.36, the board falls down about the hinged end H. The ball B is caught by the cup C. Explain how the cup C can reach the ground before the ball, even though the ball is in free fall.

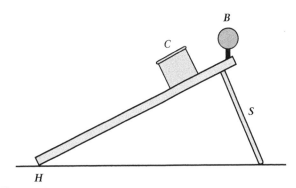

Figure 9.36
Question 9.18.

Problems

Sections 9.1 and 9.2 Angular Velocity and Angular Acceleration and Rotational Kinematics

Hints for Solving Problems

Remember the correspondence between linear quantities and rotational quantities. One revolution corresponds to 2π radians.

9.1 What is the average angular velocity of each of the three hands of a clock?

9.2 What are the initial and final speeds of the car in Example 9.2?

9.3 (a) A dentist's drill turns a 0.75-mm-diameter bit at 5.0×10^5 rev/min. What is the linear speed of the cutting edge? (b) When the drill is first turned on it takes about 1/4 s to come up to full speed. What is the average angular acceleration of the bit?

9.4 A wheel starts from rest and rotates about its axis with constant angular acceleration. After 6.8 s have elapsed, it has rotated through an angle of 25 radians. (a) What is the angular acceleration of the wheel? (b) What is the angular velocity when the time $t = 6.8$ s? (c) What is the centripetal acceleration of a point on the wheel a distance $r = 0.45$ m from the axis at $t = 6.8$ s?

9.5 A pneumatic high-speed cutter with a 7.50-cm-diameter cutting disc is advertised to have a rotation rate of between 5000 and 18,000 rev/min. (a) What is the range of angular speeds in radians per second? (b) What is the range of linear speeds of the edge of the disk? (c) What is the average angular acceleration if, starting from rest, the cutter comes up to its fastest speed in 2.8 s?

9.6• A wheel initially rotating at an angular speed of 1.6 rad/s turns through 36 revolutions during the time that it is subject to an angular acceleration of 0.32 rad/s². How long did the acceleration last?

9.7• The brakes are applied steadily on a car initially traveling at 86.5 km/hr. The braking gives the 15.3-cm-radius wheels an angular acceleration of −2.13 rad/s². (a) What is the average angular velocity of the wheels during the 16.9 s that the brakes are applied? (b) How far does the car go in that 16.9 s?

9.8• A screw with 20 threads per centimeter is driven 1.37 cm into its fixture in 12.8 s with a cordless electric screwdriver. What is the average angular speed of the screwdriver? Give your answer in radians per second (rad/s) and in rotations per minute (rpm).

9.9• A ball is tossed straight up with a spinning motion. The ball spins at 31 rad/s and makes 7.2 revolutions before it returns to its starting level. How high did the ball go?

9.10• A 3.60-cm-radius ball rolls down an inclined plane from rest at the top. The angular acceleration of the rolling ball about its center is 155 rad/s², and its angular speed at the bottom is 46.4 rad/s. How long is the plane?

9.11• A car engine idles at 800 rev/min. With the car in neutral, you depress the accelerator. After 1.2 s the tachometer indicates an engine speed of 3400 rev/min. (a) What are the initial and final angular velocities in rad/s? (b) What is the average angular acceleration during the 1.20-s interval? (c) How many revolutions does the engine make during that 1.20 s?

9.12•• A 0.50-m-radius wheel runs on a circular 1.75-m-radius horizontal track with a constant linear speed of 0.37 m/s. At $t = 0$, a dot painted on the rim of the wheel is in contact with a dot painted on the track. (a) What is the angular speed of the wheel about its axis? (b) What is the angular speed of the center of the wheel as it goes around the track? (c) Where is the dot on the wheel after the wheel makes one complete trip around the track? (d) Will the dots ever be in contact again? (e) If the dots will coincide again, how long will it take?

Section 9.3 Torque

9.13 If a force of 4.0 N is needed to open a 81-cm-wide door when applied at the edge opposite the hinges, what force must be applied to open the door if you push against the door 10 cm from the hinged side?

9.14 If a person can apply a maximum force of 50 lb, what is the minimum length of a wrench needed to apply a 35-ft-lb torque to the bolts on a motorcycle engine?

9.15 A force of 303 N is exerted on the end of a wrench in order to apply a torque of 43.2 N · m to a bolt head. The point of application of the force is 21.5 cm from the center of the bolt. What angle does the force make with respect to the wrench handle?

9.16 A clock has a second hand whose tip rubs against the inside of the glass cover. If the frictional force between the glass cover and the tip of the second hand is 0.0020 N and the length of the hand is 8.0 cm, what is the minimum torque that must be applied to the second hand if the clock is not to be stopped?

Section 9.4 Static Equilibrium

Be sure to start with a diagram of the situation. Include the coordinate axes and indicate the direction of positive torques. Choose counterclockwise torques to be positive and clockwise torques to be negative.

9.17 A claw hammer is used to pry up a nail. Approximately how much force is applied to the nail when a force of 100 N is applied to the handle, as shown in Fig. 9.37?

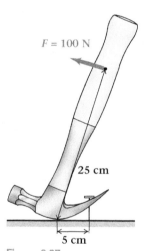

$F = 100$ N

25 cm

5 cm

Figure 9.37
Problem 9.17.

9.18 Two children are playing on a balanced seesaw. One child with a mass of 42 kg sits 1.4 m from the center. Where on the other side must the second child sit if her mass is 34 kg?

9.19 A person with upper arm vertical and forearm horizontal holds a 4.5-kg iron cannon ball (Fig. 9.38). Assume the mass of the forearm and hand is 1.5 kg, with a center of mass 15 cm from the elbow. The center of the cannonball is 32 cm from the elbow, and the force of the biceps is applied 5.0 cm from the elbow. (a) What force is exerted on the forearm by the biceps muscle? (b) What force is exerted on the upper arm at the elbow contact? Assume that all horizontal components are negligible.

9.20• A trucker needs to weigh a truck that is too long to fit on a platform scale. When the front wheels of the truck are run onto the scale, the scale reads W_1. When the rear wheels

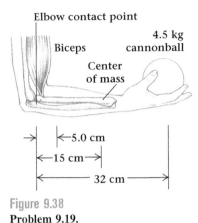

Figure 9.38
Problem 9.19.

400 N

Figure 9.40
Problems 9.23 and 9.24.

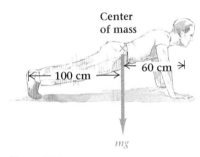

Figure 9.41
Problem 9.25.

are run onto the scale so that the front wheels are off, it reads W_2. (a) Prove that the total weight of the truck is $W_1 + W_2$. (b) Prove that if the truck is loaded so that its center of gravity is halfway between the front and rear wheels, the total weight is $2W_1$.

9.21• A bar balances 30.0 cm from one end. When a 0.75-kg mass is hung from that end, the balance point moves 8.0 cm toward that end. What is the mass of the bar?

9.22• A 4.0-m-long iron bar of uniform cross section is held perpendicular to the wall by a wire from the end of the bar to the wall (Fig. 9.39). What is the tension in the wire if the iron bar weighs 400 N and the wire is 5.0 m long?

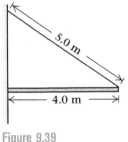

Figure 9.39
Problem 9.22.

9.23• A sign weighing 400 N is suspended at the end of a uniform rod 4.00 m long weighing 500 N (Fig. 9.40). (a) What is the tension in the support cable if it makes an angle $\theta = 40°$ with the rod? (b) What would be the tension if the cable were attached higher on the wall so that $\theta = 55°$?

9.24• Suppose the sign in Fig. 9.40 is suspended from the center of the boom rather than at the end. The cable is still connected to the end of the boom. What would be the tension in the cable if it made an angle $\theta = 40°$ with the bar?

9.25• A 75-kg Marine does pushups as shown in Fig. 9.41. What are the forces on his hands and feet?

9.26•• A bicycle carrier attached to a car by two horizontal straps carries a 11.3-kg bicycle (Fig. 9.42). What is the tension in each of the two straps marked S? Ignore the mass of the carrier.

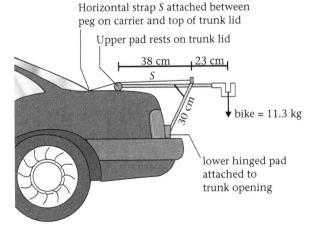

The distance between the center of the upper pad and the center of the lower pad is 31 cm.

Figure 9.42
Problem 9.26: A bicycle carrier mounted on a car.

9.27•• Figure 9.43(a) shows a person's outstretched arm holding a 5.0-kg dumbbell. The deltoid muscle is attached so that the force is applied at an angle of 17° from the horizontal at a point halfway between the shoulder joint and the center of mass of the arm (Fig. 9.43b). If the mass of the arm is 3.5 kg, what must be the tension in the deltoid muscle?

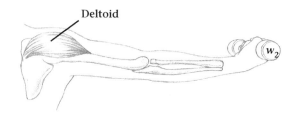

(a)

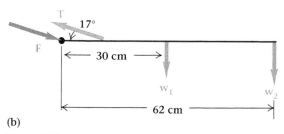

(b)

Figure 9.43
Problem 9.27.

*Section 9.5 Elasticity: Stress and Strain

Hints for Solving Problems

Remember that stress has units of N/m^2; strain is dimensionless.

9.28 A 1.7-m long brass bar has a square cross section 2.4 cm on an edge. The bar is compressed by a force of 5.0×10^3 N applied to its ends. By how much does the bar shorten?

9.29 A steel cable, 1.27 cm in diameter, stretches by 8.7 mm when subjected to a force of 6.27×10^4 N. How long is the unstretched cable?

9.30 Use the information in Table 9.2 to plot a figure similar to the region Oa in Fig. 9.19 for aluminum, steel, nylon, and tungsten.

9.31 What force is required to compress a 2.50-cm cube of aluminum to 99.9% of its original height (Fig. 9.44)?

9.32• The breaking stress of steel is 11.0×10^8 N/m^2. What is the minimum diameter for a steel wire that can safely support a 70.0-kg person?

9.33•• Find an expression for the work needed to stretch a circular wire by an amount ΔL as a function of the applied force F when the wire has a Young's modulus Y.

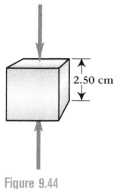

Figure 9.44
Problem 9.31.

Section 9.6 Torque and Moment of Inertia

9.34 A torque of 12 N · m is applied to a heavy wheel whose moment of inertia is $I = 36$ kg · m^2. (a) What is the angular acceleration of the wheel? (b) If the wheel was initially at rest and the torque is applied for 10 s, what will be the rotational frequency ω of the wheel at the end of the 10 s?

9.35 A wheel whose moment of inertia is 32 kg · m^2 is subjected to a torque of 12 N · m. If the wheel is initially moving with an angular velocity $\omega = 6.0$ rad/s when the torque is applied, what will be its angular velocity if the torque is applied for 9.0 s?

9.36 An iron disk has a radius of 0.515 m and a mass of 307 kg. The disk is mounted on its axis so that it is free to spin. (a) What torque is required to give it an angular acceleration $\alpha = 1.00$ rad/s^2? (b) If the torque is applied at the edge of the disk, how much force is required? (c) How much force is required if the force is applied at a distance 10.5 cm from the axis of rotation?

9.37 A wheel of radius R and moment of inertia I is subjected to a torque τ for a time t. (a) If the wheel was initially at rest at $t = 0$, what is its angular velocity at time t? (b) Calculate the tangential speed of the outer edge of the wheel.

9.38• A shaft extending from the side of an enclosed box is said to be connected to a flywheel inside. It is known that the mass of the flywheel is 1.37 kg and its radius is 7.50 cm. A 0.130-N · m-constant-torque motor connected directly to the shaft goes from rest to 500 rev/min in 3.0 s. Is the flywheel a uniform disk or is it some other shape? If it is some other simple shape, what might it be?

9.39• A student holding a rod by the center subjects it to a torque of 1.4 N · m about an axis perpendicular to the rod, turning it through 1.3 radians in 0.75 s. When the student holds the rod by the end and applies the same torque to the rod, through how many radians will the rod turn in 1.00 s?

9.40• A uniform 2.45-kg spinning disk with a radius of 0.243 m is brought to rest by a brake-pad pressed against the side 0.183 m from the rotation axis. The wheel is brought to rest from an angular velocity of 15.4 rad/s in a time of 24.3 s. What frictional force was applied by the brake pad?

9.41• In a student experiment, a torque of $2.0 \times 10^{-2}\,N \cdot m$ is applied to a rigid aluminum pipe, causing it to move about an axis through its center and perpendicular to its length with an acceleration $\alpha = 0.43\,rad/s^2$. (a) What is the moment of inertia of the pipe? (b) The rigid pipe is made from light tubing with a mass of 0.20 kg inserted in each end. How far apart are the two masses? (Refer to Table 9.3.)

9.42•• A piece of metal is pressed against the rim of a 1.6-kg, 19-cm-diameter grinding wheel that is turning at 2400 rev/min. The metal has a coefficient of friction of 0.85 with respect to the wheel. When the motor is cut off, with how much force must you press to stop the wheel in 20 s?

Sections 9.7 and 9.8 Angular Momentum and Conservation of Angular Momentum

Hints for Solving Problems

A net torque causes a change in angular momentum with time, which is equivalent to angular acceleration times the moment of inertia. When there is no net torque, the final angular momentum equals the initial angular momentum.

9.43 A toy airplane moves at the end of a string about a fixed point in a horizontal circle of 1.00-m radius. If the linear speed is 4.86 m/s, what will the speed become if the string is pulled in to give a radius of 0.750 m? Assume there is no torque.

9.44 A 0.5-kg flashlight is swung at the end of a string in a horizontal circle of 0.80-m radius with a constant angular speed. If no torque is applied, what must the radius become if the angular speed of the flashlight is to be halved?

9.45 What is the angular momentum of the earth as it rotates about its axis? Approximate the earth by a sphere of uniform density.

9.46• A sphere with a mass of 4.37 kg and a radius of 6.29 cm is spun at 37.3 rad/s around an axis through its center. Independent measurements show that the angular momentum of the sphere is $0.186\,kg \cdot m^2/s$. Is the sphere of uniform density? Explain your answer.

9.47• A 12-in. record is dropped on a large 12-in. phonograph turntable that is freely turning at $33\frac{1}{3}$ rev/min. The mass of the record is 0.150 kg, and the mass of the turntable is 1.00 kg. What is the final speed of the turntable in revolutions per minute? (In this case you may add the angular momenta in a manner analogous to the way you add linear momenta.)

9.48•• A playground merry-go-round has a disk-shaped platform that rotates with negligible friction about a vertical axis. The disk has a mass of 200 kg and a radius of 1.8 m. A 36-kg child rides at the center of the merry-go-round while a playmate sets it turning at 0.25 rev/s. If the child then walks along a radius to the outer edge of the disk, how fast will the disk be turning?

Section 9.9 Rotational Kinetic Energy

Hints for Solving Problems

Refer to Table 9.3 for the moments of inertia of solid objects of assorted shapes.

9.49 What is the kinetic energy of a 0.145-kg, 12-in. phonograph record when rotated at 45 rev/min?

9.50 A solid iron cylinder has a radius of 0.250 m and a mass of 145 kg. Calculate the kinetic energy of this cylinder when it is rotating about its axis at a rate of 13.5 rev/s.

9.51• What is the approximate rotational kinetic energy of a 66-cm diameter bicycle wheel of mass 4.0 kg when the bicycle is traveling at 15 km/h?

9.52• (a) A solid 4.0-kg wheel of radius 0.23 m is initially at rest. How much work is required to make it rotate at 3.0 rev/s about its axis? (b) If the energy of the rotating wheel is doubled, how many revolutions per second will it make?

9.53•• A 400-g, 16-cm-diameter disk is suspended in a horizontal position from a helical spring as shown in Fig. 9.45. The disk is rotated through a certain number of turns, thereby storing energy in the spring. When released, the disk is observed to have an angular speed of 18 rad/s when the spring returns to its equilibrium position. The disk is removed and replaced with a 400-g, 16-cm rod attached at the center. The rod is rotated through the same number of revolutions as was the disk to wind up the spring, and then it is released. What is the angular speed of the rod as it passes through the equilibrium position?

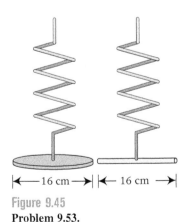

|←— 16 cm —→| |←— 16 cm —→|

Figure 9.45
Problem 9.53.

Section 9.10 Conservation of Energy: Translations and Rotations

9.54 A hoop and a disk, both of 0.50-m radius and 2.0-kg mass, are released from the top of an inclined plane 3.0 m high and 8.0 m long. What is the speed of each when it reaches the bottom? Assume that they both roll without slipping.

9.55 You simultaneously release a 1.0-kg hoop of 0.50-m radius and a 1.0-kg disk of 0.25-m radius from the upper end of an inclined plane of 2.5-m height. Calculate the speed of each at the bottom of the plane, assuming that they roll without slipping.

9.56 A disk released from the top of an inclined plane has a speed of 4.52 m/s at the bottom. How high is the upper end of the inclined plane? Assume that the disk rolled without slipping.

9.57• In a demonstration an iron hoop rolls without slipping down an inclined plane from a height h to the bottom. In another demonstration the plane is lubricated and the hoop slides down the plane from the same height without rolling. What is the ratio of the speeds at the bottom?

9.58• A sphere is released from rest at the top of an inclined plane. Derive an expression for the speed of the sphere at a point a distance h below its starting point. Assume that the sphere rolls without slipping.

9.59• A hoop of mass m and radius r is released from rest and rolls without slipping down a hill to a point that is a distance h lower than the starting point. Show that at this time the hoop will be rotating with an angular velocity

$$\omega = \sqrt{\frac{gh}{r^2}}.$$

9.60• A solid bowling ball with a radius of 10.9 cm and a mass of 7.0 kg rolls along a bowling alley at a linear speed of 2.0 m/s. (a) What is its translational kinetic energy and (b) what is its rotational kinetic energy?

9.61• A solid 0.558-kg disk rolls without slipping down an inclined plane that makes an angle of 30° with the horizontal direction. The disk is released from rest a distance 0.834 m from the lower end of the plane. (a) How fast is the disk moving as it reaches the end of the plane? (b) What fraction of the total kinetic energy of the disk is rotational kinetic energy?

9.62• A physics teacher stands on a freely rotating platform (Fig. 9.46). He holds a dumbbell in each hand of his outstretched arms while a student gives him a push until his angular velocity reaches 1.5 rad/s. When the freely spinning professor pulls his hands in close to his body, his angular velocity increases to 5.0 rad/s. What is the ratio of his final kinetic energy to his initial kinetic energy? How do you account for the change in energy?

9.63•• An Atwood's machine of the type shown in Fig. 9.47 has hanging masses of mass m_1 and m_2 and a disk-shaped pulley of mass m_p. Show that if $m_1 = m_p = M$ and $m_2 = 2M$, the acceleration of the hanging masses is $\frac{2}{7} g$. Use the principle of the conservation of energy to solve this problem.

9.64•• The Atwood's machine of Fig. 9.47 consists of masses $m_1 = 1.35$ kg and $m_2 = 1.15$ kg and a solid pulley with a diameter of 6.70 cm and a mass $m_p = 0.546$ kg. When released from rest, what is the speed of the heavier mass after it has fallen a distance of 1.45 m? Treat the pulley as a uniform disk.

9.65•• Use the principle of conservation of energy to find the acceleration sought in Example 9.11. First find the speed of the bucket after traveling a distance s. Then find the acceleration necessary to give this velocity.

$\omega_1 = 1.5$ rad/s $\omega_2 = 5$ rad/s

Figure 9.46
Problem 9.62.

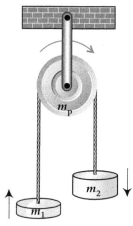

Figure 9.47
Problems 9.63 and 9.64.

9.66•• A 1.00-kg mass is attached to a string wrapped around a shaft of negligible mass and having a 6.0-cm radius. A dumbbell-shaped "flywheel" made from two 0.500-kg masses is attached to one end of the shaft and perpendicular to its axis (Fig. 9.48). The mass is released from rest and allowed

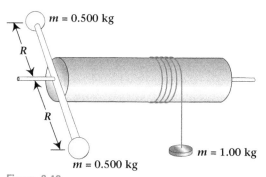

$m = 0.500$ kg

R

R

$m = 0.500$ kg

$m = 1.00$ kg

Figure 9.48
Problem 9.66.

to fall 1.00 m to the floor. It reaches a speed of 2.68 m/s just before striking the floor. How far apart are the masses of the dumbbell?

Additional Problems

9.67 An electric motor is used to lift a 20-kg bucket of water at constant speed from a well. If the diameter of the pulley is 10.0 cm, what must be the torque of the motor?

9.68• An unpowered flywheel is slowed by a constant frictional torque. At time $t = 0$ it has an angular velocity of 200 rad/s. Ten seconds later its velocity has decreased by 15%. What is its angular velocity at (a) time $t = 50$ s and (b) $t = 100$ s?

9.69• In Example 9.6, determine the mass m_3 by calculating torques about a point 0.50 m to the right of the left-hand end of the bar.

9.70• In Example 9.6, determine the mass m_3 by calculating torques about a point 0.10 m to the left of the right-hand end of the bar.

9.71• Figure 9.49 is a diagram of the jaw. Chewing is accomplished by the force of the masseter muscle closing the jaw about the fulcrum A. The distance $x_2 = 3x_1$. If the muscle exerts a force of 400 N, what force is applied by the front teeth?

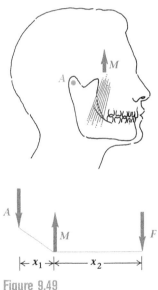

Figure 9.49
Problem 9.71.

9.72• A uniform solid disk of radius R_D and mass m and a hoop of radius R_H and mass m are simultaneously released from rest from the top of an incline. Can the ratio of the radii of the two objects be fixed so that they both reach the bottom of the plane at the same time?

9.73• Find the vertical and horizontal components of force exerted by the wall on the bar suspended as shown in Fig. 9.50. The weight of the bar is 300 N.

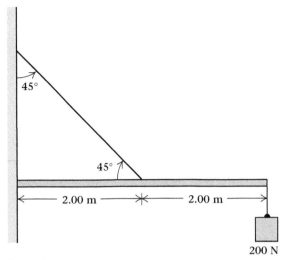

Figure 9.50
Problem 9.73.

9.74• A $\frac{1}{4}$-hp motor rotates at 1200 rpm. How much torque does it develop? (*Hint:* You may want to make an analogy with Eq. 6.19.)

9.75• A yo-yo resting on a horizontal table is free to roll (Fig. 9.51). When the string is pulled horizontally to the left, the yo-yo rolls to the left. When the string is pulled vertically, the yo-yo rolls to the right. Prove that the yo-yo will slide without rolling when the string is pulled at an angle θ given by $\sin \theta = r/R$.

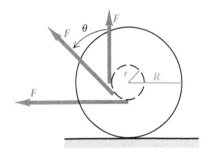

Figure 9.51
Problem 9.75.

9.76•• A cylinder of mass m and radius R is rigidly mounted to the same shaft as a lightweight cylinder of radius $r = R/2$. The shaft is free to turn with negligible friction. Cords are wound in opposite directions about the cylinders, and identical masses m are hung from the cords as shown in Fig. 9.52. (a) Which way do the cylinders turn? (b) What is the acceleration of the right-hand mass?

9.77•• A 1-m-radius flywheel is to be made from steel in the form of a solid disk. If the flywheel, when turning at 60 rev/min, is to store as much energy as a 100-watt lamp uses in 1.0 min, how thick must the flywheel be? The density of steel is 7.8 g·cm^{-3}.

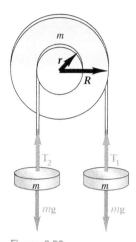

Figure 9.52
Problem 9.76.

9.78•• Two masses, one of value m and the other of $2m$, hang from light strings wrapped around a uniform solid cylinder of mass M and radius R that is free to rotate about a horizontal axis (Fig. 9.53). Find the acceleration of the masses when the cylinder is released from rest. Neglect effects of friction and the mass of the string.

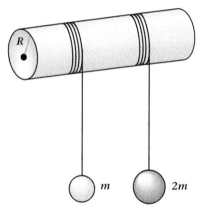

Figure 9.53
Problem 9.78.

9.79•• (a) Show that the kinetic energy of a satellite in circular orbit of radius r about the earth is one half the magnitude of its gravitational potential energy. (b) What is its total mechanical energy?

9.80•• A solid cylinder rolls without slipping on a horizontal surface. It collides with a resting hollow cylinder of the same mass and radius in a collision in which kinetic energy and momentum are conserved. If the initial speed of the rolling cylinder is 0.25 m/s, what is the final speed of the struck cylinder if it also rolls without slipping?

9.81•• When fitted over a narrow inclined plane and released, a yo-yo rolls slowly down the plane and then speeds up when it hits the floor (Fig. 9.54). The diameter of the center rod of the yo-yo is one-fifth of the diameter of the outer disks. (a) Show that the speed at the bottom of the plane is

$$v = \sqrt{\frac{4gh}{27}},$$ where h is the vertical distance through which

the center of mass descends. (b) What is the speed on the floor? Neglect the mass of the rod that joins the disks.

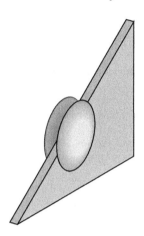

Figure 9.54
Problem 9.81.

9.82•• Find an expression for the speed with which a bowling ball must roll on a horizontal surface in order to roll up a ramp through a vertical distance equal to the ball's radius. (*Hint:* Include translational and rotational energy when in motion.)

9.83•• If the 0.70-kg block in Fig. 9.55 is released from rest, what speed will it have just before it hits the floor if there is no friction at the wheel's axis? Use conservation of energy and consider both translational and rotational kinetic energy.

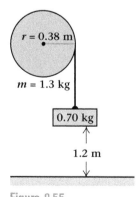

Figure 9.55
Problem 9.83.

9.84•• Assume that the axis of the wheel in Problem 9.83 is not frictionless. What is the frictional torque if the speed just before the 0.70-kg block hits the floor is half of the speed it would have without friction?

10.1 Hydrostatic Pressure
10.2 Pascal's Principle
10.3 Achimedes' Principle

Physics in Practice: Measuring Blood Pressure

*10.4 Surface Tension
10.5 Fluid Flow: Streamlines and the Equation of Continuity

Physics in Practice: Surface Tension and the Lungs

10.6 Bernoulli's Equation
*10.7 Viscosity and Poiseuille's Law
*10.8 Stokes's Law and Terminal Speed

Physics in Practice: How Airplanes Fly

*10.9 Turbulent Flow

Fluids

The study of fluids dates back to some of the earliest discoveries in physics. Many of the principles we examine in this chapter are associated with great scientists of the past, such as Archimedes (third century B.C.), Pascal (seventeenth century), Bernoulli (eighteenth century), and Stokes (nineteenth century). However, the study of fluid flow remains an active area of research. For example, the principles of fluid flow are used to minimize the aerodynamic resistance of a moving car or plane. Weather forecasters use computer simulation methods to model the fluid flow of our atmosphere, trying to understand the origin of hurricanes as well as of stable air currents like the jet stream. The occurrence of stable patterns of fluid flow from seemingly random initial conditions has become an exciting area of contemporary research in physical model building and computer science.

In this chapter, we discuss the fundamental properties of fluids at rest (the study of *hydrostatics*) and in motion (the study of *hydrodynamics*). The treatment here is somewhat different from that of other chapters in that we present most results without derivation. Instead, we rely on physical intuition to show that these results are reasonable. We do this because in many cases the derivations are prohibitively long. However, these ideas are all developed from classical mechanics, primarily Newton's laws and conservation of energy.

After studying this chapter, you should be able to recognize the proper conditions for applying the various laws of fluid behavior, particularly those of fluid flow. These laws are strictly valid only for certain types of fluids and particular types of flow. They cannot give reliable results beyond their proper domain of applicability. ■

10.1   Hydrostatic Pressure

A **fluid** is any substance that cannot maintain its own shape; in other words, it is a substance that has no rigidity. It can flow and alter its shape to conform to the outlines of its container. This definition includes liquids, such as water; gases, such as air; very slowly flowing substances, such as tar and some plastics; and even some mixtures of solids and liquids that can flow, such as mud. Gases are easily compressible and have no natural volume; that is, they expand to uniformly fill the container in which they are held. Liquids, on the other hand, are practically incompressible, and a given mass of liquid has a characteristic volume. If the liquid volume is less than that of its container, the liquid will have a well-defined surface bounding its volume.

Unless otherwise stated, we deal in this chapter with fluids that cannot be compressed, that is, with liquids. However, we consider fluids to have viscosity, which is the friction that resists the motion of objects through the fluid.

Consider an upright cylinder containing a liquid (Fig. 10.1). The weight of the liquid exerts a force on the bottom of the cylinder. This force produces a pressure on the bottom of the cylinder, where the **pressure** P is defined as the mag-

Figure 10.1

A fluid exerts a pressure on the bottom of its cylindrical container equal to the total weight of the fluid divided by the area of the bottom of the container.

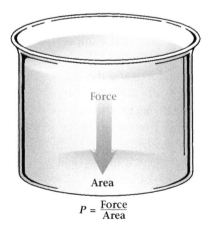

Force

Area

$$P = \frac{\text{Force}}{\text{Area}}$$

nitude of the perpendicular force acting on an area divided by that area. Thus, pressure is the *force per unit area:*

$$P \equiv \frac{\text{force}}{\text{area}}. \tag{10.1}$$

If we insert the weight of the liquid for the force in Eq. (10.1), we find that

$$P = \frac{\text{weight}}{\text{area}} = \frac{mg}{A},$$

where m is the mass of the liquid, A is the area of the bottom of the cylinder, and g is the acceleration of gravity. Note that pressure is a scalar quantity.

The different conditions under which pressure measurements are made have led to the development of a variety of commonly used units. The SI unit of pressure, N/m^2, is given the name **pascal** (Pa). Table 10.1 lists several other common units of pressure, along with their relationship to the pascal.

A tire gauge is a familiar pressure-measuring device (Fig. 10.2). One form consists of a hollow cylinder fitted with a spring-loaded piston. When you press the gauge against a tire valve stem, the pressurized air from the tire enters the cylinder. The air exerts a force on the piston that is equal to the pressure in the cylinder times the area of the face of the piston ($F = P \cdot A$). If the spring obeys Hooke's law, the piston is pushed a distance that is proportional to the force and therefore to the pressure. The rod on the end of the piston can be calibrated to read the pressure directly. We will discuss some other pressure-measuring devices later.

It is common to calibrate pressure gauges, such as the tire gauge, so that they indicate only the pressure in excess of atmospheric pressure. This pressure is called *gauge pressure*. As we will discuss in more detail in Chapter 12, the atmosphere exerts a pressure of about 1.013×10^5 N/m^2 (101.3 kPa or 14.7 $lb/in.^2$) at sea level, and this value must be added to the gauge pressure to give the total pressure.

Table 10.1	Some Common Units of Pressure	
Name	**Value (N/m² = Pa)**
1 pascal (Pa)	1
1 bar	1.00×10^5
1 atmosphere (atm)	1.01×10^5
1 mm Hg	1.33×10^2
1 torr	1.33×10^2
1 lb/in.² (psi)	6.89×10^3

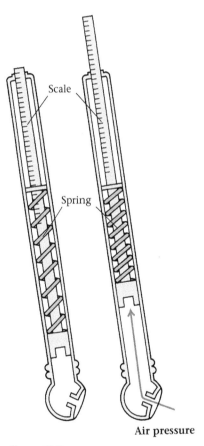

Air pressure

Figure 10.2
A tire-pressure gauge. The extension of the scale is proportional to the force on the spring (Hooke's law), which is proportional to the air pressure in the tire. When the gauge is removed from the tire, the scale, which is not attached to the spring, remains extended, held in position by friction with the sleeve that holds it.

Master the Concept

Air Pressure

Question: A driver with a flat tire measures its pressure with a tire-pressure gauge. The gauge gives a reading of zero. Does this reading indicate that there is no air in the tire?

Answer: The gauge for measuring tire pressure registers the difference between the pressure inside the tire and the atmospheric pressure outside the tire. Thus, a reading of zero only indicates that the pressure inside is equal to the pressure outside. There is still air within the tire, but the air present is at the same pressure as the outside air. There is no pressure difference to hold up the walls of the tire.

It is convenient to use the concept of density when discussing pressure. The **density** of a substance, ρ, was defined in Chapter 5 as its mass per unit volume,

$$\rho = \frac{m}{V}, \qquad (10.2)$$

The SI unit for density is kg/m^3. Table 10.2 gives the densities of several gases, liquids, and solids. A related quantity, the **specific gravity** of a substance, is defined as the ratio of its density to the density of water at 4°C, which is 1.00×10^3 kg/m^3. Thus lead, which has a density of 11.4×10^3 kg/m^3, has a specific

Table 10.2	*Densities of Some Common Materials* ▼	
Material	**Temperature (°C)**	**Density (kg/m³)**
Gases*		
Hydrogen	0	0.09
Helium	0	0.18
Nitrogen	0	1.25
Air	0	1.29
Oxygen	0	1.43
Carbon dioxide	0	1.98
Liquids		
Gasoline	20	0.68×10^3
Methyl alcohol	20	0.791×10^3
Water	20	0.998×10^3
Sea water	20	1.03×10^3
Glycerin	20	1.26×10^3
Mercury	20	13.6×10^3
Solids		
Wood, balsa	—	$(0.12–0.20) \times 10^3$
Wood, pine	—	$(0.37–0.64) \times 10^3$
Wood, oak	—	$(0.67–0.79) \times 10^3$
Butter	—	$(0.86–0.87) \times 10^3$
Ice	—	0.92×10^3
Brick	—	$(1.4–2.2) \times 10^3$
Bone	—	$(1.7–2.0) \times 10^3$
Glass, common	—	$(2.4–2.8) \times 10^3$
Granite	—	$(2.64–2.76) \times 10^3$
Aluminum	20	2.70×10^3
Iron	20	7.87×10^3
Brass	—	$(8.41–8.86) \times 10^3$
Lead	20	11.4×10^3
Uranium	20	18.95×10^3
Gold	20	19.3×10^3

*The density given here is for a pressure P_0 of one standard atmosphere = 1.01325×10^5 Pa. The density ρ of a gas at other temperatures and pressures is given by

$$\rho = \rho_0 \left(\frac{P \times 273.15}{P_0 \times (T + 273.15)} \right),$$

where P is the pressure and T is the temperature in degrees Celsius.

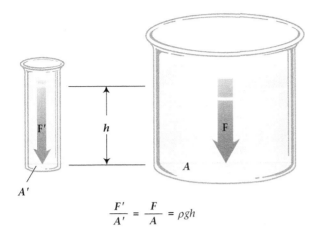

$$\frac{F'}{A'} = \frac{F}{A} = \rho g h$$

Figure 10.3
Containers of different size, filled to
the same depth with identical fluids of
uniform density, have equal pressure at
the bottom.

gravity of 11.4. Because the specific gravity is a ratio of two quantities with the same units, it is a pure number without units or dimensions.

Equation (10.1) for pressure can be written in terms of density if we write the mass as the product of density and volume:

$$P = \frac{mg}{A} = \frac{\rho V g}{A} = \frac{\rho h A g}{A},$$

or

$$\boxed{P = \rho g h,} \tag{10.3}$$

where ρ is the density and h is the depth of the liquid (Fig. 10.3).

We can now see that pressure is directly proportional to both the density and the depth of the liquid. Thus, separate containers of different size, holding identical liquids of uniform density, have equal pressure at equal depth. If the two containers are filled to the same height, they have equal pressure at the bottom, even though the total force on the bottom surface due to the liquid is greater at the bottom of the larger container (see Fig. 10.3). The pressure depends on the depth and not on the cross section. A thin upright tube filled to a height of 3 m with water has the same pressure at its bottom as does a large lake that is 3 m deep.

A force also is exerted on the sides of the container, and a corresponding pressure is present there. Moreover, a pressure exists at any point within the body of the liquid. If the liquid is at rest, this pressure is independent of direction. Thus, the pressure on the small rubber membrane in Fig. 10.4 is the same regardless of the orientation of its surface, provided that the center of the membrane is kept at a constant depth. If the pressures in opposite directions were not the same, a pressure difference would arise, resulting in an unbalanced force acting on the liquid. This force would cause the liquid to flow, which contradicts our original assumption that the liquid is at rest. So the pressure must depend only on the height of the liquid above the point in question, according to Eq. (10.3). Thus, the difference in pressure ΔP between two points that differ in depth by Δh is

$$\Delta P = \rho g \, \Delta h. \tag{10.4}$$

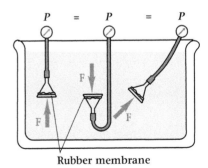

Rubber membrane

Figure 10.4
At constant depth, the pressure exerted by the fluid is the same in all directions.

Example 10.1

A tank is filled with water to a depth of 1.5 m. What is the pressure at the bottom of the tank due to the water alone?

Solution We can compute the pressure directly from Eq. (10.3). The density of water is approximately 10^3 kg/m^3, and the height h is 1.5 m. So

$$P = \rho g \,\Delta h = (10^3 \text{ kg/m}^3)(9.81 \text{ m/s}^2)(1.5 \text{ m}) = 1.5 \times 10^4 \text{ N/m}^2.$$

The combination of units N/m^2 is the pascal (Pa). Thus, the pressure at the bottom of the tank due to the water is 1.5×10^4 Pa, or 15 kPa.

Discussion Note that the pressure due to the water is completely independent of the size and shape of the tank. Note also that, if we wish to know the total pressure on the bottom of the tank, we must add atmospheric pressure to our answer here.

Example 10.2

A nurse administers medication in a saline solution to a patient by infusion into a vein in the patient's arm (Fig. 10.5). The density of the solution is 1.0×10^3 kg/m^3, and the gauge pressure inside the vein is 2.4×10^3 Pa. How high above the insertion point must the container be hung so that there is sufficient pressure to force the fluid into the patient?

Solution The container must be hung high enough that the gauge pressure due to the liquid in the tube and container is at least as great as the gauge pressure inside the vein:

$$P_{\text{liquid}} = \rho g h = 2.4 \times 10^3 \text{ Pa}.$$

Solving for the height h yields

$$h = \frac{2.4 \times 10^3 \text{ Pa}}{\rho g} = \frac{2.4 \times 10^3 \text{ Pa}}{9.81 \text{ m/s}^2 \times 1.0 \times 10^3 \text{ kg/m}^3}$$

$$h = 0.24 \text{ m} = 24 \text{ cm}.$$

To actually establish a flow through the needle, the container would need to be higher than this result.

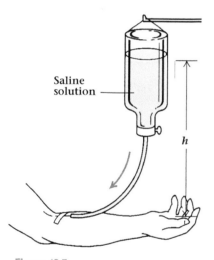

Saline solution

h

Figure 10.5
Example 10.2: A fluid is fed into a patient's arm from a suspended container. The pressure of the fluid must exceed the pressure in the arm.

10.2 Pascal's Principle

It is often desirable to know the pressure at one point in a fluid when we know it at another. The pressure at any point in the liquid in Fig. 10.6 depends on its depth below the surface h and on any additional pressure (such as atmospheric pressure, P_{atm}) exerted on the liquid above that point. If we know the pressure on the surface of the liquid (P_{atm}) and wish to determine the pressure at point B, our equation reads

$$P_B = P_{\text{atm}} + \rho g h. \qquad (10.5)$$

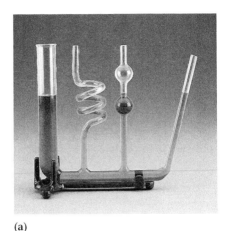
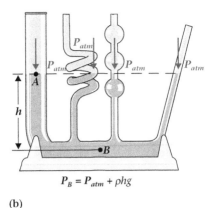

$$P_B = P_{atm} + \rho h g$$

(a)   (b)

If the pressure at A (that is, P_{atm}) is increased, then the pressure at B is correspondingly increased by the same amount. This fact was recognized by Blaise Pascal (1623–1662) and is embodied in the statement known as **Pascal's principle:** *The pressure applied at one point in an enclosed fluid is transmitted undiminished to every part of the fluid and to the walls of the container.* Pascal's principle holds for gases as well as for liquids, with some minor modifications due to the change in volume of a gas when the pressure is changed.

Hyperbaric medicine treats many physical problems through the application of high-pressure air or air-oxygen mixtures. Patients are enclosed in chambers pressurized at up to 6 atmospheres. By Pascal's principle, the pressure is distributed throughout the hyperbaric chamber. Patients breathing air at 6 atmospheres take in six times the amount of oxygen with each breath. The increased oxygen intake is useful in treating a variety of problems such as carbon-monoxide poisioning, slow-healing wounds, and burns.

A patient being placed in a hyperbaric chamber. The chamber provides a demonstration of Pascal's principle.

Example 10.3

A scuba diver searches for treasure at a depth of 20.0 m below the surface of the sea. At what pressure must the scuba (self-contained underwater breathing apparatus) device deliver air to the diver?

Strategy The pressure at the diver's depth is greater than atmospheric pressure because of the weight of the water above the diver. If the air breathed in is not at the same pressure as the external pressure on the diver's chest, the excess pressure will collapse the chest. Thus, the breathing apparatus must deliver air to the diver at the pressure of the surrounding water. We can calculate this pressure from Eq. (10.5).

Solution The pressure on the diver is

$$P = P_{atm} + \rho g h,$$

where P_{atm} is the pressure due to the atmosphere pressing down on the sea, ρ is the density of sea water, and h is the depth of the diver below the surface. The numerical values for P_{atm} (101.3 kPa) and ρ (approximately 1030 kg/m^3)

are found in Table 10.2. When the values for P_{atm}, ρ, and h are inserted into the equation, we get

$$P = 101.3 \times 10^3 \text{ Pa} + (1030 \text{ kg/m}^3)(9.81 \text{ m/s}^2)(20.0) = 303 \text{ kPa}.$$

When expressed in terms of atmospheres, the pressure becomes

$$P = 303 \text{ kPa} \left(\frac{1 \text{ atm}}{101.3 \text{ kPa}} \right) = 2.99 \text{ atm} \approx 3 \text{ atm}.$$

In other words, at a depth of 20.0 m, the pressure is three times the pressure at the surface.

Example 10.4

You can make a simple hydraulic lift by fitting a piston attached to a handle into a 3-cm-diameter cylinder, which is connected to a larger cylinder of 24-cm diameter (Fig. 10.7). If a 50-kg (110-lb) woman puts all her weight on the handle of the smaller piston, how much weight can be lifted by the larger one?

Strategy By Pascal's principle, the same applied pressure is transmitted every-where within the enclosed liquid system. In particular, if the heights of the pistons a and b are the same, the pressure on the pistons must be the same, including the pressures due to the applied force. We can set the pressure on the pistons equal, express the pressures in terms of the forces and areas, and then solve for the force on the larger piston.

Solution Using subscripts a and b to denote the quantities at each place, we can write $P_a = P_b$. But the pressure is the force per unit area: $F_a/A_a = F_b/A_b$. The area of the circular pistons is πr^2, so

$$\frac{F_a}{\pi r_a^2} = \frac{F_b}{\pi r_b^2}.$$

Solving for F_b gives

Figure 10.7
Example 10.3: A woman pushes down on the piston a. The pressure is transmitted undiminished to piston b.

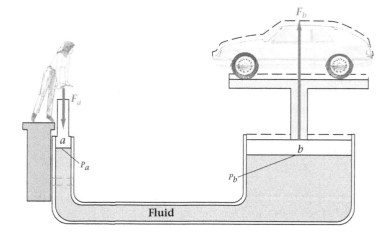

$$F_b = F_a\left(\frac{r_b}{r_a}\right)^2.$$

We see that the force at b is the applied force multiplied by the square of the ratio of the radii of the cylinders. In this case, the applied force is $F_a = mg$, so the answer becomes

$$F_b = mg\left(\frac{r_b}{r_a}\right)^2 = 50 \text{ kg} \times 9.81 \text{ m/s}^2\left(\frac{12 \text{ cm}}{1.5 \text{ cm}}\right)^2 = 3.14 \times 10^4 \text{ N}.$$

This is enough force to lift two Jeeps, which together weigh 3.10×10^4 N.

In addition to the tire gauge mentioned earlier, there are several other pressure-measuring devices. One of these is the *manometer*, which measures a pressure by balancing the force due to the pressure with the weight of a column of liquid (Fig. 10.8). The pressure to be measured by this open-tube manometer is the pressure in the chamber C. If the density of air is neglected or the height h' is not too great, then Pascal's principle says that the pressure at A is the same as at C. Pascal's principle further says that the pressure at B is the same as at A. Therefore we can determine the gauge pressure at C by measuring the difference in the levels (heights) of the liquid h. This, as we saw in Section 10.1, is ρgh, where ρ is the density of the liquid. In some cases, it is common to state the pressure in terms of the height h. Thus, blood pressures are given as so many millimeters of mercury (mm Hg).

A *barometer* is a type of manometer used for measuring atmospheric pressure. A long tube is filled with mercury and inverted in a bowl of mercury (Fig. 10.9). The mercury drops in the tube until it is about 76 cm above the level of the mercury in the bowl. The atmosphere exerts a pressure on the mercury in the bowl that just balances the column of mercury. Small changes in atmospheric pressure, which are associated with changes in the weather, can be read from the barometer. Aneroid (without liquid) barometers are also commonly used to measure atmospheric pressure. The basic component of an aneroid barometer is a partially evacuated, sealed chamber made of thin metal with corrugated sides. The chamber expands and contracts in response to changes in atmospheric pressure. This movement of the chamber walls is transmitted to a pointer by a mechanical linkage.

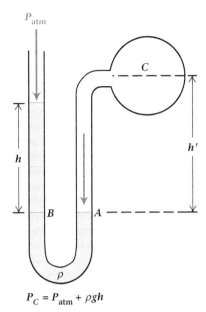

$$P_C = P_{atm} + \rho gh$$

Figure 10.8
An open U-tube manometer. The difference in the heights of the liquid indicates the pressure in the chamber C.

10.3 Archimedes' Principle

The story has been told that Archimedes (287–212 B.C.) conceived of the principle that bears his name after King Hiero of Syracuse asked Archimedes to determine the actual composition of the king's crown, which was alleged to be pure gold. Archimedes was ordered to do so without damaging the crown. According to legend, the Greek scientist's inspiration came to him as he lay partially submerged in his bath. On getting into the tub, he observed that the more his body sank into the tub, the more water ran out over the top. He immediately jumped out of the tub and rushed through the streets naked, shouting excitedly in a loud voice "Eureka" ("I have found it"). **Archimedes' principle** says: *A body, whether completely or partially submerged in a fluid, is buoyed upward by a force that*

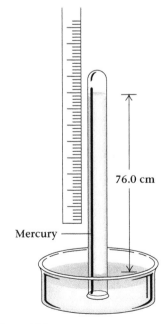

Figure 10.9
Mercury barometer.

MEASURING BLOOD PRESSURE

Almost any time you get a medical checkup, someone measures your blood pressure. The procedure is one of the most common in medicine: Someone wraps a cuff around your arm, inflates the cuff until it's tight, then listens through a stethoscope held to your arm while letting the cuff slowly deflate. What is happening during this procedure? The person is measuring the pressure in a fluid, your blood.

The heart is a large muscle, responsible for pumping oxygen-supplying blood to all parts of the body. The blood returns from the body through the veins to the right side of the heart, which pumps the blood to the lungs. The lungs remove carbon dioxide from the blood and add oxygen. The left side of the heart receives the oxygenated blood from the lungs and pumps it throughout the body by way of the arteries. The blood flows from the arteries to the veins through capillary beds.

Two pressures in the heart's action are of particular medical interest: the *systolic* pressure, when the heart is contracted, and the *diastolic* pressure, when the heart is relaxed between beats. Normal heart action causes arterial blood pressure to oscillate between these two values. Abnormally high or low arterial blood pressure can sometimes indicate physical and mental conditions of varying degrees of seriousness.

The most direct way of measuring blood pressure is to insert a fluid-filled tube into the artery and connect it to a pressure gauge. Though this is sometimes done, it is neither comfortable nor convenient. The commonly used indirect method involves a device called a sphygmomanometer. A nonelastic cuff that has an inflatable bag within it is placed around the upper arm, roughly at the same vertical level as the heart. The cuff is connected directly to some pressure gauge, such as a manometer (Fig. B10.1). When the cuff is inflated, the tissue in the arm is compressed; if sufficient pressure is applied, the flow of arterial blood in the arm stops. If the cuff is long enough and if it is applied snugly, the pressure in the tissues in the arm is the same as the pressure in the inflated part of the cuff, and is also the same as the pressure in the artery. In effect, Pascal's principle holds for the system composed of cuff, arm, and artery.

After the blood flow has been cut off, the pressure in the cuff is reduced by releasing some of the air. The falling pressure corresponds to the dashed line in Fig. B10.1. At some point, the maximum arterial pressure slightly exceeds the pressure in the surrounding tissue and cuff, allowing the blood to resume flowing. The acceleration of the blood through the arteries gives rise to a characteristic sound, which can be

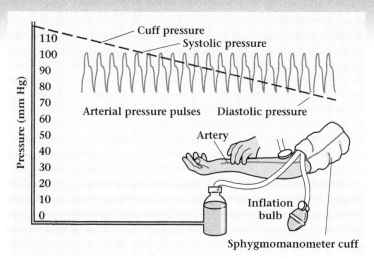

Figure B10.1 Measuring blood pressure with a sphygmomanometer. Identifiable sounds occur in the arm when the cuff pressure falls below the systolic and diastolic pressures.

identified by means of a stethoscope. When this sound occurs, the manometer indicates the maximum, or systolic, pressure. As the pressure in the cuff falls further, a second change in the sound is heard, characteristic of the drop below diastolic pressure. The readings shown in Fig. B10.1 correspond to the two pressures and are reported as "100 over 75," which is a typical value of the pressures for a healthy person.

The measurements made by this technique may vary because of the need to fit the cuff properly and the need to reliably estimate the point at which the sound changes. The condition of the manometer, the size of the arm, and the rate at which the cuff is inflated and deflated can have an effect. Figure B10.2 shows a comparison between pressures measured directly in the artery and pressures measured indirectly by a type of sphygmomanometer.

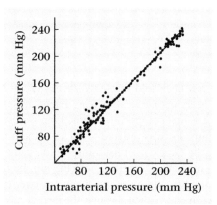

Figure B10.2 Comparison of blood pressure measurements by sphygmomanometry with direct measurements of arterial pressure.

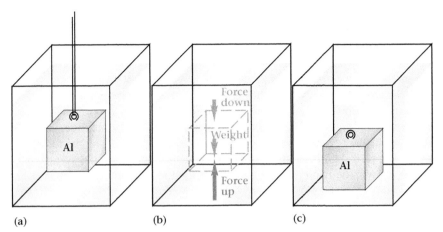

(a) (b) (c)

Figure 10.10
(a) An aluminum cube suspended in water. (b) An imaginary volume in the water, equal to the volume of the cube. The difference between the upward force and the downward force on the volume is equal to the weight of the water in the volume. (c) If the string is cut, the cube sinks because it is denser than water.

is equal to the weight of the displaced fluid. How this principle allowed Archimedes to solve the problem of the king's crown is seen in Problem 10.30.

Archimedes' principle can be obtained by a simple nonmathematical argument. Consider an object of arbitrary but known shape, such as an aluminum cube, that hangs completely submerged in a fluid, such as water (Fig. 10.10a). Now imagine that you remove the cube and replace it with a volume of water having the same size and shape as the "missing cube." (This is the amount of fluid displaced by the object.) Since this volume of fluid does not sink to the bottom of the container, the surrounding fluid must provide a net upward force, which counteracts the downward force due to the weight of fluid in the volume (Fig. 10.10b).

This upward force due to the surrounding water is the **buoyant force** and is equal to the weight of fluid in the volume displaced by the object. If you replace the aluminum cube with a lead cube of the same size, the buoyant force remains the same: It depends only on the volume of the submerged object, not on its mass or density. Of course, since aluminum is denser than water, the buoyant force alone cannot support the cube, which sinks to the bottom of the container if the supporting string is cut (Fig. 10.10c). If the fluid were mercury, which has a density greater than that of aluminum, the aluminum cube would float. We can generalize to a case in which the body is partially submerged, such as that of the iceberg in Example 10.6.

Blimps, hot-air balloons, and other lighter-than-air craft furnish another example of Archimedes' principle. They float in the air just as a submerged fish floats in the water. The blimp in Fig. 10.11 obviously has individual parts that will not float in air. However, if the *average* density of the whole craft, including passengers, is less than the density of air, the craft will take off without power. To meet this requirement in a practical way, the blimp contains a large volume of helium. The same type of observation can be made about large ships, which float even though they are made of steel and carry dense objects. The explanation is that the average density of the entire ship, including all of the air spaces, is less than the density of water.

Health professionals use Archimedes' principle to determine the percentage of fat in a person's body composition. The technique used, commonly known as the *hydrostatic weighing* method, requires two measurements of weight. A person is first weighed in air and is then weighed when submerged in water. The

Figure 10.11
The Goodyear airship *Europa* above the British research vessel *Eye of the Wind*. Although both the airship and the boat contain materials of high density, their average density is less than that of the fluid in which they float.

difference in the weight in air and the weight in water is the buoyant force, which is equal to the weight of the volume of water displaced. From these two weight measurements the person's mass and volume can be found. The person's average density can then be computed from these numbers. In practice, corrections are made for the air contained in the lungs.

The amount of body fat is then computed using an appropriate model. Usually a two-component model is assumed in which the body mass is divided into a fat mass and a fat-free mass. Furthermore, based on prior measurements, the densities of the two components are assumed to be 0.9×10^3 kg/m^3 for the fat and 1.10×10^3 kg/m^3 for the fat-free component. Then, since the average density is known, the two-component model is used to compute the fraction of fat in the body. The fraction is usually given as a percentage of body mass. Measurements made this way are precise to within a few percent of the body's fat composition.

Master the Concept

Buoyancy

Question: A bucket of water rests on a scale. Does the scale reading change when a lead block is suspended from a thread and lowered into the water where it is held submerged without touching the bottom or sides of the bucket?

Answer: The lead block displaces a volume of water equal to its own volume. Consequently, the water pushes the block upward with a buoyant force equal to the weight of the displaced water. By Newton's third law, there must be an equal but opposite force pushing down. The scale reading will increase by an amount equal to the buoyant force.

Question: If the lead block just described was suspended from a spring scale, what happens to the reading of that scale when the block is submerged in the water?

Answer: If the lead block is not accelerating, the upward forces acting on it must equal the downward force of gravity on it. When the block is in the air, the spring scale provides all of the upward force. When the block is submerged in the water, the water provides part of the upward force, so the spring scale reading is decreased by an amount equal to the buoyant force.

Example 10.5

An object of density ρ and mass m is submerged in a liquid with a smaller density ρ_0. Show that the effective weight of the submerged object is

$$w_{\text{eff}} = mg\left(1 - \frac{\rho_0}{\rho}\right).$$

Strategy Because the density of the object is greater than that of the surrounding liquid, the object will sink when dropped in the liquid. However, if we suspended it with a thread, we find that the force needed to hold it up (its effective weight) is less than its weight in air by the amount of buoyant force exerted by the liquid. It is this difference in forces that we need to find.

Solution The weight of the object is mg. The buoyant force is equal to the weight of the displaced liquid.

$$\text{buoyant force} = \rho_0 V g,$$

where V, the volume of the liquid displaced, is equal to the volume of the submerged object. The volume of the object can be expressed in terms of its density as

$$V = \frac{m}{\rho}.$$

The effective weight w_{eff} is the gravitational force less the buoyant force:

$$w_{\text{eff}} = mg - \rho_0 V g = mg - \rho_0\left(\frac{m}{\rho}\right)g$$

$$w_{\text{eff}} = mg\left(1 - \frac{\rho_0}{\rho}\right).$$

Example 10.6

Icebergs are made of fresh-water ice, which has a density ρ_i of 0.92×10^3 kg/m^3 at 0°C. Ocean water, largely because of the dissolved salt, has a density ρ_w of about 1.03×10^3 kg/m^3. What fraction of an iceberg lies below the surface?

Strategy For simplicity, assume the iceberg to be a cube of volume L^3. The downward force acting on it is due to gravity:

$$F_{\text{grav}} = mg = \text{volume} \times \text{density} \times g = L^3 \times \rho_i \times g.$$

The buoyant force, according to Archimedes' principle, depends on the volume of ice submerged in the water. If the bottom of the floating cube is at a depth d below the surface of the water, then the upward buoyant force is

$$F_{\text{buoyant}} = d \times L^2 \times \rho_w \times g.$$

When the iceberg is floating in equilibrium, these forces are equal in magnitude. We can solve for the ratio of d to L to obtain the desired fraction.

Solution In equilibrium, the upward buoyant force must be equal in magnitude to the downward gravitational force.

$$F_{\text{buoyant}} = F_{\text{grav}},$$

or

$$d\,L^2\,g\rho_w = L^3 g\rho_i.$$

Rearrange the equation and insert the numerical values to get

$$\frac{d}{L} = \frac{\rho_i}{\rho_w} = \frac{0.92}{1.03} = 0.89.$$

Thus, 89% of the iceberg lies below the surface.

Discussion We have just computed how much of an iceberg lies below the surface for the particular case of a cubic iceberg. What happens if the iceberg is not cubic? The volume of the iceberg below the surface will be 89% of the total volume regardless of the shape of the iceberg. However, the ratio of the linear extent of berg below the surface to its total height will not, in general, be 0.89, but will depend on its exact shape.

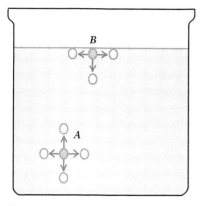

Figure 10.12
A molecule inside a liquid (point A) is attracted to other molecules on all sides. A molecule on the surface (point B) has attractive forces only to other molecules in the surface and below the surface. As a result, the surface acts like a membrane under tension.

*10.4   Surface Tension

Most people have observed the phenomenon called surface tension. You have seen spherical water drops hanging from a spider's web; or objects denser than water, like a needle or a razor blade, floating on the surface; or a water bug skittering over a pond. In each case, the liquid surface exhibits some of the characteristics of a stretched membrane under tension.

The molecules that compose a liquid attract one another; otherwise the liquid would not have a definite volume. Most liquids are nearly incompressible because the intermolecular forces are repulsive at distances less than their normal separations. At any point A inside a liquid at rest, the net molecular force on a molecule of the liquid is zero because the molecules surrounding it provide opposing forces in balance (Fig. 10.12). However, as shown, at a point B on the surface of the liquid, the situation changes. A molecule experiences attractive forces only in the direction of the other molecules of the liquid, and since at the surface these forces are not balanced by attractive forces in the outward direction, there is a net inward force. This inward force makes the surface act like a stretched drumhead. The surface of a liquid resists any effort to increase its area.

We can determine values of surface tension by measuring the force necessary to lift a ring out of the liquid (Fig. 10.13). The required force is proportional to C, the circumference of the ring. As the ring rises, a thin film of liquid clings to it until the weight of the film exceeds the attractive forces holding the film together. The film has two surfaces, one inside and one outside of the ring. Thus, the total length along which the lifting force acts is 2C. The **surface tension** γ is the ratio of the surface force to the length along which it acts:

$$\gamma = \frac{F}{2C}. \qquad (10.6)$$

Notice that the surface tension is not simply a force, but a force divided by a length. The units of surface tension are N/m. Table 10.3 lists the surface tensions of some common liquids.

An equivalent way of thinking about surface tension is to think of it as the energy per unit area of the surface. That this is reasonable can be seen by writing the units N/m as $N \cdot m/m^2$, which is J/m^2. The equilibrium configuration of a surface corresponds to its lowest possible energy. One consequence is that liquids try to minimize their surface area. As a result, liquids tend to assume the shape of a sphere, which is the shape with the smallest surface area (and therefore energy) for a given volume. Figure 10.14 is a view of a splash of milk, showing the detached spheres in the process of separating from the body of liquid. For the same reason, soap bubbles tend to take the shape of spheres.

The attractive force between like molecules that acts to hold a liquid together is called cohesion. The attractive force between unlike molecules—say, between

Figure 10.13
A force is required to lift a ring out of the liquid.

Table 10.3	Measured Values of Surface Tension	
Liquid in Contact with Air	Temperature (°C)	Surface Tension (10^{-3} N/m)
Water	0	75.6
Water	25	72.0
Water	80	62.6
Ethyl alcohol	20	22.8
Acetone	20	23.7
Glycerin	20	63.4
Mercury	20	435

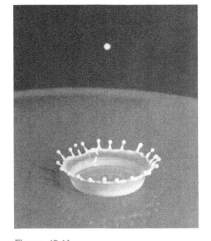

Figure 10.14
Close-up of the splash of a milk drop falling on a hard surface.

those of water and glass—is called adhesion. The adhesive forces may be as great as, or even greater than, cohesive forces. For example, the adhesion of water to clean glass is greater than the cohesion of water to itself, so the water wets the glass. By contrast, the adhesion of water to a newly waxed surface is less than the cohesion, so water does not wet the surface, but beads up into drops.

The surface tension of a liquid, such as water or oil, may be greatly reduced by the addition of certain chemicals called surfactants, or surface-active agents. Detergents are one type of surface-active agent. The lowering of the surface tension of water by detergents increases the ability of water to wet a surface. This improved wetting allows more water molecules to penetrate cloth fibers and wash away particles of soil.

If a tube of relatively small internal diameter (a capillary) is placed in a liquid that wets it, the liquid rises up in the tube (Fig. 10.15). This effect, known as *capillary action,* is due to the cohesive forces of surface tension and the adhesive forces between the liquid and the glass tube. The liquid rises until the upward force due to surface tension is equaled by the weight of the liquid in the tube.

In the weightless environment of an orbiting spacecraft, surface tension can pull liquids from their containers. Astronauts attempting to use a straw to drink a liquid find that the liquid climbs up the straw and collects as a spherical drop at the open end because there is no force (weight) opposing the capillary forces. The straws used aboard the space shuttle come with clamps to squeeze the straws shut lest the drinks come oozing out the top.

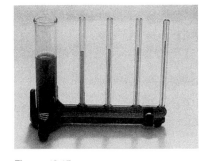

Figure 10.15
The internal diameters of the four tubes decrease from left to right.

Example 10.7

Show that the height to which a liquid rises in a narrow tube is given by $h = 2\gamma \cos \theta / r\rho g$, where r is the radius of the column of liquid, ρ is its density, g is the acceleration of gravity, γ is the surface tension, and θ is the angle the liquid surface makes with the wall at the line of contact (Fig. 10.16).

Solution First note that, for equilibrium, the weight of the liquid in the tube must be equal to the upward component of the adhesive force due to surface tension. The weight, or downward force F_d, is given by the density of the liquid times the volume of the column ($h\pi r^2$) times the acceleration of gravity:

$$F_d = \rho g V = \rho g h \pi r^2.$$

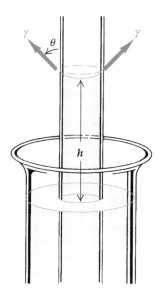

Figure 10.16

Example 10.7: Analysis of the height to which a liquid rises in a capillary tube.

Figure 10.17

The flow of the river is laminar in some regions and turbulent in others.

The upward force F_u, due to the surface tension acting all around the inside of the cylindrical surface, is the product of the upward force per unit length times the inner circumference of the cylinder. The upward force per unit length is the component of the surface tension along the vertical direction, $\gamma \cos \theta$. Thus, the upward force is

$$F_u = 2\pi r \gamma \cos \theta.$$

Equating the upward and downward forces gives

$$\rho g h \pi r^2 = 2\pi r \gamma \cos \theta,$$

or

$$h = \frac{2\gamma \cos \theta}{r \rho g}.$$

10.5 Fluid Flow: Streamlines and the Equation of Continuity

Let us now turn our attention to fluids in motion. The two main types of fluid flow are easily recognized in the river shown in Fig. 10.17. One type is the orderly flow of neighboring layers of fluid moving past each other smoothly. Each small element of fluid follows a path called a **streamline,** which does not cross over or become tangled with other streamlines. This smooth streamline flow is known as **laminar** flow. The other type of flow occurs when the fluid exceeds a certain critical velocity. Then the flow no longer is laminar but becomes **turbulent** and is characterized by an irregular, complex motion. (Turbulent flow will be considered in Section 10.9.)

Let us look at the steady laminar flow of an incompressible fluid moving through a tube or pipe. How does the flow change when the diameter of the pipe changes? Consider the case of a fluid moving from a region of cross-sectional area A_1 to a region of area A_2 (Fig. 10.18). Because the fluid is incompressible, the same amount of it leaves each region toward the right as enters from the left during the same time interval. The volume of fluid that flows into the tube across A_1 in a time interval Δt is $\Delta V_1 = A_1 v_1 \, \Delta t$, where v_1 is the velocity of the fluid at A_1. If the density of the fluid is ρ, then the mass of fluid that flows into the tube in time Δt is $\rho A_1 v_1 \, \Delta t$. Similarly, the mass of fluid that flows out of the tube through A_2 in the same time Δt is $\rho A_2 v_2 \, \Delta t$. Since the mass of fluid entering is the same as the mass leaving, we get

$$\rho A_1 v_1 \, \Delta t = \rho A_2 v_2 \, \Delta t.$$

We can divide out the density because it is constant for an incompressible fluid. We then get

$$v_1 A_1 = v_2 A_2. \tag{10.7}$$

This equation is called the **equation of continuity** and will be useful throughout our discussion of fluids in motion. It says that the flow of material (mass) through a tube of changing cross section is constant when the density of the fluid does not change. That is, the equation of continuity is a statement of conservation

SURFACE TENSION AND THE LUNGS

Take a deep breath. You've probably never thought about it, but some interesting physics goes on in your lungs every time you breathe. It all takes place without your having to think about it, but the interplay is fascinating.

The air passages into the two lungs branch and branch again until they end in tiny air sacs called *alveoli* (Fig. B10.3). It is here that the exchange of gases with the blood takes place. An adult's lungs contain on the order of 300 million alveoli, each with an average radius of 120 μm. Specialized cells in the walls of the alveoli produce a detergentlike material called surfactant that coats the inside of the alveoli, thus reducing the surface tension.

First, consider two soap bubbles connected to a pipe that contains a valve (Fig. B10.4). This arrangement is sometimes shown to a class and the question asked: "What will happen if the valve is opened?" When the valve is opened, the larger bubble grows and the smaller bubble becomes smaller until it completely goes away. We can understand this observation from the standpoint of energy. Just as a free drop of liquid takes on a spherical shape to minimize its total surface energy, the bubbles change relative sizes in such a way as to minimize their combined surface area, and therefore the surface energy. The surface area of a single bubble is about 30% less than the surface area of two smaller bubbles of equal size that together have the same volume as the larger bubble. So, when the valve is opened, the two bubbles become one system and form a single bubble.

If the effect of large bubbles absorbing smaller ones were to take place in the lungs, the smaller alveoli would all collapse and the larger ones would grow. This does not happen because of the pulmonary surfactant that coats the inside of

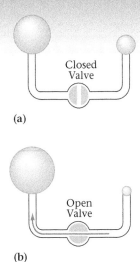

(a)

(b)

Figure B10.4   (a) Two soap bubbles of different radius are connected through a pipe. (b) When the valve is opened, the larger bubble grows as the smaller one shrinks.

the lungs. Experiments have shown that the surface tension of the pulmonary surfactant *increases* with its area, in contrast with the behavior of water and most other liquids. This means that the surface energy of larger alveoli, in spite of the smaller surface-to-volume ratio, can be the same as that of the smaller alveoli. Therefore, the larger and smaller air sacs can exist in equilibrium.

The experimental results that show the variation of surface tension with area also explain another observation about the lungs. If you take a big breath and then relax your chest muscles, the air is expelled from your lungs. Part of the reason that the air flows out is that the lungs have been blown up, much like a balloon, and the elasticity of the tissues causes them to contract and force the air out. However, tests have shown that the elasticity of the lung tissue itself is not sufficient to completely explain what happens. A large part of the effect is due to the surface tension in the alveoli, which causes them to contract and expel the air. Furthermore, the effect depends on a material for which the surface tension increases with area, or else the tendency of the lungs to expel air when inflated would be much less than it is.

Normal breathing is possible only when the pulmonary surfactant is present in the proper amount and has the proper surface tension. If the surface tension is greater than normal, the lungs tend to collapse and expansion of the alveoli is difficult. Some newborn babies, especially premature ones, do not have enough surfactant, making lung expansion difficult. Unless they receive immediate treatment, these infants die soon after birth because of inadequate ventilation. This condition is known as respiratory distress syndrome.

Figure B10.3   A plastic cast of the air passages in the lungs. The passages end in tiny sacs called alveoli.

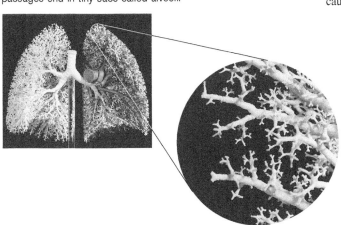

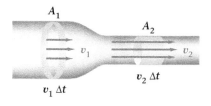

$$v_1 A_1 = v_2 A_2$$

Figure 10.18
Fluid passing cross section A_1 with speed v_1 passes through cross section A_2 with a new speed v_2, as required by the equation of continuity.

of mass. Notice that the product Av is the volume rate of flow, that is, the volume of fluid passing a given cross section per unit time. In SI units, the volume rate of flow is measured in m^3/s.

▼

Example 10.8

A horizontal pipe of 25-cm^2 cross section carries water at a velocity of 3.0 m/s. The pipe feeds into a smaller pipe with a cross section of only 15 cm^2. What is the velocity of water in the smaller pipe?

Solution We can determine the velocity of water in the smaller pipe from the equation of continuity. The velocity and area in the large pipe are $v_1 = 3.0$ m/s and $A_1 = 25$ cm^2. The area of the smaller pipe is $A_2 = 15$ cm^2. Thus, we have

$$v_2 = \frac{v_1 A_1}{A_2} = \frac{3.0 \text{ m/s} \times 25 \text{ cm}^2}{15 \text{ cm}^2} = 5.0 \text{ m/s}.$$

▼

10.6 Bernoulli's Equation

We wish to find a relationship among the variables describing the steady laminar flow of a fluid, assuming the fluid not only is incompressible but also has no internal friction, or viscosity. (We will introduce the effects of viscosity in Section 10.7.) The result, called Bernoulli's equation,* describes the relationship of a fluid's pressure, velocity, and height as it moves along a pipe or other tube of flow.

The fluid flowing smoothly from region A to region B in Fig. 10.19 need not be constrained to a real pipe. Think, for example, of a portion of the water flowing in a river. However, if we draw all of the streamlines from the boundary of region A surrounding a portion of the fluid to their later positions when the fluid reaches B, we outline a *tube of flow*. The equation of continuity (Eq. 10.7) applies to such a tube of flow.

Figure 10.19
Fluid passing through area A later passes through area B. The streamlines mark the paths of small elements of the fluid. The tube that connects A to B along the streamlines is the tube of flow.

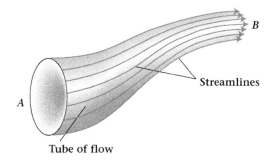

Streamlines

A

Tube of flow

---

*This problem was first solved by the Swiss mathematician and physicist Daniel Bernoulli (1700–1782), who published the result in a book on fluid flow in 1738.

We can find the relationship that we seek by making use of the principle of conservation of energy. In particular, we calculate the work done on a small element of fluid moving along a tube of flow and then use the work-energy theorem (Section 6.4) to equate the change in kinetic energy to this work. To move a small element of fluid through a distance of Δx_1 at region 1 (Fig. 10.20) requires an amount of work $P_1 A_1 \Delta x_1$. At the same time, the same amount of fluid (given by $A_2 \Delta x_2$) moves a distance Δx_2 at region 2. The work in this case is $-P_2 A_2 \Delta x_2$. The negative sign indicates that the element of fluid at region 2 moves against the force due to the pressure of the fluid to its right.

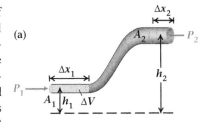
(a)

Because the fluid is incompressible, the volume of the fluid displaced at region 1 is equal to the volume of the fluid displaced at region 2; $A_1 \Delta x_1 = A_2 \Delta x_2$. The work done by gravity in the net motion of fluid from region 1 to region 2 is $-mg(h_2 - h_1)$, where the mass $m = \rho A_1 \Delta x_1 = \rho A_2 \Delta x_2 = \rho \Delta V$. Thus, the work done by gravity is $-g\rho \Delta V(h_2 - h_1)$. The net work done is

$$W = P_1 \Delta V - P_2 \Delta V - g\rho \Delta V(h_2 - h_1).$$

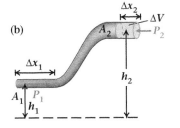
(b)

According to the work-energy theorem, the change in kinetic energy of the mass $\rho \Delta V$ is equal to this work, so

$$\Delta \text{KE} = W,$$

or

$$\tfrac{1}{2}\rho \Delta V v_2^2 - \tfrac{1}{2}\rho \Delta V v_1^2 = P_1 \Delta V - P_2 \Delta V - \rho g \Delta V h_2 + \rho g \Delta V h_1.$$

Dividing through by ΔV and rearranging terms gives

$$\boxed{P_1 + \rho g h_1 + \tfrac{1}{2}\rho v_1^2 = P_2 + \rho g h_2 + \tfrac{1}{2}\rho v_2^2 = \text{constant.}} \qquad (10.8)$$

Figure 10.20
A volume ΔV of incompressible fluid is moved along a tube of flow from (a) region 1 to (b) region 2.

Equation (10.8) is called **Bernoulli's equation,** for the steady, nonviscous flow of an incompressible fluid. Under these conditions, Bernoulli's equation expresses conservation of energy in a moving fluid. To some extent, we can also apply Bernoulli's equation to compressible fluids of negligible viscosity in laminar flow.

If we consider a horizontal pipe ($h_1 = h_2$), the equation of continuity tells us that the fluid flows more rapidly in a constricted region of the pipe. If we combine the equation of continuity [$v_1 = (A_2/A_1)v_2$] with Bernoulli's equation we get

$$P_2 = P_1 + \frac{\rho v_2^2(A_2^2 - A_1^2)}{2A_1^2}. \qquad (10.9)$$

The second term on the right-hand side is negative if A_1 is greater than A_2. In that case, the pressure P_2 is less than the pressure P_1. This result, which arises from the principles of conservation of energy and of mass, tells us that the pressure is less in the constricted region of the pipe. Similarly, if A_2 is greater than A_1, then P_2 is larger than P_1. In other words, when a moving fluid enters a narrower section of pipe (or artery), its speed increases but the pressure on the fluid decreases.

Equation (10.9) holds strictly only for incompressible nonviscous fluids. But the general qualitative conclusion above applies to both gases and liquids. If we consider an incompressible but viscous fluid, such as water or blood, we get

$$P_2 < P_1 + \frac{\rho v_2^2 (A_2^2 - A_1^2)}{2A_1^2}.$$

The inequality arises from noticing that in a viscous fluid, some of the work done is dissipated by the internal frictional forces in the liquid.

▼

Example 10.9

Determine the pressure change that occurs on going from the larger-diameter pipe to the smaller pipe for the conditions of Example 10.8; that is, take $A_1 = 25$ cm², $A_2 = 15$ cm², and $v_2 = 5.0$ m/s.

Solution Since the pipe is horizontal, we can find the pressure change $P_2 - P_1$ from Eq. (10.9). It is

$$\Delta P = P_2 - P_1 = \rho v_2^2 \frac{(A_2^2 - A_1^2)}{2A_1^2}.$$

Here ρ is the density of water $= 10^3$ kg/m³.

$$\Delta P = (10^3 \text{ kg/m}^3)(5.0 \text{ m/s})^2 \left(\frac{(15 \text{ cm}^2)^2 - (25 \text{ cm}^2)^2}{2(25 \text{ cm}^2)^2} \right)$$

$$\Delta P = -8 \times 10^3 \text{ Pa}.$$

The negative result tells us that the pressure is smaller in the smaller pipe.

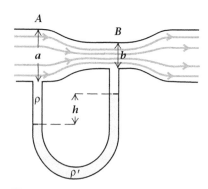

Figure 10.21

A Venturi meter enables us to measure fluid speed by observing height differences in a U-shaped tube.

The speed of a fluid flowing in a pipe can be measured with a device called a *Venturi meter* (Fig. 10.21). If the fluid in the pipe is flowing, the pressure at B is lower than the pressure at A. The difference in pressures is a function of the rate at which the fluid flows. The Venturi meter measures this difference in pressure with the U-shaped tube. Using Bernoulli's equation (Eq. 10.8) and the equation of continuity (Eq. 10.7), we can derive the following relationship for the velocity of the fluid at position A:

$$v = b \left(\frac{2(\rho' - \rho)gh}{\rho(a^2 - b^2)} \right)^{1/2},$$

where a and b are the cross-sectional areas at A and B, respectively, ρ is the density of the fluid flowing in the pipe, and ρ' is the density of the liquid in the U-tube. The difference in height of the liquid in the two arms of the U-tube is h, and the gravitational acceleration is denoted by g. Thus, the Venturi meter enables us to determine the flow velocity from a measurement of the height difference h.

▼
*10.7   Viscosity and Poiseuille's Law

Bernoulli's equation predicts that for a horizontal pipe of uniform cross section, the pressure in a moving fluid is constant. If there were no fluid friction, or viscosity, this would indeed be the case. However, for a viscous fluid flowing through a horizontal pipe of uniform cross section, the fluid pressure decreases with distance along the direction of flow.

Viscosity is that property of a fluid that indicates its internal friction. The more viscous a fluid, the greater the force required to cause one layer of fluid to slide past another. Viscosity is what prevents objects from moving freely through a fluid or a fluid from flowing freely in a pipe. The viscosity of gases is less than that of liquids, and the viscosity of water and light oils is less than that of molasses and heavy oils. Your experience with liquids such as motor oils and syrups tells you that viscosity increases with decreasing temperature. Thus, it is hard to start a car engine in subzero weather when the oil is thick and flows slowly, but it is easy to start the same car on a hot summer day when the oil is warm and flows readily.

Let us return to the situation of a fluid moving through a horizontal pipe. The walls of the pipe exert a resistive force, or drag, on the adjacent layers of fluid. These layers, in turn, slow down the next adjacent layers, and so on. As a result, the rate of flow is slowest near the pipe walls and fastest in the center of the pipe. Therefore, for a given rate of flow the pressure difference between two points along the length of the pipe depends on the radius of the pipe (Fig. 10.22). The pressure difference between the two points is also related to a quantity known as the coefficient of viscosity or simply the viscosity of the fluid. The exact relation is given by the following equation, called **Poiseuille's law:***

$$P_1 - P_2 = 8\frac{Q\eta L}{\pi R^4}, \qquad (10.10)$$

where Q is the flow rate in m^3/s, η is the coefficient of viscosity, R is the radius of the pipe, and L is the separation between the test points. If R and L are given in meters and the pressure is given in pascals, the unit of the coefficient of viscosity is the pascal-second (Pa · s). This equation is often used experimentally to determine the coefficient of viscosity of a liquid. Table 10.4 lists the coefficients of viscosity for a number of fluids.

An important observation about the behavior of real fluids is easily made from Eq. (10.10). A viscous fluid will not flow through a pipe unless there is a pressure difference between the ends.

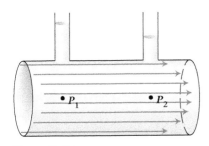

Figure 10.22
The pressure in a viscous fluid along a horizontal pipe of uniform cross section diminishes with distance along the direction of flow. Thus, pressure P_2 is less than pressure P_1. Note, too, that fluid flows fastest in the center of the pipe.

---

*Poiseuille is pronounced "pwa-zoy′."

Table 10.4	Viscosities of Some Common Fluids	
Fluid	Temperature (°C) (10^{-3} Pa · s)	Viscosity
Air	20	0.018
Water	40	0.656
Water	20	1.005
Motor oil (SAE 10)	30	200
Glycerin	20	1490
Castor oil	20	986
Mercury	20	1.550

Example 10.10

Blood in the extremities of the body is carried by arterioles, small vessels with an average diameter of about 0.1 mm. The muscles in the walls can contract and change the diameter of the "pipe," thereby decreasing the flow of the blood, a viscous fluid. Sometimes great strain or shock causes a severe reduction in blood flow. By approximately what amount would the arterioles have to contract to reduce the blood flow to 30% of its former value if we assume that the pressure drop remains constant?

Solution We use Poiseuille's law, writing subscripts 1 for the normal condition and 2 for the reduced-flow case. Then, because the pressure drop is constant, we have

$$8\frac{Q_1\eta_1 L}{\pi R_1^4} = 8\frac{Q_2\eta_2 L}{\pi R_2^4}.$$

Though the viscosity of the blood is not independent of its velocity or of the diameter of the tube through which it flows, we assume it to be constant over the range considered here. Then we have

$$\frac{R_2^4}{R_1^4} = \frac{Q_2}{Q_1},$$

or

$$\frac{R_2}{R_1} = \left(\frac{Q_2}{Q_1}\right)^{1/4}.$$

If the flow is reduced to 30% of its initial value, then $Q_2/Q_1 = 0.30$. Inserting this value in the above equation, we find that

$$\frac{R_2}{R_1} = (0.30)^{1/4} = 0.74.$$

The arteriole has constricted to 74% of its original diameter. For example, if the diameter of the arteriole were 0.10 mm originally, then its diameter after constriction would be 0.074 mm. The relative change in flow is greater than the relative change in the diameter of the tube.

Discussion In general, the diameter of blood vessels, unlike that of glass or metal tubes, increases as the internal pressure increases, because the blood vessels are distensible. Moreover, in blood vessels as small as capillaries, the viscosity of whole blood is as little as half of what it is in large vessels. This effect is due to the alignment of the red blood cells as they pass through the narrow vessels.

▼

*10.8   Stokes's Law and Terminal Speed

Viscous Drag

An object moving through a fluid experiences a resistive force, or drag, that is proportional to the viscosity of the fluid. If the object is moving slowly enough, the drag force is proportional to its speed v. If the object is a sphere of radius r, the force is

$$F = 6\pi\eta r v, \tag{10.11}$$

where η is again the coefficient of viscosity. This equation is known as **Stokes's law,** after Sir George Stokes (1819–1903), who first conceived it in 1845. Stokes's law can be used to relate the speed of a sphere falling in a liquid to the viscosity of that liquid.

Consider a solid sphere of radius r dropped into the top of a column of liquid (Fig. 10.23). At the top of the column, the sphere accelerates downward under the influence of gravity. However, there are two additional forces, both acting upward: the constant buoyant force and a speed-dependent retarding force given by Stokes's law. When the sum of the upward forces is equal to the gravitational force, the sphere travels with a constant speed v_t, called the **terminal speed.** To determine this speed, we write the equation for the equilibrium of forces:

$$F_{\text{grav}} = F_{\text{buoyant}} + F_{\text{drag}}.$$

We can express the gravitational force in terms of the density ρ of the sphere, its volume $\frac{4}{3}\pi r^3$, and g:

$$F_{\text{grav}} = \frac{4}{3}\pi r^3 \rho g.$$

The buoyant force is equal to the weight of the displaced liquid, which has a density ρ':

$$F_{\text{buoyant}} = \frac{4}{3}\pi r^3 \rho' g.$$

The retarding force is expressed by Stokes's law with the speed v_t:

$$F_{\text{drag}} = 6\pi\eta r v_t.$$

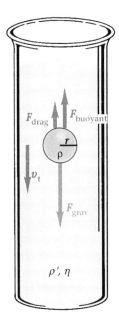

Figure 10.23
A sphere falling in a viscous liquid reaches a terminal speed v_t that depends upon the radius and density of the sphere and the density and viscosity of the liquid.

HOW AIRPLANES FLY

Air travel is one of the great triumphs of the twentieth century. Every day hundreds of thousands of people are carried through the air to destinations all around the world. In every case the flight of heavier-than-air craft results from the flow of air around their wings.

Before their first powered flight in December 1903, the Wright brothers tested many different wing shapes in a wind tunnel to find the shape that produced the most lifting force. This shape, often called an airfoil, is shown in Fig. B10.5 along with the streamlines of the air moving past. The fluid moving over the top travels a greater distance than that moving just under the bottom of the wing. Consequently, the fluid moving over the top must travel faster in order to conform with the shape of the wing and still maintain the natural streamline. The shape of the wing also crowds the streamlines together above the wing, just as in the case of a constricting pipe. The result is that the region immediately above the wing experiences reduced pressure relative to the region immediately below the wing. Because the downward force on the top of the wing is less than the upward force on the bottom, a net upward force, or lift, arises from the air flow. (Beyond the airfoil the flowing air has a downward component of velocity. By Newton's third law, the reaction force to the net downward force exerted on the air is the lift.) Note that for lift to occur, a flow of air is required relative to the wing. The lift occurs equally well for a wing moving through stationary air or for air moving past a stationary wing.

You can demonstrate this effect with a small piece of paper, about 10 × 15 cm. Hold the short edge close below your lower lip and blow vigorously across the top of the paper (Fig. B10.6). The motion of the air above the paper will cause it to rise. This same effect helps to lift a plane into the air.

In addition, the angle of attack, or tilt of the wing relative to the air flow, can be changed to get additional lift from the deflection of the air stream (see Fig. B10.5). If the leading edge of the wing is higher than the trailing edge, the force of air against the underside of the wing is greater than its force

Figure B10.5 An airfoil in a moving fluid.

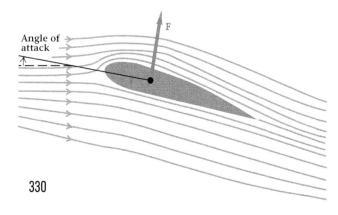

Figure B10.6 A demonstration of lift. Blowing across the paper causes it to rise.

against the upper side. In this case lift occurs even for a flat wing. However, if the angle of attack becomes too great, the streamline flow gives way to turbulence and the pressure difference is reduced. If the turbulence is great enough, the lift diminishes and the plane stalls.

In general, as the flow of air past the wing increases, both the lift force and the drag force (the resistance to forward motion) increase. Aircraft wings are designed so that pilots can change the wing shape during flight, producing greater lift for the slower speeds of takeoff and landing and producing less drag at cruising speeds. During takeoff and landing, flaps are extended backward and downward from the trailing edge of the wing (Fig. B10.7), increasing lift by imparting a greater downward velocity to the air. On some planes, extending the flaps increases the wing area as much as 25%, resulting in a much increased drag. At the same time, the leading edge of the wing may be moved forward, creating a slot that directs a high-speed layer of air over the top surface of the wing to reduce turbulence and increase lift. At higher speeds, the pilot closes the slot and retracts the flaps to reduce the drag forces. Passengers in commercial aircraft can easily see these changes in the wing during flight.

We should point out that lift is not in strict accord with Bernoulli's equation. The reason is that the Bernoulli equation holds exactly only for incompressible nonviscous fluids, yet air is both compressible and viscous. However, the pressure difference, and hence the lift, does occur in air, even if the amount is not in exact agreement with Eq. (10.8).

Figure B10.7 Flaps are extended during takeoff and landing to increase the lift.

Combining these equations, we get an expression for the terminal speed:

$$v_t = \frac{2r^2 g}{9\eta}(\rho - \rho').$$ (10.12)

The terminal speed is also called the sedimentation speed by biologists and geologists.

Example 10.11

An aluminum sphere of radius 1.0 mm is dropped into a bottle of glycerin at 20°C. What is the terminal speed of the sphere?

Solution Using Eq. (10.12), we calculate the terminal speed directly as

$$v_t = \frac{2r^2 g}{9\eta}(\rho - \rho').$$

The radius in meters is 1.0×10^{-3} m. The densities, from Table 10.2, are $\rho = 2.7 \times 10^3$ kg/m^3 and $\rho' = 1.26 \times 10^3$ kg/m^3. The viscosity, from Table 10.4, is 1.49 Pa · s. Thus,

$$v_t = \left(\frac{2 \times 1.0 \times 10^{-6}\ \text{m}^2 \times 9.81\ \text{m} \cdot \text{s}^{-2}}{9 \times 1.49\ \text{N} \cdot \text{m}^{-2} \cdot \text{s}}\right)(2.7 - 1.26) \times 10^3\ \text{kg} \cdot \text{m}^{-3}$$

$$v_t = 2.1 \times 10^{-3}\ \text{m}^2 \cdot \text{s}^{-2} \cdot \text{kg} / \text{N} \cdot \text{s}$$

But the units of N are kg · m · s^{-2}, so the speed is in m/s:

$$v_t = 2.1 \times 10^{-3}\ \text{m/s, or 2.1 mm/s.}$$

Stokes's law suggests a method of measuring the size of small particles. If the rate at which material settles from a suspension is measured and the other parameters are known, then Eq. (10.12) gives the particle size. In the case of particles whose radius is less than about 5×10^{-6} m, the settling rate is prohibitively slow, even when the densities of the particles and fluid are quite different. However, we can increase the rate by using a centrifuge (see Section 5.2). The centripetal force per unit mass in an ordinary centrifuge may be 100 g, while that in a modern ultracentrifuge may go as high as 5×10^5 g.

Stokes's law is also useful in the consideration of geological processes in which the rate of sedimentation is important. Modifications are made to take account of nonspherical particles.

Form Drag

Stokes's law applies for situations in which the fluid flow is laminar, but not when the flow becomes turbulent. An important class that shows the effects of turbulence is illustrated by the retarding force of air on a moving car (Fig. 10.24), a falling raindrop, or a skydiver. In these cases it is observed that whenever an object moves rapidly enough, the retarding force F depends not on the speed (Stokes's law), but on the square of the speed:

$$F = bv^2,$$

where b is a constant determined for each different case.

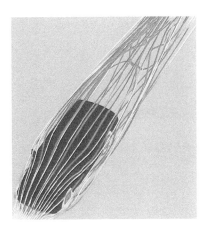

Figure 10.24
Computer modeling of air flow around a moving car showing both laminar and turbulent flow.

An object falling from rest through the air falls with increasing speed until, at the terminal speed v_t, the retarding force of the air is equal in magnitude to the gravitational force:

$$mg = bv_t^2.$$

Thus, the terminal speed can be written as

$$v_t = \sqrt{\frac{mg}{b}}.$$

Elementary analysis (see Problem 10.59) shows that the constant b depends on the density ρ of the air and the area A of the body presented to the air flow. Then the equation for the terminal speed is

$$v_t = \sqrt{\frac{mg}{C_D \frac{\rho}{2} A}},$$

where C_D is called the **drag coefficient.** This equation also holds for objects moving horizontally through the air at any speed if mg is replaced by the retarding, or drag, force on the object. Thus, the aerodynamic drag on a moving object, such as a car, becomes approximately

$$\boxed{F_{drag} = 0.65 C_D A v^2.} \tag{10.13}$$

One of the objects of modern automobile design is to reduce the drag in order to improve fuel economy. This is especially true for electric vehicles such as the General Motors EV$_1$. The small drag coefficient of the EV$_1$ is due in part to its smooth belly pan, its rear wheel skirts, and its teardrop shape resulting from a rear wheel track some nine inches smaller than that of the front wheels. (Some drag coefficients are given in Table 10.5.) On the other hand, the object of parachute design is to have a large value of both C_D and A, so that descent is slow (Fig. 10.25).

Table 10.5	Aerodynamic Drag Coefficients ▼
Shape	**C_D**
1997 General Motors EV$_1$	0.19
1995 Lexus LS 400	0.28
1997 BMW 850ci	0.29
1997 BMW 750iL	0.32
1997 Dodge Intrepid	0.33
1997 Dodge Caravan	0.35
Typical 1970 U.S. auto	0.50
Typical 1970 U.S. station wagon	0.60
Small truck	0.70

For a skydiver falling through air, the terminal speed is approximately 60 m/s (about 120 mi/h); for a feather, it may be as small as 0.1 m/s. For a 2-mm-diameter raindrop, the terminal speed is about 7 m/s. Without air resistance, such a raindrop starting from rest would reach a speed of 7 m/s in less than three-quarters of a second, while it fell a distance of only 2.5 m. In this case the effects of air resistance are very important.

In our discussion of projectile range in Chapter 3, we used a simplified model that neglected the air resistance. Our model predicted that a thrown baseball would follow a parabolic path. In a more realistic model including air resistance, the path of the ball is nonparabolic and the ball lands short of the range predicted with the simple model. Furthermore, the launch angle for maximum range is less than 45° and depends on the initial speed of the ball. If the ball spins, additional forces arise from the resulting turbulence that can also affect its path. These additional forces are described in the next section.

Figure 10.25
A parachutist falling with terminal speed. Parachutes are designed with large drag coefficients and large areas.

Turbulent Flow

When you move your finger slowly through a liquid, such as water, you feel only a moderate force of resistance. This resistance arises from two sources: an inertial resistance to the acceleration of the water being displaced and a viscous drag force. As you move your finger faster, the resistance becomes larger because you are moving more water in the same time. The ratio of the inertial force to the viscous force, called the **Reynolds number,*** is a useful parameter for describing fluid flow and for determining the onset of turbulence. It is given by

$$\text{Re} = \frac{\rho v L}{\eta}, \tag{10.14}$$

where ρ and η are the density and viscosity of the fluid, v is the speed of the object, and L is a length characteristic of the object. In this case, L is the length of your finger.

A large value of Re indicates large motion of the fluid. When motion through the fluid exceeds a certain critical speed, the laminar flow of the fluid around the object becomes turbulent and is characterized by an irregular, complex motion. It is the motion of the object relative to the fluid that is important; that is, a stationary object and a moving fluid give the same results. Similar behavior is observed in the flow of a fluid through a pipe. Laminar and turbulent flow are illustrated in Fig. 10.26.

For fluid flow through a tube, the Reynolds number becomes

$$\boxed{\text{Re} = \frac{\rho v D}{\eta},} \tag{10.15}$$

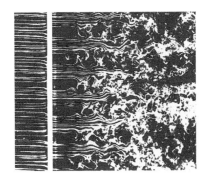

Figure 10.26
An example of turbulent flow. A laminar flow of smoke trails moving from left to right passes through a grid, which induces turbulent flow.

---

*The Irish-born engineer Osborne Reynolds (1842–1912) discovered in 1883 that laminar flow can become turbulent if the speed is sufficiently large.

where D is the diameter of the tube. The Reynolds number is dimensionless and has the same value in any consistent system of units. Observations show that for flow through a pipe, Reynolds numbers of less than about 2000 correspond to laminar flow and Reynolds numbers greater than 3000 correspond to turbulent flow. At values between 2000 and 3000, the flow is unstable and may change back and forth from one type of flow to another.

The frictional forces are much greater in turbulent flow than in nonturbulent flow. It is therefore often desirable to maintain laminar flow, whether in the case of water in pipes or blood in arteries and veins. In rigid pipes, this is accomplished primarily through using large pipes and low velocities. Blood vessels, however, are flexible and may expand with an increase in pressure. Turbulence in pipes can also be reduced by the appropriate placement of deflecting vanes and wires.

As a fluid moves past an object, it interacts with the object's surface forming a thin *boundary layer*. The interaction of the object with the boundary layer is the source of viscous drag. For very low Reynolds number (Re < 1), the flow is laminar and the drag is entirely viscous. At larger flow rates, the flow is not completely laminar. The boundary layer begins to separate from the surface leaving a turbulent wake in the trailing fluid. In this region (Re < 200,000), the resistive forces are partly due to viscous drag and partly due to form drag. As the flow increases further, the boundary layer separation begins to move closer to the front of the object—that is, the boundary separation moves in the upstream direction. The result is a larger wake and greater drag. At still larger flow velocities (Re > 200,000), the boundary layer becomes completely turbulent and the drag is entirely form drag.

At the transition to fully turbulent flow, there is a drop in the form drag, which then grows larger as the flow velocity is increased still further. The velocity at which the transition to fully turbulent flow occurs can be reduced by roughening the surface. For an object (a ball) moving through a fluid (air) at a speed near the transition to fully turbulent flow, the result of increasing the surface roughness is to lower the drag. Surface roughness affects the behavior of balls used in many sports. The dimples on a golf ball play a significant role in reducing the drag and thus increase the ball's time of flight. The fuzzy surface of tennis balls and the seams on baseballs play a role similar to the golf ball's dimples and contribute to the fully turbulent flow about them.

A related effect of turbulent air flow, this time around a spinning ball, causes the curve of a baseball or golf ball. To see this effect, imagine a stationary ball subjected to a flow of air (Fig. 10.27a). The motion of the air past the ball departs from streamline flow at the velocities normally attained by a thrown baseball, and some turbulence occurs, as shown. However, because of the symmetry of the ball, there is no net force on the ball perpendicular to the direction of flow.

When the ball is spinning, the friction between the ball's surface and the air drags a layer of air around with the ball (Fig. 10.27b). The pattern of turbulence becomes asymmetric, and the streamlines become more crowded at the top of the figure than at the bottom. The net result is a lowering of the pressure at the top and a force transverse to both the direction of flow and the axis of spin. This transverse force is the force that causes the ball to curve. By Newton's third law, there must also be a net force acting on the air whose effect is to deflect the air downward (Fig. 10.27c).

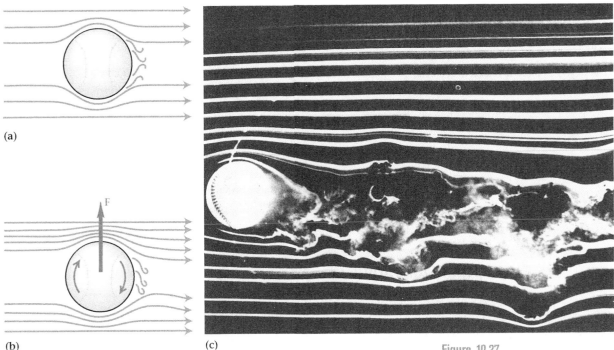

(a)

(b)   (c)

Figure 10.27
(a) Air flow about a baseball that is not spinning. (b) Air flow about a spinning baseball. (c) Photograph of smoke trails around a spinning baseball.

In golf, the impact of the slanted club head gives the ball spin around a horizontal axis (similar to Fig. 10.27c). The force resulting from the spin gives an additional lift to the ball, allowing it to travel farther. When the club does not strike the ball squarely, it gives the ball additional spin about a vertical axis, causing the ball to "hook" or "slice" to one side.

▼ Summary

Useful Concepts

■ Pressure is defined as the force per unit area,

$$P = \frac{F}{A}.$$

The gauge pressure due to the weight of a fluid of density ρ at a depth h is

$$P = \rho g h.$$

■ Pascal's principle: The pressure applied at one point in an enclosed fluid is transmitted undiminished to every part of the fluid and to the walls of the container.

■ Archimedes' principle: A body, whether completely or partially submerged in a fluid, is buoyed upward by a force that is equal to the weight of the displaced liquid.

■ The equation of continuity,

$$v_1 A_1 = v_2 A_2,$$

is a statement of the principle of conservation of mass for fluids of constant density.

■ Bernoulli's equation is a statement of conservation of energy for fluids of constant density. For an incompressible nonviscous fluid in laminar flow, Bernoulli's equation is

$$P + \rho g h + \tfrac{1}{2}\rho v^2 = \text{constant}.$$

■ For a viscous fluid flowing in a horizontal pipe, Poiseuille's law gives

$$P_1 - P_2 = \frac{8 Q \eta L}{\pi R^4},$$

where Q is the flow rate, L is the distance along the direction of flow, η is the coefficient of viscosity, and R is the radius of the pipe.

■ The force on a sphere moving in a viscous liquid is given by Stokes's law:

$$F = 6 \pi \eta r v.$$

■ Aerodynamic drag is given by

$$F_{\text{drag}} = 0.65 \; C_D A v^2,$$

where C_D is the drag coefficient.

■ The Reynolds number is used to characterize turbulent flow, and for a tube is given by

$$\text{Re} = \rho v D / \eta$$

Important Terms

You should be able to write the definition or meaning of each of the following:

fluid	laminar flow
pressure	turbulent flow
pascal	equation of continuity
density	Bernoulli's equation
specific gravity	viscosity
Pascal's principle	Poiseuille's law
Archimedes' principle	Stokes's law
buoyant force	terminal speed
surface tension	drag coefficient
streamline	Reynolds number

Conceptual Questions

10.1 You are floating on a rubber raft in a small swimming pool in which the water level has been carefully measured. You throw overboard some wooden blocks that had been on the raft and watch the blocks float on the water. What happens to the water level as measured on the edge of the pool? Would the water level behave differently if the blocks were concrete and sank to the bottom of the pool?

10.2 Explain how a siphon works.

10.3 Three containers have the same base area but not the same shape. According to Pascal's principle, when they are filled to the same height with water, the same force acts on the base of each one. Yet when they are weighed on a scale, they do not weigh the same. Explain this apparent contradiction, which is sometimes called the *hydrostatic paradox.*

10.4 A block of wood floats half submerged in a container of water. If the same container were in an earth-orbiting satellite, how would the block float? Explain your reasoning.

10.5 The port of Hamburg is about 60 mi inland from the North Sea on the river Elbe. When a container ship left the port, a sailor noticed that there was a paint spot just at the water line. Where was the paint spot when the ship reached the open sea? Explain.

10.6 A sealed hollow glass tube is weighted at one end so that it floats upright when placed in a liquid. The level at which the tube floats depends on its weight and the density of the liquid. When calibrated, such a device can be used to measure fluid densities and is called a hydrometer. Discuss the effect of adhesive and cohesive forces on the level at which the tube floats.

10.7 A thin piece of wood is cut into the shape shown in Fig. 10.28, and a small piece of soap is placed at the point marked *A*. When the "boat" is placed in a pan of water, it moves in the direction indicated by the arrow. Explain.

10.8 A Ping-Pong ball can be suspended in a vertical stream of air, such as that from the exhaust pipe of a vacuum cleaner.

Figure 10.28
Question 10.7.

If the ball is given a small impulse to the side, it will return to the center of the stream rather than being ejected from the stream. Explain.

10.9 The card in the diagram in Fig. 10.29 will not fall away from the spool as long as one blows through the hole. Explain this effect. (The pin in the center is only to eliminate sideways motion and does not exert any vertical force.)

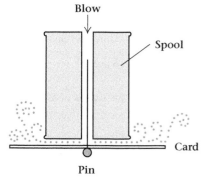

Figure 10.29
Question 10.9.

10.10 The viscosity of liquids decreases with increasing temperature. Give as many examples as you can of situations in which this effect can be encountered in everyday experience.

10.11 An upright cylindrical tank filled with water to a height h has three holes in its side through which the water escapes. The holes are at distances $h/4$, $h/2$, and $3h/4$ above the bottom of the tank. Which of the drawings in Fig. 10.30 corresponds to the streams of water that emerge? Explain your choice.

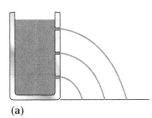

(a)

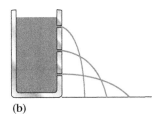

(b)

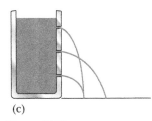

(c)

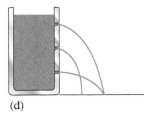

(d)

Figure 10.30
Question 10.11.

10.12 List some sports in which it is desirable to reduce turbulent fluid flow, and give some of the ways in which this is done.

10.13 Are there sports in which it is desirable to maximize turbulent fluid flow? If there are, give examples and indicate how turbulence is maximized.

10.14 How does the external design of a car affect its high-speed behavior? Why do race cars have spoilers (Fig. 10.31) on the back?

Figure 10.31
Question 10.14: The spoiler can be seen on the rear of the race car.

10.15 The explanation often given of how airplanes fly depends on the fact that the cross section of the wings usually is not symmetric but is curved on the upper surface and flat on the lower surface. How, then, do stunt flyers manage to fly upside down for considerable distances?

10.16 When syrup or oil is slowly poured from a container, the diameter of the stream decreases for a distance below the point at which it leaves the container. Explain this observation.

10.17 (a) If your mass is 62 kg and you float in water with only a negligible amount of your body above the surface, what is your approximate volume? (b) Determine your own volume by using either this technique or an improvement on it that takes account of how deep you really float.

Problems

Section 10.1 Hydrostatic Pressure

Hints for Solving Problems

Pressure is a scalar, not a vector. Remember that gauge pressure measures pressure above atmospheric pressure.

10.1 A block of wood 10 cm $\times$ 30 cm $\times$ 5.5 cm thick has a mass of 1240 g. (a) What is the density of this wood? (b) Is the wood balsa, oak, or pine?

10.2 A liter of corn oil has a mass of 0.925 kg. What is the (a) density and (b) specific gravity of the oil?

10.3 At the base of the Hoover Dam on the Colorado River, the depth of the water is 726 ft. What is the pressure at the base of the dam? Neglect the pressure due to the atmosphere.

10.4 A swimming pool is 50 m long by 23 m wide and is less deep at one end than at the other. The depth at the shallow end is 1.22 m, and the depth at the deep end is 4.35 m. The slope is continuous (smooth) from one end to the other. What is the difference in pressure on the bottom at opposite ends of the pool?

10.5 Organisms have been found living in the oceans where the pressure is as high as 1000 atm. To what depth does this pressure correspond? (Take the density of seawater to be 1.026×10^3 kg/m^3.)

10.6 An automobile tire is properly inflated at a pressure of 32.0 psi. What is its pressure expressed in kPa?

10.7 A 1350-kg automobile is supported by four tires inflated to a gauge pressure of 220 kPa. Ignoring the effects of tread thickness, calculate the area of contact between each tire and the road.

10.8 The gauge pressure at the bottom of a reservoir is four times what it is at a depth of 1.2 m. How deep is the reservoir?

10.9• A woman wearing high-heeled shoes places about 50% of her full weight on a single heel when walking. (a) Assuming the woman weighs 530 N, what is the pressure on the ground under one heel if the area of contact is 6.5 cm²? 1.0 cm²? (b) How does this compare with the pressure underneath an elephant's foot? For computation, assume that a full-grown elephant weighs 37,000 N and is standing evenly on four feet. Approximate the feet as circles 38 cm in diameter.

10.10• A rectangular fish tank measures 30 cm by 65 cm by 40 cm high. (a) If the tank is filled with water to a depth of 37 cm, what is the pressure at the bottom due to the water? (b) What is the total force of the water on the bottom?

10.11• A 1.000-m-tall pipe is filled to the halfway level with glycerin and then to the top with water. What is the gauge pressure at the bottom?

Section 10.2 Pascal's Principle

In using Pascal's principle at some point in a fluid, make sure you know the pressure due to depth at that point before you consider the effect of an applied pressure.

10.12 A hydraulic jack is made with a small piston 1.2 cm in diameter that is used to move a large piston 5.4 cm in diameter. If a man can exert a force of 280 N on the small piston, how heavy a load can he lift with the jack?

10.13 A hydraulic press has a large piston with a cross-sectional area of 420 cm² and a small piston with a cross-sectional area of 5.00 cm². What is the force on the large piston when a force of 1.50 kN is applied to the small piston?

10.14 An air compressor maintains a pressure of 700 kPa over the hydraulic fluid in a tank (Fig. 10.32). The large piston that lifts the car has a cross-sectional area of 0.280 m². What is the maximum weight that it can lift?

10.15 A hydraulic lift of the type shown in Fig. 10.32 is used to raise a car weighing 15,000 N. The piston that supports the car has a diameter of 36 cm. What pressure of air within the system is required to just hold the car in place?

10.16 The column of mercury in a barometer stands 76.0 cm high. How tall would the barometer have to be if the mercury were replaced by water?

10.17• A U-shaped tube is partially filled with equal volumes of water and mercury (Fig. 10.33). If each liquid fills a 20-cm-long section of the tube, what will be the difference in the levels of the upper surfaces?

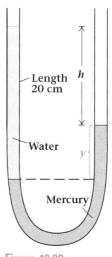

Problem 10.17.

10.18•• Corrosive liquids can be moved from containers by means of siphons rather than by pumps (Fig. 10.34). Over how high a wall can sulfuric acid (specific gravity 1.84) be siphoned?

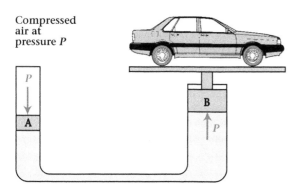

Problems 10.14 and 10.15: An air compressor provides a pressure at piston *A*. The pressure is transmitted through the hydraulic fluid to piston *B*.

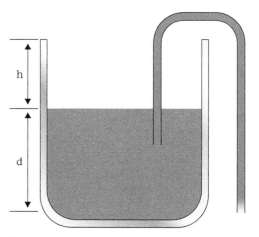

Problem 10.18.

Section 10.3 Archimedes' Principle

Hints for Solving Problems

Remember that the buoyant force equals the weight of the *displaced fluid* and is independent of the *weight* of the object. When working problems that use Archimedes' principle with gases, remember that the density of a gas depends on the pressure and the temperature through the relationship given in the footnote to Table 10.2.

10.19• A solid cube of unknown composition is seen floating upright in water with 30% of it above the surface. Calculate the density of the material.

10.20• A block of iron is suspended from one end of an equal-arm balance by a thin wire. To balance the scales, 2.35 kg are needed on the scale pan at the other end. (a) What is the volume of the block? (b) Next, a beaker of water is placed so that the iron block, suspended as in part (a), is submerged in the beaker but not touching the bottom (Fig. 10.35). What mass is now necessary to balance the scales?

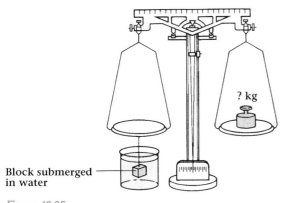

Figure 10.35
Problems 10.20 and 10.30.

10.21• A Goodyear blimp has a volume of 5750 m³ and a mass of 4300 kg when empty. What additional load is it able to lift when the entire volume is filled with helium at a temperature of 20°C? (Your answer will differ from the actual load because the entire volume is not filled with helium, the helium is not at atmospheric pressure, and the temperature of the air and helium may not be the same.)

10.22• The helium gas capacity of the dirigible Macon was 184,000 m³. The weight of the dirigible (less gas) was about 1,092,000 N. (a) Approximately how much additional load could the dirigible lift from the ground? Assume a temperature of 21°C. (b) What percent more load could it lift if hydrogen were used for the gas?

10.23• A plastic bag is filled with helium at atmospheric pressure and 21°C. How large a volume of helium is required to lift a 50-kg girl off her feet? Assume that the mass of the bag is negligible. (See Table 10.2.)

10.24• If, in Problem 10.23, hot air is used instead of helium, what is the required volume for the balloon if the air inside can be maintained at a temperature of 44°C? Assume the outside air is at 21°C.

10.25• A wooden dowel is placed in a test tube containing water. The dowel floats with 60% of its length below the water surface. How much of the dowel is submerged when it floats in methyl alcohol?

10.26• A 1.0-kg container of water sits on a scale A. A piece of aluminum 10 cm × 10 cm × 10 cm is suspended from a spring scale B so that half of the block is submerged in the water. (a) What is the reading on spring scale B? (b) What is the reading on scale A?

10.27• A 0.0132-kg seashell of density $\rho = 3.54 \times 10^3$ kg/m³ is suspended by a thread from a spring scale. The seashell is then lowered into seawater until it is completely submerged. If the scale is calibrated in units of newtons, what is the reading of the scale?

10.28•• A block of pine wood ($\rho = 0.40$ g/cm³) is floating on a pond. The block is 10 cm × 40 cm × 5 cm thick. (a) How much of the block protrudes above the water? (b) If the block is made to carry a load by placing additional mass on top of it, how much mass must be added to just submerge the block?

10.29•• A wooden block 20 cm × 20 cm × 10 cm has a density of 0.60 g/cm³. (a) How much iron ($\rho = 7.86$ g/cm³) can be placed on top of the block if the top of the block is to be level with the water around it? (b) If iron were attached to the bottom of the block instead, what mass of iron would it take to bring the top of the wooden block down to the level of the water? Why?

10.30•• A king's crown is said to be solid gold but may be made of lead and covered with gold. When it is weighed in air, the scale reads 0.475 kg. When it is submerged in water, the scale reads 0.437 kg. (a) Is it solid gold? (b) If not, what percentage by mass is gold? (Refer to Fig. 10.35.)

10.31•• An inverted Atwood machine is constructed by fixing a pulley P near the bottom of a container filled with a liquid of density ρ (Fig. 10.36). Two floats with the same mass

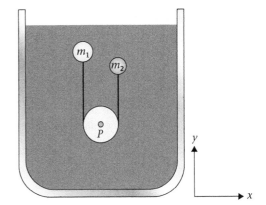

Figure 10.36
Problem 10.31.

($m_1 = m_2$) but different density are joined together by a string passing around the pulley. Because the masses are not the same size, the upward forces on them are unequal. The upward force F_1 on mass m_1 is greater than the upward force F_2 on mass m_2. The floats are released from rest. (a) Draw a free-body diagram for each float including all of the forces that act on the float. (b) What is the net force on each float? (c) Find an expression for the initial acceleration of each float. Ignore the pulley's mass, any friction in the pulley, and any fluid friction.

*Section 10.4 Surface Tension

10.32 What force is required to overcome surface tension when raising a horizontal 8.0-cm-diameter ring out of water at 25°C?

10.33 A 5.0-cm-diameter ring is used to determine the surface tension of a liquid. What is the liquid's surface tension if, in addition to the ring's weight, a force of 2.3×10^{-2} N is required to lift the ring from the liquid?

10.34 A wire frame with a sliding crosspiece is dipped into a soap solution and held vertically (Fig. 10.37). The crosspiece is 5.0 cm long and has a mass of 0.265 g. What is the value of the surface tension of the soap solution if the weight of the crosspiece is just balanced by the surface tension force?

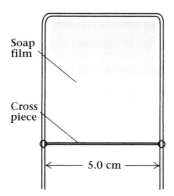

Soap film

Cross piece

|← 5.0 cm →|

Figure 10.37
Problem 10.34.

10.35 How high will water rise in a capillary tube with inside diameter of 0.10 mm? Assume the contact angle to be $\theta = 0°$. Take the temperature to be 25°C.

10.36• Water is poured into an upright U-shaped tube in which the legs have different internal diameters. If the diameter of one is 0.6 mm and the diameter of the other is 1.2 mm, what will be the difference in the height of the water in the two legs? Take the contact angle to be 0°.

10.37• By what factor is the surface energy of a 2.0-cm-diameter soap bubble increased when it is blown up to a diameter's of 6.0 cm?

Sections 10.5 and 10.6 Fluid Flow: Streamlines and the Equation of Continuity; Bernoulli's Equation

Hints for Solving Problems

Remember that Bernoulli's principle applies to incompressible, nonviscous fluids in laminar flow. Be especially careful with units, since many of the quantities used in fluid flow involve derived units rather than fundamental units.

10.38• What is the pressure change in water going from a 4.0-cm-diameter pipe to a 2.0-cm-diameter pipe if the velocity in the smaller pipe is 3.0 m/s?

10.39• What is the pressure change in methyl alcohol flowing from a 4.0 cm diameter pipe to a 1.5 cm diameter pipe if the velocity in the larger pipe is 0.40 m/s?

10.40• Water is flowing in a horizontal pipe of variable cross section. Where the cross-sectional area is 1.0×10^{-2} m^2, the pressure is 5.0×10^5 Pa and the velocity 0.50 m/s. In a constricted region where the area is 4.0×10^{-4} m^2, what are the pressure and velocity?

10.41• A large storage tank is filled with water. Neglecting viscosity, show that the speed of water emerging through a hole in the side a distance h below the surface is $v = \sqrt{2gh}$. This result is known as *Torricelli's theorem*. Try using Bernoulli's equation.

10.42• Suppose you blow air at a speed of 10 m/s across one end of a U-shaped tube containing water. What will be the difference in the heights of the water surfaces on the two sides? Which one will be higher?

10.43•• Use the results of Problem 10.41 to show that you obtain the maximum range for water leaving a hole in the side of a tank resting on the ground when the hole is halfway between the top and bottom surfaces of the liquid.

10.44•• Assume that you wish to find the speed of a moving fluid that obeys Bernoulli's equation. Use the equation of continuity and Bernoulli's equation to derive the equation for the speed measured by a Venturi meter (refer to Fig. 10.21).

*Section 10.7 Viscosity and Poiseuille's Law

10.45 A horizontal garden hose 15 m long with an interior diameter of 1.25 cm is used to deliver water at the rate of 150 cm^3/s. What is the pressure drop from one end of the hose to the other? Assume a temperature of 20°C.

10.46 Mercury flows through a horizontal pipe 4.0 cm in diameter and 0.50 m long. If the pressure drop from one end of the pipe to the other is 1.0×10^4 Pa (about 1/10 atm), what is the rate of flow through the tube?

10.47 By what fraction would the blood flow be reduced if an arteriole were reduced to 0.95 of its former diameter? Assume the pressure and viscosity to be constant.

10.48• How high above the point of injection must a container of blood plasma be if the plasma is to enter the patient's arm at a rate of 3.0 cm³/min through a needle that is 50 mm long and has an inside diameter of 0.55 mm? Assume the pressure in the vein to be 15 mm Hg. (Assume also that the density of blood plasma is 1.05 g/cm³ and its viscosity is about 1.5×10^{-3} Pa · s.)

*Section 10.8 Stokes's Law and Terminal Speed

10.49 Compare the sedimentation rates for a mixture of spherical particles that are all of the same material but have diameters that differ in the ratio of 1:2:3.

10.50 A steel ball bearing 8.00 mm in diameter is dropped into a cylinder of glycerin. The densities of steel and glycerin are 7.80×10^3 and 1.26×10^3 kg/m³, respectively. What is the terminal speed of the ball bearing?

10.51 (a) A bottle of corn syrup is taken from a refrigerator ($T = 5°C$), and a glass marble of density 2.5×10^3 kg/m³ is dropped into it. The marble takes 45 s to sink to the bottom. The diameter of the marble is 1.57 cm, the depth of the liquid is 12.1 cm, and its density is 1.2×10^3 kg/m³. What is the viscosity of the syrup at that temperature? (b) If the bottle is kept out of the refrigerator for several hours and the experiment is done again, the marble takes 5.0 s to fall through the liquid. What is the viscosity of the syrup at room temperature?

10.52 Measurements of falling coffee filters show that they experience a drag force proportional to the square of their speed. If three filters are nested together so that their effective cross-sectional area is the same as that of a single filter, what would be the ratio of their terminal speed to the terminal speed of a single filter?

10.53 A small balloon is inflated to a diameter of 20 cm and has a total mass of 0.40 g. When it is allowed to fall in air, the balloon has a drag force predominantly due to v^2, where v is its speed. Calculate the balloon's terminal speed given that the coefficient b equals 9.0×10^{-3} kg/m.

10.54 The speed of an automobile increases from 80 km/h (50 mi/h) to 115 km/h (71 mi/h). What is the ratio of the drag forces at the two speeds?

10.55● When the engines of a jet airliner develop 1.00×10^5 N of thrust (driving force), the jet reaches an air speed of 750 km/h. Calculate the thrust required for speeds of 800 km/h and 600 km/h. What does your result suggest about the relationship between fuel consumption and speed if the thrust is proportional to fuel consumption?

10.56● Two spherical objects have the same size and same surface roughness. One of them is heavier than the other. Show that if both objects are simultaneously released from rest from the same height, the heavier one strikes the ground first.

10.57● A geological sample from a river bed forms sediment at the rate of 1.0 g/day. How many revolutions per second would a centrifuge have to achieve to increase the sedimentation rate to 3.0 g/h? Assume that the sample is placed 5.0 cm from the axis of rotation of the centrifuge.

10.58● A baseball falling through the air experiences a drag force

$$F(\text{newtons}) = 8.06 \times 10^{-4} \, v^2,$$

where v is in m/s. What is the terminal speed for the ball if it falls from a great height? The ball has a mass of 0.145 kg.

10.59●● Show that the terminal speed of an object falling in air, such as a ball or parachute, can be estimated by

$$v_t = \sqrt{\frac{mg}{kA\rho}},$$

where m is the mass of the object, A is its cross-sectional area, ρ is the density of air, and k is a dimensionless constant whose value is 1 or less and depends on the shape of the object. (*Hint:* During its fall, the object "sweeps out" a vertical tube of air. Assume that the drag force is proportional to the rate at which the falling object transfers momentum to this tube of air, and that the rate of change of momentum is the product of the speed and the rate at which the mass of the air in the tube is displaced.)

*Section 10.9 Turbulent Flow

10.60 What is the order of magnitude of the lowest speed that a Ping-Pong ball can have in air at 20°C if the flow remains turbulent? The diameter of a Ping-Pong ball is 3.75 cm.

10.61 Show that the Reynolds number is dimensionless.

10.62● (a) Calculate the terminal speed for a steel ball of radius 0.50 cm and density 7.8×10^3 kg/m³ falling through water. Assume that Stokes's law applies. (b) Calculate the Reynolds number by setting L in Eq. (10.14) equal to the diameter of the ball. (c) Is the flow really laminar? What does this suggest about the value for the terminal speed? Assume a temperature of 20°C.

10.63● What is the minimum diameter of a pipe through which 1.00 m³ of glycerin at 20°C can be made to flow per hour if the flow is to be laminar?

10.64● If the flow of a liquid in a 2-cm-diameter pipe is just barely laminar, what size pipe would be needed to maintain laminar flow if the flow rate were to be twice as much as in the first pipe?

10.65● How much water per hour can be delivered by a $\frac{3}{4}$-in. pipe in which laminar flow is maintained? Assume a temperature of 20°C.

Additional Problems

10.66 What is the pressure at the bottom of a 2.0-km-deep oil well filled with oil of density 860 kg/m³?

10.67 A water tower provides pressure for a water supply system. What is the maximum water pressure available at the bottom of the tower, given that the water level is 33 m above the place where the pressure is to be measured?

10.68 A Rolex Sea-Diver wrist watch is guaranteed to be water resistant down to a depth of 4000 ft below sea level. A special version of this model ran after having been submerged to a depth of 35,000 ft in the Marianas Trench in the Pacific Ocean. To what pressures do these depths correspond? (Take the density of sea water to be 1.026×10^3 kg/m^3.)

10.69 Water is flowing in a horizontal pipe of varying cross section. At one point where the cross-sectional area is 1.0×10^{-2} m^2, the velocity of the water is 2.0 m/s and the pressure is 15 kPa. In another region of the pipe the velocity is 3.0 m/s. What is the cross-sectional area at the second position and what is the pressure there?

10.70 A glass marble of density 2.5×10^3 kg/m^3 and diameter 5.0 mm is dropped into a cylinder containing castor oil of density 900 kg/m^3. What is the terminal speed of the marble?

10.71• The deep research vessel Alvin can dive to depths of 4000 m. What is the force of the water on one of the submarine's 30.5-cm-diameter circular ports? The pressure inside the titanium hull is one atmosphere.

10.72• A garden hose has an interior diameter of 0.95 cm and a nozzle with a 0.40-cm-diameter opening. (a) If 30 liters per minute flow through the hose, what is the speed of the water emerging from the nozzle? (b) If the nozzle is held horizontally 1.1 m above level ground, how far will the stream go before it hits the ground?

10.73• A Venturi meter of the type shown in Fig. 10.21 has mercury in the U-shaped tube. The meter is used to measure the flow speed of water. At A the pipe diameter is 10.0 cm, at B it is 5.0 cm. What is the speed of the water at A if the differential height h is 5.0 cm?

10.74• On each heartbeat about 70 cm^3 of blood is forced from the heart at an average pressure of approximately 105 mm Hg. What is the average power output if the heart beats 70 times each minute?

10.75•• A glass disk G is held tightly against the end of a vertically held cylindrical tube C while the tube is lowered so that the bottom of the disk is 20 cm below the surface of the water (Fig. 10.38). What is the maximum thickness the disk can have and not fall away from the cylinder? The density of the glass is $\rho = 2.5 \times 10^3$ kg/m^3.

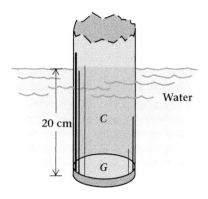

Figure 10.38
Problem 10.75.

10.76•• A hollow Ping-Pong ball is tethered to the bottom of a water-filled cylinder by a short string of length L. When the cylinder is mounted on a moveable arm and set into rotation, the ball is deflected toward the center of rotation (Fig. 10.39). Find an expression for the deflection angle θ in terms of the rotational frequency ω and the distance R.

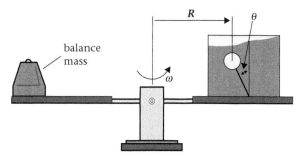

Figure 10.39
Problem 10.76.

10.77•• A cylinder of solid uranium weighs 9.34 kg in air, 8.84 kg in water, and 2.54 kg in another liquid. (a) What is the volume of the cylinder? (b) What is the density of the uranium cylinder? (c) What is the density of the liquid? (d) Identify the liquid.

10.78•• A block of oak wood floats at the interface between gasoline and water (Fig. 10.40). One-third of the volume of the block is in the water and two-thirds of the block is in the gasoline. What is the density of the block?

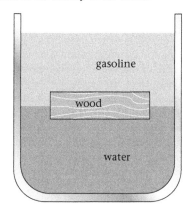

Figure 10.40
Problems 10.78 and 10.79.

10.79•• An ice cube floats at the interface between olive oil and water in the same manner as the block in Problem 10.78 (Fig. 10.40). If the olive oil has a specific gravity of 0.91, what fraction of the ice cube is submerged below the level of the oil-water interface?

10.80•• A dense liquid is poured into a 1-m-deep container and a less dense liquid carefully poured on top of it, so as to form two layers. After many days the liquids have become mixed, but not thoroughly so. At the bottom of the container the density is still that of the denser liquid and at the top the density is that of the lighter liquid. Tests show that the density is given by

$$\rho = (1 + 0.26x^2) \times 10^3 \text{ kg/m}^3,$$

where x is the distance below the surface in meters. What is the pressure in this liquid mixture at a depth of 0.5 m below the surface? (Try using the graphical technique of Chapters 2 and 6. Add up the weight of individual thin layers whose density is nearly constant.)

10.81•• If the internal volume of a hot-air balloon is 2180 m³, at what temperature must the air be to keep a 475-kg balloon and loaded gondola in the air when the outside temperature is 20°C? (See the footnote in Table 10.2.)

10.82•• Show that the problem posed in Example 10.3 can be solved without resorting to Pascal's principle by assuming that the output work is equal to the input work. (*Hint:* Remember that the volume of liquid remains constant.)

10.83•• A triangular prism of ice with uniform thickness floats in sea water with its base above the water (Fig. 10.41). (a) Show that the fractional volume of ice below the water is $V_{\text{below}}/V_{\text{total}} = \rho_{\text{ice}}/\rho_{\text{sea water}}$. (b) Show that the ratio of the depth of the peak below the water to the total height of the prism is $d/h = \sqrt{\rho_{\text{ice}}/\rho_{\text{sea water}}}$.

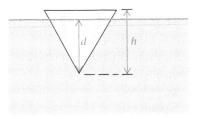

Figure 10.41
Problem 10.83.

chapter 11

Thermal Physics

11.1   Temperature and States of Matter

11.2   Thermometry

Back to the Future: Fahrenheit's Thermometer

11.3   Thermal Expansion

11.4   The Mechanical Equivalent of Heat

11.5   Calorimetry

11.6   Change of Phase

11.7   Heat Transfer

The development of thermal physics was greatly influenced by the practical concerns and search for efficiency that characterized the Industrial Revolution in the eighteenth and nineteenth centuries. By that time, mechanics was relatively well developed, but electricity had not yet become of practical or commercial importance. As a consequence, the disciplines of mechanics, heat, and electricity all evolved along different paths. As recently as the late eighteenth century, the study of heat was not related to the study of mechanics. As a result, the definitions and units of measurement for temperature and heat were developed independently of the definitions and units for work and mechanical energy. Not until the mid-nineteenth century did James Prescott Joule quantitatively connect the unit of thermal energy with the unit of mechanical work, allowing us to see mechanics and thermal physics as parts of a greater whole.

Today we think of heat as a form of energy transfer. The effects of heat and temperature changes are a fundamental aspect of many physical situations, from the study of star formation to research in lasers. ■

11.1 Temperature and States of Matter

We begin our discussion of thermal physics by briefly describing what we mean by different states of matter. As an example, water can have the form of ice (solid), water (liquid), or steam (gas). Many other materials can also exist as solids, liquids, or gases. Such distinct forms, or states, of matter are called *phases* (Fig. 11.1). The change from one state, or phase, to another, such as the melting of ice, is usually caused by a transfer of thermal energy.

The molecules of a gas move about freely, except when they collide with other gas molecules or the walls of the container. The average separation between molecules is large compared with their own size, and as a result, a gas has no definite volume. Consequently, a gas may be compressed or expanded and will fill a container of any shape or size. In a liquid, the average separation between molecules is comparable to their own diameters. Individual molecules are free to move about, but because of the forces between them they move so that the average separation between near neighbors remains essentially constant. As a result, a liquid is virtually incompressible and has a definite volume, although its shape can change to match the shape of its container. In solids the separations are comparable to the separations in liquids, but the binding forces are so strong that the atoms in a solid are not free to move about. Instead, the atoms of a solid are confined to small oscillations about fixed positions. Thus, a solid has not only a definite volume but a definite shape as well.

Energy is associated with the motion of molecules in any state of matter. In fact, as we will see, changes in temperature and changes from one state to another are simply large-scale manifestations of changes in the energy of the random motions of the atoms and molecules that compose the material.

The concept of temperature originated in human sensory perception of the environment. When you touch an object, you say it is relatively "hot" or "cold." This response early led to attempts to describe the feeling in terms of the objects; for example, this rock is warmer than that rock. The desire to quantify and measure such differences in warmth culminated in the idea of **temperature:** the number assigned to an object as an indication of its warmth. A device used to measure temperature is called a **thermometer.** Thermometers are used not only as quantitative indicators to measure what the hand can feel, but also to extend the range of measurements far beyond the sense of touch. The range of thermometers extends from temperatures low enough to freeze the gases of the air to the enormous temperatures at the interiors of stars.

Our sensory perception allows us to define another useful term. Place an object A, which feels hot to your hand, in contact with an object B of the same material, which feels cold to your hand. After a period of time has passed, they will give the same sensation to your hand. Objects A and B are said to be in **thermal equilibrium,** and their temperatures are equal (Fig. 11.2). We can extend this idea to say that two objects that are not touching are in thermal equilibrium if, upon being placed in contact, their temperature would not change. This principle, which is discussed in greater detail in Chapter 13, is very useful in making a thermometer as described in the following section.

Figure 11.1
Matter that we commonly encounter exists in one of three phases: solid (glacier), liquid (water), and gas (air and water vapor).

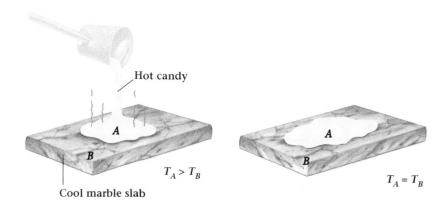

Figure 11.2
The hot molten candy and the cool marble slab reach thermal equilibrium after a period of time. At thermal equilibrium, their temperatures are equal.

Hot candy

A

B

$T_A > T_B$

Cool marble slab

A

B

$T_A = T_B$

11.2   Thermometry

The development and calibration of thermometers and the establishment of temperature scales are the essence of *thermometry,* the science of temperature and its measurement. The basis of thermometry is that some physical properties vary with temperature in a quantitative and repeatable fashion. Some of these thermometric properties are the volume of a gas or liquid, the length of a metallic strip, the electrical resistance of a conductor, and the light-transmitting properties of a crystal. Any physical system whose properties change with variations in temperature can be used as a thermometer. The choice of a particular thermometer depends primarily on the range of temperatures to be studied. We measure the change in some property, say the length of a column of liquid, and then associate a change in temperature with our measurement of the change in length.

The liquid-in-glass thermometer was invented about 1650 by the Grand Duke of Tuscany, Ferdinand II, one of Galileo's fellow countrymen and a patron of science. In this thermometer, a liquid indicator is sealed into a glass capillary tube having a bulb at one end. When the temperature increases, both the volume of the glass bulb and the volume of the liquid increase. If they both expanded at the same rate, we would observe no change. But because the liquid expands at a greater rate than the glass does, the liquid is forced to expand into the tube as the temperature increases. By using a relatively large bulb and a narrow tube, it is possible to make a thermometer that we can read easily from a scale scribed on the glass. The common fever thermometer is made this way.

We choose to discuss the liquid-in-glass thermometer here because of its simplicity and great familiarity. However, we emphasize that it is only one of many possible types of thermometers. For example, some thermometers determine temperature by measuring the electrical resistance of a platinum wire or a semiconductor crystal (Fig. 11.3). For a fixed applied voltage, the amount of current transmitted by the wire or crystal depends on the temperature and is reproducible. Thermometers of the type shown are used in medical applications. Similar thermometers are used in applications that require precision measurement over a wide range of temperatures.

Any thermometer, whether liquid-in-glass or one that depends on other thermal properties, must be calibrated to make it a useful instrument, capable of quantitative and reproducible measurements. For example, a liquid-in-glass ther-

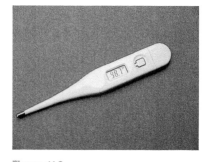

Figure 11.3
A digital fever thermometer uses the temperature dependence of the electrical resistance of a semiconductor crystal to measure temperature.

mometer can be calibrated by marking on the glass the position of the liquid column at a set of reference temperatures or standards. Temperatures between the reference marks are interpreted as proportional to the length of the liquid column. In fact, this is just how the **Celsius temperature scale** is defined. The two fixed points of reference are the ice point and the steam point. The ice point is defined as the equilibrium temperature of a mixture of ice and water at a pressure of one atmosphere; the steam point is defined as the equilibrium temperature of water and steam at a pressure of one atmosphere. The numbers assigned to these two points in the Celsius scale are arbitrarily chosen as 0 for the ice point and 100 for the steam point.

Assuming that the cross section of the thermometer capillary is uniform and that the rate of expansion of the liquid with changes in temperature is constant, we then can mark the distance between the ice and steam points into 100 equal parts. We can easily compare the level of the liquid to the nearest mark, called a degree.* We thus measure temperature in units of degrees Celsius, abbreviated as °C. (This scale was originally known as the centigrade scale because it has one hundred divisions between the principal reference marks. The present name was adopted to honor the Swedish astronomer Anders Celsius, who popularized the scale in 1742.)

Figure 11.4 shows a Celsius scale thermometer at a temperature T_C, at which the liquid is extended a distance L beyond the zero position. We may calculate the temperature by

$$T_C = \left(\frac{L}{L_0}\right) \times 100,$$

where L_0 is the distance between the 0° and 100° marks. Here we have defined the temperature scale to be a linear function of the length L of the liquid column. (There is no fundamental reason for doing this; we could define other functions equally well. However, the linear relationship is the simplest.) When the temperature scale is defined this way, other important physical properties turn out to be approximately independent of temperature.

Although the Celsius temperature scale is widely used, there is nothing fundamental about choosing the ice point to be 0° and the steam point as 100°. The **Fahrenheit temperature scale** assigns a value of 32° to the ice point and 212° to the steam point, a difference of exactly 180°. It is easy to transform temperatures in one system into temperatures in the other system. For example, let us find the relationship that transforms temperature in °C to temperature in °F. Just remember that 0°C is equivalent to 32°F, and that a range of 180° on the Fahrenheit scale is 100° on the Celsius scale. Therefore, one Celsius degree is equivalent to $\frac{180}{100}$, or $\frac{9}{5}$, of one Fahrenheit degree. We can then write the Fahrenheit temperature T_F as

$$\boxed{T_F = \frac{9}{5}T_C + 32.} \qquad (11.1)$$

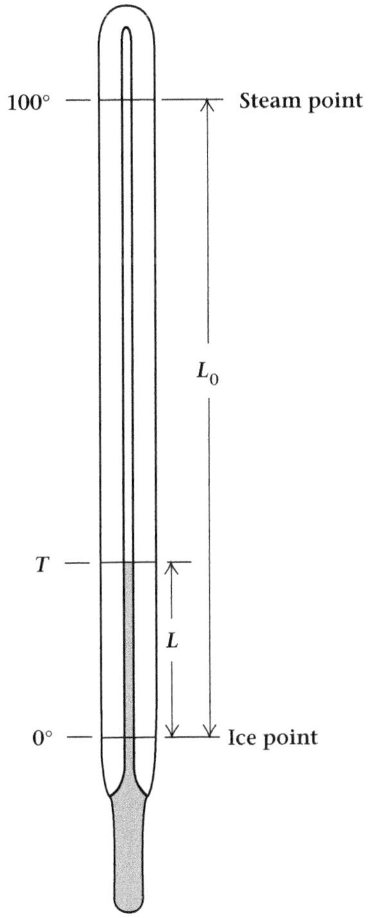

You can convince yourself that this is correct by substituting the Celsius values for the freezing and boiling temperatures of water and seeing whether you get

Figure 11.4
A liquid-in-glass thermometer with a Celsius scale. The temperature is proportional to the ratio of the distance L to the reference distance L_0.

---

*Some early thermometers were marked in 360 divisions, like the parts of a circle; thus, the term *degree* became applied to temperature.

the correct Fahrenheit values. You can use this same substitution to check whether you have remembered the formula correctly when you must recall it without the book.

Equation (11.1) gives the Fahrenheit temperature if the Celsius temperature is known. It can easily be rearranged to express the Celsius temperature in terms of Fahrenheit. Two examples of these transformations follow.

Example 11.1

What Fahrenheit temperature is equivalent to 37.0°C?

Solution Application of Eq. (11.1) yields

$$T_F = \tfrac{9}{5}T_C + 32 = \tfrac{9}{5}(37.0) + 32 = 66.6 + 32 = 98.6°F.$$

Example 11.2

On a day when the temperature is 86°F, what is the reading of a Celsius thermometer?

Solution From Eq. (11.1) we have

$$T_F = \tfrac{9}{5}T_C + 32,$$

which can be rearranged to give

$$T_C = \tfrac{5}{9}(T_F - 32),$$
$$T_C = \tfrac{5}{9}(86 - 32) = \tfrac{5}{9}(54) = 30°C.$$

In both the Fahrenheit and Celsius temperature scales, the assignment of the zero point is arbitrary. We can readily achieve temperatures below these zero points. However, one temperature scale has a more fundamental choice of zero. This scale was proposed in 1848 by William Thomson, Lord Kelvin (1824–1907), and arose from the study of gases. Kelvin's scale uses intervals equal to those of the Celsius degree, but with zero set at the lowest theoretical temperature that a gas can reach. The scale is based on the fact that a gas at 0°C will lose 1/273.15 of its volume for a 1°C drop in temperature. If this reduction in volume were to continue with decreasing temperature and if the gas did not liquefy, the volume would become zero at −273.15°C, a temperature called **absolute zero.** The temperature scale based on this zero is the **Kelvin temperature scale.** We will discuss the physical meaning of this observation in more detail in Chapter 12. In this chapter you can just consider the Kelvin scale to be a temperature scale with degree intervals of the same size as the Celsius degree, but with the zero point at −273.15°C. Thus a temperature *change* of 1°C is the same as a *change* of 1 K.

The conversion between Celsius and Kelvin temperatures is a simple one,

$$\boxed{T_K = T_C + 273.15.}$$ (11.2)

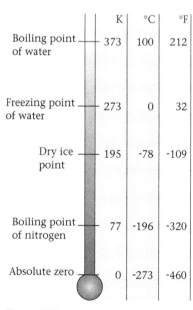

	K	°C	°F
Boiling point of water	373	100	212
Freezing point of water	273	0	32
Dry ice point	195	-78	-109
Boiling point of nitrogen	77	-196	-320
Absolute zero	0	-273	-460

Figure 11.5
A comparison of the Fahrenheit, Celsius, and Kelvin scales of temperature.

Back to the Future

FAHRENHEIT'S THERMOMETER

Although the Celsius scale is becoming increasingly common in the United States, most people in the United States still think in terms of Fahrenheit temperatures when deciding what to wear outside. Have you ever wondered why the freezing temperature is 32°F? Why not 0° or 100°? What's so special about the numbers in 32°F, 212°F, or even 98.6°F?

At the beginning of the eighteenth century, the Danish astronomer Ole Roemer (famous for making the first measurements that showed that the velocity of light is finite) devised a temperature scale of his own for use with the alcohol-in-glass thermometers that he constructed. His thermometers attracted the attention of Gabriel Fahrenheit (1686–1736), a manufacturer of meteorological instruments in the Netherlands. In 1708, Fahrenheit traveled to Copenhagen to meet Roemer and see his thermometers, which were based on two reference points. For one reference Roemer used a mixture of ice, water, and salt to reach the lowest temperatures then attainable in the laboratory, which he called zero. His other reference was the boiling point of water, which he arbitrarily designated as 60 degrees.

Fahrenheit returned home to make thermometers like Roemer's. In 1714 he overcame technical difficulties with alcohol thermometers by substituting mercury as the expanding liquid. The use of mercury extended the range of temperature measurements from well below Roemer's zero to well above the boiling point of water. Furthermore, mercury expanded and contracted more uniformly than the other liquids then in use. As a result, Fahrenheit could mark his mercury thermometers more accurately and with finer divisions.

By 1724, Fahrenheit had adopted a new scale, similar to Roemer's but with much finer divisions. For the zero point he chose the same reference as Roemer. However, since his thermometer was intended for meteorological observations, he wanted a second reference point that would be nearer the maximum observed temperature for weather. He chose the normal temperature of the human body as the upper reference point, which he called 96°. Fahrenheit gave no reason for his choice of 96, but it may have been due to his desire for a finer scale and because 96 is evenly divisible by 2, 3, 4, 8, and 12.

Why didn't Fahrenheit choose the freezing point of water for his zero reference, as Newton had done before him and as Celsius did later on? Perhaps Fahrenheit was influenced by Roemer, or he may have wanted to avoid the inconvenience of repeatedly using negative temperatures during winter. Also, in the early 1700s it was widely believed that water did not always freeze at the same temperature. Soon, using his newly calibrated thermometers, Fahrenheit learned that water always froze at 32° on his scale. He immediately added this third reference point to his instruments.

A report of Fahrenheit's thermometers was published in the *Philosophical Transactions* in 1724. Almost at once his scale was adopted in Great Britain and the Netherlands and gained wide acceptance throughout the English-speaking countries.

The Fahrenheit scale in use today differs slightly from the original. The two fixed points are the ice point, assigned a value of 32°F, and the steam point, assigned a value of 212°F. On this scale the normal human body temperature is 98.6°F, slightly higher than the 96° originally chosen by Fahrenheit.

Today the Celsius scale and the Kelvin scale have replaced the Fahrenheit scale for scientific work. Also, the range of temperatures that can now be measured has been extended by many orders of magnitude since Fahrenheit's time. Modern thermometry uses many different physical properties to indicate temperatures, spanning a range from the extreme lows near 10^{-6} K to the surface temperature of the stars at about 10^4 K. The choice of thermometer depends on the temperature to be measured. For example, infrared pyrometers, which use the infrared radiation from hot matter to measure temperature, can measure temperatures ranging from $-30°C$ to $3000°C$. Steelworkers use pyrometers to find the temperature of molten steel. Parents quickly take their baby's temperature with special pyrometers that sense the radiation generated by the child's eardrum and surrounding tissue (Fig. B11.1).

Figure B11.1 A radiation thermometer (pyrometer) uses infrared to accurately measure a child's temperature in just one second.

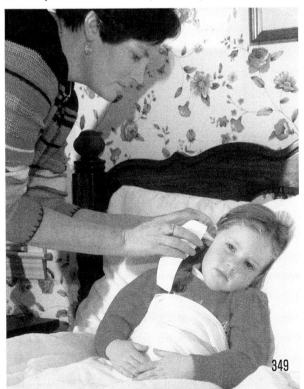

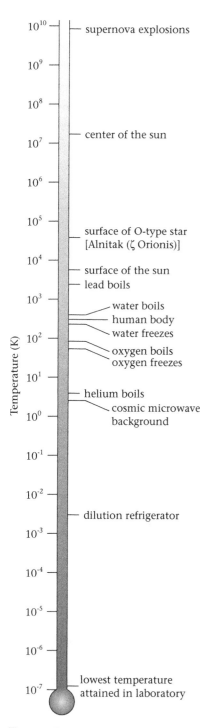

Figure 11.6
Temperature range and corresponding physical situations that occur in nature. Note that the scale is logarithmic.

The unit of absolute temperature is the kelvin (K). It is not written with a degree sign. A temperature of 0°C is simply 273.15 K. A comparison of the various scales is shown in Fig. 11.5.

Today the range of temperatures that can be measured has been extended by many orders of magnitude since Fahrenheit's time. Modern thermometry uses many different physical properties to indicate temperatures, spanning a range from the extreme lows below 10^{-6} K to the surface temperature of the stars at about 10^4 K. The particular choice of thermometer depends on the temperature to be measured. No single thermometer can span the enormous range of temperatures that occur in nature. Figure 11.6 shows the range of temperatures and the corresponding physical phenomena associated with them.

11.3 Thermal Expansion

When you loosen the metal cap on a glass bottle by holding it in a stream of hot water, you are making use of thermal expansion. The liquid-in-glass thermometer described in the preceding section works because of the difference in the rates of thermal expansion of the indicating liquid and of the glass envelope. We can calibrate such a thermometer without ever knowing the individual expansion rates. However, once a temperature scale is established, we can show that, to a good approximation, most solid objects change length in direct proportion to a change in temperature. Also, the change in length is proportional to the initial length of the object. Thus, for the same increase in temperature, a long copper bar expands more than a shorter one, but the ratios of change in length to initial length are the same for both bars (Fig. 11.7). We call this behavior **linear thermal expansion,** that is, expansion in one dimension. The reason for this expansion is that the increase in temperature causes greater amplitudes of vibration of the atoms in the solid, giving a greater average distance between them.

Let us describe linear thermal expansion mathematically. For an object of initial length L_0, the change in length ΔL due to a change in temperature ΔT can be expressed as

$$\Delta L = L_0 \alpha \, \Delta T. \tag{11.3}$$

The proportionality constant α, called the **linear thermal expansion coefficient,** has the dimension of inverse temperature, or $°C^{-1}$. Table 11.1 (p. 353) lists thermal expansion coefficients for a number of common materials. The coefficients themselves have some slight temperature dependence and are given here for 20°C, but you may take them as constant for the purposes of your study.

For an increase in temperature $\Delta T = T - T_0$, a rod of initial length L_0 expands to a new length $L = L_0 + \Delta L$. With the aid of Eq. (11.3), we can express the length L at the new temperature T in terms of the initial length L_0 at the initial temperature T_0:

$$L = L_0 \, (1 + \alpha \Delta T),$$

or

$$L = L_0[1 + \alpha(T - T_0)]. \tag{11.4}$$

Example 11.3

The Verrazano-Narrows Bridge between Brooklyn and Staten Island in New York City is one of the world's longest suspension bridges, with a center span of 1300 m (Fig. 11.8). Because the temperature variation over a year may be quite large, allowance must be made for thermal expansion and contraction of its materials. Assuming that the bridge is steel and, for safety, allowing for a temperature range of 120°C, how much thermal expansion must be allowed for in the center span? (This allowance is made by using expansion joints and components that can move with respect to each other.)

Solution We can obtain the change in length of the center span from our definition of thermal expansion:

$$\Delta L = L_0 \alpha\, \Delta T.$$

Upon inserting the numerical values, including α from Table 11.1,

$$\Delta L = (1300\ \text{m})(12 \times 10^{-6}\ °\text{C}^{-1})(120°\text{C}) = 1.9\ \text{m}.$$

Discussion The total allowance for expansion must be 1.9 m. This total expansion allowance is divided among a number of expansion joints, each allowing only a small amount of expansion.

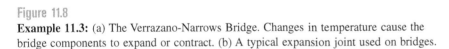

Example 11.4

A copper hot-water pipe is 10.0 m long when cut and installed in a building on a day when the temperature is 10°C. How long is the pipe when it carries hot water at 60°C if the pipe is free to expand?

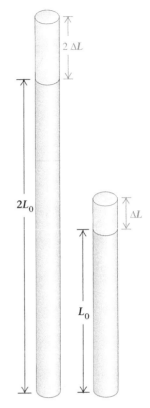

$$\Delta L = L_0\, \alpha\, \Delta T$$

Figure 11.7
A copper bar that is twice as long as a shorter copper bar undergoes twice as much expansion for the same temperature change.

Figure 11.8
Example 11.3: (a) The Verrazano-Narrows Bridge. Changes in temperature cause the bridge components to expand or contract. (b) A typical expansion joint used on bridges.

(a)

(b)

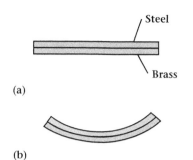

(a)

(b)

(c)

Figure 11.9

(a) A bimetallic strip of steel and brass at room temperature. (b) At a higher temperature, the brass expands more than the steel, causing the strip to bend. (c) A thermostat for controlling a home heat pump. The coil is a thermometer made from a bimetallic strip. The glass tubes containing drops of mercury are electrical switches.

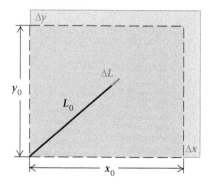

Figure 11.10

A rectangular plate expands in all directions with the same linear thermal expansion coefficient α.

Solution We can use Eq. (11.4):

$$L = L_0[1 + \alpha(T - T_0)]$$
$$L = (10.0 \text{ m})[1 + (17 \times 10^{-6} \text{ °C}^{-1})(60\text{°C} - 10\text{°C})]$$
$$L = (10.0 \text{ m})[1.00085] = 10.0085 \text{ m} = 1000.85 \text{ cm}.$$

The pipe is 0.85 cm longer.

A common application of linear thermal expansion is the bimetallic strip, which is made by joining along their length two strips of metal with different thermal expansion coefficients (Fig. 11.9). Because of unequal expansion or contraction of the two metals with change in temperature, one side of the bimetallic strip becomes longer than the other, causing the strip to bend or curl. Bimetallic strips are frequently used to make thermometers and sensing elements in thermostats.

In some cases we do not observe the expansion anticipated with increasing temperature because the object is clamped or otherwise held fixed. This is the case with modern continuous-welded railroad track. The higher temperature produces a thermal stress in the rail, resulting in a force acting on the ties. Formerly, rail was laid in short sections containing gaps called expansion joints between them. The rails were free to slide back and forth on the ties as the temperature changed. Continuous-welded rail is laid in unbroken segments of any length, with a practical limit of 25 mi imposed by the need for electrically insulating breaks for signal purposes. Spikes clamp the rail firmly to the ties, which distribute the forces caused by temperature changes to the ballast (the small rocks and gravel packed around the railroad ties), and thereby to the earth. The large forces are distributed because the rails are clamped down at closely spaced intervals.

Because the linear dimensions of an object change with temperature, it follows that the area and the volume also change. For example, consider the expansion of a rectangular metal plate as its temperature changes by ΔT (Fig. 11.10). A straight line drawn on the plate in any direction would expand with the linear expansion coefficient of the metal. Along the horizontal (x) direction, the plate would expand with a coefficient α. If the material is homogeneous, the plate expands with the same α in the vertical (y) direction or, indeed, in any other direction. Thus, the plate enlarges horizontally by an amount $\Delta x = x_0\alpha \Delta T$ and vertically by an amount $\Delta y = y_0\alpha \Delta T$, giving an increase in area of approximately $2\alpha \Delta T$ (see Problem 11.19). Furthermore, if the plate contains a hole, the area of the hole increases by the same amount as would the portion of the plate that was removed to make the hole.

If we consider the thickness of the plate, it, too, increases with increasing temperature. If the temperature change is not too great, the change in volume ΔV of a homogeneous material is also proportional to the change in temperature ΔT and to the original volume V_0, so we have

$$\Delta V = \beta V_0 \Delta T, \tag{11.5}$$

where β is the volume coefficient of thermal expansion. The units of β are also °C^{-1}. The volume coefficient of thermal expansion β is approximately three times the value of the linear coefficient of thermal expansion α: $\beta = 3\alpha$. Values for β are given in Table 11.1.

	Coefficients of Thermal Expansion at 20°C	
Table 11.1		
Material	**Linear Coefficient α** $(10^{-6}\ °C^{-1})$	**Volume Coefficient β** $(10^{-6}\ °C^{-1})$
Aluminum	24	72
Brass	19	57
Brick and concrete	10–12	30–36
Copper	17	51
Glass (ordinary)	9	27
Glass (Pyrex)	3	9
Invar	0.7	2.1
Iron and steel	12	36
Lead	29	87
Ice	51 (−20 to −1°C)	153 (−20 to −1°C)
Gasoline	—	950
Mercury	—	180
Water	—	210

The values given are approximate. They vary with the composition of alloys, glasses, and composite materials, and with temperature.

Master the Concept

Linear Expansion

Question: A circular copper plate of uniform thickness has a circular hole in its center. The plate expands when it is heated from room temperature to 500°C. Does the hole in the center expand or contract? Why?

Answer: The hole in the center of the plate expands because its diameter increases in the same proportion as does the diameter of the plate. To understand why, imagine that the hole is completely filled with a copper disk. As the plate is heated, the center disk expands at the same rate as the rest of the plate because it is made of the same material. Then, if the center disk is knocked out of the hot plate, the hole that remains is the size of the disk that is removed. Because the disk is bigger than it was when the plate was cold, the hole must also be bigger by the same amount.

Example 11.5

A 1.00-liter glass bottle is filled to the brim with water at a room temperature of 20°C. The temperature of the bottle and the water is then raised to 95°C. Does the water spill over, or does the level go down, and by how much? Because the volume coefficient of thermal expansion of water changes with temperature, use the average value of $\beta = 525 \times 10^{-6}$ °C for the range of 20°C to 95°C.

Strategy Think of the glass bottle as the "skin" of a solid piece of glass, all of which expands uniformly. Then the change in volume of the inside of the bottle is just the same as the change in volume of the solid interior. We may then compare this change in volume to the change in volume of the liquid.

Solution We may write the change in volume ΔV_{glass} for the bottle as

$$\Delta V_{glass} = \beta V_0 \, \Delta T$$
$$\Delta V_{glass} = (27 \times 10^{-6} \, °C^{-1})(1.00 \times 10^{-3} \, m^3)(95°C - 20°C)$$
$$\Delta V_{glass} = 2.03 \times 10^{-6} \, m^3 = 2.03 \, cm^3.$$

For the water the change in volume ΔV_{water} is

$$\Delta V_{water} = \beta V_0 \, \Delta T$$
$$\Delta V_{water} = (525 \times 10^{-6} \, °C^{-1})(1.00 \times 10^{-3} \, m^3)(95°C - 20°C)$$
$$\Delta V_{water} = 39.4 \times 10^{-6} \, m^3 = 39.4 \, cm^3.$$

The expansion of the water is greater than the expansion of the bottle. The amount of water that will run over the edge is

$$\Delta V_{water} - \Delta V_{glass} = 39.4 \, cm^3 - 2.03 \, cm^3 = 37.4 \, cm^3.$$

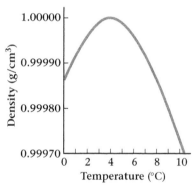

Figure 11.11
The density of water as a function of temperature.

Most liquids expand smoothly with increasing temperature. Alternatively, we can say that they become less dense with increasing temperature. Water, however, is an exception (Fig. 11.11). Its density is greatest at 4°C and less for both higher and lower temperatures. Water also becomes less dense on freezing, again in contrast to most liquids. This effect has important consequences for aquatic life. When a body of water, such as a lake, cools, the cooler water at the top flows to the bottom because of its greater density. When the lake reaches 4°C, this flow stops because the colder top of the lake is less dense as the temperature drops below 4°C. As a consequence the top of the lake freezes first, while the lower depths remain at 4°C. So water freezes from the top down. If water behaved like other substances, lakes would freeze from the bottom up, and the continuous circulation of warmer water to the top would cause more efficient freezing. Under those conditions lakes would freeze solid more frequently than they actually do. But as it is, lakes do not frequently freeze solid, even in the coldest climates. This effect is aided by the fact that the ice layer acts as an insulating blanket over the water. Fish survive by staying on the bottom, where the temperature is at least 4°C.

11.4 The Mechanical Equivalent of Heat

Before the mid-eighteenth century, the distinction between temperature and heat was not clear and the two were often confused. At that time it was generally thought that heat was some kind of fluid, called *caloric,* which could be added to or taken away from a substance to make it hot or cold. We now know that **heat** is a form of energy transfer that occurs when there is a temperature difference between objects. An example of the distinction between heat and temperature is sometimes given by comparing a flaming candle and a warm radiator in the same cool room (Fig. 11.12). The candle flame is at a much higher temperature than the radiator, but you don't expect it to appreciably warm the room. On the other hand, although the radiator is at a lower temperature than the flame, enough heat flows from it to keep you warm. In both cases energy is transferred from an object at a higher temperature to surroundings at a lower temperature.

The first evidence for the connection between heat and energy transfer came when the American-born Benjamin Thompson, Count Rumford (1753–1814), was serving as minister of war in Bavaria. While supervising the boring of cannon, he became curious about the tremendous amount of heat generated. His interest led to some detailed experiments on the nature of heat and heat capacities. (See the definitions in Section 11.5.) He concluded that the increase in temperature was due to the work done in the boring process. Despite the implications of Rumford's work, the popular notion of heat as the fluid caloric still persisted, since that theory explained all the results in which people were generally interested.

In 1842, Julius Mayer (1814–1878) suggested that heat and mechanical work were equivalent and that one could be transformed into the other. He even went so far as to show that the temperature of water could be raised 1°C by mechanical agitation alone. However, he failed to determine the amount of work required for such a change.

(a)

The quantitative connection between heat flow and work was conclusively demonstrated a year later, in 1843, by James Prescott Joule (1818–1889). Joule devised an experiment in which the change of potential energy of falling weights was used to churn the water in an insulated container (Fig. 11.13). This famous apparatus contained paddles for stirring the water and stationary vanes to break up the flow, so that the water was not merely set into rotational motion (kinetic energy). The frictional drag of the water caused the weights to fall very slowly, so that their kinetic energy was quite small. The potential energy lost by the falling weights was imparted to the water and was detected as a change in temperature. In this way Joule showed that the temperature of one pound of water could be raised one degree Fahrenheit by the expenditure of 772 ft-lb of mechanical work.* He proved the direct conversion of mechanical energy into thermal energy (heat) and measured the numerical factor relating mechanical units to heat units.

As mentioned earlier, the definitions and units for mechanical energy developed independently of the definitions and units for heat, which grew out of the study of the properties of water. Two separate units for measuring heat were devised. In Britain, the primary unit was the British thermal unit (Btu), the amount of heat required to raise the temperature of one pound of water one degree Fahrenheit. In Europe, where a metric system was in use, the calorie (cal) was defined as the heat required to raise the temperature of one gram of water by one degree Celsius. The Calorie (spelled with a capital C) used in discussing diet and nutrition is a kilocalorie (10^3 cal).

(b)

Figure 11.12
Heat and temperature are different physical quantities. (a) A candle has a high temperature but does not give off much heat; (b) a radiator can warm a room, but does not reach a very high temperature.

In honor of Joule's contribution to science, his name was given to the common unit of energy. The joule equals one newton-meter and is roughly one-fourth the size of the calorie:

$$1 \text{ calorie} = 4.187 \text{ joules.}$$

This relation is called the *mechanical equivalent of heat.* The relationships between several energy units are given for reference in Table 11.2.

---

*Better measurements place this value as 778 ft-lb, less than 1% greater than Joule's carefully determined number.

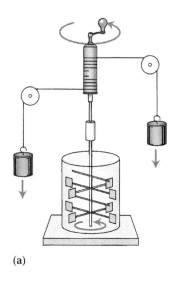

(a)

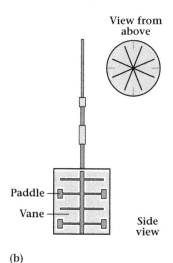

View from above

Paddle

Vane

Side view

(b)

Figure 11.13
(a) A sketch of Joule's apparatus. Falling weights turn a set of paddles in a water-filled container. (b) A cross-sectional view showing the paddles and the stationary vanes. Joule's apparatus measured the quantitative conversion of mechanical energy into thermal energy.

Table 11.2		Conversion Table for Some Common Energy Units				
		J	cal	kcal	Btu	kWh
1 J	=	1	0.239	2.39×10^{-4}	9.48×10^{-4}	2.78×10^{-7}
1 cal	=	4.187	1	10^{-3}	3.97×10^{-3}	1.16×10^{-6}
1 kcal	=	4187	1000	1	3.97	1.16×10^{-3}
1 Btu	=	1060	252	2.52×10^{-1}	1	2.93×10^{-4}
1 kWh	=	3.60×10^{6}	8.60×10^{5}	8.60×10^{2}	3.41×10^{3}	1

Neither the calorie nor the Btu is an SI unit. The appropriate SI unit for energy is the joule. However, the calorie is still used in many practical applications and in several fields of research and the Btu is common in engineering. We will use both the joule and the calorie in our examples. You should be able to work with either unit.

Example 11.6

A 1500-W heater is submerged into one kilogram of water that is well below 100°C. At what rate, in °C/s, does the temperature rise when the heater is operating at its rated power?

Strategy Energy is supplied by the heater at a rate of 1500 W = 1500 J/s, which can be converted to units of cal/s. Then, since one calorie changes the temperature of one gram of water 1°C, we can find the rate of temperature increase by dividing the rate of energy input by the mass of water in units of grams.

Solution The rate of energy input is

$$1500 \text{ J/s} \times \frac{1 \text{ cal}}{4.187 \text{ J}} = 358.3 \text{ cal/s}.$$

The rate of energy input per gram is

$$\frac{358.3 \text{ cal/s}}{1000 \text{ g}} = 0.3583 \text{ cal/g} \cdot \text{s}.$$

Since each gram of water receives 0.3583 cal/s, the temperature of each gram of water, and therefore the entire volume of water, increases by 0.3583°C/s.

11.5 Calorimetry

The measurement of quantities of heat exchanged, a process known as *calorimetry,* was introduced in the 1790s. Chemists of the time found that when a hot object, such as a brass block, was immersed in a water bath, the resulting change in temperature of the water bath depended on both the mass and the initial temperature of the block. Further observations showed that, when two similar brass blocks at the same initial temperature were immersed in identical water baths, the more massive block caused a greater temperature change. Similarly, for two identical blocks at different temperatures, the hotter block gave rise to a greater temperature change in the bath. Finally, for blocks of the same mass and initial temperature but of different composition, the change in temperature was different for different materials.

We can synthesize these observations by describing the objects in terms of their **heat capacity,** which is the amount of heat required to change an object's temperature by 1°C. Blocks of the same material but of different masses have heat capacities proportional to their mass. Thus, we define an intrinsic quantity peculiar to each material, called its *specific heat capacity,* the ratio of the heat capacity to the mass. The specific heat capacity, or simply the **specific heat,** as it is usually called, is **the heat required per unit mass to change the temperature of a substance by one degree.** A material with a high specific heat, like water, requires a lot of heat to change its temperature, while a material with a low specific heat, like silver, requires little heat to change its temperature.

The amount of heat Q required to warm an object of mass m by raising its temperature ΔT is given by

$$Q = mc\ \Delta T, \qquad\qquad (11.6)$$

where c is the specific heat of the material from which the object is made. If the object cools, then the temperature change is negative and the heat Q is given off by the object. The units of specific heat are cal/g · °C, J/kg · °C, or Btu/lb · °F. A list of specific heats is given in Table 11.3.

Table 11.3	Specific Heat for Some Common Materials at 25°C	
Substance	Specific Heat (J/kg · °C)	Specific Heat (cal/g · °C) or (kcal/kg · °C)
Water (0°C −100°C)	4187	1.00
Ethyl alcohol	2430	0.581
Ethylene glycol	2390	0.571
Ice (−10°C–0°C)	2090	0.50
Steam (100°C)	2010	0.48
Wood	1700	0.4
Aluminum	900	0.215
Sodium chloride	871	0.208
Marble	860	0.21
Glass	840	0.200
Iron	448	0.107
Copper	390	0.0920
Zinc	386	0.0922
Silver	236	0.0564
Lead	128	0.0305

The specific heat of most materials varies slightly with temperature; however, you may take it to be constant.

We have said that heat is a form of energy transfer. Therefore, we can predict temperature changes when two or more substances are in thermal contact by applying the principle of conservation of energy: The heat (or energy) lost by the cooling objects must equal the heat (or energy) gained by the substances being warmed. We take the quantity of heat *added* to a body to be positive, and the heat *lost* by a body to be negative. Then we say that the sum of all the heat flows to all bodies in thermal contact is equal to zero. That is,

$$\text{heat gained (positive)} + \text{heat lost (negative)} = 0. \qquad (11.7)$$

When we use this convention, the temperature change ΔT is *always* the difference between the final and initial temperatures, or $\Delta T = T_f - T_i$. A negative value of ΔT means that energy has left the body. Example 11.7 illustrates this principle using a Styrofoam cup as an insulating, low-heat-capacity container. You can easily do this experiment and compare your measured final temperatures with your calculations.

▼
Problem-Solving Strategy

Calorimetry

Calorimetry problems are applications of energy conservation. The total of the heat lost and the heat gained must be zero. Take care to consider the heat lost or gained by each object or item that is exchanging thermal energy. If you treat all temperature changes as $T_{final} - T_{initial}$, the signs will take care of themselves. Just sum all the heat exchanges and set the total to zero.

Be consistent with units. For safety, carry the units and cancel them as appropriate. Doing so is a good way to avoid errors due to improper units.

▼
Example 11.7

A Styrofoam cup of negligible heat capacity contains 150 g of water at 10°C. If you add 100 g of water at a temperature of 85°C, what is the final temperature of the mixture after it has been thoroughly mixed?

Strategy By the principle of conservation of energy, we expect that

$$\text{heat gained (positive)} + \text{heat lost (negative)} = 0.$$

We also expect that the final temperature T of the mixture will be between 10° and 85°C. We can calculate the two heat changes in order to determine T, and then check that our answer is in the expected range.

Solution The heat gained by the cooler water is

$$\text{heat gained} = m_1 c\, \Delta T_1 = m_1 c(T_f - T_{1i}) = (150\text{ g})c(T_f - 10°\text{C}).$$

The heat lost by the hotter water is

$$\text{heat lost} = m_2 c \, \Delta T_2 = m_2 c (T_f - T_{2i}) = (100 \text{ g}) c (T_f - 85°C).$$

When the heat lost plus the heat gained is set equal to zero, the resulting expression determines a unique value for the final temperature T_f:

$$\text{heat lost} + \text{heat gained} = 150 c (T_f - 10°C) + 100 c (T_f - 85°C) = 0,$$

$$(150 + 100) T_f = (8500 + 1500)°C,$$

$$T_f = \frac{10,000°C}{250} = 40°C.$$

Discussion Our result falls within our expected temperature range. Note that in this particular problem there was no necessity for knowing the specific heat because both components of the mixture were of the same material, water, and had the same specific heat.

Example 11.8

A small metal block (mass of 74 g) is heated in an oven to 90°C. It is then taken from the oven and immediately placed in a calorimeter, a thermally insulated container designed for measurements of heat exchange. The calorimeter contains 300 g of water at 10°C. The heat capacity of the calorimeter is negligible, and the final temperature is 14°C. Identify the composition of the block from the following list: aluminum, iron, silver, or zinc.

Strategy Again we apply the rule of energy conservation: Heat lost plus heat gained equals zero. This will enable us to calculate the block's specific heat, which we can compare with the values in Table 11.3 in order to identify the metal.

Solution The heat lost by the block was

$$Q_1 = m_1 c_1 \, \Delta T_1 = (74 \times 10^{-3} \text{ kg}) c_1 (14°C - 90°C)$$
$$Q_1 = -5.62 \, c_1 \, (\text{kg} \cdot °C).$$

The heat gained by the water was

$$Q_2 = m_2 c_2 \, \Delta T_2 = (300 \times 10^{-3} \text{ kg})(4187 \text{ J/kg} \cdot °C)(14°C - 10°C)$$
$$Q_2 = 5024 \text{ J}.$$

Conservation of energy gives

$$\text{heat lost} + \text{heat gained} = 0,$$
$$-5.62 \, c_1 \, (\text{kg} \cdot °C) + 5024 \text{ J} = 0.$$

We rearrange to find

$$5.62 \, c_1 \, (\text{kg} \cdot °C) = 5024, \quad \text{or} \quad c_1 = \frac{5024 \text{ J}}{5.62 \text{ kg} \cdot °C} = 894 \text{ J/kg} \cdot °C.$$

By comparing this value for c with those in Table 11.3, we see that the metal block in this example is probably made of aluminum.

Discussion Notice that at one point in the computation of the heat gained by the water we multiplied by $(14°C - 10°C) = 4°C$, a number that has only one

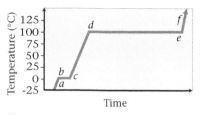

Figure 11.14

Temperature as a function of time for heat applied to water at a constant rate. The temperature remains constant during a change of phase. Ice is warmed to 0°C (*a* to *b*) and melts (*b* to *c*), the resulting water is heated (*c* to *d*) and boils (*d* to *e*). The final steam can obtain higher temperatures (*e* to *f*).

Figure 11.15

Ice cream is made in a churn by surrounding the can containing the ice cream mix with ice and salt. The surrounding salt water solution is much colder than 0°C, allowing the mix to freeze.

significant figure. Consequently, we give our result in a way that reflects this limitation: $c_1 = 9 \times 10^2$ J/kg · °C.

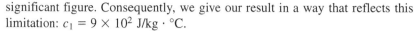

11.6 Change of Phase

We know from experience that when heat is supplied to ice, it melts into water and that steam, when cooled, condenses into water. The transformation from one physical state to another (for instance, from solid to liquid or from gas to liquid) takes place *with no change in temperature* and is called a change of phase. If we perform a careful calorimetric measurement during a phase change, we find that our previous description of heat exchange is incomplete. In addition to the heat absorbed or released in proportion to changes in temperature, there is an amount of heat energy associated with a phase change (Fig. 11.14). This quantity is called the **heat of transformation** (sometimes the *latent heat of transformation*) L, defined as the ratio of the amount of heat Q absorbed (or released) to the mass m of material undergoing the phase change:

$$L \equiv \frac{Q}{m}.$$

We can express the heat absorbed (or released) in terms of L:

$$\boxed{Q = mL.} \tag{11.8}$$

The heat of transformation is expressed in units of J/kg or cal/g. The term *latent heat* goes back to the early days of the study of heat, when it referred to the absorption of heat without an accompanying change in temperature. In more recent times, people refer simply to the heat of transformation. If the phase change is from the solid to the liquid phase (or from the liquid to the solid), we refer to the **heat of fusion** (L_f); for the liquid-vapor phase change, we use the term **heat of vaporization** (L_v). The energy added (or removed) in the form of the heat of transformation goes into rearranging the internal structure of the substance. For example, when a solid becomes a liquid, energy is required to overcome the intermolecular forces that keep the material in the solid state.

Table 11.4 lists heats of transformation for several substances. We see from the table that the heat of fusion for ice is 3.34×10^5 J/kg (79.7 cal/g). This means that 3.34×10^5 J must be supplied to melt each kilogram of ice. Conversely, 3.34×10^5 J are removed from each kilogram of water that freezes.

A home ice cream churn provides a useful application of heat of fusion. The mixture to be turned into ice cream is placed in a metal can (with good heat-conducting properties) surrounded by ice (Fig. 11.15). Rock salt is then poured onto the ice. At the ice-salt interface, the ice melts because there is a chemical interaction with the salt. The resulting salt solution has a freezing point much lower than that of pure water. The solution can thus provide the energy for melting the rest of the ice. The melting ice absorbs heat energy from the salt solution, making the solution much colder than 0°C. Even though the temperature of the ice is also lowered, it continues to melt at its surface because of the effects

Substance	Melting Point (K)	Heat of Fusion L_f (J/kg)	(cal/g)	Boiling Point (K)	Heat of Vaporization L_v (J/kg)	(cal/g)
Water	273	3.34×10^5	79.7	373	22.6×10^5	539
Mercury	234	0.115×10^5	2.74	630	2.97×10^5	71
Iron	1808	2.89×10^5	69.1	3023	63.4×10^5	1520
Lead	600	0.232×10^5	5.54	2023	5.69×10^5	205
Copper	1356	2.05×10^5	48.9	2840	48.0×10^5	1150
Oxygen	54.4	0.14×10^5	3.3	90.2	2.13×10^5	50.9
Nitrogen	63.3	0.26×10^5	6.1	77.3	2.01×10^5	48.0
Helium	—	—	—	4.2	21	5×10^{-3}

Table 11.4 *Heat of Transformation of Various Substances at Atmospheric Pressure*

of the salt. The salt solution, in turn, absorbs heat energy from the ice cream mixture through the walls of the metal can, allowing the mixture to cool enough to become firm. Without the addition of salt to the ice, the temperature of the mixture would never become low enough to form ice cream.

Master the Concept

Heat of Vaporization: Steam Burns

Question: Why does exposure to steam at 100°C produce a more severe burn than exposure to the same amount of hot water at 100°C.

Answer: When hot water at 100°C touches your much cooler skin, the transfer of energy in the form of heat raises the temperature of the surrounding tissue thereby causing a burn. When steam at 100°C touches your skin it gives up its energy of vaporization as it condenses to water at 100°C. Because the heat of vaporization of water is so large, the energy transferred to the skin by condensing steam greatly exceeds the heat transferred by the hot water. Consequently, the burn caused by the steam is much worse than that due to the hot water.

Heat of Vaporization: Cooling by Perspiration

Question: Athlete's engaged in strenuous activities often sweat profusely. How does the perspiration help cool the athlete?

Answer: The athlete's body heats up as a result of the physical activity. In response, the body directs more blood to the surface where heat is lost by radiation, conduction, and the evaporation of sweat. When sweat evaporates from the skin, heat from the body provides the heat of vaporization. Under severe conditions, an athlete may sweat a liter or more of liquid (water) per hour. The evaporation of 1 liter of sweat can remove up to 2.26 MJ of thermal energy from the body. Thus perspiration cools the body by its evaporation.

Perspiration cools the body by removing energy needed for evaporation.

Example 11.9

A 105-g copper calorimeter contains 307 g of water at room temperature ($T = 23°C$). If 52 g of ice at 0°C is added to the calorimeter, what is the final temperature of the system?

Strategy As before, we can solve this problem by applying the principle of conservation of energy:

$$\text{heat lost} + \text{heat gained} = 0.$$

However, in this case heat is gained by the ice in melting, as well as by the melted ice in being warmed from 0°C to the final temperature T.

Solution The heat gained by the ice is

$$Q(\text{gain}) = m_{ice}L_f + m_{ice}c_{water}\ \Delta T$$
$$Q(\text{gain}) = (52\ g)(80\ cal/g) + (52\ g)(1\ cal/g\ °C)(T - 0°C)$$
$$Q(\text{gain}) = 4160\ cal + 52T\ cal/°C.$$

Note that we have rounded off the heat of fusion of ice to 80 cal/g because the amount of ice and the temperatures are given to only two significant figures.

The heat lost is given up by the calorimeter (subscript c) and the original water (subscript w):

$$Q(\text{lost}) = m_w c_w\ \Delta T + m_c c_c\ \Delta T = (m_w c_w + m_c c_c)(T - T_0)$$
$$= [(307\ g)(1\ cal/g \cdot °C) + (105\ g)(0.092\ cal/g \cdot °C)](T - 23°C)$$
$$Q(\text{lost}) = (317\ cal/°C)(T - 23°C)$$
$$Q(\text{lost}) = 317T\ cal/°C - 7290\ cal.$$

When the heat gained is added to the heat lost, we find

$$4160\ cal + 52T\ cal/°C + 317T\ cal/°C - 7290\ cal = 0.$$

Upon rearranging, we find

$$369T\ cal/°C = 3130\ cal,$$
$$T = 8.5°C.$$

Example 11.10

Repeat the calculations for Example 11.9, but this time use 95 g of ice. What happens now?

Solution The expression for heat lost is the same as before,

$$Q(\text{lost}) = 317T\ cal/°C - 7290\ cal$$

and is a maximum of −7290 cal when the final temperature is 0°C. For the heat gained we find

$$Q(\text{gain}) = m_{ice}L_f + m_{ice}c_{water}\ \Delta T$$
$$Q(\text{gain}) = (95\ g)(80\ cal/g) + (95\ g)(1\ cal/g\ °C)(T - 0°C)$$
$$Q(\text{gain}) = 7600\ cal + 95T\ cal/°C,$$

which is a minimum of 7600 cal at $T = 0°C$. When we apply the conservation equation, we arrive at a negative value for T, an obvious error. (If T were negative, all the water would turn to ice. In addition, we expect the final temperature to lie in the range between $0°C$ and $23°C$.) What went wrong?

We see that the maximum amount of heat available from the water and calorimeter is 7290 cal. Therefore *not all of the ice will melt,* since that would require 7600 cal, an amount that exceeds the heat available. If all of the available energy goes into melting ice, the amount melted is

$$\frac{7290 \text{ cal}}{80 \text{ cal/g}} = 91 \text{ g}.$$

The remaining mixture of water and 4 g of ice has a temperature of $0°C$. (In time, that ice will also melt as a result of the slow leakage of heat through the insulation of the calorimeter.)

11.7 Heat Transfer

Heat energy can be transferred in three ways: conduction, convection, and radiation (Fig. 11.16). When one end of a metal rod is heated, the other end gets warm. This is an example of **conduction,** in which thermal energy is transferred without any net movement of the material itself. Conduction is a relatively slow process. A more rapid process of heat transfer is accomplished through the mass motion or flow of some fluid, such as air or water, and is called **convection.** This transfer takes place when warm air flows about a room and when hot and cold liquids are poured together. A still more rapid transfer of thermal energy is accomplished by **radiation,** a process that requires neither contact nor mass flow. The energy from the sun comes to us by radiation. We also feel radiation from warm stoves, fires, and radiators. Although the processes of conduction, convection, and radiation may all take place at the same time, frequently one of them is dominant in a given situation. In this section, we will principally discuss some aspects of conduction and radiation. Because of the mathematical complexities, the details of convection will not be discussed.

An object's usefulness as a thermal conductor (or insulator) depends on a number of things, including its thickness and the nature of the material from which it is made. For example, no sensible person would try to use a good heat conductor like aluminum as a protective layer when picking up a hot pan. On the other hand, a padded cloth potholder is a good insulator and works quite well.

Suppose we imagine a wall of uniform material, such as plasterboard, that separates a warm room from a cold one. After a period of time, a steady temperature difference occurs across the wall and a steady flow of heat goes from the warmer room to the cooler one (Fig. 11.17). Experiments show that the time rate at which heat flows ($\Delta Q/\Delta t$) through the wall is proportional to its area A, proportional to the temperature difference ($T_2 - T_1$), and inversely proportional to the thickness L of the wall. This information is contained in the heat flow equation:

$$\frac{\Delta Q}{\Delta t} = KA \frac{(T_2 - T_1)}{L}. \qquad (11.9)$$

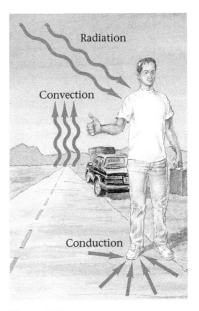

Figure 11.16
Thermal energy transfers by conduction, convection, and radiation.

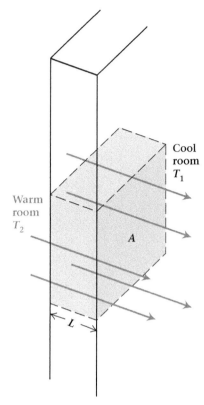

Figure 11.17
The rate of heat flow by conduction through a wall of area A depends on the temperature difference divided by the thickness, $(T_2 - T_1)/L$, as well as the thermal conductivity K of the wall's material.

The constant K is called the **thermal conductivity** and is characteristic of the material making up the wall. The SI units of heat flow are J/s or W, so the SI units of K are J/(s · m · °C) or W/m · °C.

A high thermal conductivity indicates a good heat conductor; a low thermal conductivity indicates a good heat insulator. Some representative values of K for common materials are tabulated in Table 11.5. In designing a good insulator, such as a potholder or the outside walls of a house, the first requirement is to choose a material with a small thermal conductivity, so that the heat flow in Eq. (11.9) is small. In addition, by minimizing the area of contact A and making the path length L as long as possible, we can further reduce the heat flow.

Example 11.11

A Styrofoam cooler has a surface area of 0.50 m² and an average thickness of 2.0 cm. How long will it take for 1.5 kg of ice to melt in the cooler if the outside temperature is 30°C? (The thermal conductivity of the Styrofoam used to make the cooler is 0.030 W/m · °C.)

Strategy First we compute the rate of energy transfer (heat) into the cooler due to conductivity through its walls, assuming an inside temperature of 0°C. Then we can compute the rate of melting of the ice and thus determine the time required to melt it.

Solution The rate of energy transfer is computed from

$$\frac{\Delta Q}{\Delta t} = KA \frac{(T_2 - T_1)}{L}$$

$$\frac{\Delta Q}{\Delta t} = (0.030 \text{ W/m} \cdot °\text{C})(0.50 \text{ m}^2)\frac{30°\text{C} - 0°\text{C}}{0.020 \text{ m}} = 22.5 \text{ W}.$$

The heat of fusion of ice is $L_f = 3.34 \times 10^5$ J/kg. The mass of ice Δm melted in a time Δt is related to the rate of energy transfer through

$$\frac{\Delta Q}{\Delta t} = \frac{\Delta m}{\Delta t} L_f.$$

If we let Δm be the entire mass of ice, then Δt becomes the time required for it to melt,

$$\Delta t = \frac{\Delta m L_f}{\Delta Q / \Delta t} = \frac{(1.5 \text{ kg})(3.34 \times 10^5 \text{ J/kg})}{22.5 \text{ W}} = 2.23 \times 10^4 \text{ s}.$$

Upon dividing Δt by 3600 s/h, we find that it takes 6.2 h for all the ice to melt.

The effectiveness of insulation is rated by another quantity, called thermal resistance, or R value. The **R value** is the ratio of a material's thickness to its thermal conductivity:

$$R \equiv \frac{L}{K}.$$

(11.10)

In the United States, the R value is given in the British system units of ft$^2 \cdot$ h $\cdot$ °F/Btu. For the outside walls of your home you want a good heat insulator; that is, you want materials and insulation with a high R value. Some examples are found in Table 11.6. The R values are useful because you can simply add them to obtain the R value resulting from multiple layers of insulation (Problem 11.80). For example, a $6\frac{1}{4}$-in.-thick layer of fiberglass insulation has an R value of 19. Insulation made from two layers of $6\frac{1}{4}$-in. fiberglass has an R value of 38. For a given material, the R value is directly proportional to the thickness, which is represented by L in Eq. (11.10).

A hot object also loses energy by radiation.* This radiation, which is known as electromagnetic radiation, is similar to light (see Chapter 22) and can pass through empty space (a vacuum). The warmth you feel when you warm yourself by a fire is due to this radiation. If the object is hot enough, some of the radiation is visible and can indeed be seen. This emission is the blackbody radiation discussed in Section 1.1.

The rate at which an object radiates energy is proportional to its surface area A and to the fourth power of its absolute temperature T. The total energy radiated from an object per unit time (that is, its radiated power) is found experimentally to be

$$P = \sigma e A T^4, \qquad (11.11)$$

where σ is the Stefan-Boltzmann constant, which has the value $\sigma = 5.67 \times 10^{-8}$ W $\cdot$ m$^{-2} \cdot$ K^{-4}, and e is a constant called the *emissivity*. The emissivity is a dimensionless number between 0 and 1 that describes the nature of the emitting surface. The emissivity is larger for dark, rough surfaces and smaller for smooth, shiny ones. For example, the emissivity of a black cast iron stove is near one

Table 11.5 — *Thermal Conductivities of Some Common Materials at 27°C*

Material	K (W/m · °C)
Silver	427
Copper	398
Aluminum	237
Tungsten	178
Iron	80.3
Brick	0.4–0.8
Water	0.61
Asbestos	0.083
Glass	0.72–0.86
Air	0.026
Wood (pine)	0.11–0.14
Fiberglass	0.046
Polystyrene foam	0.033
Polyurethane foam	0.020

Table 11.6 — *R Values of Some Common Building Materials*

Material	Thickness (in.)	R Value (ft$^2 \cdot$ h $\cdot$ °F/Btu)
Gypsum board	$\frac{1}{2}$	0.45
Plywood	$\frac{1}{2}$	0.62
Brick	$3\frac{5}{8}$	0.6–1.2
Glass, single pane		1
Glass, double pane		2
Polystyrene foam	$\frac{3}{4}$	2.9
Fiberglass insulation	$3\frac{1}{2}$	11
Fiberglass insulation	$6\frac{1}{4}$	19

*This radiation is the blackbody radiation described mathematically by Planck (Chapter 1).

while the emissivity of the silver coating of a thermos bottle is near zero. Equation (11.11) is known as the **Stefan-Boltzmann law.**

According to the Stefan-Boltzmann law, all objects radiate energy, no matter what their temperature happens to be. Why then do they not lose all their thermal energy by radiation and cool down to 0 K? The answer is that they also absorb radiation from surrounding objects and eventually come to thermal equilibrium with their environment. The book in your hand is radiating, but it is also absorbing radiation from its surroundings. If the book (or other object) is at a temperature T and its surroundings are at a different temperature T_s, the net energy gained (or lost) per second by the book is given by

$$P_{net} = \sigma e A(T^4 - T_s^4), \tag{11.12}$$

where A is the surface area of the book. Notice that we have used the same value for the emissivity for absorption as for radiation. This must be correct, because the net heat exchange must go to zero when $T = T_s$. Thus a good radiator is also a good absorber.

Because of the T^4 term in Eq. (11.11), the total power radiated grows rapidly as the temperature increases as seen in Fig. 1.3 (p. 4). For example, an object radiates 16 times more power at a temperature of 273°C (546 K) than it does at 0°C (273 K). The distribution of the radiation, which is composed of many different wavelengths, is also a function of temperature. It is the change in this distribution that accounts for the change of color of a glowing hot object as its temperature is raised. We will discuss these issues further when we describe blackbody radiation in Chapter 27 (p. 858).

Example 11.12

A patient waiting to be seen by his physician is asked to remove all his clothes in an examination room that is at 16°C. Calculate the rate of heat loss by radiation from the patient, given that his skin temperature is 34°C and his surface area is 1.6 m². Assume an emissivity of 0.80.

Solution From Eq. (11.12), the rate of heat loss by radiation is

$$P_{net} = \sigma e A(T^4 - T_s^4),$$

where the temperatures are expressed in kelvins. Inserting the numbers, we get

$$P_{net} = (5.67 \times 10^{-8} \text{ W} \cdot \text{m}^{-2} \cdot \text{K}^{-4})(0.80)(1.6 \text{ m}^2)[(307 \text{ K})^4 - (289 \text{ K})^4]$$

$$P_{net} = 140 \text{ W}.$$

A patient feels cool because of loss of energy radiated to the room.

The problem of choosing good insulation is not always merely that of finding a poor thermal conductor. Air is a poor conductor, yet a hot object left exposed in the air cools rapidly as a result of convection currents in the air, which continually bring cool air in contact with the object. These convection currents are caused by the expansion of the air as it is warmed. The warmer air is lighter than the cooler surrounding air and rises as a result of buoyancy. Energy is also lost by direct radiation. To reduce these effects and still capitalize on the low conductivity of air, we may use an insulating material that contains many tiny pockets of air so that convection is reduced to nearly zero. Pockets of trapped air

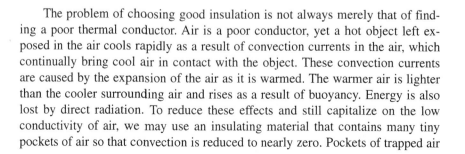

account for the good insulating qualities of Styrofoam, fiberglass, down, felt, and woolen clothing. In addition, the many surfaces of the insulating material help reduce the radiant loss by reflection and by radiation back toward the object.

The vacuum flask, used so effectively to keep hot foods hot and cold foods cold, has an inner glass container surrounded by an outer one (Fig. 11.18). The space between is evacuated and sealed. The vacuum between the containers offers little heat loss through either conduction or convection. Radiation losses are minimized by coating the wall of the evacuated space with a highly reflecting layer of silver. Thus, the principal means of heat leakage is through the plug at the mouth of the container and through the glass joining the inner and outer containers. This type of flask is called a *Dewar* flask after the Scottish scientist Sir James Dewar, who first used it in 1892 in his studies of liquid oxygen. It is also known by the trade name, Thermos bottle.

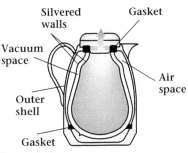

Figure 11.18

Cross-sectional view of a vacuum flask. The vacuum space reduces heat loss by conduction or convection, and the reflecting surfaces reduce heat loss by radiation.

Summary

Useful Concepts

■ Heat is a form of energy transfer between two objects; temperature is a measure of an object's warmth.

■ The relationship between Fahrenheit and Celsius temperatures is

$$T_C = \tfrac{5}{9}(T_F - 32).$$

■ The relationship between the Kelvin and Celsius temperature scales is

$$T_K = T_C + 273.15.$$

■ A body expands or contracts when the temperature changes. The change in length due to a change in temperature ΔT is

$$\Delta L = L_0 \alpha \, \Delta T,$$

where α is the linear expansion coefficient. The length at new temperature T in terms of the initial length L_0 at T_0 is

$$L = L_0[1 + \alpha(T - T_0)].$$

■ Joule showed experimentally that heat and mechanical work are equivalent, determining the relationship

$$1 \text{ calorie} = 4.187 \text{ joules}.$$

■ Calorimetry is based on the idea of conservation of thermal energy. In a thermally isolated system,

$$\text{heat gained (positive)} + \text{heat lost (negative)} = 0.$$

■ The heat Q required to change the temperature of a body of mass m is

$$Q = mc \, \Delta T,$$

where c is the specific heat capacity. The heat required to change the phase of a mass m of material with latent heat of transformation L is

$$Q = mL.$$

■ Heat of transformation is absorbed or given off during a substance's change of phase; however, the temperature remains constant during the phase change.

■ The heat conduction equation is

$$\frac{\Delta Q}{\Delta t} = \frac{KA(T_2 - T_1)}{L}.$$

■ The R value of insulation is the ratio of thickness to thermal conductivity:

$$R \equiv \frac{L}{K}.$$

■ Energy is radiated from all objects. The rate at which the energy is radiated is given by the Stefan-Boltzmann law:

$$P = \sigma e A T^4.$$

Important Terms

You should be able to write the definition or meaning of each of the following:

temperature	heat capacity
thermometer	specific heat
thermal equilibrium	heat of transformation
Celsius temperature scale	heat of fusion
Fahrenheit temperature scale	heat of vaporization
absolute zero	conduction
Kelvin temperature scale	convection
linear thermal expansion	radiation
linear thermal expansion	thermal conductivity
coefficient	R value
heat	Stefan-Boltzmann law

Conceptual Questions

11.1 What differences are there between a fever thermometer that measures from 35 to 42°C and a laboratory thermometer that measures from −10 to 110°C?

11.2 Devise a thermometer that relies on some property other than thermal expansion to indicate changes in temperature.

11.3 How does thermal expansion affect the accuracy of a pendulum clock?

11.4 A square brass plate has a large circular hole cut in its center. If the plate is heated, it will expand. Will the diameter of the hole expand or contract? Explain your answer.

11.5 On a warm summer day you hold a thermometer by a thread while standing in front of an electric fan. When the fan is turned on, your hand feels cooler. Does the thermometer indicate a change in temperature? Explain what is happening.

11.6 Why are concrete highways made in short sections with tar-filled gaps between them?

11.7 A sports car going 80 km/h is braked to a stop without skidding. What happens to its kinetic energy?

11.8 Can you warm up a cup of coffee by stirring it vigorously?

11.9 Why is the climate of coastal cities milder than that of cities in the midst of large land areas?

11.10 What happens to the heat of transformation absorbed during a phase transition?

11.11 People in hot arid regions frequently store water in canvas bags through which some of the water can seep. What is the purpose of doing this?

11.12 How does the thickness of a pot or frying pan affect the way it cooks? What effect does the pot's composition (e.g., aluminum, steel, or ceramic) have on the way it cooks?

11.13 Why do some materials, such as glass and metal, usually feel cold and other materials, such as cloth, usually feel warm? (Refer to Tables 11.3 and 11.5.)

11.14 Do windows made of three panes of glass separated by two air spaces have any insulating advantage over those made of the equivalent total thickness of material in two panes of glass separated by one air space? Explain your reasoning.

Problems

Section 11.2 Thermometry

Hints for Solving Problems

Be especially careful to use a consistent set of units, based on the same temperature scale.

11.1 What is generally regarded as the record high terrestrial temperature of 57.8°C occurred in Tripoli in Northern Africa in 1922. The record low of −89.2°C was recorded at the Soviet Antarctica station Vostok in 1983. Convert these temperatures to the Fahrenheit scale.

11.2 Human body temperature is about 98.6°F. Convert this to the Celsius scale and the Kelvin scale.

11.3 At atmospheric pressure, the boiling point of helium is 4.2 K. What is the boiling point of helium on the Celsius scale? On the Fahrenheit scale?

11.4 Express the following Kelvin temperatures in degrees Celsius and in degrees Fahrenheit: 77.3 K, 300 K, and 1356 K.

11.5 At atmospheric pressure, the boiling point of nitrogen is −195.8°C. What is the boiling point of nitrogen on the Kelvin scale? On the Fahrenheit scale?

11.6• Find a relationship expressing the temperature in degrees Fahrenheit in terms of the temperature in kelvins.

11.7• An approximate way of converting from the Fahrenheit scale to the Celsius scale is to subtract 32 from the Fahrenheit temperature and divide the result by two. How much error in

degrees Celsius does this give for Fahrenheit temperatures of 80°, 40°, 10°, and −10°?

11.8• At what temperature do the Fahrenheit and Celsius scales have the same numerical value?

11.9•• A physicist defines a new temperature scale that has its zero at a room temperature of 70°F and its 10° mark at approximately body temperature (say 98°F). (a) Derive an expression for converting from the Fahrenheit scale to this new scale. (b) Derive an expression for converting from the Celsius scale to this new scale.

Section 11.3 Thermal Expansion

Hints for Solving Problems

A homogeneous material expands (or contracts) with the same coefficient of thermal expansion in any direction. A circular hole expands just as a solid circle would.

11.10 A tall steel flagpole was erected in Vancouver for Canadian Expo 86. If the flagpole gets 5.1 mm taller when the average ambient temperature increases by 5.0°C, approximately how tall is the flagpole?

11.11 A metal rod that is 100.0 cm long at 10°C is observed to be 100.2 cm long at a temperature of 80°C. What is its coefficient of linear expansion?

11.12 A copper rod is measured to be 3.00 m long at a temperature of 15°C. How much does it expand when heated to a temperature of 150°C?

11.13 A building with a steel framework is 50 m high. How much taller is it on a summer day when the temperature is 30°C than on a −5°C winter day?

11.14 In the days of horse-drawn wagons, iron tires used to be placed on wooden wagon wheels by heating the iron rims and slipping them over the wheels before they cooled. If an iron tire is made to fit tightly around a 1.50-m-diameter wheel at 15°C, what diameter will the tire have when it is heated to 800°C?

11.15 A motorist fills the 60-liter tank of his automobile with gasoline at 60°F. The automobile is left in the sun, and the temperature of the gasoline rises to 110°F. Approximately how much gasoline is lost to overflow caused by thermal expansion? Ignore the expansion of the tank.

11.16 A framework of rods is made as shown in Fig 11.19. How far and in what direction will the point A move when the temperature is increased by 100°C?

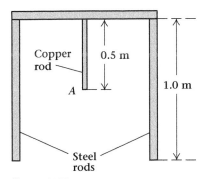

Figure 11.19
Problem 11.16.

11.17 An iron bar is exactly one meter long at 15°C. A brass bar is 0.5-mm shorter than the iron bar at 15°C. They are both heated in the same oven. At what temperature will they be the same length?

11.18 A steel plate with a circular hole of 2.005-cm radius and a copper ball with a radius of 1.998 cm are initially at 15°C. (a) If the temperature of the copper ball is raised to 275°C, will the ball still fit through the hole? (b) Will the ball fit through the hole if both the plate and the ball are at 275°C?

11.19 A flat plate with area A_0 at temperature T_0 is characterized by a linear expansion coefficient α. Show that to a good approximation the area A of the plate at temperature T is given by

$$A = A_0[1 + 2\alpha (T - T_0)].$$

11.20 A bottle made of ordinary glass has an internal volume of 1.00 liter at 20°C and contains 0.99 liter of water at the same temperature. At what temperature will water begin to overflow the bottle?

11.21 A motorist fills the 61-liter tank of her automobile

with gasoline at 15°C. The automobile is left in the sun, and the temperature of the gasoline rises to 44°C. Approximately how much gasoline is lost to overflow caused by thermal expansion? Assume the volume expansion coefficient of the tank is 70×10^{-6} °C^{-1}.

Section 11.4 The Mechanical Equivalent of Heat

11.22 (a) How many joules are required to raise 1.0 kg of water from room temperature of 22°C to its boiling point? (b) If this work were used to lift a 50-kg boy instead, how high could he be lifted?

11.23 When you do work against a frictional force, mechanical energy is transformed into thermal energy. Suppose you push a 2.4-kg textbook 0.85 m across a level table at a constant speed. If the coefficient of friction between the book and the table is 0.25, how much energy is dissipated? Give your answer in calories.

11.24 The food energy of a jelly donut is about 250 kcal. Show that the jelly donut could be used as a unit of energy where 1 jelly donut ≈ 1 MJ.

11.25 What is the kinetic energy of a 61-kg person running at 4.5 m/s? Express your answer in kcal.

11.26 What would be the maximum possible increase in temperature of water as it fell from the top to the bottom of a 23-m-high waterfall? Assume that the drop does not cool by evaporation as it falls.

11.27 What is the energy in calories of a 1780-kg car traveling at 20.4 km/h?

11.28 The Btu is defined to be the amount of thermal energy needed to raise the temperature of one pound of water by 1°F. Show that 1 Btu = 252 cal.

11.29 A 1500-W heater is submerged into one kilogram of water that is well below 100°C. At what rate, in °C/s, does the temperature rise when the heater is operating at its rated power?

Section 11.5 Calorimetry

Hints for Solving Problems

For an object or a group of objects insulated from the surroundings, the heat lost plus the heat gained is zero, where heat gained is positive and heat lost is negative. Specific heat is the heat required per unit mass to change the temperature of a substance by one degree.

11.30 Two hundred grams of lead shot is placed in a 1.5-m-long cardboard tube, which is closed at both ends. If the tube is in a vertical position and then quickly inverted, the shot falls through the length of the tube. If this is done 50 times in succession, what is the maximum increase in temperature of the shot?

11.31 In an experiment similar to the one done by Joule (Fig. 11.13), a 10-kg weight is allowed to fall through a distance of 1.6 m. If there is 2.0 kg of water in the container, what will the temperature rise be?

11.32 Suppose that 250 g of water at 85°C is mixed with 95 g of water at 15°C in an insulated container of negligible heat capacity. What is the final temperature?

11.33 Assume that the specific heats of coffee and water are the same. How much cool water at 59°F must be added to an insulated cup that contains 145 g of coffee at 188°F to cool it to 135°F? Ignore the mass of the cup.

11.34 You pour 150 g of hot coffee at 85°C into a 210-g glass cup at 22°C. If they come to thermal equilibrium quickly, what is the final temperature? Assume no heat is lost to the surroundings.

11.35 A cook pours 400 g of hot water at 98°C into a 235-g aluminum pot initially at 15°C. If they come to thermal equilibrium quickly, what is the final temperature? Assume no heat is lost to the surroundings.

11.36 If 1.0 kg of lead shot at 150°C is poured into 1.0 kg of water at 23°C, what is the final temperature? Neglect the effect of the container and assume that no steam escapes and that no heat is lost to the surroundings.

11.37• A 2.0-cal/s heater is submerged in a 1.0-liter beaker full of water for 10 min. What is the temperature rise if all of the heat goes into raising the temperature of the water?

11.38• Two hundred fifty grams of water at 80°C is poured into a Styrofoam cup of negligible heat capacity containing 180 g of water at 10°C. An additional 300 g of water is added to the cup, the mixture comes to an equilibrium temperature of 30°C. What was the temperature of the additional 300 g of water?

11.39• A thermometer with a mass of 0.055 kg and a specific heat of 0.20 kcal/kg · °C reads 15.0°C. The thermometer is then inserted into 0.300 kg of water and comes to a common temperature with the water of 44.4°C. What was the temperature of the water before the thermometer was inserted if other heat losses can be neglected?

11.40• A 175-g copper block at 90°C is dropped into an aluminum calorimeter cup initially at 20°C. The calorimeter cup has a mass of 400 g and contains 430 g of water, also at 20°C. What is the final temperature of the system?

Section 11.6 Change of Phase

Hints for Solving Problems

Heat exchanged includes $Q = mc \, \Delta T$, due to temperature change, and $Q = mL$, due to phase change. The final temperature of a mixture of hot and cold liquids will be intermediate between their initial temperatures.

11.41 How many joules are required to change one kilogram of ice at −15°C to water at 15°C?

11.42 From your experience, estimate the final temperature that will result if a single ice cube is placed in a cup of hot coffee that has just been boiled. Make reasonable estimates of the size of the ice cube and the volume of coffee.

11.43 How many calories are required to change 400 g of ice at −12°C to steam at 110°C?

11.44 How many joules are required to change 1.0 kg of solid lead at 23°C to a liquid at 2000°C? (Assume the specific heats of both solid and molten lead to be the same.)

11.45 If 20 g of steam at 100°C is mixed into 80 g of water at 20°C, what will be the final temperature if no thermal energy is lost and no steam escapes?

11.46 If the energy that goes into evaporating one kilogram of water from Lake Michigan at 15°C were used instead to raise that amount of water above the surface of the lake, how high would it be lifted?

11.47 A container of negligible heat capacity is filled with 5.0 kg of crushed ice and then placed on a hot plate that supplies heat to the ice at a rate of 30 W. What volume of water is produced per minute?

11.48• (a) If 120 g of hot coffee at 85°C is poured into an insulated cup containing 200 g of ice initially at 0°C, how many grams of liquid will there be when the system reaches thermal equilibrium? (b) How much ice will remain?

11.49• If you remove 1000 cal from 1.5 g of steam at 100°C, what will you have left?

11.50• A 50-W electrical heating element is placed in a well-insulated container into which has just been placed 500 g of water at 20°C and 300 g of ice at 0°C. How long will it take before all of the contents are evaporated?

11.51•• A 50-g piece of iron and a 40-g piece of copper at the same temperature of 80°C are put into an insulated container that has 400 g of water and 100 g of ice, all at 0°C. What is the equilibrium temperature?

Section 11.7 Heat Transfer

11.52 A wall is insulated with glass wool of thermal conductivity $K = 0.046$ W/m · °C. What is the rate of heat loss through an area 1.0 m wide by 1.8 m high, insulated with a layer of glass wool 15 cm thick, if the temperature difference across the layer is 20°C?

11.53 A large window of ordinary plate glass is 1 m wide, 1.5 m high, and 3.0 mm thick. Use the heat flow equation to estimate the rate of heat loss through the window on a day when the inside temperature is 22°C (72°F) and the outside temperature is 0°C. (In practice, the actual rate of heat loss through the window is much smaller than the value calculated on the basis of the heat flow equation with T_1 = inside temperature and T_2 = outside temperature. The layers of air on both sides of the glass act as additional insulation, so the temperature difference across the glass is substantially reduced.)

11.54 A small oven has a surface area of 0.20 m². The insulated walls are 1.5 cm thick with an average thermal conductivity of 4.0×10^{-2} W/m · °C. What is the rate of heat loss if the temperature inside the oven is maintained at 245°C and the outside temperature is 20°C?

11.55 What is the rate of energy radiated per unit area from a blackbody with emissivity = 1.00 at temperatures of 300 K, 1000 K, 3000 K, and 3200 K?

11.56 A lamp is designed to operate at a temperature of 3200 K. If the lamp is operated at a higher voltage that raises its temperature to 3400 K, what will be the fractional increase in radiant energy?

11.57● A recreational vehicle (RV) can be modeled as a rectangular box with exterior dimensions of 23′ × 7′10″ × 7′6″. The uninsulated exterior walls have an average R value of 4. The RV is heated with a furnace that delivers 19,000 Btu/h. Can the furnace keep the inside of the RV at 70°F on a day when the outside temperature is −10°F?

11.58● The bottom of an aluminum pot has an area of 177 cm^2 and a thickness of 3.25 mm. The pot is placed on a stove and heated until water boils away at a rate of 0.235 g/min. What is the temperature difference between the outside and the inside of the bottom of the pot? Be sure to state all assumptions needed to solve the problem.

11.59● The rate of radiation from the sun is determined to be 6.25×10^7 W/m^2. Use this value to compute the effective temperature of the sun. Assume an emissivity of 1.00.

11.60● An outside wall of a room is 2.44 m (8 ft) high by 5.0 m (16.4 ft) wide. (a) Calculate the rate of heat loss through the wall, assuming there are no windows and the wall has an average R value of 15. Take the temperature difference across the wall to be 25°C. (b) What is the rate of heat loss through the wall if it has a single glass window with an R value of 1.0 and an area of 1 m^2 = 10.76 ft^2? Give your answers in units of watts.

11.61● A Styrofoam cooler has dimensions of 0.20 m × 0.30 m × 0.35 m and an average thickness of 1.5 cm. How long will it take for 6.5 kg of ice to melt in the cooler if the outside temperature is 35°C? The thermal conductivity of the Styrofoam is 0.030 W/m · °C.

11.62● An iron bar 50 cm long is braised to a copper bar 50 cm long and of the same diameter. The free end of the iron bar is kept at 0°C while the free end of the copper bar is at 100°C. (a) What is the temperature of the junction point? (b) What is the heat flow down the rod if its cross-sectional area is 1.5 cm^2?

11.63● The radiation from the sun is received from all parts of the sun's disk, including the less luminous outer edges. One estimate places the radiation rate at the center to be 16% greater than the average value of 6.25×10^7 W/m^2. Use this estimate to determine the temperature of the sun near the center of the sun's disk. Assume an emissivity of 1.00.

11.64●● Derive an expression for heat flow in terms of the R value.

Additional Problems

11.65 A concrete highway has expansion joints at intervals of 18 m. How wide must the expansion joints be to allow for thermal changes over the temperature range from −10°C to 40°C? Use $\alpha = 10 \times 10^{-6}$ °C^{-1}.

11.66 What is the increase in volume of an aluminum sphere with a radius of 11.6 cm when it is heated from 0°C to 100°C?

11.67 What is the rate of heat flow along a copper bar 1.08 m long having a cross section of 1.64 cm^2 if one end of the bar is at 0.0°C and the other one is at 100.0°C?

11.68● Show that the density ρ of an object with respect to its density ρ_0 at some reference temperature is given approximately by $\rho = \rho_0(1 - \beta \, \Delta T)$, where β is the thermal coefficient of volume expansion and ΔT is the difference between the object's temperature and the reference temperature.

11.69● A 3.75-kg iron crucible holds 4.23 kg of silver at 20°C. How much thermal energy must be supplied to the system to melt the silver? Silver melts at 962°C with a heat of fusion of 1.11×10^5 J/kg. Assume that the specific heats given in Table 11.3 are appropriate.

11.70● If a one-cubic-meter sealed container of air at 0°C and one atmosphere pressure is heated by supplying heat at the rate of 10.0 W for three minutes, by how much will the temperature rise? Assume the container to be perfectly insulated. Under these conditions, the density of air is 1.293 kg/m^3 and the specific heat is 804 J · kg^{-1} · K^{-1}.

11.71● An automobile having a mass of 1900 kg and traveling at a speed of 30 m/s is braked smoothly to a stop without skidding in 15 s. (a) How much energy is dissipated in the brakes? (b) What is the average power delivered to the brakes during stopping? (c) If the total heat capacity of the braking system (shoes, drums, etc.) is 0.75 kcal/°C, what is the temperature rise of the brakes during the stop?

11.72● What is the R value of a wall that loses heat at the rate of 10 W/m^2 when the temperature difference across the wall is 20°C? Express your answer in units of ft^2 · h · °F/Btu.

11.73● An iron bar is braised to a 50-cm long copper bar of the same diameter. The free end of the iron bar is kept at 0°C while the free end of the copper bar is at 100°C. How long is the iron bar if the temperature of the junction point is 50°C when the system reaches a steady state?

11.74● A person's metabolic rate can be measured using what is called a flow calorimeter. The person is placed in a large insulated container through which water can flow. The flowing water carries away the heat produced by the body. If a resting person is known to have a thermal power output of 85 W, what will the temperature difference between the intake and outflow water be when the flow rate is 1.0 liter each 5.0 min?

11.75● If you start with a container of 500 g of water at 20°C and add 300 g of ice, how many grams of steam at 100°C will you have to condense into the water, by bubbling it through a tube from the bottom, in order to return the mixture to its original temperature?

11.76● Two rods of equal length and diameter are connected end to end. The extreme ends of the rods are kept at different temperatures. The coefficient of thermal conductivity of one rod is 425 W/m°C and its free end is kept at 0°C. The coefficient of thermal conductivity of the other rod is 80 W/m°C and the free end of that rod is kept at 75°C. What is the temperature of the junction between the rods?

11.77●● A certain material has a linear expansion coefficient α. Show that, to a good approximation, the volume expansion coefficient is $\beta = 3\alpha$.

11.78●● A clock with a brass pendulum keeps correct time at 20°C. (a) What is the fractional change in pendulum length when the temperature rises to 38°C? The thermal expansion coefficient of brass is $\alpha = 18.5 \times 10^{-6}/°C$. (b) The period of a pendulum depends on the square root of its length L through $T = 2\pi\sqrt{L/g}$. By how many seconds will the clock be in error after running 24 h at 38°C? (*Hint:* You may find it helpful to use the binomial theorem.)

11.79●● A liquid of unknown specific heat at a temperature of 20°C was mixed with water at 80°C in a well-insulated container. The final temperature was measured to be 50°C, and the combined mass of the two liquids was measured to be 240 g. In a second experiment with both liquids at the same initial temperature, 20 g less of the liquid of unknown specific heat was poured into the same amount of water as before. This time the equilibrium temperature was found to be 52°C. Determine the specific heat of the liquid.

11.80●● Show that the effect of using two layers of insulation made of pieces of different material placed one after the other, with R values of R_1 and R_2, is to give an equivalent R value of $R_1 + R_2$.

11.81●● A 0.50-kg piece of glowing-hot iron at a temperature of 1000°C is put into an insulated container holding one kilogram of water at 23°C. How much water will be left after equilibrium has been reached? Assume that no steam escapes.

11.82●● A hollow insulating cube whose inside dimensions are 10 cm × 10 cm × 10 cm contains 300 g of water at 30°C. A 4.0-cm cube of aluminum at 95°C is lowered quickly into the water. Is it possible to reduce the temperature of the cube to 12°C by pouring cold water into the insulating container without allowing any water to spill over the sides of the container?

12.1　The Pressure of Air
12.2　Boyle's Law

Back to the Future: Gas Laws and Balloons

12.3　The Law of Charles and Gay-Lussac
12.4　The Ideal Gas Law
12.5　The Kinetic Theory of Gases
12.6　The Kinetic-Theory Definition of
　　　Temperature
12.7　Internal Energy of an Ideal Gas
*12.8　The Barometric Formula and the Distribution of Molecular Speeds

Appendix: The Exponential Function

Gas Laws and Kinetic Theory

In this chapter we examine for the first time the concept of atoms. The atomic concept is that matter consists of enormous numbers of tiny components called atoms. The properties and interactions of atoms, or of the molecules into which they may combine, are responsible for the observed properties and behavior of matter in bulk form. Up to now we have dealt only with objects large enough to see and measure. Here we apply the ideas from mechanics to predict how a gas composed of a large number of atoms or molecules will behave.

Because we can neither see nor measure individual atoms directly, we must make some assumptions about what they are like. As we have discussed before, this process is part of making a theoretical model. In addition, because we clearly cannot follow the motions of every individual atom, we must decide how to evaluate average behavior. Our model will not be perfect—that is, it will not correspond to reality in every way—but the model will allow us to make predictions about the large-scale thermal behavior of gases. We can then test those predictions experimentally. The

373

value of our model, called the kinetic theory of gases, depends on how close it comes to correctly describing the experimental observations.

Before considering the construction and use of a model of a gas, we briefly review the gas laws as they were determined over the years by observations and experiments. An understanding of the nature of air, and subsequently of other gases, could come only with the development of new devices and measuring instruments. The seventeenth century saw the discovery of such new instruments as the telescope, microscope, thermometer, barometer, pendulum clock, and air pump. These developments, as well as the founding of the first scientific societies, gave impetus to many kinds of scientific study, including the investigation of gases.

Today many researchers actively investigate the behavior of gases, using the latest computer simulation techniques and other modern methods of investigation. Much of their research has been spurred by environmental problems connected with the atmosphere, such as the depletion of the earth's ozone layer. Solutions to such problems depend on understanding the behavior of gases. ■

12.1 The Pressure of Air

Galileo was the first person to record a fact that others had surely observed: that a lift pump (Fig. 12.1) could raise water only as high as 10.4 m (34 ft). In 1643, Evangelista Torricelli (1608–1647), who was briefly associated with Galileo, provided an explanation for this fact. Previously it had been said that "nature abhorred a vacuum." People thought the lift pump worked because the water rose up into the chamber to avoid the formation of a vacuum at the top. But Torricelli believed that the water was forced up the pipe by the pressure of the atmosphere on the surface of the water at the bottom of the pump. He reasoned that since mercury is about 14 times as dense as water, if he was correct, atmospheric pressure should support a column of mercury approximately $\frac{1}{14}$ as high as the maximum water column:

$$(10.4 \text{ m water})\left(\frac{\text{density of water}}{\text{density of mercury}}\right) = (10.4 \text{ m})\left(\frac{1}{13.6}\right)$$
$$= 0.76 \text{ m mercury.}$$

Figure 12.2 shows a *Torricellian tube,* the forerunner of today's barometer. If a glass tube, closed at one end, is completely filled with mercury and then inverted into a bowl of mercury, the column of mercury in the tube drops until it reaches a height of about 76 cm above the lower surface, just as Torricelli predicted. In accord with Pascal's principle (Chapter 10), the pressure of the atmosphere on the surface of the mercury in the bowl is equal to the pressure due to the weight of the mercury in the tube. If this were not so, the mercury would flow because it would not be in static equilibrium. The space between the top of the liquid and the end of the tube contains no air and was named the *Torricellian vacuum.*

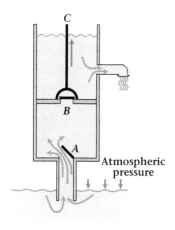

Figure 12.1

A lift pump. When rod *C* is lifted, valve *B* closes and valve *A* opens. Then water below the piston flows into the chamber and the water above flows out at the same time. When rod *C* is pushed down, *A* closes and *B* opens, allowing water to flow above the piston.

Example 12.1

Determine the pressure due to the atmosphere, using Torricelli's results.

Strategy We could make immediate use of the results contained in Chapter 10 on fluids, but it is instructive to consider the problem from a more fundamental standpoint. The weight of mercury in the tube in Fig. 12.2 is the product of its density ρ times the volume times the acceleration of gravity:

$$\text{weight} = \rho V g = \rho \cdot hA \cdot g,$$

where h is the height and A the cross-sectional area of the mercury column. For the fluid to be in static equilibrium, an upward force must be present. In this case it comes from the atmospheric pressure acting downward on the mercury in the bowl and then, according to Pascal's principle, being transmitted equally to all parts of the fluid. The upward force on the bottom of the tube is therefore

$$F = PA,$$

where P is the pressure due to the atmosphere.

Solution Because the fluid is in equilibrium, the magnitude of the upward force equals the magnitude of the downward force (the weight). Setting the two forces equal to each other gives

$$\rho \cdot hA \cdot g = PA,$$

or

$$P = \rho g h.$$

This is the same expression we found earlier, in Section 10.1. Inserting the numbers for g, h, and the density of mercury, we have

$$P = (13.6 \times 10^3 \text{ kg/m}^3)(9.81 \text{ m/s}^2)(0.760 \text{ m})$$
$$P = 101 \times 10^3 \text{ N/m}^2$$
$$P = 1.01 \times 10^5 \text{ N/m}^2 = 1.01 \times 10^5 \text{ Pa}.$$

This pressure is atmospheric pressure. An atmosphere is a unit of pressure equal to the pressure of the earth's atmosphere at sea level. It is defined to be 1.01325×10^5 N/m^2.

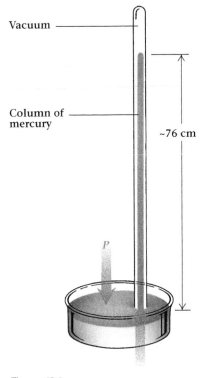

Figure 12.2
In a Torricellian tube, atmospheric pressure supports a column of mercury 76 cm tall.

Within a few years of Torricelli's experiments, Pascal suggested that the atmosphere is like an ocean of air, in which the pressure is greater at the bottom than at higher altitudes. This suggestion was soon confirmed when a Torricellian tube was carried from sea level to a mountain top and the mercury column was observed to be shorter at the higher elevations.

A dramatic example of atmospheric pressure was provided by Otto von Guericke (1602–1686), who used his own invention, the air pump, in the famous demonstration of the Magdeburg hemispheres (Fig. 12.3). Two hemispheres, each about 55 cm in diameter, were fitted together and most of the inside air removed. The hemispheres were held together by the pressure of the surrounding air. Two teams of eight horses each, when hitched to the hemispheres, could not pull them apart. Problem 12.12 asks you to find the force holding them together.

(a)

(b)

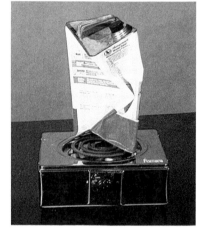

(c)

(a) A one-gallon metal can open to the air contains a small amount of boiling water. (b) The can is fitted with a tight-fitting stopper and the heat turned off. (c) As it cools the can is crushed by atmospheric pressure.

Figure 12.3
Otto von Guericke's experiment in Magdeburg, Germany, utilized an early vacuum pump. Two teams of eight horses could not separate the sealed and evacuated hemispheres against the force of atmospheric pressure.

Because we are always immersed in the atmosphere, we often overlook its effects. Its presence can be easily demonstrated, however. Consider the one-gallon can shown in Fig. 12.4(a). When a small amount of water was placed in the can and heated to the boiling point, the steam drove out the air and filled the can. While the water was still boiling, the can was closed with a rubber stopper and the heat source turned off. Immediately the can began to collapse as the steam condensed leaving a partial vacuum inside (Fig. 12.4b). With little internal pressure to resist, the pressure of the atmosphere outside crushed the can (Fig. 12.4c).

12.2   **Boyle's Law**

Robert Boyle* (1627–1691) advanced the study of gases using an air pump made by Robert Hooke, which was greatly improved over that of von Guericke. The result for which Boyle is best known today is the observed relationship between the pressure and the volume of an enclosed gas at a constant temperature.

---

*Boyle was one of the founders of the Royal Society, chartered in 1662, which published Newton's first papers and of which Newton was later president. Among the interests of this group were pneumatic experiments, which were often carried out as a diversion.

Boyle's law states that **the pressure exerted by a gas at constant temperature is inversely proportional to the volume in which it is enclosed.** Boyle's law is usually written

$$PV = \text{constant},$$

where P is the gas pressure, V its volume, and the value of the constant depends on the initial conditions. A complete statement of Boyle's law includes the condition that both the temperature and the amount of gas must be held constant.

Alternatively, Boyle's law may be written

$$P_1V_1 = P_2V_2, \qquad (12.1)$$

where the subscripts 1 and 2 refer to different physical states of the same sample of gas with the temperature held constant. Figure 12.5 illustrates Boyle's law.

We should point out that while Boyle's law is applicable over a wide range of pressures, it does not always apply. For example, if the temperature is low enough, a sample of gas will condense to a liquid at sufficiently high pressure. For carbon dioxide at 31°C, this pressure is about 7.38×10^6 N/m^2, or 72.9 atm.

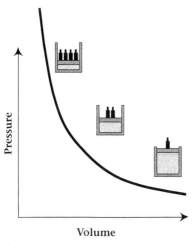

Figure 12.5
A graph of pressure versus volume for a gas enclosed in a cylinder at constant temperature. According to Boyle's law, PV is constant.

Example 12.2

A cylinder with a height of 0.20 m and a cross-sectional area of 0.040 m^2 has a close-fitting piston that may be moved to change the internal volume of the cylinder (Fig. 12.6). Air at atmospheric pressure (1.01×10^5 N/m^2) fills the cylinder. If the piston is pushed until it is within 0.12 m of the end of the cylinder, what is the new pressure of the air? Assume that the temperature of the gas remains constant and that the volume of gas in the gauge is small compared with the volume of the cylinder.

Solution Let subscripts 1 and 2 indicate the situation before and after the piston is pushed in. Then, according to Boyle's law, we can write

$$P_1V_1 = P_2V_2,$$

which can be written

$$P_2 = \frac{P_1V_1}{V_2}.$$

Inserting the numerical values, we find

$$P_2 = \frac{(1.01 \times 10^5 \text{ N/m}^2)(0.20 \text{ m} \times 0.040 \text{ m}^2)}{0.12 \text{ m} \times 0.040 \text{ m}^2}$$

$$P_2 = 1.7 \times 10^5 \text{ N/m}^2.$$

The new pressure is 1.7×10^5 N/m^2, or 1.7×10^5 Pa.

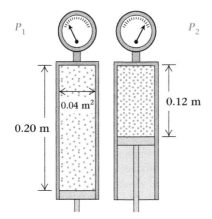

Figure 12.6
Example 12.2: Gas enclosed in a cylinder at constant temperature. The volume of gas in the gauge is small compared to the volume of the cylinder.

Back to the Future

GAS LAWS AND BALLOONS

The first human flight occurred in Paris on November 21, 1783, when two passengers made a 25-minute flight in a hot-air balloon designed by Joseph and Etienne Montgolfier. The brothers had been experimenting with balloons for several years. Benjamin Franklin, then serving as ambassador to France, was an official observer of this first manned flight. When asked what was the use of flying he is said to have replied, "What use is a newborn baby?"

A few days after the Montgolfier flight, J. A. C. Charles, in a balloon of his own design, made an ascent with a companion. At the end of the flight his companion got out of the gondola and Charles alone soared to a height of 9000 ft in about ten minutes, making temperature and pressure measurements along the way.

According to Archimedes' principle, a balloon rises if its overall density is less than the density of the air it displaces. Thus, a balloon needs very-low-density gas to carry people through the air. Although the Montgolfiers knew about the discovery of hydrogen by Henry Cavendish in 1766, they elected to use hot air, for practical and economic reasons. Professor Charles, with encouragement from Franklin, selected hydrogen instead. (Hydrogen is the least dense of all gases.) For balloons of the same size, a hydrogen-filled balloon has several times more lifting force than a hot-air balloon. The first few years of ballooning were filled with controversy over the relative merits of hydrogen versus hot air, spurring studies of the laws of gas behavior by people who were often associated with ballooning. For instance, the first qualitative work on the thermal expansion of gases was probably done by Charles in about 1787, several years after his first hydrogen balloon flight.

Another balloonist, J. L. Gay-Lussac, was one of the first to make ascents for scientific purposes. He was an active chemist and made two important discoveries about gases. He independently studied the thermal expansion of gases and published his results in 1802, fifteen years after Charles's work. In his paper, Gay-Lussac referred to the earlier work of Charles, noting that Charles had obtained incorrect results for wet gases. The law of thermal expansion of gases is given the names of both Gay-Lussac and Charles.

During the next hundred years, ballooning evolved into sporting, military, and commercial applications, culminating in the invention of the rigid-frame airship by Count Ferdinand von Zeppelin in the last part of the nineteenth century. Zeppelin's airships became the luxury liners of the sky. The Zeppelin was made of a light, rigid metal framework covered with fabric. Inside were sealed bags of hydrogen gas and compartments

Figure B12.1   The Zepplin NT, a modern rigid-frame airship, on its maiden flight in 1997.

for passengers. The cabin that hung beneath the Zeppelin contained the bridge and navigation rooms. The *Hindenburg,* a Zeppelin built in 1936, was the largest flying machine ever made. It had space to carry 72 passengers at 80 mph for over 8000 mi. The *Hindenburg* made more than 50 successful flights, including 36 across the Atlantic, before it exploded on landing at Lakehurst, New Jersey, in 1937, ending the Zepplin era. A new technology airship was launched in 1997 using helium as the lifting gas (Fig. B12.1).

Today most ballooning takes place with colorful hot-air sports balloons (Fig. B12.2). From shortly after the time of the Montgolfiers until the 1950s, most balloons used hydrogen or helium, the two lightest gases. The expense of large quantities of these gases effectively kept private individuals from participating. On October 10, 1960, the age of the modern hot-air sports balloon was born when Ed Youst flew a hot-air balloon, using propane burners of his own design. These heat sources, which are at the heart of modern sports ballooning, are capable of delivering several million Btu per hour (10 million Btu/h = 2.9 MW), giving temperatures near 100°C inside the top of a rising balloon. Hot-air balloons must be relatively large because even very hot air is only slightly less dense than the atmosphere. A typical three- or four-person balloon has a volume of about 2200 m³.

Figure B12.2   Modern hot-air balloons.

12.3 The Law of Charles and Gay-Lussac

Boyle's law relates the pressure and the volume of a gas at constant temperature. However, we can also investigate the effect of temperature change on the volume of a gas at constant pressure, using the apparatus shown in Fig. 12.7(a,b). We introduce some particular gas, say gas A, into the cylinder and place a weight on the piston. This arrangement creates an enclosed variable volume in which the pressure (due to the weight) remains constant. Then we bring the gas to thermal equilibrium at several different temperatures. We record these temperatures and the corresponding volumes and graph the data (Fig. 12.7c, line A). If we repeat this procedure with another gas, say B, with the same initial volume and temperature, we get the same results (line B). However, if we use gas B with a different initial volume, we obtain data producing a new line, marked B' in Fig. 12.7(c). Whatever gas we use, the behavior is the same: The plotted data always lie along a straight line.

To see what this result means, we may write the equation of any of these straight lines in the form

$$V = V_0(1 + \beta T),$$

where V is the volume at temperature T and where V_0 and β are constants. The experimental result is that β is the same for all gases. If T is measured in degrees Celsius, β is found to have the value of $1/273.15°C$.

If a gas is brought to some temperature T_1, then its volume V_1 is given by

$$V_1 = V_0(1 + \beta T_1).$$

If the gas is brought to a different temperature T_2, its volume V_2 is

$$V_2 = V_0(1 + \beta T_2).$$

Dividing one of these equations by the other and writing in the numerical value for β gives

$$\frac{V_1}{V_2} = \frac{273.15 + T_1}{273.15 + T_2}.$$

It is evident that, at least so far as gases are concerned, it would be convenient to introduce a new temperature scale in which the temperature T is related to the Celsius temperature T_C by

$$T = 273.15 + T_C. \tag{12.2}$$

As we learned in Chapter 11, this temperature scale is called the Kelvin scale. The scale was introduced in 1848 by Lord Kelvin, who observed that if the lines for all gases in Fig. 12.7(c) were extrapolated to lower temperatures, they would intersect at $-273.15°C$ and zero volume. That does not mean that a gas would vanish at this temperature, even if it could be cooled so low before liquefying. It means, as we will see in more detail in Section 12.6, that the molecules of the gas would have a minimum amount of energy at that temperature. The scale is an absolute scale in the sense that its zero ($-273.15°C$) is the lower limit for temperatures as defined by macroscopic thermometers. *We will use the Kelvin scale throughout the remainder of this chapter.*

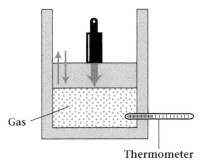

(a) Low temperature

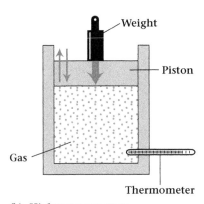

(b) Higher temperature

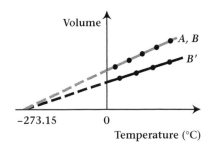

(c)

Figure 12.7
Apparatus for measuring the volume of a gas as a function of temperature at constant pressure shown at (a) lower temperature and (b) higher temperature. (c) Typical graphical representation. The volume is directly proportional to the temperature.

If the temperature is expressed in kelvins, we find that, when the pressure is held constant, the volume is proportional to the temperature. This statement is the **law of Charles and Gay-Lussac,** which can be expressed mathematically as

$$\frac{V_1}{V_2} = \frac{T_1}{T_2} \quad or \quad \frac{V}{T} = \text{constant}. \tag{12.3}$$

As with Boyle's law, the amount of gas also must be held constant for Eq. (12.3) to be valid.

▼

Example 12.3

To what temperature would the air in a hot-air balloon have to be heated so that its mass would be 0.980 times that of an equal volume of air at a temperature of 25°C?

Strategy As the air in a hot-air balloon is heated, it expands. Some of the air escapes through the hole at the bottom of the balloon in order for the interior of the balloon to remain at constant atmospheric pressure. The mass of air remaining inside the constant volume of the bag is less than the mass of an equivalent volume of the surrounding cooler air. Thus, the density of the air inside the bag is reduced and the balloon floats, in accord with Archimedes' principle. The mass of cool gas m_1 at temperature T_1 that was originally inside the volume V_1 of the bag expands to a new volume V_2 upon heating to temperature T_2. Since the volume of the bag is constant, the amount of hot gas m_2 that remains inside is proportional to the original mass and to the ratio of V_1/V_2. Thus

$$m_2 = \frac{V_1}{V_2}m_1,$$

which can be rearranged as

$$\frac{V_2}{V_1} = \frac{m_1}{m_2}.$$

We can combine this equation with Eq. (12.3) to find the required temperature.

Solution The law of Charles and Gay-Lussac, Eq. (12.3), can be written as

$$T_2 = \frac{V_2}{V_1}T_1 = \frac{m_1}{m_2}T_1.$$

The ratio of m_1/m_2 is

$$\frac{m_1}{m_2} = \frac{1}{0.980}.$$

The temperature T_1 must be expressed in kelvins to be used in the law of Charles and Gay-Lussac,

$$T_1 = 25°C = (273 + 25) \text{ K} = 298 \text{ K}.$$

Inserting the values for T_1 and the ratio of the masses into the equation for T_2, we get

$$T_2 = \frac{1}{0.980}\ 298\ \text{K} = 304\ \text{K}.$$

Upon converting back to degrees Celsius, we get

$$T_2 = 31°\text{C}.$$

▼

12.4   The Ideal Gas Law

Boyle's law and the law of Charles and Gay-Lussac are special cases of a more general expression called the **ideal gas law.*** It can be inferred from them and is usually written

$$\boxed{PV = nRT.} \tag{12.4}$$

Here, as before, P, V, and T stand for pressure, volume, and temperature, respectively; R is a constant that is the same for all gases and so is called the **universal gas constant.** If pressure is measured in the SI unit of pascals, volume in cubic meters, and temperature in kelvins, then R has the value 8.314 Joule/mole · K.

The quantity of gas, measured in moles, is given by n. A **mole** (abbreviated mol) is the amount of material whose mass in grams is numerically equal to the molecular mass of the substance. For example, the molecular mass of oxygen gas is 32; a mole of oxygen gas is 32 g. (Oxygen molecules are diatomic; that is, each molecule consists of two atoms, each with atomic mass 16.) Avogadro's principle, discussed in Chapter 26, leads to the conclusion that a mole of any gas contains the same number of molecules. This number is called **Avogadro's number,** N_A, and is $N_A = 6.02 \times 10^{23}$ molecules/mole. The modern definition of the mole encompasses the concept of isotopes, discussed in Chapter 29. *The mole is the amount of substance of a system that contains as many elementary entities as there are atoms in 0.012 kg of carbon-12.* Table 12.1 lists the molecular masses of a few common gases. The dependence of the ideal gas law on n, the number of moles, can be seen from the observation that doubling an amount of gas at constant temperature and volume will double its pressure. One mole of nitrogen gas at 273.15 K occupying a volume of 22.4 L has a pressure of 101 kPa; two moles of nitrogen gas at the same temperature and occupying the same volume have a pressure of 202 kPa.

An equation that links the pressure, volume, and temperature of a sample of matter is called an **equation of state.** Equation (12.4) is one such equation. It is the equation of state for an ideal gas, which is described in detail in the next section. Quantities that describe the condition or state of a system are called **state variables.**

---

*The definition of an ideal gas is given in Section 12.5. In brief, an ideal gas obeys Eq. (12.4). The behavior of real gases is closely approximated by Eq. (12.4).

Table 12.1	*Approximate Molecular Masses of Some Common Gases* ▼	
Substance	Symbol	Molecular Mass (g/mol)
Molecular hydrogen	H_2	2
Helium	He	4
Water vapor	H_2O	18
Neon	Ne	20
Molecular nitrogen	N_2	28
Molecular oxygen	O_2	32
Argon	Ar	40
Carbon dioxide	CO_2	44

In ordinary situations, the ideal gas law predicts the behavior of many gases quite well. The agreement between the observed and predicted behavior of real gases is good near atmospheric pressure and ordinary temperatures. Deviations from the predictions are greatest when the pressure is very great or the temperature is very low. At the extremes of these conditions, the gases condense to liquids. For the examples and problems given in this chapter, the deviations from the ideal gas law are small.

Example 12.4 ▼

During a chemistry laboratory experiment, a sample of hydrogen gas is collected into a 0.50-liter flask at room temperature (23°C) and pressure (1.00 atm). It is cooled to 5.0°C and transferred to a container whose volume is 0.12 L. What pressure does the gas exert on the walls of the final container?

Solution Using the subscript 1 to indicate the initial conditions, we have

$$P_1V_1 = nRT_1.$$

Using the subscript 2 to denote conditions in the new container, we write

$$P_2V_2 = nRT_2.$$

Because the number of moles of gas is constant, we can combine the equations of state for the two situations to get

$$\frac{P_1V_1}{T_1} = \frac{P_2V_2}{T_2},$$

or

$$P_2 = \frac{V_1T_2P_1}{V_2T_1}.$$

Substituting the data gives

$$P_2 = \frac{(0.50 \text{ L})[(273 + 5.0) \text{ K}](1.00 \text{ atm})}{(0.12 \text{ L})[(273 + 23) \text{ K}]} = 3.9 \text{ atm.}$$

Discussion Notice that pressure and volume enter only as ratios and can be given in any system of units as long as they are the same. Temperatures, however, must always be given in kelvins.

Example 12.5

What is the density of carbon dioxide gas at a temperature of 23°C and atmospheric pressure?

Solution The mass m of a sample of matter is related to the number of moles by

$$m = nM,$$

where n is the number of moles and M is the gram molecular mass. For carbon dioxide, CO_2, the gram molecular mass is

$$M_{carbon} + 2M_{oxygen} = 12.0 + 2(16.0) = 44.0 \text{ g/mol}.$$

The density is given by

$$\rho = \frac{m}{V} = \frac{nM}{nRT/P} = \frac{MP}{RT}.$$

Substituting for the molecular mass of CO_2 in the units of kg/mol and for the other variables, we have

$$\rho = \frac{(44 \times 10^{-3} \text{ kg/mol})(1.01 \times 10^5 \text{ N/m}^2)}{(8.31 \text{ J/mol} \cdot \text{K})[(273 + 23) \text{ K}]}$$

$$\rho = 1.81 \text{ kg/m}^3.$$

This value compares well with the experimentally measured one of 1.84 kg/m^3.

Example 12.6

An automobile tire is filled to a gauge pressure of 240 kPa early in the morning when the temperature is 15°C. After the car is driven all day over hot roads, the tire temperature is 70°C. Estimate the new gauge pressure.

Strategy We assume the volume of the tire to be approximately constant. Then from the ideal gas law we get

$$\frac{P_1}{T_1} = \frac{P_2}{T_2}.$$

The appropriate pressure to use is the absolute pressure. Recall that the absolute pressure is gauge pressure plus atmospheric pressure.

Solution Rearrange the equation above to get the pressure P_2,

$$P_2 = P_1 \frac{T_2}{T_1}$$

$$P_2 = \frac{(240 \text{ kPa} + 101 \text{ kPa})(273 + 70) \text{ K}}{(273 + 15) \text{ K}} = \frac{(341 \text{ kPa})(343)}{288}$$

$$P_2 = 406 \text{ kPa}.$$

But this is the absolute pressure, so

$$\text{gauge pressure} = 406 \text{ kPa} - 101 \text{ kPa} = 305 \text{ kPa.}$$

12.5 The Kinetic Theory of Gases

The gas laws describe what happens to a gas under various conditions, but they say nothing about why gases act this way. Explaining the "why" behind observed behavior of matter has always been a fundamental motivation in physics. As early as the time of Boyle and Newton (that is, late seventeenth century), there were efforts to explain the observed behavior of gases on a fundamental basis. Newton proposed that a gas might consist of tiny particles called molecules, which exert a repulsive force on each other. Such an idea can lead to Boyle's law, though Newton and Boyle did not claim this to be the only possible explanation.

The development of a successful theory of gas behavior did not take place until the middle of the nineteenth century. Many people contributed to this development, and the theory has not been named after any particular scientist. However, since the theory assumes that a gas consists of particles in motion, it is usually called the **kinetic theory of gases.**

In the kinetic theory of gases, we assume that a gas consists of many particles. Here "many" means so numerous that we cannot hope to trace out their individual paths (Fig. 12.8). In fact, it may not be desirable to do this even if we could. The things we want to determine from a model of a gas are the things that determine its behavior—an equation of state and the thermal and mechanical properties of a gas—not the directions and speeds of a large number of individual particles. If we do not treat the molecules individually, then we must determine their average behavior. This implies that we need to develop a statistical theory that includes the rules of probability.

We will first construct a model of a gas by making detailed assumptions about its nature. Then we will calculate how this gas should behave, by using our knowledge of Newton's laws and of the conservation of momentum and mechanical energy and by taking the appropriate averages. For instance, we will derive a relationship between the pressure and volume of this model gas. One test of the validity of our assumptions about the gas model will be how closely our predictions agree with what we observe for a real gas.

This example of model making is typical of many theories in modern science. We cannot, in the ordinary sense, "see" individual molecules, atoms, or their constituent parts, so our explanations of what happens in many biological, chemical, and physical phenomena must be made in terms of an abstract model. Such models should not be taken as absolute replicas of reality. Furthermore, we will see that in many cases, as we examine smaller and smaller physical constituents of a system and therefore consider more of them, we are forced to calculate the observed behavior as statistical averages. This will be the case with a gas.

Our rules for formulating a model are as follows:

1. We will not make any assumptions that are not specifically needed in our derivation.

Figure 12.8
Model of a gas composed of a large number of identical molecules in random motion.

2. The assumptions made will be as simple as possible.

3. The assumptions will, when possible, have some basis in physical experience.

We will first list the *principal assumptions of the kinetic theory of gases* and then use them in deriving a relationship between the pressure and the volume of a gas. These assumptions constitute the definition of an ideal gas. Any gas that obeys the relationships derived from these assumptions at all temperatures and pressures is called an **ideal gas.**

1. *A sample of gas consists of many identical molecules. In this context "many" means so many that one could not hope to trace out their individual paths.*

2. *The molecules are very far apart in comparison to their size; that is, the total volume of the molecules is negligible when compared with the size of their container.*

3. *The direction of motion of any molecule is random; on the average, no direction is preferred above another and the molecules move with a variety of speeds.*

4. *The molecules are treated as if they were hard spheres. This assumption, which gives rise to the name "billiard ball model," means that there are no forces acting between molecules except when the molecules collide and that the collisions are elastic. In addition, we treat collisions with the walls of the container as elastic collisions.*

5. *The molecules obey Newton's laws of motion.*

These assumptions are to some extent based on everyday experience. For instance, we know that molecules of air cannot be seen by the unaided eye. This means they must be much smaller than spheres with a radius of about 0.1 mm. The assumption of random directions seems reasonable because if the molecules of a gas had a preferred direction, the gas would have a net flow in that direction.

The assumption that molecules of a gas are like hard spheres is not the only, or even the most realistic, assumption we could make. However, it is the simplest assumption and therefore, lacking specific information to the contrary, the most appropriate in this case. We have listed the use of Newtonian mechanics in order to emphasize that the results of our calculations with this model depend not only on the physical properties of the model, but also on the mathematical techniques used to obtain its predictions.

Now that we have stated the assumptions of the kinetic theory of gases, let us analyze their consequences and compare these with observable properties of a real gas. We will do this by deriving mathematical expressions for those physical quantities of importance in mechanics, such as momentum, force, and kinetic energy. We start by considering an ideal gas confined to a cubical box with sides of length L. The gas molecules move in a manner determined by Newton's three laws and the laws of conservation of energy and momentum. We assume that the number density, that is, the number of molecules per unit volume, is on the average the same throughout the box. For convenience we choose a coordinate system aligned with the edges of the box (Fig. 12.9).

Consider a molecule of mass m moving parallel to the x axis in the positive direction. For the moment, we neglect collisions between molecules and consider only collisions between the molecules and the walls of the box. If the molecule

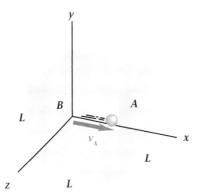

Figure 12.9
A model for calculating the pressure of a gas from kinetic theory. The gas molecule is confined to a box of length L as shown.

has a velocity v_x it will rebound from wall A with a velocity $-v_x$, because we assumed that the collisions are elastic, and the walls are essentially immobile. The molecule's change in velocity is $-2v_x$, and its change in momentum is $-2mv_x$. The momentum transferred to the wall is $+2mv_x$.

If the molecule encounters no other molecules but moves until it strikes wall B and rebounds again to strike wall A, the time between collisions with face A is

$$\Delta t = \frac{2L}{v_x}.$$

The average momentum change per unit time at face A is

$$\frac{\Delta p}{\Delta t} = \frac{2mv_x^2}{2L}.$$

We can interpret this expression as the average force on the wall due to any molecule that has an x component of velocity given by v_x. The total force due to N molecules is

$$F_{\text{total}} = N \frac{\overline{\Delta p}}{\Delta t} = \frac{Nm\overline{v_x^2}}{L},$$

where the bar indicates, as before, the average of that quantity.

By dividing both sides of the equation by the area of the face L^2, we have the pressure P,

$$P = \frac{F_{\text{total}}}{A} = \frac{F_{\text{total}}}{L^2} = \frac{Nm\overline{v_x^2}}{L^3} = \frac{Nm\overline{v_x^2}}{V},$$

or

$$PV = Nm\overline{v_x^2}, \tag{12.5}$$

where P is the pressure on the wall and $V = L^3$ is the volume of the box.

The square of the total velocity of a single molecule is the sum of the squares of the three component velocities:

$$v^2 = v_x^2 + v_y^2 + v_z^2.$$

For a large number of molecules, the assumption of no preferred direction (assumption 3) leads to an average squared velocity of

$$\overline{v^2} = \overline{v_x^2 + v_y^2 + v_z^2} = \overline{v_x^2} + \overline{v_y^2} + \overline{v_z^2}.$$

The average values of the components are identical because the x, y, and z directions are equivalent and independent. Therefore

$$\overline{v_x^2} = \overline{v_y^2} = \overline{v_z^2}$$

and

$$\overline{v^2} = 3\overline{v_x^2}.$$

Thus $\overline{v_x^2}$ in Eq. (12.5) can be replaced by $\overline{v^2}/3$ to give

$$PV = \tfrac{1}{3}Nm\overline{v^2}. \tag{12.6a}$$

Since $\overline{KE} = \frac{1}{2}m\overline{v^2}$, where $\overline{KE}$ is the average translational kinetic energy per molecule associated with random molecular motions, we have

$$PV = \tfrac{2}{3}N\overline{KE}. \qquad \text{(12.6b)}$$

The quantities on the left-hand side of Eq. (12.6) are macroscopic (large-scale) quantities. The quantities on the right-hand side are microscopic (molecular-scale) variables. We have derived an expression linking the microscopic, and generally unobservable, properties of molecules, such as their masses and speeds, with the easily observed large-scale properties, such as pressure and volume. For example, we can use Eq. (12.6a) to find the average of the speed squared or, as it is also called, the mean square speed. Then we can compute the quantity $\sqrt{\overline{v^2}}$, which is called the *root-mean-square speed* v_{rms}. The rms speed is a type of "average" speed used in describing the motion of a collection of particles.

In deriving Eq. (12.6), we assumed that there were no collisions between the particles. However, if we include elastic collisions, the result is unchanged. Because of the perfect exchange of velocities in elastic collisions between identical particles, the component of momentum mv_x of a particle leaving face B is still carried to face A of the box in Fig. 12.9 by some other particle. The time duration of elastic collisions is negligible compared with the time between collisions. So the absence of collisions in our derivation does not affect its validity.

Example 12.7

Estimate the rms speed of oxygen molecules at the standard temperature and pressure of 0°C and one atmosphere. Assume that oxygen can be treated as an ideal gas.

Strategy We can use Eq. (12.6a) to find the mean square speed. We can then compute the rms speed $v_{rms} = \sqrt{\overline{v^2}}$.

Solution Equation (12.6a) can be rewritten as

$$\overline{v^2} = \frac{3PV}{Nm}.$$

But since Nm is the total mass of the gas, we can write

$$\overline{v^2} = \frac{3P}{\rho},$$

where $\rho = Nm/V$ is the mass density.

The rms speed is computed from the square root of $\overline{v^2}$:

$$v_{rms} = \sqrt{\overline{v^2}} = \sqrt{\frac{3P}{\rho}}.$$

Inserting a pressure of one atmosphere and the density of oxygen at one atmosphere and 0°C (from Table 10.2), we get

$$v_{rms} = \sqrt{\frac{3(1.01 \times 10^5 \text{ N/m}^2)}{1.43 \text{ kg/m}^3}}$$

$$v_{rms} = 460 \text{ m/s} \approx 1700 \text{ km/h } (1000 \text{ mi/h}).$$

Discussion This result for the rms speed of oxygen molecules is of the same order of magnitude as the speed of sound (317 m/s) observed in oxygen at this temperature and pressure. This similarity is to be expected, since sound waves are transmitted by the motion of air molecules. According to our model, the molecules of a gas in a closed container are moving with great speeds.

▼

12.6 The Kinetic-Theory Definition of Temperature

According to the ideal gas law (Eq. 12.4), the product of pressure and volume of a confined gas is proportional to the temperature,

$$PV = nRT.$$

We have also seen in Eq. (12.6b) that the product of pressure and volume is proportional to the average kinetic energy per molecule,

$$PV = \tfrac{2}{3}N\overline{KE}.$$

If our kinetic theory model is correct, the terms on the right-hand sides of these two equations must be equal.

$$\tfrac{2}{3}N\overline{KE} = nRT.$$

We can rearrange the equation to get

$$\overline{KE} = \tfrac{3}{2}\frac{n}{N}RT.$$

The number of molecules N is the number of moles n times Avogadro's number ($N = nN_A$). Thus

$$\overline{KE} = \tfrac{3}{2}\frac{RT}{N_A},$$

or

$$\boxed{\overline{KE} = \tfrac{3}{2}kT,} \tag{12.7a}$$

where the constant $k = R/N_A$ is called the **Boltzmann constant** and has a value of 1.3807×10^{-23} J·K^{-1}. The Boltzmann constant occurs frequently in the physics of gases and is sometimes called the gas constant per molecule. The Boltzmann constant can be used to write the ideal gas law as

$$PV = NkT.$$

Equation (12.7a) provides a new definition of temperature in terms of the microscopic mechanical properties of a gas. Specifically, temperature is a measure of the average random translational kinetic energy of the molecules of a gas (Fig. 12.10),

$$T = \frac{2}{3}\frac{\overline{\text{KE}}}{k}. \tag{12.7b}$$

Furthermore, we see that the average translational kinetic energy of a molecule in an ideal gas depends only on the temperature, not on the pressure or type of gas. Remember that the temperature in these equations is given in kelvins.

The connection between temperature and the average kinetic energy of the molecules is an important result. It tells us what is happening on a molecular scale. An increase in temperature corresponds to an increase in the average speed of the molecules; a decrease in temperature corresponds to a slowing down of the molecules. Neither phenomenon is cause or effect; instead, temperature is a large-scale manifestation of motion at the molecular level of gases, solids, and liquids. Knowing this helps us to better understand the relationships among temperature, heat flow, and energy that we discussed in Chapter 11.

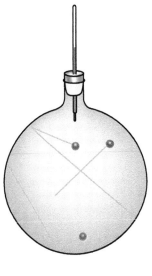

Example 12.8

What is the rms speed of a nitrogen molecule at a temperature of 300 K? Assume that nitrogen behaves as an ideal gas. The mass of a nitrogen molecule is $m = 4.65 \times 10^{-26}$ kg (nitrogen is another diatomic molecule).

Solution From Eq. (12.7a) we have

$$\overline{\text{KE}} = \tfrac{3}{2}kT = \tfrac{1}{2}m\overline{v^2},$$

so

$$\overline{v^2} = \frac{3kT}{m},$$

$$v_{\text{rms}} = \sqrt{\overline{v^2}} = \sqrt{\frac{3kT}{m}}.$$

Upon inserting the values for k, T, and m, we find that

$$v_{\text{rms}} = \sqrt{\frac{3(1.38 \times 10^{-23}\ \text{J} \cdot \text{K}^{-1})(300\ \text{K})}{4.65 \times 10^{-26}\ \text{kg}}}$$

$$v_{\text{rms}} = 517\ \text{m/s}.$$

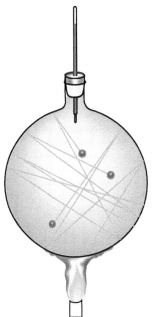

Figure 12.10
The average kinetic energy of a gas depends only on the temperature of the gas. The greater the temperature, the greater the average kinetic energy of the molecules.

12.7 Internal Energy of an Ideal Gas

We have seen that the product of pressure and volume of a confined ideal gas can be expressed in terms of the average translational kinetic energy per molecule, $\overline{\text{KE}}$:

$$PV = \tfrac{2}{3}N\overline{\text{KE}}.$$

The product $N\overline{KE}$ is the total translational kinetic energy of the gas due to the random thermal motion of its molecules. This kinetic energy represents the total **internal energy** U of an ideal monatomic gas. For that case there is no energy associated with rotations or internal vibrations of the molecules. Consequently we can write

$$PV = \tfrac{2}{3}U.$$

This equation is the same as Boyle's law if we assume that keeping the temperature constant and keeping the internal energy constant are the same thing.

By combining this equation with the ideal gas law (Eq. 12.4), we can relate the internal energy to the temperature through

$$nRT = \tfrac{2}{3}U.$$

We can rearrange to find

$$\boxed{U = \tfrac{3}{2}nRT.} \tag{12.8}$$

We will make use of the concept of internal energy when we discuss the laws of thermodynamics in the next chapter.

Equation (12.8) defines the internal energy in a monatomic gas such as helium or neon. Diatomic gases such as nitrogen and oxygen have additional internal energy associated with rotational and vibrational motions. Nevertheless their internal energy is still proportional to RT.

Figure 12.11
Example 12.9: Helium-filled balloons are popular items in the annual Macy's parade.

Example 12.9

A parade balloon contains 368 m³ of helium at a pressure of 115 kPa (Fig. 12.11). What is the internal energy of the helium in the balloon?

Strategy We need to find the internal energy from knowledge of the volume and pressure of the gas. The internal energy of the helium gas was given in Eq. (12.8) as $U = \tfrac{3}{2}nRT$. Although we are not given the temperature of the gas, we know from the ideal gas law that $nRT = PV$, so that the internal energy may be expressed as

$$U = \tfrac{3}{2}PV.$$

Solution The internal energy may be computed by substituting the numerical values for P and V to get

$$U = \tfrac{3}{2}(115 \times 10^3 \text{ Pa})(368 \text{ m}^3) = 6.35 \times 10^7 \text{ J}.$$

*12.8   ### The Barometric Formula and the Distribution of Molecular Speeds

So far in this chapter, we have considered only the average speeds of molecules. However, there are times when we need to know the distribution of molecular speeds in a gas. By distribution we mean a mathematical expression that tells us what fraction of the molecules have speeds in a given range.

The distribution of molecular speeds was first worked out by James Clerk Maxwell (1831–1879) in 1860. Maxwell's significant contribution was the introduction of statistical ideas into classical mechanics. To describe his conclusions, we first derive a formula for pressure as a function of height in the atmosphere as a way of introducing you to the exponential function. Then we will present Maxwell's results, which are expressed with this mathematical function. (We discuss the exponential function in detail in an appendix to this chapter.)

Consider a tall column of air, which might represent a cross section of the atmosphere (Fig. 12.12). We assume the temperature to be the same at all points in this atmosphere. Let us now examine the gas between two horizontal planes at altitudes z and $z + \Delta z$. The pressure at height z is greater than the pressure at height $z + \Delta z$ because of the weight of the air contained between z and $z + \Delta z$. Although the atmosphere does not have a well-defined height, we are able to write the difference in pressures because it depends on the difference in heights:

$$P_{z+\Delta z} - P_z = \Delta P = -\rho g\, \Delta z,$$

where ρ is the mass density of the gas. The minus sign indicates that the pressure decreases as the altitude increases. If we assume that the density of the air does not vary over a small change in height, we may use the ideal gas law to express this density. The total mass M of the gas is the number of moles n times the number of molecules in a mole N_A times the mass of one molecule m. The density is then

$$\rho = \frac{\text{mass}}{\text{volume}} = \frac{M}{V} = \frac{nN_A m}{nRT/P}$$

$$\rho = \frac{m}{kT}P,$$

where k is the Boltzmann constant. We can insert this value for ρ into the equation for ΔP to get

$$\frac{\Delta P}{\Delta z} = -\rho g = -\frac{mg}{kT}P. \qquad (12.9)$$

This equation is a relationship between changes in pressure and changes in height. We wish to find an expression for pressure as a function of height alone. If we interpret Eq. (12.9) graphically, we see that we are looking for a function P whose slope $\Delta P/\Delta z$ is proportional to the value of P. The result is that

$$\boxed{P(z) = P_0 e^{-mgz/kT},} \qquad (12.10)$$

where P_0 is the pressure at $z = 0$ and e is an irrational number with a value approximately equal to 2.718. (If you are not already familiar with the exponential function e^x, see the appendix to this chapter.) Although we would not expect full agreement between the prediction of Eq. (12.10) and the observed pressure in the earth's atmosphere because T is not constant, there is rather good general accord.

We may also express Eq. (12.10) in terms of the number density n, the number of molecules per unit volume. We can do so because at constant temperature, the pressure and density of an ideal gas are proportional. Thus

$$n = n_0 e^{-mgz/kT} \qquad (12.11)$$

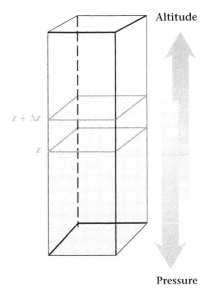

Altitude

Pressure

$z + \Delta z$

z

Figure 12.12
A simplified model of the atmosphere at constant temperature. Pressure is greater at lower altitudes.

This equation is called the *barometric formula*. It gives the number of molecules per unit volume as a function of height z in our idealized atmosphere.

▼

Example 12.10

People who have been to high elevations on mountains know that it is more difficult to breathe at higher altitudes than at lower ones. This effect is due to the reduced air pressure or, equivalently, to the reduced number of air molecules (including oxygen) per unit volume. Estimate the number of molecules of air per unit volume on Pike's Peak (4300 m above sea level) relative to the number in Denver, Colorado (1610 m above sea level).

Solution We need the average mass of the air molecules for m in Eq. (12.11). The atmosphere is about 21% oxygen (at 5.31×10^{-26} kg per molecule) and 79% nitrogen (at 4.67×10^{-26} kg per molecule). Thus, the average mass is

$$m = (0.21)(5.31 \times 10^{-26} \text{ kg}) + (0.79)(4.67 \times 10^{-26} \text{ kg}) = 4.80 \times 10^{-26} \text{ kg}.$$

The temperature is not uniform, but because we use the Kelvin scale, only a small error is introduced by assuming a constant value of $0°C = 273$ K. We can use Eq. (12.11) to find the ratio of the density of air molecules if we let n_0 represent the density at Denver and n represent the density at Pike's Peak. Then z is the difference in their altitudes, 2690 m. When we insert the numerical values into the equation we find

$$\frac{n}{n_0} = e^{-mgz/kT} = e^{-\frac{(4.80 \times 10^{-26} \text{ kg})(9.81 \text{ m/s}^2)(2690 \text{ m})}{(1.38 \times 10^{-23} \text{ J/K})(273 \text{ K})}} = 0.71.$$

Discussion The difficulty of breathing on Pike's Peak is understandable because the number of molecules per unit volume is only 71% as great as in Denver. How does the density of air molecules on Pike's Peak compare with the density where you live?

Altitude sickness (or mountain sickness as it is also known) is the body's reaction to the reduced atmospheric pressure of high altitude. People whose travels include a change in altitude of about 8000 ft (2438 m) or more may experience symptoms that include shortness of breath, headache, and fatigue. Usually such symptoms subside after 2 or 3 days of acclimatization at the new altitude. Airlines pressurize the cabins of high-flying planes to the equivalent of a height of 6000 ft for the comfort of passengers and crew and to prevent altitude sickness.

By continuing to analyze gases in the same way and by using the results of the kinetic theory, we can extend the derivation of the barometric formula to get an expression for the fraction of particles in a gas within a range of speeds. This result was obtained (though by another method) by Maxwell, who showed that the distribution in speeds is given by

$$f(v)\Delta v = 4\pi \left(\frac{m}{2\pi kT}\right)^{3/2} v^2 e^{-mv^2/2kT}\Delta v, \tag{12.12}$$

where $f(v)\Delta v$ is the fraction of molecules that have speeds between v and $v + \Delta v$. Eq. (12.12) is called the **Maxwell-Boltzmann distribution** function. Figure 12.13 displays this function, computed for oxygen, neon, and helium gases at a temperature of 295 K. Figure 12.14 shows the distribution for oxygen at 295 K and 1000 K. Notice that the Maxwell-Boltzmann distribution function is not an exponential curve, although the equation does contain an exponential function. We do not expect you to memorize the details of this formula, but you should become familiar in a general way with the factors that determine the distribution and their significance. In particular, the shift of the curve with temperature and the factor in the exponent of kinetic energy $\frac{1}{2}mv^2$ divided by kT are worth noting.

The peak of each curve represents the most probable molecular speed for that temperature and gas. That is, the curve peaks at that speed exhibited by the largest fraction of molecules in the gas. The most probable speed depends on the temperature through

$$v_{\mathrm{mp}} = \sqrt{\frac{2kT}{m}}. \qquad (12.13)$$

Although many molecules have speeds near v_{mp}, the overall range of speeds is large in every case. More massive molecules have lower most probable speeds, in agreement with the predictions of kinetic theory for a given temperature. For a given gas, the most probable molecular speed becomes greater with increasing temperature. In particular, more molecules have high speeds and fewer molecules have low speeds, throughout the range of speeds. This ties in with our earlier results from kinetic theory that higher temperatures mean higher molecular kinetic energies.

In 1955, Miller and Kusch conducted a high-precision experiment to compare a measured speed distribution with the Maxwell-Boltzmann equation. They placed a container A, filled with a known gas, and a molecule detector B at opposite ends of a cylinder C of length L (Fig. 12.15). A large number of helical grooves were cut into the surface of the cylinder, only one of which is shown in the diagram. The cylinder rotated about its axis at a constant angular velocity ω. As the cylinder rotated, it was bombarded by molecules coming out of an aperture in the heated container A. A molecule from A would reach detector B only if its velocity matched the motion of the slit as the cylinder turned. The velocity of those molecules that reached B was proportional to the cylinder's speed of rotation ω. Miller and Kusch recorded the number of molecules detected (beam

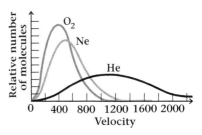

Figure 12.13
Maxwell-Boltzmann molecular-speed distribution for three different gases at $T = 295$ K. The differences are due to the different molecular masses.

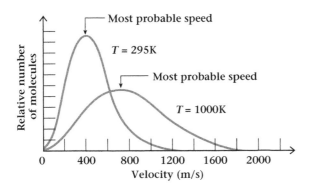

Figure 12.14
The distribution of molecular speeds for oxygen gas according to the Maxwell-Boltzmann distribution function at two different temperatures.

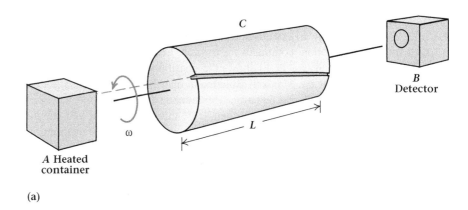

(a)

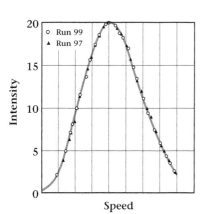

Figure 12.16
Distribution of molecular speeds in a gas. The points represent experimental observations; the solid line represents the Maxwell-Boltzmann distribution. (From R. C. Miller and P. Kusch, "Velocity Distributions in Potassium and Thallium Atomic Beams," *Physical Review,* vol. 99, August 15, 1955, p. 1314.)

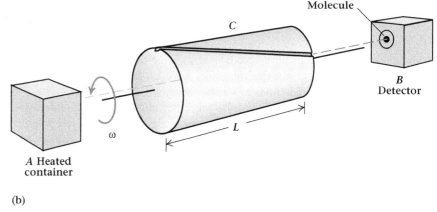

(b)

Figure 12.15
Apparatus for measuring the distribution of molecular speeds. As the grooved cylinder rotates, a molecule entering the groove at one end at just the right speed can continue in straight line motion and emerge from the far end. Molecules with other speeds will strike the edge of the groove and be scattered.

intensity) as a function of ω. This distribution of beam velocities was then used to get the distribution of molecular speeds in the container (Fig. 12.16). For other gases, the results were similar. In all cases, the distribution was consistent with the predictions of the Maxwell-Boltzmann distribution function.

▼ Summary

Useful Concepts

■ Boyle's law states that if the temperature and the amount of gas are held constant, then

$$P_1V_1 = P_2V_2 \quad \text{or} \quad PV = \text{constant}.$$

■ The law of Charles and Gay-Lussac states that for a gas at constant pressure,

$$\frac{V}{T} = \text{constant}.$$

■ We can predict the behavior of gases using the ideal gas law,

$$PV = nRT.$$

The agreement between prediction and observation is best when temperatures and pressures are near ordinary values.

■ The kinetic theory of gases shows how it is possible to connect the macroscopic properties of a gas, such as pressure and volume, with its microscopic properties, such as average molecular kinetic energy. The kinetic theory gives, for an ideal gas,

$$PV = \frac{2}{3}N\overline{KE}.$$

■ The kinetic-theory definition of temperature is

$$\overline{KE} = \frac{3}{2}kT.$$

■ The internal energy in a monatomic gas is the total translational kinetic energy of the gas due to random thermal motion of its molecules. It is given by

$$U = \frac{3}{2}nRT.$$

■ The pressure at a given height in the atmosphere is given by

$$P(z) = P_0 e^{-mgz/kT}.$$

Important Terms

You should be able to write the definition or meaning of each of the following:

Boyle's law	state variables
law of Charles and Gay-Lussac	kinetic theory of gases
ideal gas law	ideal gas
universal gas constant	Boltzmann constant
mole	internal energy
Avogadro's number	Maxwell-Boltzmann distribution
equation of state	

Conceptual Questions

12.1 A barometer of the type shown in Fig 12.2 is carried on an earth-orbiting satellite in which the cabin is pressurized to one atmosphere. Describe what an astronaut would observe if the apparatus were first laid on its side and then turned upside down.

12.2 If the atmosphere were made of only oxygen, instead of being primarily nitrogen, would barometers read higher or lower than they do now?

12.3 A car owner's manual says to measure the tire pressure before driving. What difference would it make if the pressure were measured after driving several miles at highway speeds?

12.4 Explain in words why the pressure of a gas increases when its volume is reduced.

12.5 Two gastight balloons are filled with helium at atmospheric pressure. One of the balloons is made from a latex material that stretches easily and the other is made from a material that does not stretch. Which balloon will rise higher?

12.6 Explain how the buoyancy of a submarine can be adjusted.

12.7 In the kinetic model of a gas we assumed elastic collisions between the molecules. How would the model change if inelastic collisions were allowed?

12.8 How would the results of our kinetic model be modified if we assumed that the size of the molecules is not negligible in comparison to the distance between them?

12.9 Give an explanation for the difference between heat and temperature, based on the kinetic theory.

12.10 At high altitude, the ratio of nitrogen to oxygen in the atmosphere increases above the ratio at sea level. Why?

12.11 Is the total kinetic energy of the molecules of air in a warm room greater than the total kinetic energy of the molecules of air in the same room when it is cool? Why? (*Hint:* The pressure is unchanged.)

12.12 An attempt is made to construct a barometer as indicated in Fig. 12.17. The barometer differs from the ordinary Torricellian tube only in that two liquids are employed as shown. (a) Can such a barometer be made if liquid *A* is mercury and liquid *B* is water? (b) Can such a barometer be made if liquid *A* is water and liquid *B* is mercury? Explain your reasoning in each case.

12.13 What is the difference between the average speed of the molecules in a gas and the rms speed?

12.14 How does the average velocity of the molecules in a gas differ from their average speed?

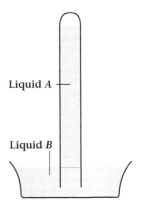

Figure 12.17
Question 12.12.

Problems

Section 12.1 The Pressure of Air

Hints for Solving Problems

Remember that pressure is force per unit area. The gauge pressure due to the weight of a fluid of density ρ and depth h is $P = \rho g h$.

12.1 How high will the liquid stand in a Torricellian tube filled with methyl alcohol if the atmospheric pressure is 101 kPa and the temperature is 20°C? The density of methyl alcohol is 791 kg/m³.

12.2 A Torricellian tube similar to the one in Fig. 12.2 supports a column of liquid 8.17 m high when the atmospheric pressure is 101 kPa. What is the liquid? (*Hint:* You may want to refer to the table of densities in Chapter 10.)

12.3 A mercury barometer is tilted at an angle of 45° from the vertical (Fig. 12.18). How far up the tube is the end of the mercury column, as measured along the tube? Assume that the temperature is 20°C and the atmospheric pressure is 101 kPa.

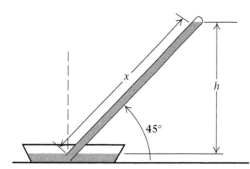

Figure 12.18
Problem 12.3.

12.4 What is the total downward atmospheric force on the top of a 0.21-m by 0.26-m book lying on a table? Why doesn't this force break the table?

12.5• Estimate the "total weight" of the atmosphere, using your knowledge of barometers and given the radius of the earth.

12.6• The air-conditioning system of a department store is designed to maintain a pressure of 0.20 in. of water above atmospheric pressure. What is the net force due to pressure on a rectangular display window that is 3.0 m × 4.0 m? (*Hint:* First convert the pressure of 0.20 in. of water to pascals.)

Section 12.2 Boyle's Law

Hints for Solving Problems

Remember to express temperatures in kelvins. It is often helpful to establish ratios of old and new state variables (P, V, T) when calculating changes in a gas.

12.7 If you can use your abdominal and chest muscles to decrease the volume of your lungs by 20%, what pressure can you develop by this method alone?

12.8 A cylinder with a cross-sectional area of 10.0 cm² is fitted with a movable piston. Air is introduced into the cylinder at atmospheric pressure and a temperature of 20°C. The temperature is held constant as the volume is compressed to half its initial volume. How much force must be applied to the piston to maintain it in its new position?

12.9• A 1.0-m long cylinder 6.0-cm in diameter is closed at one end and fitted with a moveable piston. The interior pressure is 1.0 atm when the piston is 0.50 m from the closed end. Make a graph of the pressure in the cylinder versus distance of the piston from the closed end for distances from 0.10 m to 0.80 m if the temperature of the cylinder and its contents is held constant.

12.10• The cylinder of a bicycle pump has an interior diameter of 2.0 cm and a length of 25 cm. It is used to put air into a tire where the pressure is already 240 kPa. How far down must you push the piston before air begins flowing into the tire?

12.11• A spherical bubble rises from the bottom of a lake. If the lake temperature is uniform and the bubble doubles its volume by the time it reaches the surface, how deep is the lake?

12.12• (a) How much force would the teams of horses have had to apply to pull the Magdeburg hemispheres apart? Their diameter is 55 cm. A rough estimate is that 90% of the air was removed from the sphere by the vacuum pump.
(b) Is there anything surprising in this result?

Section 12.3 The Law of Charles and Gay-Lussac

Hints for Solving Problems

When working problems in this chapter, you may use the approximation $T_K = T_C + 273$ when converting temperatures.

12.13 A 1.00-L sample of an ideal gas at room temperature (23°C) is taken outside on a cool day (6°C) in a constant-pressure container similar to the one in Fig. 12.7(a). What is the new volume?

12.14 A one-meter-long glass tube is sealed at one end. A drop of mercury large enough to close off the tube is placed at the midpoint when the temperature is 0°C. Where will the mercury be when the closed end of the tube is immersed in boiling water?

12.15 We wish to double the volume of a gas held at constant pressure. To what temperature must we heat it if its original temperature was (a) 0°C, (b) 100°C, and (c) 1000°C?

12.16 (a) By what fraction of its initial volume does the volume of a gas decrease at constant pressure if the temperature is lowered from 100°C to 0°C? (b) What will be the fractional change if the temperature is lowered from 0°C to −100°C?

12.17 A column of dry air was sealed off from the atmosphere by closing one end of a glass tube and placing a drop of mercury in the tube 0.50 m from the closed end. This was done at some unknown temperature. The tube was then placed into a freezer where the temperature was known to be −10°C. After the tube reached the temperature of the freezer, the mercury slug was found to be 42 cm from the closed end. What was the original temperature?

Section 12.4 The Ideal Gas Law

Hints for Solving Problems

The value of the gas constant R in the ideal gas equation $PV = nRT$ is $R = 8.314$ J/mol · K.

12.18 The temperature of a 1.00-L sample of gas at atmospheric pressure is 33°C. How many moles of gas are in the sample?

12.19 Calculate the volume occupied by one mole of hydrogen gas at STP.

12.20 (a) How many molecules are there in one cubic meter of argon at STP? (b) How many molecules of radon are there in one cubic meter at STP? (STP means standard temperature and pressure: 0°C and 101 kPa.)

12.21 A cylinder closed at both ends has a piston in between that is free to slide. At 20°C, the piston is exactly in the center when hydrogen gas is in one end and helium in the other (Fig. 12.19). (a) What is the ratio of the number of hydrogen molecules to the number of helium molecules? (b) Where will the piston be if the temperature is raised to 57°C?

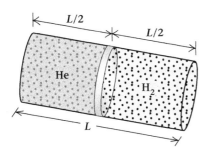

Figure 12.19
Problem 12.21.

12.22• Calculate the volume occupied by 50 g of carbon dioxide gas at a pressure of one atmosphere and a temperature of 25°C. Assume that the ideal gas law is obeyed.

12.23• A cylindrical propane tank used for portable cooking stoves has an interior length of 16.5 cm and a diameter of 6.5 cm. The mass of the gas inside is 400 g. Approximately how much pressure is exerted on the walls of the container when the temperature is 75°F? Propane has a molecular mass of 44 g/mol.

12.24• An unknown gas has a density of 1.784 kg/m³ at STP. (STP, for standard temperature and pressure, means a temperature of 0°C and a pressure of 101 kPa.) The gas does not

burn, support combustion, or react strongly with polished metal surfaces. (a) What is the gram molecular mass? (b) What is the most probable identity of the gas?

12.25• One cubic centimeter of water is converted to steam at atmospheric pressure and 100°C. What is the volume of the resulting steam?

12.26•• A spherical bubble rises from the bottom of a lake whose temperature is 7°C at the bottom and 27°C at the surface. If the bubble doubles its volume by the time it reaches the surface, how deep is the lake?

Sections 12.5 and 12.6 The Kinetic Theory of Gases and the Kinetic-Theory Definition of Temperature

12.27 Show, using the numbers 1, 3, 7, and 8, that the root-mean-square value and the average value are not the same.

12.28 What is the rms speed of hydrogen molecules at a temperature of 23°C? The mass of a hydrogen molecule is 3.34×10^{-27} kg.

12.29 A student plans to build a cubical box to hold a gas at a temperature of 17°C and a pressure of 101 kPa. He wants the number of gas molecules inside to equal the population of the United States (260 million). What length are the edges of the box?

12.30 (a) At what temperature is the rms speed of a molecule of hydrogen gas equal to 2200 m/s? (b) If you wished to reduce the rms speed of the molecules in hydrogen gas to 1100 m/s, what temperature would be required? The mass of a hydrogen molecule is 3.34×10^{-27} kg.

12.31 Find the average kinetic energy of helium atoms at a temperature of 500 K. Assume ideal gas behavior.

12.32 What is the average kinetic energy of oxygen molecules (O_2) at a temperature of 300 K? Assume oxygen to be an ideal gas.

12.33 What is the density of a gas, at a pressure of one atmosphere, in which the molecules have an rms speed of 450 m/s? (*Hint:* Study Example 12.7.)

12.34• Hydrogen (H_2) and helium (He) gases are mixed in a container. What is the ratio of the rms velocity of the heavier gas to that of the lighter gas? The mass of a helium molecule is approximately twice the mass of a hydrogen molecule.

12.35• The speed of sound in a gas is proportional to the rms speed of the molecules. What is the ratio of the speed of sound at 27°C to that at 0°C?

12.36• The speed of sound in a gas is proportional to the rms speed of the molecules. Show that the speed of sound in an ideal gas depends on the temperature and molecular mass, but not on the density. (See Example 12.8.)

12.37• (a) If the root-mean-square velocity of a molecule in a gas at 300 K were 100 m/s, what would be its mass? (b) Is this a realistic example?

12.38•• Starting with $v_{rms} = \sqrt{\dfrac{3P}{\rho}}$, where P is the pressure and ρ is the density of an ideal gas, show that the rms speed can be put in the form $v_{rms} = \sqrt{\dfrac{3kT}{m}}$, where k is Boltzmann's constant, T the temperature, and m the molecular mass.

Section 12.7 Internal Energy of an Ideal Gas

12.39 Calculate the total internal energy of an ideal gas confined to a volume of 10 L at a pressure of 2.0 atm and a temperature of 300 K.

12.40 Calculate the internal energy of one mole of helium gas at a temperature of 300 K. Assume ideal gas behavior.

12.41 Calculate the internal energy of 12 g of argon gas at a temperature of 300 K. Assume ideal gas behavior.

*Section 12.8 The Barometric Formula and the Distribution of Molecular Speeds

12.42 Plot a graph of the number density versus height for an atmosphere consisting of oxygen (O_2) only at a temperature of 23°C. Assume a unit density ($n = 1$) at $z = 0$. Plot your graph from $z = 0$ to $z = 15$ km.

12.43 Calculate the atmospheric pressure at a height of 5900 m for air with average molecular mass of 29 g/mol and uniform temperature of 290 K, given that the sea level pressure is P_0.

12.44• Use the barometric formula to estimate the ratio of the atmospheric pressure at Myrtle Beach, South Carolina (sea-level elevation), when the air temperature is 27°C, to the pressure at Denver, Colorado (1610 m above sea level), when the temperature is 10°C. (Use the mass given in Example 12.10.)

12.45• (a) At what height above sea level is the atmospheric pressure half the pressure at sea level? Assume that the temperature is a constant 0°C. (b) How high must you go for the pressure to drop to one-fourth the pressure at sea level? (Use the mass given in Example 12.10.)

12.46• Calculate the height at which atmospheric pressure is half the sea-level pressure P_0 for an atmosphere consisting solely of nitrogen (N_2) at a uniform temperature of 300 K.

12.47•• The maximum value of the Maxwell-Boltzmann distribution function occurs for a speed $v_{mp} = \sqrt{\dfrac{2kT}{m}}$. Find an expression for the magnitude of the distribution function at this speed.

Additional Problems

12.48 Air at a pressure of one atmosphere is confined to a volume V_0. If it is compressed at constant temperature to a volume of $\frac{1}{3}V_0$, what is the resulting pressure?

12.49 The velocity of sound in air is given by $v = \sqrt{\dfrac{1.4P}{\rho}}$, where P is the pressure and ρ the density of the air. What is the ratio of the rms velocity of the air molecules to the velocity of sound?

12.50• (a) Approximately how many molecules of air at STP (0°C and 101 kPa) are there in a room measuring 10 ft × 12 ft × 8 ft? (b) How much do the molecules weigh if the average molecular mass for air is 28.8 g/mol? (c) What is their average separation? (d) If they were all compacted so that the material had the same density as water, what volume would they occupy?

12.51• Nitrogen gas (N_2) is held in a 1.0-L container at a pressure of 15 atm and a temperature of 18°C. (a) How many moles of nitrogen are inside the container? (b) What is the total mass of nitrogen in the container?

12.52•• An upright cylinder, 1.00 m tall and closed at its lower end, is fitted with a light piston that is free to slide (Fig. 12.20). Initially the piston is in the center. A cuplike cavity is formed by the top of the piston and the upper cylinder walls. Water is poured into the cavity until it is full. At what fraction of the total height of the cylinder will the piston be when the cavity is full? Assume that the lower portion of the cylinder contains an ideal gas at constant temperature.

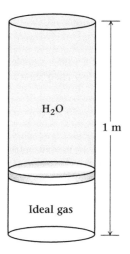

Figure 12.20
Problem 12.52.

12.53•• A bubble of 1.00-cm diameter is released at the bottom of a lake that is 30 m deep. The temperature at the bottom is 5°C, and near the surface it is 17°C. What is the diameter of the bubble when it reaches the surface?

12.54•• A 1.00-cm-diameter bubble is released at the bottom of a lake. The temperature at the bottom is 7°C, and near the surface it is 17°C. When the bubble reaches the surface its diameter is 1.80 cm. How deep is the lake?

12.55•• (a) How many molecules are there in a cubic meter of argon at a temperature of 23°C and a pressure of one atmosphere? (b) What is the total kinetic energy of these molecules? (c) How fast would someone have to throw a baseball (0.17 kg) in order for it to have a kinetic energy equal to the total kinetic energy in part (b)?

12.56•• A 1.0-L container of an ideal gas at 300 kPa and 20°C is connected through a small tube to a 10-L container of the same gas at 100 kPa and 25°C. After the gas has come to equilibrium, its temperature is 22°C. What is the pressure of the gas?

12.57•• (a) At what temperature is the rms speed of nitrogen gas equal to the escape velocity from the earth? (b) At what temperature is the rms speed of oxygen gas equal to the

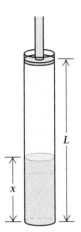

Figure 12.21
Problem 12.59.

escape velocity? (c) How would this result affect the composition of the air in the upper atmosphere, where the temperature is about 1000 K? The masses of oxygen and nitrogen molecules can be determined from Table 12.1.

12.58●● What is the ratio of the probability that a molecule of a gas has the most probable speed to the probability that it has a speed of twice the most probable speed?

12.59●● An instrument once used for measuring ocean depths from sailing ships consisted of a long heavy tube open at the bottom. When the tube was lowered into the water by a wire attached to the upper end (Fig. 12.21), the increased water pressure with depth compressed the air in the tube. When the tube was withdrawn from the water, the point to which the water had risen in the tube could be measured and used to determine the depth to which the tube had been lowered. Derive an expression for the approximate depth d in terms of the length of the tube L, the height x to which the water rises in the tube, atmospheric pressure P_0, the density of sea water ρ, and the acceleration of gravity g. For simplicity, assume that the temperature of the water is uniform and that the temperature of the gas in the tube is constant.

12.60●● Imagine making a proverbial lead balloon from a very thin lead foil. (a) Estimate the thickness of the foil for a lead balloon 1.00 m in diameter if it is to just float in air at STP when filled with hydrogen at STP. The average molecular mass for air is 28.8 g/mol. (b) Is this a realistic situation? Explain.

The Exponential Function

In many cases in the physical and biological sciences, the rate of change of a variable is proportional to the variable itself. The growth rate of a biological cell, the rate of growth of a population (whether people, plants, or bacteria), the rate of decay of a radioactive material, the rate of cooling of a hot object—all these examples represent rates of change that are proportional to the amount of material present. The function that reflects this characteristic is called the *exponential function.*

Let us examine some of the properties of the exponential function. We call our function, the dependent variable, y, and call the independent variable x. The variable x can be displacement, time, temperature, or any other quantity. In Fig. A12.1 we have drawn curve a whose slope $\Delta y/\Delta x$ increases as x increases. Curve b has a constant slope, and curve c has a slope that decreases with increasing x. The relationship between x and y in the exponential function has a graphical form that looks more like curve a than the other curves in Fig. A12.1. For the moment, we are considering only increasing rates of change.

Now let us look for a specific relationship between x and y that satisfies our requirements. Table A12.1 shows the powers-of-ten notation that we have frequently used earlier in this book. Powers of other numbers can be

Table A12.1	Several Base Numbers Raised to Various Powers		
$10^0 = 1$		$1.5^0 = 1$	$2^0 = 1$
$10^1 = 10$		$1.5^1 = 1.5$	$2^1 = 2$
$10^2 = 100$		$1.5^2 = 2.3$	$2^2 = 4$
$10^3 = 1000$		$1.5^3 = 3.4$	$2^3 = 8$
$10^4 = 10000$		$1.5^4 = 5.1$	$2^4 = 16$
$10^{4.5} = 31622$		$1.5^{4.5} = 6.2$	$2^{4.5} = 22.6$
$10^5 = 100000$		$1.5^5 = 7.6$	$2^5 = 32$

treated in the same way. The table gives several examples and shows that neither the base numbers nor the powers to which they are raised need to be integers. We display these relationships graphically in Figs. A12.2 and A12.3. Notice that the slope increases with increasing x for all of these curves. In Fig. A12.2, we have drawn a tangent to the curve at two points, A and B, and have determined the slope of the curve at these particular values of x. We can plot the slope $\Delta y/\Delta x$ of the curve as a function of x. The gray lines drawn in Fig. A12.3 are the slopes of the respective colored curves.

After studying Fig. A12.3, we can conclude that there is only one curve for which the slope and the original curve are identical. Such a curve corresponds to a base

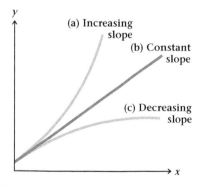

Figure A12.1
Curves with various slopes. The slope increases with increasing x for curve a. The slope is constant for curve b. The slope decreases with increasing x for curve c.

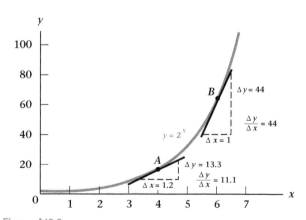

Figure A12.2
A graph of $y = 2^x$. The tangents at A and at B are the slopes of the curve at those points.

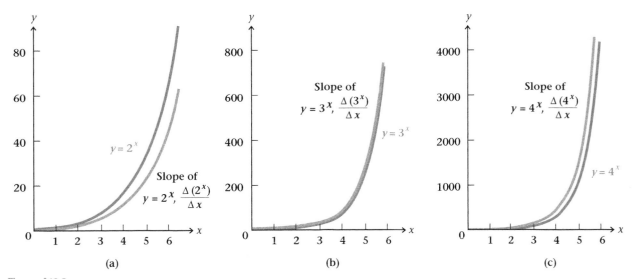

Figure A12.3

Graphs of the form $y = a^x$ and their slopes. The red lines give the values of y, the gray lines give the slopes of the red lines.

number we call e, whose magnitude is such that, for every point x,

$$\text{slope } (e^x) = \frac{\Delta(e^x)}{\Delta x} = e^x.$$

You should be able to guess from the figure that the number e must be between 2 and 3. In fact, it is an irrational number with a value of approximately 2.718. We see, then, that there is a function of x for which the slope of that function is just equal to the function itself. This function is the exponential function e^x. Table A12.2 gives values of e^x for some values of x.

In the equation for pressure in the atmosphere (Eq. 12.9), we required only that the slope of the curve be proportional to the curve, not equal to it. This requirement, too, is satisfied by an exponential function. For example, consider the number e raised to the power ax, where a is a constant. From the above equation we have

$$\text{slope } (e^{ax}) = \frac{\Delta(e^{ax})}{\Delta ax} = e^{ax},$$

where we have replaced x with ax. Since a is constant, $\Delta(ax) = a(\Delta x)$ and the equation becomes

$$\frac{\Delta(e^{ax})}{a\Delta x} = e^{ax}$$

$$\frac{\Delta(e^{ax})}{\Delta x} = ae^{ax}.$$

The exponential function e^x closely represents many processes observed in nature. It is characterized not only by its rapid increase with increasing x, but also by the increase in the rate of change with increasing x. To get a

Table A12.2	*Values of e^x*
x	**e^x**
0.0	1.000
0.5	1.649
1.0	2.718
1.5	4.482
2.0	7.389
2.5	12.182
3.0	20.09
3.5	33.12
4.0	54.60
4.5	90.02
5.0	148.4
5.5	244.7
6.0	403.4
6.5	665.1
7.0	1097
7.5	1808
8.0	2981

Note: $e^{-x} = 1/e^x$.

feeling for how rapidly the values of $y = e^x$ grow with increasing x, think of graphing the function on a large blackboard, with the axes scaled in centimeters. At $x = 1$ cm, the graph is $y = e^1 \approx 3$ cm above the x axis. At $x = 6$ cm, the graph is $y = e^6 \approx 403$ cm ≈ 4 m high (it is about to go through the ceiling if it hasn't done so already). At $x = 10$ cm, the graph is $e^{10} \approx 22{,}026$ cm ≈ 220 m high, higher than most buildings. At $x = 24$ cm, the graph is more than halfway to the moon, and at $x = 43$ cm from the origin, the graph is high enough to reach past the nearest star, Proxima Centauri:

$e^{43} \approx 4.7 \times 10^{18}$ cm $= 4.7 \times 10^{13}$ km

$\qquad\qquad = 1.57 \times 10^8$ light seconds

$\qquad\qquad$ (light travels at 300,000 km/s in a vacuum)

$\qquad\qquad = 5.0$ light-years.

The distance to Proxima Centauri is about 4.3 light-years. Thus, for $x = 43$ cm from the origin (less than 2 feet to the right of the y axis), the y component of the graph is nearly 5 light-years from the x axis.*

If we have a case in which the rate of change in y decreases in proportion to increasing x, then we have a result of the form $y = e^{-x}$ (Fig. A12.4), as is the case for the barometric formula of Eq. (12.11). Such a situation is called exponential decay. We will encounter equations of this form when we study radioactive decay in Chapter 26.

In the previous paragraphs, we have discussed the exponential function $y = e^x$. Table A12.2 gives values of y corresponding to a range of values of x. However, in some cases we may already know y but need to know x. We can find x by taking the logarithm of both sides of this equation. In general, if $N = a^b$, a is called the base. The logarithm of N with respect to the base a is the power to which the base must be raised to give N. In practice, both $e = 2.718 \ldots$ and 10 are commonly used as bases for

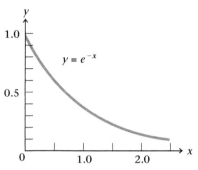

Figure A12.4
A graph of the function $y = e^{-x}$.

logarithms. When the base e is used, we refer to the logarithm as the natural logarithm and use the symbol ln. When base 10 is used, the symbol for the logarithm is log.

When we take the natural logarithm of both sides of the equation $y = e^x$, we get ln $y = x$. We can find the natural logarithm with a pocket calculator or with the aid of a table. For example, suppose we know that $7.00 = e^x$ and want to find x. In this case, we find $x = $ ln $7.00 = 1.95$. Be careful in your computations that you use the natural logarithm (ln) and not the logarithm to the base 10 (log).

The following relationships for logarithms are very useful:

$$\log (xy) = \log x + \log y,$$
$$\log (x/y) = \log x - \log y,$$
$$\log (x^n) = n \log x.$$

Although we have written these relations with log (base 10), they are valid for any base, including base e.

*From G. B. Thomas, Jr., and R. L. Finney, *Calculus and Analytic Geometry,* 8th ed. (Reading, Mass.: Addison-Wesley, 1992), p. 440.

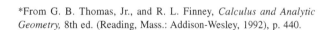

Problems

A12.1 Plot the curve $y = e^{-0.1x}$ from $x = 0$ to $x = 10$. Determine the slope at $x = 5$ by calculation and by graphical techniques.

A12.2 Plot the curve $y = e^{-0.02x}$ from $x = 0$ to $x = 100$. Determine the slope at $x = 40$ by calculation and by graphical techniques.

A12.3 Plot a graph of $y = e^x$ from $x = -2$ to $x = +2$ in steps of $\Delta x = 0.2$.

A12.4• The intensity of a beam of light traveling in a glass fiber decreases with distance x according to

$$I = I_0 e^{-kx},$$

where I_0 is the intensity at $x = 0$ and k is the absorption coefficient. What is the absorption coefficient if the intensity decreases to $0.50 I_0$ in a distance of 3.5 km?

A12.5•• The rate R_0 at which a sample of radioactive material emits radiation is measured to be 1200 particles per minute at time $t = 0$. The rate R at a later time t is given by $R = R_0 e^{-0.693t/T}$, where T equals 26 min and is called the half-life of the material. What is the rate of the radiation in particles per minute at $t = 2.0$ h?

A12.6•• In a biology experiment, the number of cells N in a particular population is given by $N = N_0 e^{at}$, where N_0 is the number of cells at time $t = 0$ and where $a = 0.30$/h. By what factor will the population increase in 24 h?

A12.7•• To what power does the base e have to be raised to give a number equal to the population of the United States (260×10^6)?

13.1 Thermal Equilibrium
13.2 The First Law of Thermodynamics
13.3 The Carnot Cycle and the Efficiency
of Engines

Physics in Practice: Gasoline Engines

13.4 Refrigerators and Heat Pumps
13.5 The Second Law of Thermodynamics
13.6 Entropy and the Second Law
*****13.7** Energy and Thermal Pollution

Thermodynamics

The area of physics concerned with the relationships between heat and work is called **thermodynamics.** Our recognition of heat as a form of energy transfer and our application of energy conservation in calorimetry provide introductory glimpses into this science. But the concerns of thermodynamics are much broader and more elegant than simply the measurement of heat. The underlying basis of thermodynamics is found in two general laws of nature abstracted from our universal observations and experience. The first law states that you cannot get more energy out of a system than you put into it, in all forms. While this sounds like a straightforward statement, its implications are quite profound and important. The second law says that the transfer of energy by heat flow has a direction; in other words, not all processes in nature are reversible. If a polar bear lies down in the snow, heat from its body will melt the snow; but the bear can't extract energy from the snow to warm itself. Thus, the flow of thermal energy has a direction—from hot to cold. By logical extension of these laws, we can correlate many measurable properties of matter with one another. Thermodynamic formulas predict many relationships between properties of matter and have the same general validity as the two laws on which they are based.

The development of thermodynamics grew out of a very practical concern with the operation of steam engines in the early nineteenth century. James Watt (1736–1819), a Scottish engineer and inventor, made steam power practical by markedly improving the efficiency of steam engines. His improvements, which resulted from his keen physical insight into thermal processes, were of such magnitude that he is often spoken of as the inventor of the steam engine.

The principles of thermodynamics that were developed in the eighteenth and nineteenth centuries made possible the tremendous advances in the power and efficiency of engines, from Watt's early steam engines to today's steam-driven electric power plants. The search for new and more efficient sources of energy continues today. But we recognize that all potential advances must still follow the laws of thermodynamics; no matter what new sources we tap, we can't get something for nothing. ■

13.1 Thermal Equilibrium

We saw in the previous chapter, that two objects in thermal contact can exchange heat as long as they are at different temperatures. The warmer object cools as the cooler one warms until they reach a common temperature at which no further changes take place. Two objects in this condition are said to be in a state of thermal equilibrium. In this state, a net flow of energy from one object to the other ceases, and they are at the same temperature throughout.

What happens if we introduce a third object? For example, suppose we take a bottle of milk *A* from the refrigerator and place it in an ideal insulating chest (Fig. 13.1a), where it exchanges heat with a can of orange juice *B* until they come to thermal equilibrium. (The chest insulates them from the outside world.) The objects remain in thermal equilibrium if they are separated. That is, if we place the juice in another insulated chest, it is still in equilibrium with the milk. Now, if a second can of juice *C* is also in thermal equilibrium with the milk *A* (Fig. 13.1b), we may ask the question: What is the relationship of *B* to *C*? Experiments show that *B* and *C* are in thermal equilibrium as well. This result may be stated as follows: **Two objects, each in thermal equilibrium with a third**

Figure 13.1
(a) Objects *A* and *B* at different temperatures come to thermal equilibrium when placed in thermal contact. (b) They remain in thermal equilibrium even when separated if no heat is exchanged with their environment. Then if object *C* is in thermal equilibrium with *A*, is it also in equilibrium with *B*?

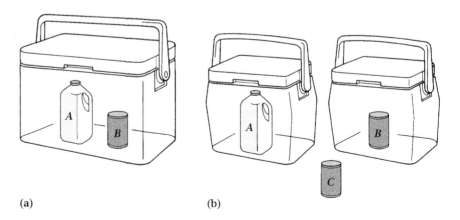

(a)   (b)

object, are in thermal equilibrium with each other. This rule is known as the **zeroth law of thermodynamics.** It is called the "zeroth" law because it logically precedes the statements of the first and second laws of thermodynamics, but was not recognized as an important and fundamental law of nature until after these other laws had been stated and named.

In the study of thermodynamics, we introduce the concept of a system and consider the transfer of energy into or out of the system by heat or work. The system could be any physical system, such as a machine (an automobile engine), a chemical system (a burning log), or a biological system (you). **A thermodynamic system** is any collection of objects considered together; the rest of the universe is the environment of the system. A thermodynamic system interacts with its surrounding environment by heat transfer and/or work. As a result of this energy exchange with the environment, the system's internal energy may change. By **internal energy,** we mean the total kinetic and potential energy associated with the internal state of the atoms composing the system. In addition, the system may also have kinetic and potential energies due to its collective motion and outside forces, such as the force of gravity.

Be sure you understand the differences among temperature, internal energy, and heat. Temperature is a measure of the warmth of an object; as we saw in Chapter 12, on an atomic level it is determined by the average random kinetic energy of the object's atoms. Internal energy is the sum of the kinetic and potential energies of the internal motion of all the atoms in the object. Heat is the transfer of energy to or from an object, either by changing the kinetic energy of the atoms (changing an object's temperature) or by changing the potential energy of the atoms (changing an object's phase).

13.2 The First Law of Thermodynamics

The first law of thermodynamics is based on the principle of the conservation of energy: that energy is neither created nor destroyed in any thermodynamic system. As is true of many other scientific laws, there is no absolute proof for the first law. Rather, it is an extrapolation of our experience and has no known exception. However, we must be sure we know all the forms in which energy can occur before we apply the first law to some specific system.

In the usual formulation of the first law, we consider the transfer of heat into a system, the work performed by the system, and the change in the system's internal energy. If we let Q be the net amount of heat flowing *into* a system during some process and W be the net work done *by* the system, then conservation of energy gives

$$Q = W + \Delta U,$$

where ΔU is the change in the system's internal energy. Upon rearranging, we find

$$\boxed{\Delta U = Q - W.} \tag{13.1}$$

The meaning of two of the terms in this equation should be clear from prior chapters: Work was encountered earlier in our study of mechanics; and heat, as a form of energy transfer, was treated in Section 11.4. A negative value of Q means that heat is being given out by the system instead of being added to the system. Similarly, a negative value of W means that work is being performed on the system rather than being done by the system. The internal energy U of the system can take a variety of forms and depends only on the temperature of the system. Equation (13.1) is the usual mathematical statement of the **first law of thermodynamics.** In words, **the change in internal energy of a system equals the difference between the heat taken in by the system and the work done by the system.** That is, when an amount of heat Q is added to a system, some of this added energy remains in the system increasing its internal energy by an amount ΔU while the rest of the added energy leaves the system as the system does work W.

Since the first law is a statement about energy, to apply it we need to specify, or measure, the energy or energy change of a system. For a purely mechanical system this is fairly easy to do because we can measure the masses and determine their velocities or positions. But with heat, things are different. There are no perfect thermal insulators to keep energy confined to a certain place. For that reason, among others, we must carefully identify the system under consideration and separate "the system" from "the rest of the universe" or what is usually called the *environment.*

A thermodynamic system, no matter what its composition, may undergo several special kinds of processes involving energy. If no heat enters or leaves the system during some process, then the system is said to be perfectly isolated from its environment and the process is called **adiabatic.** A good approximation to an adiabatic process is anything that happens so rapidly that heat does not have time to flow in or out of the system, as in the rapid compression of air in a tire pump. If $Q = 0$ in the first law (Eq. 13.1), we are left with

$$\Delta U = -W \qquad \text{(adiabatic process).}$$

Thus, in an adiabatic process, the system does not exchange heat with its environment, but undergoes a change in internal energy that is the negative of the work done by the system. For example, when the system does work on the environment, W is positive and the resulting ΔU is negative.

If the temperature of a system does not change during a process, the process is said to be **isothermal.** An approximately isothermal process proceeds so slowly that the rate of change in temperature is negligible. Slow compression of air in a tire pump is an example of such a process, provided that air is not allowed to flow out of the cylinder. Because the kinetic energy of the air molecules is proportional to the temperature, the internal energy remains constant during an isothermal process that involves no change of phase or chemical change. Therefore, from the first law, the heat absorbed by the system must equal the work done by the system:

$$Q = W \qquad \text{(isothermal process).}$$

Most processes in nature are neither strictly adiabatic nor strictly isothermal, but we can approximate many processes by treating them as one or the other, or as one followed by the other.

A process in which the volume of the system does not change is called isovolumetric or **isochoric.** Heating a gas in a rigid, tightly sealed container is an example of such a process. In a process that goes forward at constant volume, no displacement can take place, so the work done by the system is zero. (Remember, work is force times displacement.) Then, from the first law, we have only two terms,

$$Q = \Delta U \quad \text{(isochoric process).}$$

That is, in an isochoric process, no work is done by the system, and any heat added to the system goes into increasing its internal energy.

If the pressure does not change during a process, the process is called **isobaric.** One example of an isobaric process is the boiling of water in an open container. Since the container is open, the process occurs at constant atmospheric pressure. At the boiling point, the temperature of the water no longer increases with the addition of heat; instead there is a change of phase from water to steam.

Many of the thermodynamic systems we will use to illustrate new principles consist of a fluid, often a gas. So we often find it convenient to express work in terms of pressure rather than force. In practice, a thermodynamic system might be the water and steam system in a steam engine or the system of gasoline and air in an internal combustion engine.

Figure 13.2 shows a cylinder of gas fitted with a piston. If the gas pushes the piston out an amount Δx, the increment of work done $F \Delta x$ can be written in terms of the pressure P and the change in volume ΔV:

$$\Delta W = F \Delta x = \frac{F}{A}(\Delta x \, A) = P \, \Delta V. \tag{13.2}$$

The total work W done by the gas is the sum of these small increments, taking proper account of the relationship between pressure and volume in the case being investigated. A gas-filled cylinder fitted with a piston is the simplest form of what is called a *heat engine.* Such a heat engine is used to model more complicated systems, from automobile engines to biological systems.

As we noted, the change in a system's internal energy can take many different forms, including changes in temperature, changes of phase, and chemical changes. In the following examples we will consider a change in internal energy corresponding to a change in temperature. However, this is not the only possibility.

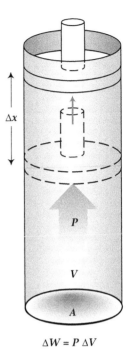

$\Delta W = P \, \Delta V$

Figure 13.2
The increment of work ΔW done by an expanding gas is $P \, \Delta V$.

Example 13.1

Show that in an isochoric process the change in temperature is proportional to the change in internal energy.

Solution As we have seen, in an isochoric process, $Q = \Delta U$. From Chapter 11 we also know that the heat added to a mass m of a substance is related to the temperature change ΔT and the specific heat c by

$$Q = mc \, \Delta T.$$

(We assume no change in phase occurs in this process.) Upon equating these two expressions for Q, we obtain

$$\Delta U = mc \, \Delta T.$$

What we have shown in this special case is generally true: Temperature is associated with the internal energy of a system.

▼

Example 13.2

Gas confined by a piston (Fig. 13.2) in a heat engine expands against a constant pressure of 100 kPa (nearly one atmosphere). When 2×10^4 J of heat are absorbed by the system, the volume of the gas expands from 0.15 m^3 to 0.25 m^3. (a) What is the work done by the system during this process? (b) What is the change in internal energy of the system?

Strategy Here we have a gas kept at constant pressure by a moveable piston, so we can use the expression $P \Delta V$ to determine the work. Because the gas expands, work is done by the system and the work will be positive. We can then use this result and the first law to find the change in internal energy of the system, keeping in mind that because heat is added to the system, the heat is also positive.

Solution (a) The work done at constant pressure is

$$W = P \, \Delta V = P(V_{\text{final}} - V_{\text{initial}})$$
$$W = (100 \times 10^3 \text{ N/m}^2)(0.25 \text{ m}^3 - 0.15 \text{ m}^3) = 1 \times 10^4 \text{ J}.$$

(b) The change in internal energy is obtained from the first law of thermodynamics:

$$\Delta U = Q - W.$$

In this case, Q is 2×10^4 J. The work W done by the gas was just found to be 1×10^4 J. Thus, the change in internal energy is

$$\Delta U = 2 \times 10^4 \text{ J} - 1 \times 10^4 \text{ J} = 1 \times 10^4 \text{ J}.$$

Discussion In this case, in which there is no change of phase, the increase in internal energy shows up as an increase in temperature.

▼

Example 13.3

A heat engine undergoes a process in which its internal energy decreases by 400 J while it is doing 250 J of work. What net heat is taken in (or given out) by the engine during this process?

Strategy Work is done by the engine, so W is a positive quantity. The internal energy decreases, so ΔU is negative. We can insert the numerical values into the expression for the first law to find the value and sign of the thermal energy flow into the system.

Solution The heat taken in (or given out) by the system can be found from the first law of thermodynamics, Eq. (13.1), which can be rewritten in the form

$$Q = \Delta U + W.$$

Here $\Delta U = -400$ J and $W = 250$ J. The heat Q is

$$Q = -400 \text{ J} + 250 \text{ J} = -150 \text{ J}.$$

Discussion The negative sign for Q indicates that the net heat is given out by the system. The negative value of ΔU indicates that, in the absence of a phase change, the temperature decreases.

The first law of thermodynamics relates two measurable quantities that pertain to changes in a system: the heat added to or given out by the system and the work performed on or done by the system. We can measure the thermodynamic properties of systems in many ways: the length of a mercury column in a thermometer; the volume, pressure, or temperature of a sample of gas; or the resistance of a resistor. All of these properties are state variables or state coordinates. A state variable is a physical property that characterizes the state of a system independently of how that particular state is reached. For example, a cup of tea at room temperature has the same temperature whether it cools from boiling or is heated from freezing; temperature is a state variable. Under some conditions, the value of two state variables, such as pressure and volume, completely specify the thermodynamic state of a system. Then we can represent any possible state by a point on a two-dimensional plot, as in a *PV* diagram (Fig. 13.3). The amount of heat added to or released by a thermodynamic system is not a state variable, and although the work done by a system often does involve state variables, such as "*P* Δ*V* work" done by a gas, work itself is not a state variable. An interesting aspect of the first law is that the internal energy of a system is a state variable; that is, the energy difference between the heat into a system and the work done by that system does not depend on the details of how that heat was added or how that work was done. In this case, the difference between two quantities that are not state variables is itself a state variable.

An important goal of thermodynamic studies is to consider systems in different thermodynamic states and follow the changes in the state variables as the systems undergo change. However, thermodynamic state variables are meaningful only for systems in equilibrium. For example, when a large sample of gas undergoes a rapid expansion, the temperature and pressure may fluctuate from place to place within the gas. Thus, describing the temperature or pressure of this sample while it changes is not meaningful. To determine clearly defined values of state variables, we must consider reversible processes. A **reversible process** is one in which the system is very nearly in equilibrium all the time. For example, in the *PV* diagram of Fig. 13.4 for a system evolving from state *A* (P_1, V_1) to state *B* (P_2, V_2), a reversal of the controlling factors causes the system to exactly retrace its path in the opposite direction, back to its initial state. Alternatively, we can say that a reversal of the controlling factors causes a reversal of the energy transformation. There is no wasted energy.

Reversible processes are allowed by the first law of thermodynamics, and we will use them as examples of how to think about thermodynamic processes. However, a reversible process cannot take place if friction or any other form of energy loss from the system is present. The situation is somewhat like learning basic mechanics without including friction in everything from the start. We will see later that the second law of thermodynamics shows that completely reversible processes do not occur in nature. However, they are still useful models for analyzing changes in the state of a system.

Because many machines operate in approximately reversible cycles, it is important to examine the implications of the first law for a cyclic process in which a system begins with an internal energy U at an initial temperature T, exchanges heat and work with its surroundings, and returns to its initial state characterized by U and T. In any number of complete cycles, $\Delta U = 0$ so that $Q = W$. Thus, the first law tells us that it is impossible for a machine (or a system) in any number of complete cycles to put out more energy in the form of work than it takes in as heat. A machine that could do this would be called a perpetual motion

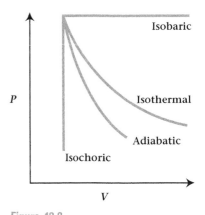

Figure 13.3

PV diagrams for isochoric, adiabatic, isothermal, and isobaric processes. The lines indicate the thermodynamic state of a system during the process, as measured by the two state variables pressure and volume.

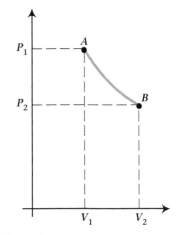

Figure 13.4

PV diagram for a system evolving from state *A* to state *B* along a reversible path.

machine of the first kind. The first law is sometimes stated in terms of such a machine as follows, *A perpetual motion machine of the first kind is impossible;* or, to put it more succinctly, *You can't win.*

13.3 The Carnot Cycle and the Efficiency of Engines

Let us now apply the first law of thermodynamics to analyzing the operation of a heat engine. Figure 13.5 shows an early steam engine built by the firm of Boulton and Watt. Steam came from the boiler (*B*) at the left and entered a condensing cylinder near the large upright cylinder (*C*). Here the steam was cooled and condensed to water, creating a partial vacuum in the large cylinder that caused a piston (*P*) to descend. This motion was transmitted to the vertical rods (*R*) on the right through the large reciprocating beam (*RB*) at the top. The upward motion of the right-hand rods pumped water from a mine. Rotary motion and the use of the pressure of expanding steam for the driving force did not come until later.

Naturally it was important to determine an engine's maximum power output. Watt accomplished this with a technique he developed and used privately for many years. In this method, Watt attached a device called an indicator to the engine. The mechanism included a card connected to a piston so that it could move back and forth as the piston moved within the cylinder (Fig. 13.6). The displacement of this main piston was proportional to the volume of the main cylinder. Another, smaller cylinder with a spring-loaded piston was connected to the main cylinder. The position of this small piston indicated the pressure. It also moved a lever with a pencil on its far end. As the card and small cylinder moved, the pencil traced out a curve of pressure versus volume. The resulting diagram was called an indicator diagram. This term is still used for measurements made on internal combustion engines. The indicator diagram is a cyclic *PV* diagram.

The area inside the curve of an indicator, or cyclic *PV*, diagram is proportional to the work done in each cycle. To see this, suppose that we divide the

Figure 13.5
An early steam engine built by the firm of Boulton and Watt. Its operation is described in the text.

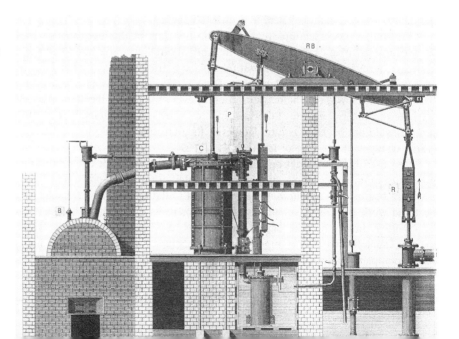

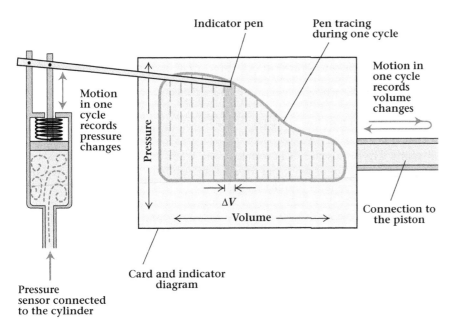

Figure 13.6
A schematic drawing of a steam engine indicator mechanism showing an indicator diagram. The area within the curve is proportional to the work done in each cycle.

area inside the indicator diagram into narrow vertical strips, just as we did in Chapter 6 for the area under the graph of force versus displacement. The width of each strip is proportional to the change in volume ΔV, and the height of each strip indicates the pressure change P. The small area of each strip $P \Delta V$ represents an increment of work. The sum of all these incremental values of work, which is the total work per cycle, corresponds to the area inside the curve. Because the time for each cycle is essentially constant for a given engine speed, the area inside an indicator diagram also measures the power of an engine.

Example 13.4

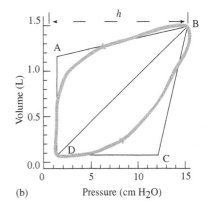

(a)

Some of the lung's functions can be tested by breathing into a calibrated device (Fig. 13.7a). Lung pressure and lung volume are measured simultaneously and plotted during a breathing cycle. Approximately how much work is done in the breathing cycle shown in Fig. 13.7(b)?

Strategy Because the breathing curve is a plot of V against P, the area inside the curve is the work done, just as in the case of the indicator diagram on the steam engine. We can approximate the area inside the breathing curve by drawing two approximately equal triangles ABD and CBD. The work done is then given by twice the area inside one of the triangles (ABD).

Solution Let the side of the triangle ABD parallel to the volume (V) axis be the base, and let the distance parallel to the pressure (P) axis be the height, marked h in Fig. 13.7(b). The area of triangle ABD is $\frac{1}{2}$ base × height. The work done is twice that area, so W = base × height. Reading directly from the graph we have

$$W = (AD)(h) = (1.17 \text{ L})(14.5 - 1.0) \text{ cm H}_2\text{O} = 15.8 \text{ L} \cdot \text{cm H}_2\text{O}$$

The measurements are not in SI units. The unit of cm H_2O represents the pressure due to a 1-cm column of H_2O. In Section 10.1 we saw that the pressure

(b)

Figure 13.7
(a) Measuring lung function. (b) Lung pressure and volume during a breathing cycle. The lower path from D to B is inspiration (breathing in) and the upper path from B to D is expiration (breathing out).

due to a column of liquid of height h is $P = \rho g h$. We can use this relationship to convert cm H_2O to pascals:

$$1 \text{ cm } H_2O = \rho g h = (0.998 \times 10^3 \text{ kg} \cdot \text{m}^{-3})(9.81 \text{ m} \cdot \text{s}^{-2})(10^{-2} \text{ m}) = 97.9 \text{ Pa}.$$

The work done by the lung in Fig. 13.7(b) then becomes

$$W = (15.8 \text{ L} \cdot \text{cm } H_2O)\left(\frac{10^{-3} \text{ m}^3}{\text{L}}\right)\left(\frac{97.9 \text{ Pa}}{1 \text{ cm } H_2O}\right) = 1.55 \text{ J}.$$

Discussion To get a sense of how much work 1.55 J represents, we can ask how far that amount of work can lift a 2.0-kg textbook. The work is given by $W = mgh$. Rearrange to find the height:

$$h = \frac{W}{mg} = \frac{1.55 \text{ J}}{(2.0 \text{ kg})(9.81 \text{ m/s}^2)} = 0.079 \text{ m} = 7.9 \text{ cm}.$$

Though steam engines were considerably improved by Watt and others, the basis for understanding the general principles of heat engines did not come until 1824, when the French engineer Sadi Carnot (1796–1832) published a treatise on this subject. In doing so, Carnot formulated the basic ideas of thermodynamics. He said that *all* movements were ultimately due to heat. It made no difference whether they occurred in natural phenomena, such as rain, storms, earthquakes, and volcanoes, or in mechanical devices such as steam engines (Fig. 13.8). In view of modern knowledge, Carnot's vision of nature was slightly simplified, but his understanding of thermal energy as the generator of motive power was essentially correct. His work was unappreciated except by his closest friends until, sixteen years after Carnot's death, Lord Kelvin pointed out its fundamental theoretical and practical importance.

Although we will discuss Carnot's ideas in terms of an ideal engine that cannot actually be built, the ideas have great practical importance even today. The ideal Carnot engine sets an upper limit on the efficiency of all real engines, including steam engines, Diesel and gasoline (Otto) engines, jet engines, and nuclear reactors. Furthermore, studies of the theoretical Carnot engine indicate some of the factors that affect the efficiency of real engines.

Carnot recognized that work could be done only when heat flowed from a higher temperature to a lower one. So Carnot proposed an *ideal* heat engine that operates cyclically and reversibly between two temperatures. This so-called Carnot engine is not 100% efficient, but is as efficient as any machine could be in transforming heat into work. Carnot analyzed the transformation of energy during one complete cycle of this engine's performance and determined the conditions for maximum efficiency. Only later was Watt's indicator diagram proposed as a basis for a mathematical discussion of Carnot's ideas.

In our example, the working substance of the engine is an ideal gas* confined within a cylinder by means of a frictionless piston (Fig. 13.9). We use an ideal gas for mathematical simplicity; however, the results would be the same for any working substance in the Carnot cycle.

Figure 13.9 shows diagrammatically the other components of a Carnot engine, in addition to the cylinder containing the working substance. A hot body

(a)

(b)

(c)

Figure 13.8

The motions of tornadoes, volcanoes, and jet engines are due to heat. Thus, their behavior is governed by the laws of thermodynamics.

---

*Chapter 12 describes an ideal gas. Use of an ideal gas allows us to calculate the exact shape of the curves for the cyclic process shown in Fig. 13.10.

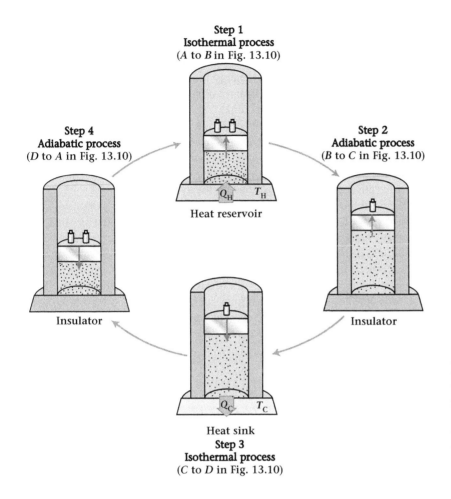

Step 1
Isothermal process
(*A* to *B* in Fig. 13.10)

Step 4
Adiabatic process
(*D* to *A* in Fig. 13.10)

Step 2
Adiabatic process
(*B* to *C* in Fig. 13.10)

Q_H T_H
Heat reservoir

Insulator

Insulator

Q_C T_C
Heat sink
Step 3
Isothermal process
(*C* to *D* in Fig. 13.10)

Figure 13.9
A diagrammatic version of a Carnot engine using an ideal gas as the working fluid. Heat is taken in isothermally at *A*, followed by adiabatic expansion at *B*, isothermal compression at *C* (where heat is expelled), and, finally, adiabatic compression at *D*.

of infinite thermal capacity, called a *heat reservoir,* supplies thermal energy without lowering its own temperature. (This reservoir can be approximated by any source of heat, such as the sun, that is much larger than the needs of the engine.) An insulating platform, together with the sides of the cylinder and piston, acts as a perfect insulator against the flow of heat. The cold body, called a *heat sink,* is also of infinite thermal capacity so that it can absorb heat without raising its own temperature. (This sink can be approximated by any large body, such as the ocean, that can absorb much more heat than the engine can generate.) Finally, there is a second insulating platform. Operation of the Carnot engine consists of moving the cylinder in a prescribed manner from one of these platforms to the other and then repeating the cycle.

The **Carnot cycle** consists of four reversible processes, two isothermal and two adiabatic:

Step 1. We start the cycle with the cylinder in contact with the heat reservoir, where the working substance (gas) takes in an amount of heat Q_H at a high temperature T_H. Because the system absorbs heat in a reversible process, its temperature is the same as the reservoir's; that is, this is an isothermal process. As the heat is absorbed, the gas expands and does work on the piston. This expansion is represented in Fig. 13.10 by going from *A* to *B* along an isothermal curve. During this isothermal process, the system's internal energy does not change, so according to the first law the work done by the system is equal to the heat input.

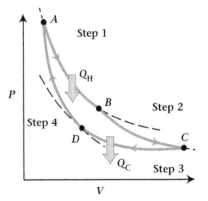

Figure 13.10
One cycle of a Carnot engine using an ideal gas as a working fluid. Curves *AB* and *CD* represent isothermal processes; curves *BC* and *DA* represent adiabatic processes. Compare with Fig. 13.9.

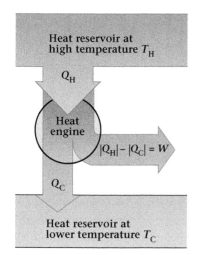

Figure 13.11

A schematic representation of a heat engine. The work done equals the net heat flow into the system, $|Q_H| - |Q_C|$.

Step 2. The cylinder is then moved to the insulating body, where the heat input (and output) is zero. The load on the piston is reduced, and the gas is allowed to expand, this time along an adiabatic curve (*B* to *C*). As the gas continues to do work by expanding, its internal energy must go down. This expansion is accompanied by a decrease in temperature along the curve *BC* until the cylinder reaches the temperature of the heat sink.

Step 3. Next the cylinder is moved to the heat sink. Here the gas undergoes an isothermal contraction in which an amount of heat $|Q_C|$ is expelled to the cold reservoir at temperature T_C.* As in the previous isothermal process, the heat intake equals the work done. However, in this case, since heat is exhausted, the work is negative; that is, work is done on the system.

Step 4. In the final step of the Carnot cycle, the cylinder is moved back to the insulating body. The load on the piston is increased, and the gas undergoes an adiabatic compression (*D* to *A*). Again the heat exchange is zero, and because the volume is decreasing (work is being done on the system), the internal energy and the temperature increase. When the temperature of the gas again reaches that of the heat reservoir, the cylinder is transferred to the heat reservoir and the cycle starts again. In this way the working substance returns to the same internal energy that it had at the start of the complete cycle. Thus, by the first law of thermodynamics, the work done must equal the net heat flow into the cylinder:

$$W = |Q_H| - |Q_C|,$$

where $|Q_H|$ and $|Q_C|$ are taken to be positive quantities. The process is shown schematically in Fig. 13.11.

You should go over Figs. 13.9 and 13.10 again to be sure you understand how they correspond.

We define the **thermal efficiency** of any system, such as a machine, to be the ratio of the work done to the heat input:

$$\text{thermal efficiency} = \frac{W}{Q_H}. \tag{13.3a}$$

Substituting for the work W, we get

$$\text{thermal efficiency} = \frac{|Q_H| - |Q_C|}{|Q_H|}. \tag{13.3b}$$

In Chapter 12 we showed that for an ideal gas the internal energy is proportional to the Kelvin temperature. From that fact and from a detailed examination of the Carnot cycle for an ideal gas, Kelvin showed that

$$\frac{|Q_C|}{|Q_H|} = \frac{T_C}{T_H},$$

where the temperatures are the absolute temperatures measured on the Kelvin scale. The thermal efficiency of an ideal engine is thus

$$\text{thermal efficiency} = 1 - \frac{T_C}{T_H} \quad \text{(ideal)}. \tag{13.4}$$

---

*Recall our sign convention that heat into the system is positive and heat out of the system is negative. Here, we consider the gas to be our system so that the heat Q_C expelled to the cold reservoir is negative.

Table 13.1	Practical Efficiencies of Real Engines

Type of Engine	Efficiency (%)
Automobile engine (gasoline)	20–25
Diesel engine	26–38
Nuclear-powered steam turbine	35
Coal-fired steam turbine	40

It can be shown that *all* reversible engines operating in cycles between the same two heat reservoirs have the same efficiency, regardless of the operating fluid. Moreover, no heat engine of any kind, operating in cycles between the same two reservoirs, can have an efficiency greater than that of a reversible Carnot engine. Thus, even if there were no losses due to friction and heat leakage, the absolute maximum efficiency of a heat engine would be given by Eq. (13.4). The efficiency of any real engine is certain to be less than that of the ideal engine. Table 13.1 gives some examples of typical efficiencies.

Problem-Solving Strategy

Comparing Quantities

1. When using the formulas for thermal efficiency remember that the temperatures are always expressed in kelvins. Take care to identify the system you are studying and its environment.
2. Remember that W is positive when the system expands and does work on the environment and negative when it is compressed. The value of Q is positive for heat coming into the system and negative for heat leaving the system.

Example 13.5

What is the maximum possible thermal efficiency of a steam engine that takes in steam at 160°C and exhausts it at 100°C?

Solution We can calculate the efficiency using Eq. (13.4), after converting the temperatures to the Kelvin scale:

$$T_H = 160°C = 433 \text{ K},$$
$$T_C = 100°C = 373 \text{ K},$$
$$\text{efficiency} = 1 - \frac{T_C}{T_H} = 1 - \frac{373 \text{ K}}{433 \text{ K}} = 0.14.$$

The theoretical efficiency of this engine is only 14%. Note that this is true regardless of the details of the engine's operation.

GASOLINE ENGINES

A ds for new cars often stress the increased efficiency of the new models compared with what you're driving now. In fact, the last few years have seen real improvements in engine efficiency. But how far can this continue? Let's find out by analyzing a simple model of a typical car engine.

Internal combustion engines form a special class of heat engines that generate the input heat by the combustion of fuel within the engine itself. Examples of internal combustion engines include gasoline engines, Diesel engines, and gas turbines. Here we consider the gasoline engine as a representative example of internal combustion engines.

The operating cycle of the gasoline engine used in most cars is a four-stroke cycle (Fig. B13.1). In the *intake stroke* a mixture of air and gasoline vapor is drawn through the intake valve into the cylinder by the downward motion of the piston. The valve closes and the fuel-air mixture is compressed. At the top of this *compression stroke,* the gases are ignited by an electric spark from the spark plug, raising the temperature and pressure of the gases. The hot gases then expand against the piston in the *power stroke,* delivering energy to the crankshaft. The exhaust valve opens as the piston moves upward again, expelling the burned gases in the *exhaust stroke.* The exhaust valve closes, the intake valve opens, and the cycle is ready to repeat.

Analysis of an indicator diagram of a real gasoline engine is very difficult (Fig. B13.2a). For this reason, the gasoline engine is usually analyzed with a simplified model of the

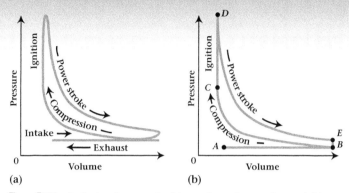

Figure B13.2 Indicator diagrams for (a) a real gasoline engine, and (b) an idealized Otto cycle.

cycle called the Otto cycle, after its developer, Nicholas Otto (1832–1891). The Otto cycle begins at point A on the PV diagram of Fig. B13.2(b). The volume expands at constant pressure to point B as the piston moves down during the intake stroke. During the compression stroke, the gases are compressed adiabatically to point C. Ignition of the gas by the spark causes an isochoric change to point D at higher temperature and pressure, which is followed by an adiabatic expansion to point E during the power stroke. Opening the exhaust valve causes the pressure to drop isochorically to point B, and this drop is followed by a decrease in volume at constant pressure as the piston moves through the exhaust stroke.

The work done by the gasoline engine is found from the area enclosed in the curve on the PV diagram, which for the idealized Otto cycle is the loop B-C-D-E-B. Comparison of the Otto cycle with a Carnot cycle operating between the same two temperatures shows that the efficiency of the Carnot cycle is more than that of the Otto cycle. The Otto cycle is, in turn, considerably more efficient than the actual gasoline engine cycle that it represents. Real gasoline engines achieve thermodynamic efficiencies of 20 to 25%, roughly half the value predicted from the simplified Otto model.

In recent years, manufacturers have been designing and building more efficient cars. Electronic sensors have been installed to monitor exhaust emissions, while computer control of air-fuel mixtures is now common. Other advances such as lean-burn engines, turbocharging, multiple valves, and cast-aluminum engine blocks have been used to make cars more fuel efficient. Future developments will undoubtedly include even more computer control of the combustion process and electronically controlled transmissions to provide the optimum gearing between the engine and the wheels for every situation.

Figure B13.1 The operating cycle of a four-stroke gasoline engine. The piston goes up and down twice during each cycle.

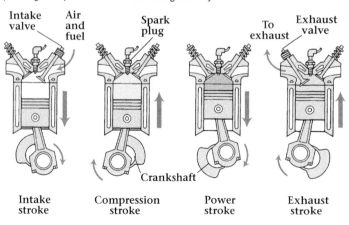

Example 13.6

Example 13.6

Calculate the maximum theoretical efficiency of a power plant that has a high-temperature reservoir at 500°C and a low-temperature exhaust (cold reservoir) at 50°C.

Solution Again we must convert to absolute temperatures:

$$T_H = 500°C = 773 \text{ K},$$
$$T_C = 50°C = 323 \text{ K},$$
$$\text{efficiency} = 1 - \frac{T_C}{T_H} = 1 - \frac{323 \text{ K}}{773 \text{ K}} = 0.58.$$

The maximum theoretical efficiency is 58%. The increase above that of Example 13.5 is due to the increase in T_H. Because real power plants do not reach ideal efficiency, a realistic value of the efficiency of a power plant is closer to 40%.

Example 13.7

An engine takes in 9220 J and does 1750 J of work each cycle while operating between 689°C and 397°C. (a) What is its actual efficiency? (b) What is its maximum theoretical efficiency?

Strategy We can calculate the actual efficiency as the ratio of the work done to the heat input. Then we can find the maximum theoretical efficiency from the efficiency of a Carnot engine operating between T_H and T_C as given in Eq. (13.4).

Solution (a) The actual efficiency of the heat engine is

$$\text{actual efficiency} = \frac{W}{Q_H} = \frac{1750 \text{ J}}{9220 \text{ J}} = 0.190.$$

(b) The maximum theoretical efficiency is that of a Carnot engine operating between $T_H = 689°C = 962$ K and $T_C = 397°C = 670$ K.

$$\text{maximum efficiency} = 1 - \frac{T_C}{T_H} = 1 - \frac{670 \text{ K}}{962 \text{ K}} = 0.304.$$

Discussion Notice that the maximum theoretical efficiency (the Carnot efficiency) is larger than the actual efficiency. This is always the case, because Carnot engines do not take into account irreversible processes such as the loss of energy by friction. The processes in real engines are irreversible. Thus, the Carnot efficiency is an upper limit to what a real engine can accomplish.

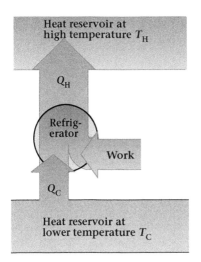

Figure 13.12
A schematic representation of a refrigerator. We have to put work into the system to transfer heat from lower temperature to higher temperature.

13.4   Refrigerators and Heat Pumps

By reversing the direction of the Carnot cycle, we can put work into the system and transfer heat from a low temperature to a higher one. A system operated in this manner is called a **refrigerator** (Fig. 13.12). In this case, the ratio of the heat extracted from the cold reservoir to the work supplied is similar to an efficiency and is called the **coefficient of performance** (c.p.):

$$c.p.(\text{refrigerator}) = \frac{Q_C}{W}. \tag{13.5a}$$

Substituting for W, we get

$$c.p.(\text{refrigerator}) = \frac{|Q_C|}{|Q_H| - |Q_C|}.$$

With ideal gas as the working substance, this becomes

$$\text{maximum } c.p.(\text{refrigerator}) = \frac{T_C}{T_H - T_C}. \tag{13.5b}$$

Because the coefficient of performance given in Eq. (13.5b) is that of a Carnot engine run in reverse, it represents the maximum c.p. of any real refrigerator. Notice that the amount of work required to run a refrigerator increases with the temperature difference between T_H and T_C. Also note that a refrigerator with a higher c.p. is a better refrigerator, that is, it extracts a given amount of heat for less work and, therefore, is less expensive to operate.

Figure 13.13(a) shows a diagram of the thermal part of a freon-cycle refrigerator, a type found in many homes. The typical refrigerator compresses a refrigerant gas (freon) to a pressure of several atmospheres. The resulting hot gas is forced through a heat exchanger (the condenser) external to or on the side walls of the refrigerator, where the gas is cooled to near room temperature and thereby condensed into a liquid. The cool liquid then flows at high pressure through a narrow tube to a much larger tube (the evaporator), which is a region of much lower pressure. In this region, the liquid evaporates because of the reduced pressure, absorbing heat from the contents of the refrigerator. The resulting cold gas is then drawn through the low-pressure tube back to the compressor, where the cycle starts over.

Compare the diagram of Fig. 13.13(a) with the schematic of Fig. 13.12. The work input is provided by the compressor; the heat input is absorbed by the gas at the evaporator at low temperature; and the heat exhausted is given up at higher temperature through the condenser. Thus, a refrigerator transfers heat energy from a cooler body to a warmer one at the expense of the work supplied.

An air conditioner (Fig. 13.13b) is a refrigerator that is designed to take heat from within a house and exhaust it to the outdoors. When such a system is reversed so that it cools the outdoors and delivers heat to the inside of the house, it is called a **heat pump.** The coefficient of performance of a heat pump is defined to be the ratio of the heat delivered inside the house (the high-temperature reservoir) to the work supplied:

$$c.p.(\text{heat pump}) = \frac{Q_H}{W}. \tag{13.6a}$$

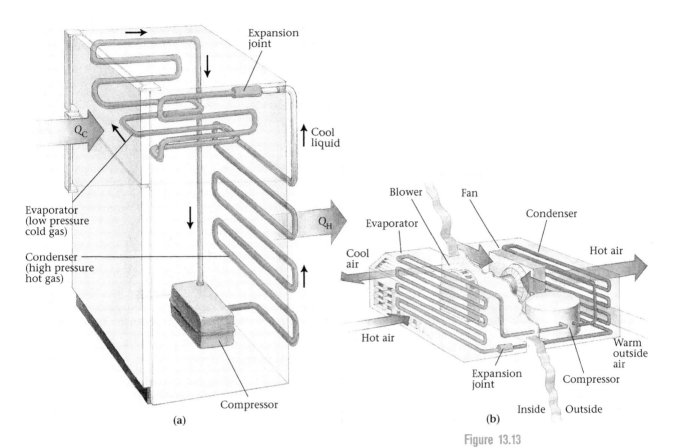

(a)

(b)

Figure 13.13
A diagram of (a) a common
refrigerator and (b) a window air
conditioner.

When we substitute for W, we get

$$\text{c.p.(heat pump)} = \frac{|Q_H|}{|Q_H| - |Q_C|}.$$

In terms of temperatures, the maximum coefficient of performance of the heat pump becomes

$$\text{maximum c.p.(heat pump)} = \frac{T_H}{T_H - T_C}. \qquad (13.6b)$$

Example 13.8

A household refrigerator has a coefficient of performance of 6.0. If the room temperature outside the refrigerator is 30°C, what is the lowest temperature that can be obtained inside the refrigerator?

Solution The maximum coefficient of performance, c.p., is

$$\text{c.p.(refrigerator)} = \frac{T_C}{T_H - T_C}.$$

We can rearrange this equation to give

$$T_C = \frac{(\text{c.p.})T_H}{1 + (\text{c.p.})}.$$

Then we obtain T_C by inserting the numerical values for the coefficient of performance and the temperature T_H. Remember that T_H must be measured on the Kelvin scale.

$$T_H = 30°C = (30 + 273) \text{ K} = 303 \text{ K},$$

$$T_C = \frac{6.0(303 \text{ K})}{1 + 6.0} = 260 \text{ K}.$$

Upon converting T_C to the Celsius temperature, we see that the coldest temperature attainable inside the refrigerator is

$$T_C = -13°C.$$

▼

Example 13.9

A household heat pump is used to maintain an inside temperature of 20°C on a day when the outside temperature is $-10°C$. (a) What is the theoretical maximum coefficient of performance for this heat pump? (b) If the heat pump delivers heat to the house at a rate 15 kW, how much power must be supplied to run the heat pump?

Strategy (a) We can calculate the maximum coefficient of performance from knowledge of the high and low temperatures by using Eq. (13.6b). The temperatures must be converted to Kelvin scale before using them in the equation.

(b) The power required may be found from the definition of the coefficient of performance (Eq. 13.6a) if we replace Q_H and W by the rate of heat delivered and the power input P.

Solution (a) We begin by converting the two temperatures from °C to kelvins.

$$T_H = 20°C = (20 + 273) \text{ K} = 293 \text{ K},$$
$$T_C = -10°C = (-10 + 273) \text{ K} = 263 \text{ K}.$$

The coefficient of performance is given by

$$\text{c.p.(heat pump)} = \frac{T_H}{T_H - T_C} = \frac{293 \text{ K}}{293 \text{ K} - 263 \text{ K}} = \frac{293}{30}$$

$$\text{c.p.(heat pump)} = 9.8.$$

(b) The definition of the coefficient of performance of the heat pump is

$$\text{c.p.(heat pump)} = \frac{Q_H}{W} = \frac{\text{rate of heat}}{P},$$

$$P = \frac{\text{rate of heat}}{\text{c.p.}} = \frac{15 \text{ kW}}{9.8} \approx 1.5 \text{ kW}.$$

Discussion Note that we have computed the maximum coefficient of performance. A real heat pump operating between the same temperatures will have a smaller c.p. As a result, the power required to deliver that same heat to the house will be greater than the value computed here.

▼ 13.5   The Second Law of Thermodynamics

It might seem to you, as it did to those who followed immediately after Carnot, that there was either some outright contradiction or at least a lack of clarity in his ideas about heat. On the one hand, we have the concept of the mechanical equivalent of heat, which Joule's experiments had confirmed. On the other hand, we have Carnot's result that even the most efficient heat engine conceivable could not convert all of its heat input into mechanical output. Doesn't this result contradict the conservation of energy?

The key to resolving this problem lies in seeing that Carnot's results refer to the amount of work available for use as output, and not to whether the total energy is conserved. The situation is somewhat analogous to that of gravitational potential. In that case, work can be done only when a body goes from one height to a lower one. The greater the difference in heights, the greater the amount of work that can be done. If the body cannot fall to a lower height, then no work can be done, no matter how much potential energy the body originally had. Similarly, for a heat engine, no work can be done unless heat can be taken in at one temperature and exhausted at a lower temperature.

Out of this seeming contradiction came the formulation of the **second law of thermodynamics.** It was first expressed mathematically by the German theoretical physicist Rudolf Clausius (1822–1888) and shortly afterwards by Lord Kelvin. Although these two formulations appear to be different, both were an outgrowth of Carnot's ideas. The two statements can be shown to be equivalent.

1. **Clausius statement of the second law:** Heat cannot, by itself, pass from a colder to a warmer body.

2. **Kelvin-Planck* statement of the second law:** It is impossible for any system to undergo a cyclic process whose *sole* result is the absorption of heat from a single reservoir at a single temperature and the performance of an equivalent amount of work.

Let us look into some of the implications of these statements. Remember that they express in general ways the results of experimenting with and observing the behavior of heat. The Clausius statement of the second law of thermodynamics is consistent with our experience. If an ice cube and a cup of hot chocolate are placed in contact, heat will flow from the hot chocolate to the ice cube until they come to the same temperature. The principle of conservation of energy—the first law of thermodynamics—does not tell us anything about how this process proceeds. It would not be a violation of the first law of thermodynamics if heat were to flow from the ice cube to the hot chocolate.

The second law of thermodynamics is different from the laws of mechanics. It does not describe the interactions between individual particles, but instead describes the overall behavior of collections of many particles. The second law of

---

*It was Planck's thermodynamic studies that led to ideas that revolutionized our notions of thermal radiation (Chapter 1).

thermodynamics says something about the sequence, or order, in which events naturally take place. In mechanics, individual events are always reversible; we say that they are symmetric in time. If we make a movie of the collision between two air-track gliders and then look at the movie, the collision that we see satisfies all the laws of mechanics, regardless of whether we show the movie forward or backward. The collision has time-reversal symmetry. However, if we make a movie of an egg frying and then show the movie backward, the result violates all our previous experience. It is in this sense that the second law tells us which way is forward in time and which way is backward.

13.6 Entropy and the Second Law

We can gain additional insight into the meaning of the second law of thermodynamics by considering it from a standpoint first introduced by Clausius in 1850. He introduced a new thermodynamic state variable called entropy, which has two Greek roots and means much the same as "turning into." **Entropy** is a measure of how much energy or heat is unavailable for conversion into work.

When a system at Kelvin temperature T undergoes a *reversible* process by absorbing an amount of heat Q, its increase in entropy ΔS is

$$\Delta S \equiv \frac{Q}{T}. \tag{13.7}$$

Notice that we are defining entropy for a reversible process, which does not occur in nature. However, for our purposes, we can use this definition for processes that are approximately reversible. When calculating ΔS for an irreversible process we must do so by substituting a reversible process that has the same initial and final states as the irreversible process.

Before we examine the meaning of this state variable further, let's see some examples of calculating changes in entropy. We will find that, just as in problems involving potential energy or heat, the changes are the significant quantity. In Example 13.10, the temperatures are not constant. Ideally, we should use the techniques of calculus to add up the increments of entropy change over many small intervals of almost constant temperature. For this example and for the problems at the end of the chapter, the difference between the exact answer from calculus and the approximate answer obtained by using the average temperature for the process in Eq. (13.7) is less than 1% in all cases. However, you should keep in mind that this method is only approximate and is not always valid. Problems 13.62 and 13.65 are concerned with the difference between the exact and the approximate solutions.

Example 13.10

A student takes a 2.5-kg block of ice at 0°C, places it on a large rock outcropping, and watches the ice melt. (a) What is the entropy change of the ice (water)? (b) If the source of heat (the rock) is very massive and remains at a constant 21°C, what is the entropy change of the rock? (c) What is the total entropy change?

Solution (a) The block of ice melts at 0°C = 273 K. The energy required to melt the ice is

$$Q = mL = (2.5 \text{ kg})(3.34 \times 10^5 \text{ J/kg}) = 8.35 \times 10^5 \text{ J}.$$

We can use the defining equation for entropy, Eq. (13.7), directly to get the entropy change of the ice:

$$\Delta S_{ice} = \frac{Q}{T} = \frac{8.35 \times 10^5 \text{ J}}{273 \text{ K}} = 3060 \text{ J/K}.$$

(b) The entropy change of the rock is also found using Eq. (13.7), but in this case the heat flow is negative and the temperature is 21°C = 294 K.

$$\Delta S_{rock} = \frac{Q}{T} = \frac{-8.35 \times 10^5 \text{ J}}{294 \text{ K}} = -2840 \text{ J/K}.$$

(c) The total entropy change is

$$\Delta S = \Delta S_{ice} + \Delta S_{rock} = 3060 \text{ J/K} - 2840 \text{ J/K} = 220 \text{ J/K}.$$

Example 13.11

A student mixes 0.100 kg of water at 60°C (sample 1) with 0.200 kg of water at 40°C (sample 2). Determine the change in entropy of the system.

Strategy Using the methods of Chapter 11, we first determine the final temperature and the heat gained or lost by each sample of water. Then we compute the entropy separately for each sample, using Eq. (13.7) and the average temperature for each sample.

Solution We start with the equation

$$\text{heat lost + heat gained} = 0,$$

where the heat gained or lost equals $mc \, \Delta T$. The heat lost for sample 1 is

$$Q_1 = m_1 c \, \Delta T = (0.100 \text{ kg})(4187 \text{ J/kg} \cdot °\text{C})(T - 60°\text{C}).$$

The heat gained by sample 2 is

$$Q_2 = m_2 c \, \Delta T = (0.200 \text{ kg})(4187 \text{ J/kg} \cdot °\text{C})(T - 40°\text{C}).$$

When these are added and set equal to zero, we obtain a final temperature of 46.667°C. The heat gained or lost is found to be

$$Q_1 = -5.58 \text{ kJ},$$
$$Q_2 = +5.58 \text{ kJ}.$$

As expected, the heat lost by one sample is equal in magnitude to the heat gained by the other.

The average temperature T_{ave} of the first sample is 53.3°C, or 326 K. The average temperature of the second sample is 43.3°C, or 316 K. The change in entropy of the initially warm water (sample 1) is then approximately

$$\Delta S_1 = \frac{Q_1}{T_{ave \, 1}} = \frac{-5.58 \text{ kJ}}{326 \text{ K}} = -17.1 \text{ J/K}.$$

The change in the entropy of the initially cool water (sample 2) is

$$\Delta S_2 = \frac{Q_2}{T_{\text{ave 2}}} = \frac{+5.58 \text{ kJ}}{316 \text{ K}} = +17.7 \text{ J/K}.$$

The change in the entropy of the system is the sum of the changes in entropy of the component parts,

$$\Delta S = \Delta S_1 + \Delta S_2 = 0.6 \text{ J/K}.$$

Discussion Notice that the change in the entropy of the system is positive. Also notice that no matter what initial temperatures we start with and no matter what the mass of each sample we choose, the change *still* will be positive. You can see this from the fact that the heat energy gained always equals the heat energy lost and that the term for the initially warmer sample has both a minus sign and the larger denominator.

▼

Example 13.12

Does the entropy of the universe change as a result of the operation of the power plant in Example 13.6?

Solution If we consider the power plant to be a reversible Carnot engine and if we assume that the surroundings interact reversibly, the entropy of the surroundings (the universe) is unchanged. This is so because the entropy lost by the high-temperature reservoir is exactly matched by the entropy gained by the low-temperature reservoir. The amount of entropy lost by the high-temperature reservoir when it gives up an amount of heat Q_H is

$$\Delta S_1 = \frac{-|Q_H|}{T_H}.$$

The entropy gained by the low-temperature reservoir when it absorbs an amount of heat Q_C is

$$\Delta S_2 = \frac{|Q_C|}{T_C}.$$

But, as we have seen, for a Carnot engine,

$$\frac{|Q_H|}{T_H} = \frac{|Q_C|}{T_C}.$$

Consequently, the net change in entropy of the surroundings is zero.

In a real power plant, however, the efficiency is always less than that of an ideal Carnot engine. As a result, the heat Q_C delivered to the low-temperature reservoir is *greater* than the amount that would be delivered by a Carnot engine. This means that the increase in entropy of the low-temperature reservoir is greater than the decrease in entropy of the high-temperature reservoir, so that there is a net increase in the entropy of the universe.

Examples 13.10 through 13.12 are special cases of a much broader principle, discovered by Clausius: *In any process the entropy of the universe increases or remains constant.* (This is another way of expressing the second law.) Entropy remains constant only in the case of reversible processes, which do not occur naturally. So the entropy principle predicts that the entropy of the natural universe always increases. It is extremely important to remember that this does *not* mean that the entropy of a local segment cannot decrease—the entropy did decrease for the warm water in Example 13.11—but the total entropy of a system and its surroundings always increases. All observations and calculations indicate that if entropy decreases in one place, it simultaneously increases by an equal or larger amount somewhere else. Thus, entropy is quite different from such concepts as energy, momentum, and angular momentum, which we have previously encountered, because entropy is not conserved. In fact, the opposite is true. Entropy can be created, and in natural processes entropy always increases if all systems taking part in the process are considered. We can examine the meaning of the entropy principle from two equivalent viewpoints, which we briefly outline in the remainder of this section.

If we have two bodies at different temperatures—say, a hot stove and a block of ice—we can connect a heat engine between them and extract useful work. If, instead, we place the two bodies in direct thermal contact, they will come to thermal equilibrium. In agreement with the first law of thermodynamics, the total energy content of the stove and the ice is the same before contact as that of the stove and water (melted ice) after they have been placed in contact. However, once they reach equilibrium, we cannot separate them again and expect to extract work from them with a heat engine. Something has changed, even though the total energy has not. What has changed is the availability of the energy to do work. An increase in entropy means a decrease in the energy available to do work, not a decrease in the total energy.

Another viewpoint connects entropy with probability and statistics. This insight is due to Ludwig Boltzmann (1844–1906), who showed that an increase in the entropy of a system or substance corresponds to an increased degree of disorder in the atoms or molecules composing the substance. The most probable—that is, the most statistically favored—arrangement of molecules is the one with the most molecular disorder. For example, suppose you have a box with a partition dividing it in two, with a gas on one side of the partition and the other side evacuated (Fig. 13.14). With all of the molecules of the gas in one side, you have a highly ordered situation. If the partition is removed, however, the gas molecules will soon distribute themselves throughout the box and be moving in random directions—a less ordered situation. We can calculate that this change of order corresponds to an increase in the entropy of the gas. The probability that the molecules will all return to their original corner position at the same time is vanishingly small. J. W. Gibbs (1839–1903), the first great theoretical physicist in the United States, once called entropy a measure of "mixed-upness."

The statistical view is represented by an example that originated with Sir Arthur S. Eddington (1882–1944). A new deck of 52 cards comes in a preestablished order. As you shuffle the deck and shuffle it again—an action corresponding to the occurrence of thermodynamic processes—the order of the cards becomes randomized (Fig. 13.15). No matter how many times you shuffle the deck, you do not expect it to return to its original order. Though this event is certainly a possibility, its *probability* is so low that it is not worth considering. Similarly, systems undergoing some physical process proceed from order to disorder because disorder is so much more probable. The first law does not say that systems will not, of their own accord, become ordered again; but the second law says that the probability of their doing so is, in practical terms, zero. The reason

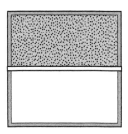

(a)

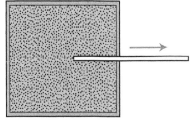

(b)

Figure 13.14

(a) A box in which all the gas molecules are confined to one side. (b) The same box after removing the dividing partition. The gas is now less ordered and has increased entropy.

(a)

(b)

Figure 13.15

(a) The cards in a new deck are arranged in order. (b) After shuffling, the cards have a random arrangement. Continued shuffling will not bring the cards back to their original sequence.

is that any physical system is made up of so many molecules that the probability of its going back to its ordered state is infinitely smaller than the probability that a deck of 52 cards will be reordered upon repeated shufflings.

An advanced area of physics called *statistical mechanics* relates entropy to collections of large numbers of particles. Though we will not go into statistical mechanics in this text, it does provide a mathematical basis for calculating entropy as a measure of disorder, as well as for calculating other thermodynamic state variables and properties. The kinetic theory model described in Chapter 12 is a simple form of statistical mechanics.

The concept of increasing disorder applies to the entire universe as well as to systems here on earth. Current understanding of the early history of the universe is that it began as a highly compressed, hot "fireball," which has been expanding for something on the order of 15 billion years. This expansion corresponds to going from a more ordered to a more disordered state. During the expansion, the temperature of the universe decreases and its entropy increases. (Most of the universe, except for the stars and their associated planets, is quite cold. As we saw in Chapter 1, the average temperature is about 2.7 K.)

Just as in the case of the two liquids mixed in Example 13.11, the entropy and disorder of the universe increase as hot bodies cool and cold bodies warm. If the entropy principle is true throughout the universe, we can envision some time in the far distant future when everything in the universe will have reached a uniform temperature. No heat could flow, no work could be done, and no change in energy or motion could take place. Neither engines nor plants nor animals would be able to extract energy. This possible occurrence is often called the *heat death of the universe.*

The heat death of the universe may happen in billions of years, or it may not happen at all. If, at some point, the universe begins to contract again into a fireball, then heat death will not occur. At the present time, it is not known which of the two cases, contraction or endless expansion, will occur.

Clausius summarized the laws of thermodynamics by saying that (1) the energy content of the universe is constant and (2) the entropy of the universe always increases. However, because of the complexity of the problem, we cannot determine in advance at what point the entropy will have reached its maximum value and the available energy will have decreased to zero.

The first law expressed the idea of conservation of energy. We stated it succinctly as *You can't win.* The second law expresses the idea that all available energy cannot be converted into useful work. So not only can you not win, but *You can't break even.*

*13.7   Energy and Thermal Pollution

We obtain most of the necessities and comforts of life from the generation of power, in one way or another. The word generation should perhaps be replaced by the word conversion. The burning of fuel, as in a car engine, converts chemical potential energy in the fuel into heat energy; the use of water power, as in a hydroelectric power station, converts gravitational potential energy of the water into electrical energy; and so on. The conversion and utilization of energy from falling water, burning fossil fuels, nuclear reactors, solar converters, or any other source cannot take place without the cost of some heat discharge somewhere.

The conversion involved in producing and using energy is always accomplished by machines or organisms whose efficiency is less than that of a Carnot engine. Thus, an inevitable consequence of energy conversion is the discharge of heat. We have no option in this respect. The unwanted release of thermal energy into the environment is known as *thermal pollution*. It can be controlled and spread over a large area to minimize local changes in temperature, but it cannot be eliminated.

The rate of energy generation by humans on the earth is about 1×10^{13} W. It is possible that with conservation and other measures, this figure need not increase as rapidly as was once thought, but it is unlikely to decrease in the foreseeable future. Overall heat production from human devices is less than 6×10^{-5} of the rate of energy absorption from the sun (less than one-hundredth of one percent) and therefore would not have an appreciable influence if it were distributed uniformly over the earth. But, of course, it is not. In heavily populated regions, the heat production rate may be several percent of the rate of energy absorption from the sun.

Approximately 91% of the electrical power in the United States is generated in steam plants heated by fossil and nuclear fuels and by gas turbines that burn fossil fuels. Most of the resulting waste heat is deposited in streams and rivers. This concentrated dumping of energy can raise the temperature of the water by several degrees. Such a small change is insignificant to humans and most warm-blooded animals, but can drastically influence which type of fish will predominate in rivers and thereby modify the entire local food chain. Other effects can be even more unpleasant, since higher temperatures often provide a more hospitable environment for pathogenic organisms.

There are several approaches to solving, or at least lessening, the problem of thermal pollution. One approach in which active research is going on is the development of alternative energy sources. The techniques being studied include the harnessing of wind power, tidal power, solar power, and ocean temperature differences, as well as a host of other ingenious ideas (Fig. 13.16). A second more promising approach to reducing thermal pollution involves measures for saving energy, from better building insulation to smaller, more efficient cars. However, the fact remains that a large amount of energy will continue to be discharged into the environment.

Figure 13.16
Alternative energy sources. (a) A solar collector for generating power in France. (b) Some of the nearly 16,000 wind turbines operating in California. (c) Hoover Dam, one of the world's largest generators of hydroelectric power.

(a)

(b)

(c)

Figure 13.17
Cooling towers at the Paradise power plant.

In response to governmental pollution abatement requirements, auto manufacturers have begun producing battery-operated electric cars. One such car is the EV-1, which General Motors has made available in California. These vehicles have been erroneously called zero-emission vehicles. While there is no direct emission of exhaust gases from the cars, there are emissions of both exhaust gases and waste heat from the power plants that provide the electricity for the cars. Moreover, there is the likelihood of increased emissions of lead and other exotic materials associated with the manufacture and disposal of the batteries needed to store the energy to propel these cars. Exhaust gas and thermal pollution are not eliminated, just relocated.

A possible remedy to thermal pollution is to extract further energy from heat exhausts. For example, exhaust heat can be used to warm buildings, resulting in lower direct-exhaust temperature and less need for additional fuel to heat the buildings. Another solution is to distribute heat exhaust more widely by depositing as much as possible into the atmosphere rather than into bodies of water. Figure 13.17 is a photograph of cooling towers that are designed for this purpose.

There is no single solution to the problems of thermal pollution, but perhaps the combination of alternative sources, conservation, and wide distribution of waste heat can make the problem manageable.

Summary

Useful Concepts

■ Thermodynamics is the branch of physics concerned with the relationships between heat and work. These relationships govern the operation of all engines and devices that convert energy from one form to another, including processes that take place in living organisms.

■ The zeroth law of thermodynamics states that when two systems are each in thermal equilibrium with a third system, they are in thermal equilibrium with each other.

■ The first law of thermodynamics is a statement of conservation of energy,

$$\Delta U = Q - W,$$

where ΔU is the change in a system's internal energy, Q is the heat added to the system, and W is the work done by the system.

■ The thermal efficiency of a Carnot engine is

$$\text{thermal efficiency} = \frac{W}{Q_{\text{H}}} = 1 - \frac{T_{\text{C}}}{T_{\text{H}}}.$$

■ The coefficient of performance of an ideal refrigerator is

$$\text{c.p.(refrigerator)} = \frac{Q_{\text{C}}}{W} = \frac{T_{\text{C}}}{T_{\text{H}} - T_{\text{C}}}.$$

■ The coefficient of performance of an ideal heat pump is

$$\text{c.p.(heat pump)} = \frac{Q_{\text{H}}}{W} = \frac{T_{\text{H}}}{T_{\text{H}} - T_{\text{C}}}.$$

■ The second law of thermodynamics can be stated in several ways. Two of them follow:

Clausius statement of the second law: Heat cannot, by itself, pass from a colder to a warmer body.

Kelvin-Planck statement of the second law: It is impossible for any system to undergo a cyclic process whose *sole* result is the absorption of heat from a single reservoir at a single temperature and the performance of an equivalent amount of work.

■ When a system at temperature T absorbs an amount of heat Q in a reversible process, the change in entropy is

$$\Delta S \equiv \frac{Q}{T}.$$

■ Entropy is a measure of the disorder of a system. In any process, the entropy of the universe increases or remains constant.

■ Thermal pollution is the unwanted release of thermal energy into the environment.

Important Terms

You should be able to write the definition or meaning of each of the following:

thermodynamics	internal energy
zeroth law of	first law of
thermodynamics	thermodynamics
thermodynamic system	adiabatic process

isothermal process	reversible process	refrigerator	second law of
isochoric process	Carnot cycle	coefficient of performance	thermodynamics
isobaric process	thermal efficiency	heat pump	entropy

▼

Conceptual Questions

13.1 Apple 1 is in thermal equilibrium with apple 2, apple 2 is in thermal equilibrium with apple 3, and so on to apple 6. Are apples 1 and 6 in thermal equilibrium? Can you prove your answer using the zeroth law of thermodynamics, or are you simply using your physical intuition (which is probably correct here)?

13.2 Assume that in Joule's paddle-wheel experiment (Chapter 11), the thermodynamic system is the water and it is well insulated from its surroundings. Has heat been added? Has work been done? Has the internal energy changed?

13.3 As you bend a wire back and forth, it becomes warm, then hot, and finally breaks. Discuss what is happening from the standpoint of the first law of thermodynamics.

13.4 According to the first law of thermodynamics, would you expect the temperature at which a substance melts or freezes to change if the substance is subject to a high pressure?

13.5 A weight is placed on top of a vertically held brass rod that has its lower end on a fixed support. Discuss what happens from an energy standpoint as the rod is heated.

13.6 If we place a hot brick in thermal contact with a cold brick, does the first law of thermodynamics allow the hot brick to become hotter and the cold brick to become colder? What is allowed by the second law?

13.7 Is there any change in the temperature of the air inside an automobile tire when you remove the valve and allow the air to escape rapidly?

13.8 A circular rod fits into a circular hole in a metal block. The interface is oiled to make it easier to turn the rod. When the rod is turned rapidly for a long time, the block and rod become warm. Extremely precise measurements show that the mechanical energy delivered in turning the rod is more than the heat energy developed. Discuss this result in terms of the first law of thermodynamics. (*Hint:* Can any changes occur in the molecular structure of oil?)

13.9 Can you cool a kitchen by leaving the refrigerator door open? What will happen?

13.10 A heat engine can extract energy from any system maintaining a temperature difference between two bodies. List as many cases as you can where this is actually done, starting with the steam engine. Give some cases in nature where a temperature difference is maintained but in which we do not, for economic or engineering reasons, extract energy.

13.11 Discuss and give specific examples of the effects that prevent real engines from reaching their Carnot efficiency.

13.12 Explain how a heat pump can add more energy to a house than is used by the electric motor driving the pump.

13.13 Assume that the exhaust from a conventional fossil fuel power plant is at a temperature of 50°C. (a) Plot the maximum theoretical efficiency as a function of the high, or input, temperature. (b) Does the shape of the curve suggest any practical considerations about the usefulness of increasing the input temperature?

13.14 A sealed container is divided into two equal parts by a removable partition. One side is filled with pure oxygen, and the other side is filled with air at the same pressure. (a) If the partition is removed, does the entropy of the system increase, remain constant, or decrease? (b) What would the answer be if both sides were originally filled with oxygen?

13.15 Discuss the statement that the eventual destiny of the physical universe is stagnation.

13.16 The earth is in approximate thermal equilibrium with its environment, absorbing radiant energy from the sun and reradiating energy at a lower temperature to its environment at the same rate. Recalling that processes on the earth increase its entropy, make an educated guess about the overall entropy change of the earth.

▼

Problems

Sections 13.1 and 13.2 Thermal Equilibrium and the First Law of Thermodynamics

Hints for Solving Problems

In using the first law of thermodynamics, you need to pay careful attention to the signs: Work done on a system is negative, work done by a system is positive, whereas heat into a system is positive, heat out of a system is negative.

13.1 One thousand joules of mechanical work are done by an insulated system that expands when 5.50 kcal of heat are added. What is the change in the internal energy of the system?

13.2 In a laboratory experiment, a heat engine takes in 200 J of heat and does 50 J of work by expanding in a reversible process. What is the change in internal energy of the engine during this process?

13.3 An insulated system takes in 6.50 kcal of heat and has

2000 J of work done on it. What is the change in internal energy of the system?

13.4 (a) What is the change in internal energy of 100 g of ice as the ice melts to water at 0°C if we assume the density of water and ice to be the same? (b) Would the answer be larger or smaller if you took into account the fact that ice is less dense than water at 0°C? Explain your answer.

13.5 An inventor tells you he has built a new type of electrical generator that produces 1000 W while using 75 Btu of fuel per minute. He mentions that an interesting side effect is that the apparatus does not heat up its environment. Is it possible for such a device to exist?

13.6 A 2.8-g piece of copper undergoes isochoric heating, which causes a temperature increase of 10°C. By how many joules does the internal energy change? (See Table 11.3.)

13.7 Gas confined by the piston in a particular heat engine expands against a constant pressure of 2.56×10^5 N/m². When 40.0 kJ of heat are added to the system, the volume expands from 0.105 m³ to 0.235 m³. What is the change in internal energy of the system?

13.8 Gas confined by the piston in a particular heat engine expands against a constant pressure of 3.0×10^5 N/m². When 10.0 kcal of heat are added to the system, the volume expands from 0.10 m³ to 0.20 m³. What is the change in internal energy of the system?

13.9 A rigid container is filled with 0.010 kg of carbon dioxide and sealed at atmospheric pressure and 20°C. It is then placed in a bath of ice water and allowed to come to thermal equilibrium. The container is then immersed in a water bath at 60°C and again allowed to come to thermal equilibrium. What is the difference in internal energy of the gas between the initial state, when the container was first filled, and the final state? The specific heat of carbon dioxide under these conditions is 638 J/kg · K.

13.10 A heat engine undergoes a process in which its internal energy increases by 275 J while it is doing 360 J of work. How much heat is taken in (or given out) by the engine during this process?

13.11 Show that the work done during an isobaric process is $W = P(V_2 - V_1)$.

13.12• (a) Consider a system that goes from a to b via the path acb on the PV diagram of Fig. 13.18. If the heat absorbed is 400 J and the system does 150 J of work, what is the change in internal energy of the system? (b) If the system does 50 J of work along path adb, how much heat energy must the system absorb?

13.13• When a system is taken from state a to b along the path acb in Fig. 13.18, 75 J of heat flow into the system while 25 J of work are done by the system. (a) How much heat flows into the system when it goes from a to b along the path adb if the work done is 10 J? (b) When the system returns to a along the curved path, the system performs -15 J of work. Does the system absorb or give out heat during that process? (c) How much heat is exchanged in part (b)?

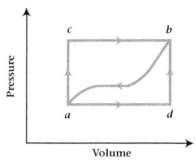

Figure 13.18
Problems 13.12 and 13.13.

Section 13.3 The Carnot Cycle and the Efficiency of Engines

Hints for Solving Problems

In formulas for thermal efficiency and coefficient of performance, the temperatures are always in kelvins. Be clear about what is the system you are studying and what are its surroundings. For simplicity in finding temperatures, take 0°C to be 273 K.

13.14 A Carnot heat engine takes in 100 J at a temperature of 100°C. At the end of the cycle, 50 J are exhausted. What is the temperature of the exhaust?

13.15 (a) What is the efficiency of an ideal engine operating between 275°C and 0°C? (b) What is the efficiency if the engine operates over the same temperature difference, but with the input and output temperature both raised by 100°C?

13.16 What is the temperature at which 45 J per cycle are added to a Carnot engine if 36 J are exhausted at a temperature of 100°C?

13.17 At the end of a cycle, 17 J are exhausted from a Carnot engine operating between 375°C and 150°C. (a) How many joules were taken in during each cycle? (b) How much work was done?

13.18 How much work is done per cycle by a Carnot engine operating between +10°C and −20°C if 12.0 J of heat are taken in at the higher temperature during each cycle?

13.19 In the summer, the temperature of water at the lower depths of Lake Geneva is 14°C. The surface temperature of the lake is about 20°C. What would the maximum efficiency be for any power-generating device that took advantage of this temperature difference?

13.20 Sketch a Carnot cycle using temperature for the vertical coordinate and volume for the horizontal coordinate.

13.21• The working fluid in a heat engine is initially at pressure P_0 and volume V_0. It is operated in a cycle shown in Fig. 13.19. What is the net work done by the engine in each cycle?

13.22• The gas in a heat engine undergoes the process shown in the PV diagram of Fig. 13.20. (a) What is the work done

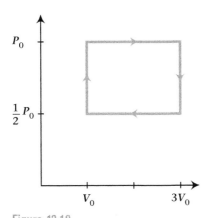

Figure 13.19
Problem 13.21.

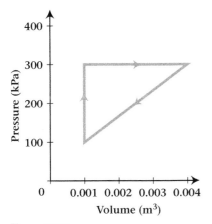

Figure 13.20
Problem 13.22.

during one complete cycle? (b) What is the net heat added to the system during one complete cycle?

13.23• A Carnot engine operating at 30% efficiency exhausts heat into a heat sink at 283 K. By how much would the temperature of the heat reservoir need to be raised to increase the efficiency of the engine to 45%?

13.24• A nuclear power plant in South Carolina produces electrical energy at the rate of 900 MW. The plant has a thermal efficiency of 30%. At what rate is energy released by the nuclear reactor? What is the rate of release of heat to the surrounding environment?

13.25• A hypothetical indicator diagram is traced out in which the pressure rises linearly with increasing volume to some value P_1 at volume V_1, then falls to zero immediately and remains there while the volume decreases to some volume V_0, at which point the cycle starts again. What is the work per cycle represented by this indicator diagram?

13.26• From the standpoint of efficiency, show whether it is better to increase the highest temperature of a Carnot engine

by ΔT or to decrease the lowest temperature by the same amount.

13.27• An engine does 2000 J of work and exhausts 2.25 kcal each cycle while operating between 700°C and 400°C. What is its actual efficiency? How does it compare with the maximum theoretical efficiency?

13.28• An engine has a maximum theoretical efficiency of 40%. If the temperature difference between the input and the output is 300°C, what is the exhaust temperature?

13.29• What is the maximum efficiency of an engine for which the ratio of the energy exhausted to the work done per cycle is 0.25?

13.30•• A steam-electric power plant delivers 900 MW of electric power. The surplus heat is exhausted into a river with a flow of 5.0×10^4 kg/s, causing a change in temperature of 12°C. (a) What is the efficiency of the power plant? (b) What is the rate of the thermal source?

13.31•• The ignition temperature of a typical automobile engine is 17,000°C, and the spent gas is exhausted from the engine at 120°C. (a) What is the maximum possible efficiency of such an engine? (b) The energy per unit volume released by combustion of gasoline is about 0.35×10^8 J/L. If the power required to overcome wind friction is 22 kW when the car is driven at 100 km/h and if the fuel consumption is 8.5 km/L, what is the actual efficiency when driving at 100 km/h? How does your answer compare with the maximum theoretical value?

13.32•• A fluid is heated so that its original volume V_0 is doubled. The pressure is observed to vary linearly with the volume according to $P = P_0(1 + bV)$, where b and P_0 are constants. Find an expression for the work done by the expanding fluid.

Section 13.4 Refrigerators and Heat Pumps

13.33 What is the maximum coefficient of performance of a refrigerator that maintains an inside temperature of 5.0°C in a room where the temperature is 25°C?

13.34 Show that the difference between the theoretical coefficient of performance for a heat pump and the same device running as a refrigerator is unity.

13.35 (a) Calculate the maximum coefficient of performance of a heat pump used to maintain an inside temperature of 21°C (70°F) on a day when the outside temperature is 7°C (45°F). (b) What is the coefficient of performance when the outside temperature drops to −12°C (10°F)?

13.36• What maximum temperature can be maintained inside a house with a heat pump whose coefficient of performance is 8 if the outside temperature is 0°C?

13.37• What is the minimum theoretical temperature that can be maintained in a refrigerator with a coefficient of performance of 5 when operated in a room where the temperature is 16°C?

13.38• Show that the efficiency e of a Carnot engine and the coefficient of performance c.p.$_{refrig.}$ of a Carnot refrigerator operating between the same temperatures are related by

$$e = \frac{1}{1 + \text{c.p.}_{\text{refrig.}}}.$$

13.39• (a) A Carnot engine operates between heat reservoirs at 420 K and 300 K. If it absorbs 500 J of heat from the hot reservoir each cycle, how much work is delivered by the engine each cycle? (b) If the engine is operated in reverse as a refrigerator acting between the two reservoirs, how much work input is required per cycle to remove 500 J of heat from the low-temperature reservoir?

13.40• Suppose that water is put into the refrigerator of Problem 13.33 at room temperature of 25°C. What is the cost of making 100 lb (45 kg) of ice if electricity costs $0.08 per kilowatt hour?

13.41•• Thermal insulation in modern refrigerators is not perfect. Consider a refrigerator with a heat leak of 2.2 kJ/min. The interior cooling coils are at −12°C and the external heat exchanger coils are in a room at 33°C. The refrigerator runs at 32% of the maximum theoretical coefficient of performance. What is the average power used to maintain the temperature inside the refrigerator?

Section 13.6 Entropy and the Second Law

Hints for Solving Problems

In calculating entropy changes, use the average temperature for a process when appropriate.

13.42 What is the change in entropy when a 230-g piece of ice melts to water at 0°C?

13.43 What is the change in entropy of the water when 500 g of water are converted to steam at 100°C?

13.44 An exhaust tube from a steam generator is submerged in a large container of cool water. When 10.0 g of steam are condensed into water at 100°C by bubbling the steam through the cold water, what is the change of entropy of the steam?

13.45 What is the change in entropy per second of the river water for the power plant in Problem 13.30? Assume the average water temperature to be 12°C.

13.46• What is the change in entropy when 500 g of water at 10.0°C are mixed with 500 g of water at 12.0°C?

13.47• What is the change in entropy when enough heat is supplied so that an 75-g piece of ice initially at 0°C melts, warms up to 100°C, and changes to steam at 100°C?

13.48• Determine the change in entropy when 50 g of cream at 14°C are put into 350 g of coffee at 80°C. Assume that the specific heat of both cream and coffee is essentially the same as that of water. Approximate by using average temperatures.

13.49• A child takes a 0.45-kg block of ice at 0°C, places it on a large marble slab, and watches the ice melt. (a) What is the entropy change of the ice (water)? (b) If the source of heat (the marble slab) is very massive and remains at a constant

20°C, what is the entropy change of the marble? (c) What is the total entropy change?

13.50• When you drink ice water, it is warmed by your body to body temperature (37°C). Energy is required to warm the water; therefore you could conceivably lose weight by consuming lots of ice water to help you burn off your food energy. (a) How much ice water at 0°C would it take to offset eating two jelly donuts? (See Problem 11.24.) (b) Estimate the change in entropy and state any assumptions made.

Additional Problems

13.51 What is the maximum efficiency of a heat engine that takes in heat at a temperature of 173°C and has an exhaust temperature of 75°C?

13.52 An inventor claims to have devised a steam turbine that is 75% efficient. The steam enters the turbine at a temperature of 300°C and exhausts at the temperature of the surrounding atmosphere. Do you believe his claim?

13.53 A 1.0-kg lead block slides slowly down an inclined plane and comes to rest at the bottom. If the initial height of the block was 0.45 m above its final resting place and if the temperature of the block, the table, and the surrounding air remains at 27°C, by how much does the entropy of the universe change as a result of this process?

13.54 Heat is added uniformly to a 1.0-kg sample of water at a constant rate of 35 W. The water is initially at a temperature of 10°C. (a) What is the change in entropy of the water over the temperature interval between 10°C and 11°C? (b) What is the change in entropy over the temperature interval from 98°C to 99°C?

13.55• A Carnot engine has an exhaust temperature of 120°C and exhausts 80 J per cycle. If the input temperature is 325°C, how much work does the engine do per cycle?

13.56• An ideal engine always takes in heat at the same input temperature T_H. When the exhaust temperature is 120°C, the efficiency is 30%. (a) What is the input temperature? (b) If the exhaust temperature is changed so that the efficiency rises to 37%, what is the new exhaust temperature?

13.57• A typical person consumes 2000 kcal of food per day and converts most of that energy into heat. (a) Under the assumption that all of the food energy is released as heat, calculate the rate of heat release in watts. (b) If all of this heat is transferred to the surrounding air, which remains at an essentially constant temperature of 24°C, what is the rate at which entropy is being delivered to the universe?

13.58• Heated metals begin to glow at temperatures near 600°C. If we take this temperature to be the temperature of the heat input, estimate the maximum efficiency of any mechanical device operated as a heat engine.

13.59•• Two similar coal-fired electric power plants generate electric energy at the same rate. One plant operates with an efficiency of 30%, while its newer companion operates with an efficiency of 40%. How much more waste heat is released to the environment by the first plant than by the newer one?

13.60•• Consider a large steam-electric plant that produces 1000 MW of electric power. (a) If the plant is 33.3% efficient, what must be the energy rate of the thermal source used? (b) What is the rate at which thermal energy is exhausted to the environment? (c) If this energy were dumped into a river whose flow was 6×10^4 kg/s, what would be the average rise in the temperature of the river?

13.61•• In order to increase the output of some heat engines, a two-step process is used. The input and output temperatures of the first engine are T_1 and T_2. The exhaust of the first engine provides the input to the second engine at temperature T_2 and with a final exhaust temperature of T_3. Show that the overall ideal efficiency is the same as that of a single engine operating between temperatures T_1 and T_3.

13.62•• (a) Using the technique of adding up the area under a curve, find the total change in entropy of a 1.0-kg sample of water as it is heated from 20°C to 40°C. You may want to divide the temperature range into 2° intervals. (b) Compute the entropy change as the total heat added, divided by the average temperature. (c) How do these two results compare?

13.63•• (a) Show that when a Carnot cycle is plotted as a temperature-versus-entropy diagram, the resulting graph is a rectangle. Calculate (b) the heat absorbed, (c) the heat exhausted, and (d) the work done by the system whose Carnot cycle is shown in Fig. 13.21.

13.64•• A copper rod 30 cm long having a cross-sectional area of 4.0 cm² is used to connect a boiler maintained at

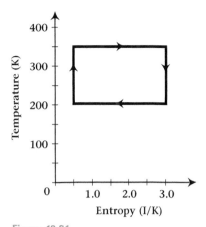

Figure 13.21
Problem 13.63.

100°C to a large block of ice at 0°C. (a) Once a steady state is reached, what is the rate of heat flow through the rod? What is the rate of change in entropy of (b) the boiler, (c) the rod, (d) the ice, and (e) the universe due to the heat flow through the bar?

13.65•• The exact expression for the entropy change of a material heated from $T_1 = 0$°C to $T_2 = 100$°C is $\Delta S = mc \ln(T_2/T_1)$, where m is the mass of the material and c is its specific heat. What percent error is made by calculating the entropy change by using the approximation $\Delta S = Q/T_{ave}$?

chapter 14

Periodic Motion

14.1   Hooke's Law
14.2   The Simple Harmonic Oscillator
14.3   Energy of a Harmonic Oscillator
14.4   Period of a Harmonic Oscillator
14.5   The Simple Pendulum
*14.6   Damped Harmonic Motion

Physics in Practice: Walking and Running

*14.7   Forced Harmonic Motion and Resonance

So far, we have used the basic laws of mechanics to study translational and rotational motions. Here we will use the same basic laws to introduce another important kind of motion: periodic motion. Such motion repeats itself, like a clock pendulum moving back and forth. It is also known as oscillatory, or vibratory, motion. We will find that oscillatory motion is also relevant to our study of electronic circuits, optics, and atomic structure.

Any behavior that repeats itself regularly is called **periodic.** Almost any physical object or system can be made to undergo periodic, or oscillatory, motion. Objects that display such motion abound in everyday life: a child's swing, a guitar string, a bell, or the quartz crystal in an electronic wristwatch. Even the earth itself undergoes oscillatory motion due to seismic activity. Many oscillating systems produce waves. For example, vibrating mechanical bodies generate sound waves, and electrical oscillations generate electromagnetic waves that make radio and television broadcasting possible. In Chapter 15, we will consider the details of wave motion.

For a mechanical system to be capable of self-sustaining oscillations, it must meet two requirements. The system must have inertia, or mass, and there must also be a force that acts to restore the system to its equilibrium, or lowest-energy, state. A stretched spring or a pendulum pulled to one side exhibits these properties. On the other hand, a light piece of thread held suspended from one end and a kicked pile of sand do not, and they also do not exhibit oscillatory behavior to any great extent.

There are many types of periodic motion, from the complicated, but repeating, pattern of the electrical impulses of a human heart (Fig. 14.1a) to the simple repeating pattern of the end of a vibrating tuning fork (Fig. 14.1b). The latter type of vibratory motion, which is both common and simple in its mathematical description, is called simple harmonic motion. In this motion, the displacement varies sinusoidally with time; that is, the graph of the displacement versus time is a sine curve, as shown in Fig. 14.1(b). Another example, which we will discuss in detail, is the oscillation of the pendulum of a grandfather clock. In this chapter, we restrict ourselves to simple harmonic motion. Even if the motion of a periodic system is more complex, its behavior has features in common with simple harmonic motion. ■

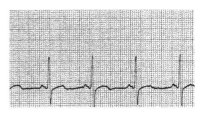

(a)

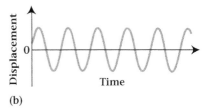

(b)

Figure 14.1
The repeating pattern of an electrocardiogram (a) is more complicated than the smooth, sinusoidal motion of the end of a tuning fork (b). However, both patterns are periodic.

14.1   Hooke's Law

One of the simplest forms of periodic motion is the up-and-down motion of a mass suspended from a spring. Because other types of oscillatory motion resemble the behavior of the mass on a spring, we can model complex systems after this behavior and apply what we learn about springs to other systems. Thus, we begin our study of periodic motion with a careful examination of the behavior of a mass moving at the end of a spring.

We saw in Chapter 6 that the force required to stretch a spring is, to a good approximation, proportional to the distance by which the spring is extended. This relationship between an applied force and the change in the length of a spring is known as **Hooke's law,** in honor of Robert Hooke,* who first enunciated it in 1678. The elastic behavior of many materials, including some woods, bone, and steel, can be described by Hooke's law if the materials are not stretched too far. Further stretching leads to a nonlinear relationship between force and extension and, finally, to breaking or rupture.

If we hang different weights from a spring that obeys Hooke's law, the elongation is proportional to the applied force (Fig. 14.2). When the spring reaches equilibrium, the gravitational force acting downward on the mass must be balanced by an upward force due to the spring. This spring force is called the **restoring force** because it acts in a direction opposite to the direction of the displacement of the end of the spring. Although we have illustrated the case of

---

*Hooke is also well known for his work in biology. His book *Micrographia,* published in 1665, contained the first drawings of tiny objects seen with the aid of a microscope; in fact, Hooke was the one who coined the word *cell* as it is used in biology.

stretching a spring, the situation of compressing a spring is exactly the same. As the spring is compressed beyond equilibrium, a restoring force acts to resist the compression.

Figure 14.3 shows a block of mass m attached to a horizontal coil spring. The block is at rest, but is free to move along a frictionless surface. We choose this arrangement so that we can avoid the changes in gravitational potential energy that occur in a situation like the one in Fig. 14.2.

What happens when we pull the block a little to the right? Let's analyze this situation mathematically. In Fig. 14.3(a), the block is at rest at the equilibrium position $x = 0$. When the block is displaced a distance x to the right, the spring exerts a restoring force F to the left (Fig. 14.3b). The relation between displacement and restoring force is

$$F = -kx. \tag{14.1}$$

If k is a constant, Eq. (14.1) is the mathematical form of Hooke's law. For many materials, k is constant if the displacement x is not too large. This proportionality constant k is called the **spring constant.** It is also known as the stiffness constant. The negative sign in the Hooke's law equation indicates that the restoring force due to the spring is in the opposite direction from the displacement. Since we are considering only one-dimensional motion of the mass at the end of a spring, we do not need to use vector notation in our equation.

Example 14.1

We would like to use a coil spring as a scale, as we discussed in defining force in Chapter 4. To do so we must determine whether its extension is proportional to the weight hung from it. Using a setup similar to the one in Fig. 14.2, we measure the equilibrium length of the spring for different weights hung on one end. The measurements are given in Table 14.1. Determine whether the spring obeys Hooke's law, and if it does, find the spring constant.

Strategy The best way to understand the behavior of the spring is to make a graph of spring length versus applied force (Fig. 14.4). Note that the measurements given are not the displacement of the spring from the unloaded equilibrium, but rather its total length. The graph is linear, which means that the spring does obey Hooke's law over the range used. The slope of the line showing length versus applied force is equal to the reciprocal of the spring constant. To see why this is so, we write an equation for the straight line. If we let L represent the length (the vertical coordinate) and F represent the applied force (the horizontal coordinate)—the negative of the force in Eq. (14.1)—the appropriate equation is $L = L_0 + mF$, where L_0 is the initial length and m is the slope. Here this equation can also be expressed as $L - L_0 = x = mF$, where x is the extension of the spring. This last expression has the form of Hooke's law with $m = 1/k$.

Solution Draw the line that best fits the data and compute the slope of the line. From the graph we see that

$$\text{slope} = m = \frac{\Delta L}{\Delta F} = \frac{\Delta x}{\Delta F} = \frac{1}{k},$$

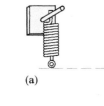

(a)

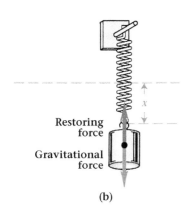

Restoring force

Gravitational force

(b)

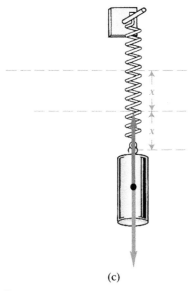

(c)

Figure 14.2
The extension of a spring is proportional to the applied force. (a) Spring with no load. (b) Spring extended a distance x by a 0.5-N load. (c) Spring extended a distance $2x$ by a 1.0-N load.

Table 14.1	*Measurements on a Spring*	
Mass *m* Applied (kg)	**Force = *mg* (N)**	**Length of Spring (cm)**
0.00	0.00	16.2
0.050	0.49	21.4
0.100	0.98	26.5
0.150	1.47	31.7
0.200	1.96	36.9
0.250	2.45	42.0
0.300	2.94	47.2
0.350	3.43	52.4

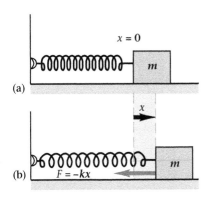

Figure 14.3
(a) A mass *m* attached to a spring rests on a frictionless surface. (b) When mass *m* is displaced by an amount *x*, the spring exerts a restoring force *F* in a direction opposite to *x*.

or

$$k = \frac{2.94 \text{ N} - 0.98 \text{ N}}{0.472 \text{ m} - 0.265 \text{ m}} = 9.47 \text{ N/m}.$$

Discussion Here we have drawn "by eye" a straight line that seems to best fit the data points. We have taken values of ΔF and ΔL from two of the data points that lie on that line. Numerical methods exist that take advantage of all of the data to determine the best fit of a line to a set of data points. One method, called the method of least squares, minimizes the square of the distances between the computed line and the data points and is used in many graphing programs. Calculating the line by such a standard method not only ensures that the resulting line is the best one to fit the data, but also allows others to arrive at the same value from the same data. A least-squares fit of the data here gives a value of $k = 9.48$ N/m. In this case, our estimate of the best line is quite close to the least-squares value.

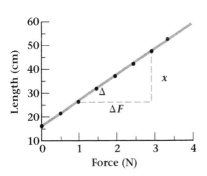

Figure 14.4
Example 14.1: A graph of spring length versus applied force.

If the block in Fig. 14.3 is displaced an amount *x* from its equilibrium position, an external force equal and opposite to the restoring force is required to keep it there. If this external force is suddenly released, the unbalanced spring force accelerates the block. The acceleration is found by combining Newton's second law with Hooke's law:

$$a = \frac{F}{m} = -\frac{k}{m}x. \tag{14.2}$$

The acceleration is proportional to the displacement and in the opposite direction. We will see that this same proportionality between acceleration and displacement occurs for children's swings, clock pendulums, and many types of vibrating bodies, as well as for some quantities that describe the behavior of electrical circuits. In the next section, we will see that whenever this relationship occurs we get an especially simple type of oscillatory behavior.

Example 14.2

The spring in Example 14.1 and a block of mass 0.350 kg are placed horizontally, as in Fig. 14.3. The spring is compressed 6.0 cm and released from rest.

(a) What is the initial acceleration of the block? (b) What is the initial force on the block?

Solution (a) If we choose our coordinate axis so that x increases to the right, compressing the spring corresponds to $x = -6.0$ cm. The acceleration is then

$$a = -\frac{k}{m}x$$

$$a = -\frac{9.48 \text{ N/m}}{0.350 \text{ kg}}(-0.060 \text{ m}) = 1.625 \text{ m/s}^2 = 1.6 \text{ m/s}^2.$$

The acceleration is positive and thus to the right, a result that agrees with your intuition about which way the block will initially move.

(b) Because we know the mass and initial acceleration, the initial force can be found directly from Newton's second law,

$$F = ma = (0.350 \text{ kg})(1.625 \text{ m/s}^2) = 0.57 \text{ N}.$$

Discussion This force of 0.57 N is the restoring force that acts on the block and causes its initial acceleration in the positive x direction. This restoring force can also be found directly from Hooke's law as

$$F = -kx = -(9.48 \text{ N/m})(-0.060 \text{ m}) = 0.57 \text{ N}.$$

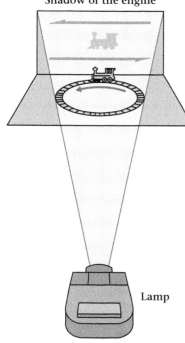

Shadow of the engine

Lamp

Figure 14.5
A simple arrangement illustrating the connection between uniform circular motion and simple harmonic motion. As the toy-train engine moves around the circular track, it casts a shadow on the wall that moves with simple harmonic motion.

| 14.2 | **The Simple Harmonic Oscillator** |

We have seen that for a spring that obeys Hooke's law, the acceleration a is proportional to the negative of the displacement x. We also noted that many oscillatory systems have motion similar to that of a spring. Now we want to find a general description of this motion. *Any system whose acceleration is proportional to the negative of the displacement undergoes* **simple harmonic motion.** As we will see, the projection (or shadow) of uniform circular motion onto a straight line is an example of simple harmonic motion.

We already know that uniform circular motion is periodic. When we view, from above, a toy-train engine going around a circular track, we see circular motion (Fig. 14.5). But if we look at the shadow of the train cast by a lamp edge-on to the track, the engine's shadow appears to oscillate back and forth. We will show this type of motion to be the same simple harmonic motion as the oscillations of a mass on a spring.

We begin by investigating the projection onto the x axis of the uniform circular motion of a point (Fig. 14.6a). If P is a point moving with constant speed v_0 in a circle of radius $R = x_0$, then the projection, or shadow, of P on the x axis oscillates back and forth between $+x_0$ and $-x_0$. The position of the point along the x axis is

$$x = x_0 \cos \theta.$$

Since $\cos \theta$ is always between -1 and $+1$, we see that x_0 is the maximum displacement of the projection of the point.

For uniform circular motion, the angle θ increases steadily with time; that is, θ is proportional to t. As we saw in Chapter 5, the time required to make one

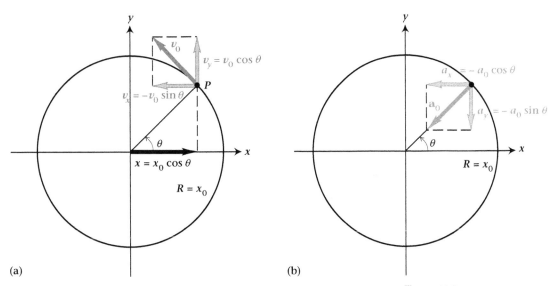

Figure 14.6
(a) A point P moving around a circular path with a constant tangential speed v_0. The projection along the x-axis of the radius vector to P is $x_0 \cos \theta$.
(b) The projection of the centripetal acceleration vector a_0 along the x-axis is $-a_0 \cos \theta$.

complete revolution ($\theta = 2\pi$) is the period T. Thus, the relationship between angle in radians and time is

$$\theta = 2\pi \frac{t}{T}.$$

Using the definition of frequency $f = 1/T$ and angular frequency $\omega = 2\pi f$ from Section 5.1, we can also write the angle as $\theta = 2\pi ft = \omega t$. The projection along the x axis of the circular motion (the x coordinate of the point in Fig. 14.6a) is therefore

$$x = x_0 \cos 2\pi ft. \tag{14.3}$$

The projection can also be expressed as $x = x_0 \cos 2\pi \frac{t}{T}$ or $x = x_0 \cos \omega t$. The quantity x_0 is the maximum displacement, the greatest distance from zero, and is called the **amplitude** of the displacement.

The velocity is also a function of time, and from Fig. 14.6(a) we find that v_x is proportional to $-\sin \theta$:

$$v_x = -v_0 \sin 2\pi ft. \tag{14.4}$$

The velocity can be expressed in terms of ω as $v_x = -v_0 \sin \omega t$. The quantity v_0 is the amplitude (or maximum value) of the velocity.

As we saw in Chapter 5, any object moving in a circle with constant speed is accelerated radially toward the center. The projection of this acceleration along the x axis (Fig. 14.6b) is

$$a_x = -a_0 \cos \theta,$$

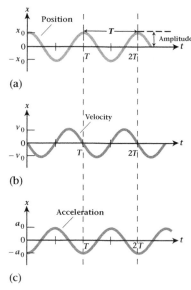

(a)

(b)

(c)

Figure 14.7
(a) The graph of x position as a function of time for the moving point of Fig. 14.6. This is also the graph of displacement as a function of time for the mass at the end of the spring of Fig. 14.3. The time interval between successive maxima is the period T. (b) Velocity along the x direction as a function of time. (c) Acceleration along the x direction as a function of time.

where a_0 is constant and positive and is the maximum acceleration of the point. The minus sign occurs because the acceleration vector is in the direction opposite to the position vector directed from the origin to the point P.

The acceleration in the x direction is a function of time. From Fig. 14.6(b) it is seen to be

$$a_x = -a_0 \cos 2\pi ft, \qquad (14.5)$$

which can be expressed as $a_x = a_0 \cos 2\pi \dfrac{t}{T}$ or $a_x = a_0 \cos \omega t$.

Upon solving Eq. (14.3) for $\cos (2\pi ft)$ and substituting into Eq. (14.5), we have

$$a_x = -\frac{a_0}{x_0} x. \qquad (14.6)$$

This equation says that for the oscillating projection of uniform circular motion on the x axis, the acceleration is proportional to the negative of the displacement. This relationship between acceleration and displacement is the same one that we had for Hooke's law. Therefore Eqs. (14.3) and (14.5) also describe the position and acceleration of a mass hung from a spring.

When the position of a harmonic oscillator is plotted as a function of time using Eq. (14.3), we obtain the graph in Fig. 14.7(a). The time required for the system to go through one complete oscillation is the period T. This is illustrated in the figure as the interval between two successive crests. More generally, the period is the interval between any two successive points along the curve that have the same magnitude and slope. In the earlier example of the toy-train engine, the time for the engine to make one complete revolution—the period—is the same as the time for one complete back-and-forth oscillation of the engine's shadow. The amplitude corresponds to the radius of the circle in circular motion, in this case the radius of the track.

If a block attached to a spring that obeys Hooke's law is displaced by an initial amount x_0 and released from rest, its motion is described by the curves in Fig. 14.7. We release it at time $t = 0$ with no initial velocity, but with an initial

Figure 14.8
Relationship between velocity and acceleration for a mass moving with simple harmonic motion at the end of a spring. The velocity is zero when the acceleration is maximum, and vice versa.

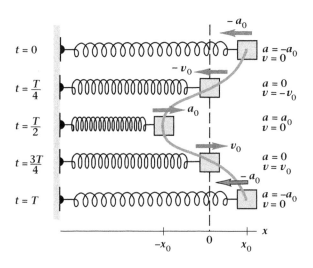

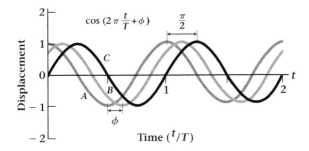

Figure 14.9
Displacement curves for a harmonic oscillator corresponding to different values of the phase angle ϕ: curve A, $\phi = 0$; curve B, $\phi = \phi$; and curve C, $\phi = \pi/2$. The amplitude $x_0 = 1$.

displacement and an initial acceleration opposite in direction to the displacement (Fig. 14.8). The block moves toward the equilibrium position $x = 0$, gaining speed as it moves. As it reaches the position of zero displacement, its momentum keeps it moving, even though the restoring force is zero at that point. The block is then displaced in the opposite direction from its initial displacement. A restoring force proportional to this new displacement gradually slows the block to a stop and then accelerates it back toward the initial position. In this way the block oscillates periodically with time. If there were no frictional forces to slow (damp) the motion, the block would oscillate indefinitely. We call this system a **simple harmonic oscillator,** and its motion is sinusoidal.

In the previous paragraphs, we described the motion by $x = x_0 \cos 2\pi f t$ and showed this motion in a number of graphs. In all of these cases we assumed that the displacement was x_0 at the time we called $t = 0$. However, the important general property of simple harmonic motion is not the displacement at time $t = 0$, but the shape of the curves that describe displacement, velocity, and acceleration. Notice that all of the following equations have the same behavior as a function of time but differ in magnitude at the time we choose to call $t = 0$ (Fig. 14.9):

$$x = x_0 \cos(2\pi f t + \phi)$$
$$x = x_0 \cos 2\pi f t \qquad\qquad (\phi = 0)$$
$$x = x_0 \cos\left(2\pi f t - \frac{\pi}{2}\right) = x_0 \sin 2\pi f t \qquad \left(\phi = -\frac{\pi}{2}\right).$$

The angle ϕ is called the **phase angle** and can be selected so that our choice of starting time and initial displacement are in agreement. The phase angle will be important in our later discussions of waves and electrical circuits.

Example 14.3

A metal block is hung from a spring that obeys Hooke's law. When the block is pulled down 12 cm from the equilibrium position and released from rest, it oscillates with a period of 0.75 s, passing through the equilibrium position with a speed of 1.3 m/s. (a) What is the displacement and (b) what is the speed of the block 0.28 s after it is released?

Strategy We must first choose a coordinate system. The initial displacement is downward, so we choose down for the positive values of x and up for negative values of x. Then a positive value for the velocity means motion in the positive, or downward, direction. Because the block starts from rest, the initial position is the maximum displacement. The motion corresponds to curve A in Fig. 14.9 with a phase angle of 0.

Solution (a) We can find the displacement by direct substitution into Eq. (14.3),

$$x = x_0 \cos 2\pi ft = x_0 \cos 2\pi \frac{t}{T} = (12 \text{ cm})\cos 2\pi \frac{0.28 \text{ s}}{0.75 \text{ s}} = (12 \text{ cm})\cos(2.35 \text{ rad})$$

$$x = (12 \text{ cm})(-0.700) = -8.4 \text{ cm}.$$

At $t = 0.28$ s, the block is 8.4 cm above the equilibrium position.
(b) Substitution into Eq. (14.4) gives the velocity,

$$v_x = -v_0 \sin 2\pi ft = -v_0 \sin 2\pi \frac{t}{T} = -(1.3 \text{ m/s})\sin 2\pi \frac{0.28 \text{ s}}{0.75 \text{ s}}$$

$$v_x = -(1.3 \text{ m/s}) \sin (2.35 \text{ rad}) = -(1.3 \text{ m/s})(0.711) = -0.92 \text{ m/s}.$$

The velocity is in the upward direction.

Discussion We could have chosen the coordinate system so that the initial displacement was negative. In that case, the signs of our answers would be different, but the physical description of what happens would be the same. For instance, we would still say that the displacement at 0.28 s is 8.4 cm above the equilibrium point.

From the preceding discussion it seems reasonable that a block on a spring oscillates in a sinusoidal manner. However, we want to know if any other type of motion is possible when the acceleration is proportional to the negative of the displacement. The answer is no, for the following reason. The velocity is the time rate of change of the displacement, and the acceleration is the time rate of change of the velocity. That is, the acceleration is given by the slope of the velocity curve, which in turn is given by the slope of the displacement curve. Curves of oscillations other than sinusoidal all give the result that the acceleration is not proportional to the displacement. We show this result explicitly for the waveform of Fig. 14.10. The solid curve in Fig. 14.10(a) departs only slightly from a cosine curve shown by the dashed line. The acceleration calculated from this displacement curve bears no resemblance to the initial curve. However, the acceleration curve of Fig. 14.7(c) is just the negative of the displacement curve of Fig. 14.7(a). Sinusoidal motion is indeed special.

14.3   Energy of a Harmonic Oscillator

We must do work to stretch a spring. As we saw in Chapter 6, the increase in the potential energy of a spring that obeys Hooke's law, due to extending the spring from $x = 0$ to $x = x_0$, is

$$\boxed{\text{PE} = \tfrac{1}{2}kx_0^2.} \tag{14.7}$$

Suppose a block of mass m is attached to the end of a spring of negligible mass. When the spring is extended to a distance x_0 and released from rest, its po-

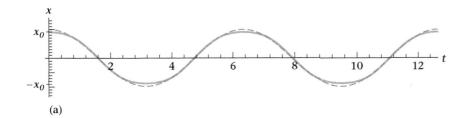

(a)

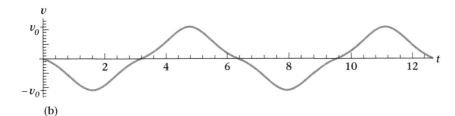

(b)

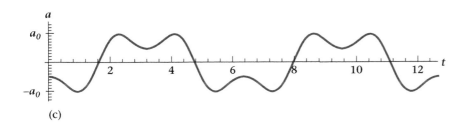

(c)

Figure 14.10
(a) The solid curve is a displacement that differs only slightly from a cosine curve (dashed line). (b) Velocity curve representing the slope of the displacement. (c) The acceleration curve is the slope of the velocity. Clearly the acceleration is not proportional to the displacement.

tential energy changes to kinetic energy as it moves toward the equilibrium position. As the block passes through $x = 0$, all its energy is kinetic and the magnitude of its velocity is a maximum. By applying the principle of energy conservation, we can find the relation between the maximum displacement x_0 and the maximum velocity v_0:

$$\tfrac{1}{2}mv_0^2 = \tfrac{1}{2}kx_0^2,$$

or

$$v_0 = x_0\sqrt{\frac{k}{m}}.$$

Note that the maximum velocity and maximum displacement do not occur at the same time or the same place. The velocity reaches a maximum v_0 when $x = 0$. Similarly, the displacement reaches a maximum x_0 when the velocity is zero.

The total energy is the sum of the kinetic and potential energies at any time and is a constant if we neglect dissipative (internal frictional) forces in the spring. We can write the total energy as

$$E = \tfrac{1}{2}mv^2 + \tfrac{1}{2}kx^2,$$

where the instantaneous values of displacement and velocity are given by Eqs. (14.3) and (14.6). We can use the energy relationship to show that the velocity at any displacement x is given by

$$v = \pm\sqrt{\frac{k}{m}(x_0^2 - x^2)}.$$

▼

Example 14.4

A 3.0-kg ball is attached to a spring of negligible mass and with a spring constant $k = 40$ N/m. The ball is displaced 0.10 m from equilibrium and released from rest. What is the maximum speed of the ball as it undergoes simple harmonic motion?

Solution   We can compute the maximum speed from the energy of the system. The maximum speed occurs at $x = 0$, when the kinetic energy is maximum and is equal to the initial potential energy. Then

$$\tfrac{1}{2}mv_0^2 = \tfrac{1}{2}kx_0^2.$$

So

$$v_0 = x_0\sqrt{\frac{k}{m}} = (0.10 \text{ m})\sqrt{\frac{40 \text{ N/m}}{3.0 \text{ kg}}} = 0.37 \text{ m/s}.$$

▼

14.4   ## Period of a Harmonic Oscillator

We have seen that the velocity of a harmonic oscillator depends on the spring constant and on the mass. Therefore, the period, or the time required to complete one cycle of the motion, also depends on them. We can obtain the exact relationship by analyzing the circular motion of the particle in Fig. 14.6. The particle moves with constant speed v_0. In one period T, it traverses a circular path of length $2\pi x_0$; that is,

$$v_0T = 2\pi x_0.$$

The period is then

$$T = \frac{2\pi x_0}{v_0}.$$

We have already seen that $v_0 = x_0\sqrt{\dfrac{k}{m}}$, so the period may be expressed as

$$\boxed{T = 2\pi\sqrt{\frac{m}{k}}.} \tag{14.8}$$

To show that this equation is consistent with our intuition, we have plotted the motion of several spring systems, each of which contains the same oscillator plus two others for which one of the parameters has been changed. Figure 14.11(a) shows the effect of displacing the block by different initial amounts. The amplitude of the oscillations is larger for larger initial displacements, but because m and k are unchanged, the period is the same. The period of the system is completely determined by the mass m and the spring constant k; how far it moves is influenced by what you do to it. In Fig. 14.11(b) we have used the same spring constant and the same initial displacement from the equilibrium position, but we have increased the mass for succeeding curves. As you would expect, the more massive systems are slower to respond and have longer periods. Figure 14.11(c) corresponds to springs of increasing k, or increasing stiffness. As expected, the stiffer the spring, the shorter the period. These curves emphasize that to change the period, you have to change the physical characteristics of the system—that is, m or k. You cannot vary the period by simply pulling the mass down farther before you release it. The period of a freely oscillating system depends on the properties of the system and is independent of the way in which the oscillation is initiated. This period is called the **natural period** of the oscillator.

As we saw in Chapter 5, the reciprocal of the period is the frequency f, the number of complete cycles per unit time:

$$f = \frac{1}{T}. \tag{14.9}$$

Recall that the dimension of frequency is inverse time and its unit is the hertz (Hz). The frequency associated with the natural period is the **natural frequency** of an oscillator. It is the frequency of an oscillator that has been set into motion and then left to oscillate freely. Examples include masses on springs, pendulums, and guitar strings. We will see in Section 14.7 that the natural frequency is the frequency at which energy is most easily fed into an oscillating system.

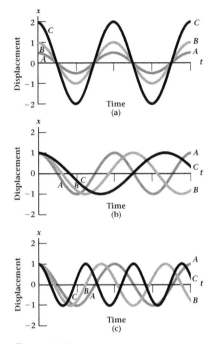

Figure 14.11
Displacement plotted against time for a simple harmonic oscillator. (a) The values of k and m are held constant while x_0 increases from curve A to B to C. (b) The values of k and x_0 are held constant while m increases from curve A to B to C. (c) The values of x_0 and m are held constant while k increases from curve A to B to C.

Master the Concept

Frequency of a Harmonic Oscillator

Question: A mass supported by a spring will oscillate when displaced from its equilibrium position and allowed to move freely. Why does a mass supported by a stiff spring oscillate with a higher frequency than does an equal mass supported by a weak spring? Ignore the mass of the springs.

Answer: When the masses on the two springs are displaced by the same amount, the stiffer spring exerts a greater force on the mass than does the weaker spring. Thus, the acceleration caused by the stiffer spring is greater than that caused by the weaker one. The mass on the stiffer spring moves more quickly between maximum and minimum displacements than does the mass on the weaker spring. As a result, the mass on the stiffer spring has the shorter period and the greater frequency.

Question: What happens if the initial amplitudes are different?

Answer: As long as we stay within the range of motions where the springs obey Hooke's law, the frequency (and the period) does not depend on the amplitude. So even if we start the two oscillators with different initial amplitudes, the mass on the stiffer spring will oscillate with the greater frequency.

▼

Example 14.5

A block of 2.4 kg oscillates on a spring of constant $k = 26$ N/m with an amplitude of 17 cm. (a) What is the period of one complete oscillation? (b) What is the natural frequency of the oscillations? (c) What is the maximum speed of the oscillating block? (d) What is the speed of the block 0.21 s after it passes through its maximum position?

Strategy (a) Because we are given the spring constant and the mass, we can find the natural period from Eq. (14.8).

(b) The natural frequency is the reciprocal of the natural period found in part (a).

(c) The maximum speed v_0 may be found from the equation that relates maximum speed to maximum displacement: $v_0 = x_0 \sqrt{k/m}$.

(d) Once we have both T and x_0, we can find the displacement at time t by using Eq. (14.3), remembering that the argument of the trigonometric function is in radians.

Solution (a) The period of oscillation is given by Eq. (14.8):

$$T = 2\pi \sqrt{\frac{m}{k}} = 2\pi \sqrt{\frac{2.4 \text{ kg}}{26 \text{ N/m}}} = 1.91 \text{ s} \approx 1.9 \text{ s.}$$

(b) The frequency is the reciprocal of the period:

$$f = \frac{1}{T} = \frac{1}{1.91 \text{ s}} = 0.52 \text{ Hz.}$$

(c) When we substitute the values for the amplitude x_0, the spring constant k, and the mass m, we have

$$v_0 = x_0 \sqrt{\frac{k}{m}} = (0.17 \text{ m}) \sqrt{\frac{26 \text{ N/m}}{2.4 \text{ kg}}} = 0.56 \text{ m/s.}$$

(d) We can now substitute the values found in parts (a) and (c) directly into Eq. (14.6) to give

$$|v_x| = \left| -v_0 \sin 2\pi \frac{t}{T} \right| = (0.56 \text{ m/s}) \sin 2\pi \frac{0.21 \text{ s}}{1.91 \text{ s}} = 0.36 \text{ m/s.}$$

Discussion In part (c), we could have obtained the maximum speed from knowledge of the amplitude and the period. The maximum speed v_0 is related to the amplitude x_0 through the expression for uniform circular motion used in the beginning of this section,

$$v_0 = \frac{2\pi x_0}{T} = \frac{2\pi (0.17 \text{ m})}{1.91 \text{ s}} = 0.56 \text{ m/s.}$$

Notice that this result is the same as the result we found in part (c).

▼

Example 14.6

The atomic force microscope consists of a sharp tip mounted on a soft cantilever spring (Fig. 14.12), a sensor that detects deflection of the spring, and a mechanical scanning system that moves the tip in a controlled path. If the

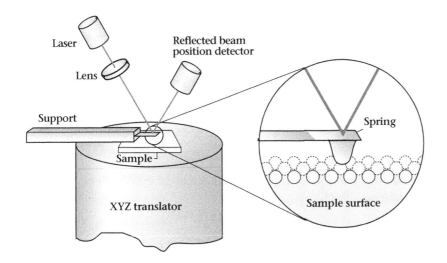

Figure 14.12
Example 14.6: Schematic of an atomic force microscope. A sharp tip is fastened to a cantilever spring having a very small spring constant. The microscope can be made to detect atomic-size displacements.

spring constant of the microscope spring is smaller than the equivalent spring constant between atoms in a solid, then the microscope can resolve positions comparable with atomic sizes without deforming the surface that is being examined. From knowledge that the vibrational frequencies of atoms in solids are of order 10^{12} Hz or higher and that the mass of an atom is of order 10^{-25} kg, calculate the effective interatomic spring constant.

Solution The relationship between the vibrational frequency and the mass is obtained from Eq. (14.8) as

$$f = \frac{1}{T} = \frac{1}{2\pi}\sqrt{\frac{k}{m}}.$$

Upon squaring both sides and rearranging, we find

$$k = (2\pi f)^2 m.$$

Inserting the approximate numerical values gives

$$k \approx (2\pi \times 10^{12} \text{ s}^{-1})^2 \, 10^{-25} \text{ kg} \approx 4 \text{ N/m}.$$

Discussion The value we have just calculated is an upper limit to the spring constant that can be used in an atomic force microscope. Working microscopes typically use spring constants in the range of 0.01 to 1 N/m. For comparison, a spring constant of that size can be obtained from a piece of ordinary aluminum foil 1 mm wide and 5 mm long.

Atomic force microscopes are capable of giving three-dimensional profiles with nanometer resolution. Figure 14.13 is an atomic force micrograph showing the surface of a stamping die used in the manufacturing of compact disks.

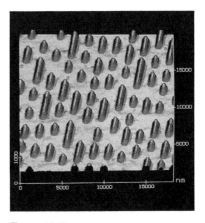

Figure 14.13
Example 14.6: Atomic force micrograph of a stamping die used to make compact disks. The audio information is encoded in bumps that are 60 nm high and arranged in tracks 1.6 μm apart.

14.5 The Simple Pendulum

A **simple pendulum** consists of a mass suspended by a light string of constant length L attached to a rigid support. When the mass, also called a bob, is pulled to one side and released, gravity causes it to swing down through the equilibrium

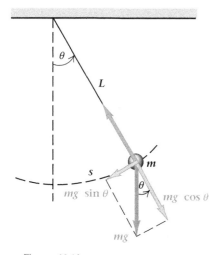

Figure 14.14
A simple pendulum consisting of a mass m at the end of a string of length L. The restoring force is $mg \sin \theta$.

point and up the other side. If the amplitude of its motion is small, the simple pendulum behaves as a simple harmonic oscillator. This is approximately the case in a grandfather clock, for example. Let us examine the pendulum and find out what determines its period.

When the bob of a simple pendulum is displaced to the side through an angle θ with the vertical (Fig. 14.14), the gravitational force $m\mathbf{g}$ has a component along the direction of the string and a component perpendicular to the string. This perpendicular component provides the restoring force F:

$$F = -mg \sin \theta.$$

When the angle θ is sufficiently small, $\sin \theta$ may be approximated by the angle θ in radians, so that*

$$F = -mg\theta.$$

The angle θ is related to the displacement s along the arc through which the pendulum swings by $s = L\theta$, giving

$$F = -\left(\frac{mg}{L}\right)s. \tag{14.10}$$

This equation has the same form as the spring equation (14.1) except that here the spring constant k is replaced by mg/L. Thus, the simple pendulum is a harmonic oscillator. The period of the pendulum is given by Eq. (14.8) with the substitution of mg/L for k. Thus,

$$T = 2\pi\sqrt{\frac{m}{k}} = 2\pi\sqrt{\frac{m}{mg/L}}$$

$$\boxed{T = 2\pi\sqrt{\frac{L}{g}}.} \tag{14.11}$$

This is an interesting result. The period of the simple pendulum is independent of the mass of the pendulum bob. The period is also independent of the amplitude of the motion (provided it is relatively small). However, the period of the pendulum does depend on its length.

The constancy of the period of a pendulum was discovered in the sixteenth century by Galileo. An often told story is that he made the discovery while observing that the periods of the chandeliers swinging in the Cathedral of Pisa were independent of their amplitudes. Although the story is instructive, it is almost certainly untrue. We do not know how Galileo made his discovery. Nevertheless, Galileo's conclusions led to the invention by Christiaan Huygens of the pendulum clock, which became the standard timekeeper for nearly 300 years. Pendulum clocks have a weight near the end of the pendulum that is used to adjust the period. Lowering the weight increases the effective length of the pendulum to make the period longer.

---

*How much error do we introduce by replacing the sine of an angle with the angle in radians for an angle of $10°$? The sine of $10°$ is 0.1736. The angle measured in radians is 0.1745, just slightly larger. The relative error is $\dfrac{\sin \theta - \theta}{\sin \theta} = \dfrac{-0.0009}{0.1736} \approx -5 \times 10^{-3}$. That is, the error is about one-half of one percent for $\theta = 10°$. For smaller angles, the relative error is even less.

Notice that when the period and length of a pendulum are well known, Eq. (14.11) provides a method for measuring the gravitational acceleration g. It is also appropriate to note that this simple result for the pendulum is valid only for small-amplitude oscillations. At larger amplitudes, the period is no longer independent of the amplitude and the motion is no longer simple harmonic, though it is still periodic.

Master the Concept

Period of a Pendulum

Question: The pendulum on the clock that strikes the hours on the bell Big Ben in London was particularly noted for its accuracy. Formerly the period was regulated by placing a penny on top of the bob of the 3.98-m-long pendulum. Will placing a penny there make the clock run faster or slower?

Answer: We can approximate the clock pendulum as a simple pendulum with a bob centered at 3.98 m below the pivot axis. If a penny is added to the top of the bob, it does two things; it increases the mass of the bob and it raises the center of mass of the bob slightly. As we have seen, the period of the pendulum is independent of its mass, but it does depend on its length. So raising the center of mass has the effect of shortening the length of the pendulum and thus reducing its period. Hence, adding the penny makes the clock run faster.

Example 14.7

A grandfather clock has a pendulum 1.0 m long. What is its period?

Solution The period is given by Eq. (14.11):

$$T = 2\pi\sqrt{\frac{L}{g}} = 2\pi\sqrt{\frac{1.0\text{ m}}{9.81\text{ m/s}^2}} = 2.0\text{ s}.$$

This length pendulum is frequently used in grandfather clocks. It is sometimes called a "seconds pendulum" because it makes a swing from one side to the other in one second, making the "tick" and the "tock" one second apart.

---

*14.6   Damped Harmonic Motion

Up to now, we have not considered the effects of friction on harmonic oscillators. Ignoring friction simplified the introduction to the topic and, as we have seen in both examples and problems, is justified because our results closely describe what actually happens when the frictional forces are weak or when we do not consider many oscillations. Yet friction is always present. Friction causes the amplitude of any real oscillating spring or pendulum to slowly decrease until the

WALKING AND RUNNING

To get some idea of the fundamental mechanical principles of walking and running, let us approximate the leg by a long thin rod of uniform cross section. We could more closely approximate a real leg with a more complicated model, but the nature of our conclusions would not change.*

Figure B14.1 shows a rod of length L supported at its upper end (point O) and free to swing. The period of a freely swinging rod supported at its upper end is

$$T = 2\pi\sqrt{\frac{2L}{3g}}.$$

This expression depends on the length of the rod and the acceleration of gravity in the same way as does the period of a simple pendulum. The factor of 2/3 is a result of the mass being distributed uniformly along the rod, rather than being concentrated at its lower end.

This expression gives an approximate value for the period of a freely swinging leg. You may wish to satisfy yourself that it is a reasonable approximation by doing the following simple experiment. Stand up and swing your leg back and forth as freely as you can. Do not use muscular effort to hold it back or to swing it rapidly. After you feel you can swing your leg freely, count the number of complete swings in ten seconds and calculate the period. Compare the period you observe with the prediction from the equation. To determine the length L, measure your leg length from the hip socket.

We can use this model to estimate a person's natural gait. Let us assume that a natural gait is the one involving the least muscular effort — the gait with the period found above. To a first approximation, we assume that the length of a stride is proportional to the length of the leg. The time for a single stride is one-half the period given above. The walking speed v thus depends on the leg length:

$$v_{walk} \propto \frac{L}{T/2} \propto \sqrt{L}.$$

This equation predicts that people with longer legs have a more rapid natural walking gait. The prediction is made on the basis of a model that assumes minimum energy expenditure and utilizes an oversimplified description of the leg. However, the prediction is borne out by common experience.

When a person runs, an important change must be made in our model. During running, the leg does not swing freely but is subject to a torque about O. The torque is a result of the force F applied by the muscles. This force is roughly proportional to the cross-sectional area of the muscles involved. If

we assume that, for people of different size, the relative proportions of the leg are the same, then the cross-sectional area, and therefore the force F, depends on the square of the length L. The torque is then proportional to the product of F with L:

$$\tau \propto FL \propto L^2 \cdot L \propto L^3.$$

The moment of inertia I is proportional to the mass times the square of the length (Chapter 9). Again we assume that all legs have essentially the same proportions; that is, width and thickness are proportional to length. Then the mass varies as the cube of the length:

$$I \propto mL^2 \propto L^5.$$

It can be shown that the period T of a long rod oscillating about one end and subject to a torque depends on the maximum torque and moment of inertia:

$$T \propto \sqrt{\frac{I}{\tau}}.$$

Upon substituting for I and τ, we find

$$T \propto \sqrt{\frac{L^5}{L^3}} \propto L.$$

The speed of running is proportional to the frequency of taking steps times the length of a step:

$$v_{run} \propto fL \propto \frac{L}{T} \propto \frac{L}{L} = 1.$$

So we have the prediction that, for animals with similarly shaped legs, the speed of running does not depend on the leg length. This prediction is not strictly true. However, the model does offer an explanation for the observation that the ordinary walking rate of people with long legs is greater than that of people with short legs, whereas the rate at which they can run is not always appreciably greater.

Figure B14.1 We can approximate the shape of a freely swinging leg by a uniform rod of length L that pivots about its upper end.

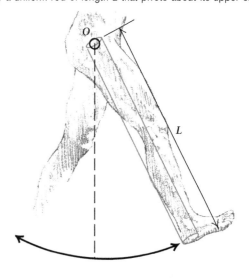

---

*This discussion of walking and running is adapted by permission of the author from P. Davidovits, *Physics in Biology and Medicine* (Englewood Cliffs, N.J.: Prentice-Hall, Inc., 1975).

oscillations eventually come to a stop. To be more complete, both Eq. (14.1) for the spring and Eq. (14.10) for the simple pendulum should have an additional term that describes the frictional force. This frictional force for an oscillator is often called **damping.**

Figure 14.15(a) shows an oscillator with damping provided by the resistance of the water in the jar to the motion of the vanes on the light rod attached to the bottom of the mass m. According to the principle of energy conservation, the amplitude of the oscillations of a damped system decreases as time goes by, unless energy is constantly supplied to replace the energy lost by friction. Thus, a spring oscillator that receives an initial displacement and is then left alone will gradually run down. For the particular system shown in Fig. 14.15, observations show that the damping is approximately proportional to the velocity of the vanes in the water. Including such a term in Eq. (14.1) leads to the result that if the mass is lifted up a distance y_0 and released, the displacement as a function of time is approximately

$$y \approx y_0 e^{-\gamma t} \cos(2\pi ft), \qquad (14.12)$$

where γ depends on the frictional force and the mass. If the damping is not too large, f is approximately the same as the natural frequency of the system.* The motion is shown by the blue curve in Fig. 14.15(b). We can look on this behavior as an oscillation at almost the natural frequency of the system but with an amplitude that decreases exponentially with time. This is shown by the gray lines in Fig. 14.15(b), which graphs the factor $e^{-\gamma t}$. Recall that the natural frequency is the frequency of the freely oscillating system.

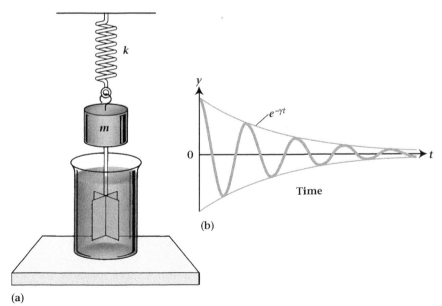

(b)

Time

(a)

Figure 14.15
(a) A simple harmonic oscillator with damping provided by viscous (frictional) forces. (b) Displacement of an underdamped harmonic oscillator as a function of time. The amplitude of the motion decreases exponentially with time.

*The frequency f is related to the natural frequency f_0 by $f^2 = f_0^2 - (\gamma/2\pi)^2$. The complete expression for the displacement under the conditions just described is
$y = y_0 e^{-\gamma t}[\cos 2\pi ft + (\gamma/\omega) \sin 2\pi ft]$. For lightly damped systems this last term is small.

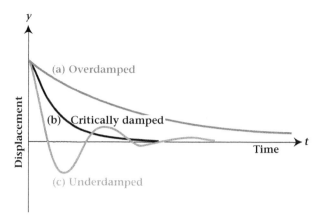

Figure 14.16

The displacement of (a) an overdamped harmonic oscillator, (b) a critically damped oscillator, and (c) an underdamped oscillator as a function of time.

Though not all harmonic oscillators have damping that is proportional to the velocity, Eq. (14.12) closely represents what happens in many real physical situations. As an extreme example, if the friction is constant but independent of velocity, a graph of the motion will be similar to Fig. 14.15(b), but the curves that form the upper and lower boundaries of the oscillatory motion will be replaced by straight lines.

If the harmonic oscillator is a pendulum, rather than a spring, Eq. (14.12) still describes the motion, but the linear displacement x is now replaced by the angular displacement of the pendulum. The same basic mathematical form holds for other damped oscillatory systems, whether they are mechanical, electrical, or acoustical systems.

Equation (14.12) and Fig. 14.15 describe the case of relatively weak damping and correspond to what is called *underdamped* motion. If the frictional force is too strong, the oscillator will not move at all. For damping that is strong, but yet allows the system to move, a related equation describes the motion that is called *overdamped,* shown by curve (a) in Fig. 14.16. A particularly important case lies between the underdamped and overdamped cases. This case is called *critical damping* and corresponds to the situation in which the damping coefficient γ is equal to the natural frequency of the system. In this case, a damped spring that is displaced and released returns as quickly as possible to the equilibrium position without overshooting (Fig. 14.16b). If we apply a constant force to a critically damped system, it moves to a new equilibrium position in the minimum time with no overshoot. The design of pointers on meters, shock absorbers, hydraulic and pneumatic door closers, and other practical devices is based on the proper design of damped harmonic oscillators.

▼

Example 14.8

A swing with 2.50-m ropes is pulled aside and let go. After 20 oscillations, the maximum amplitude is one-half of its original value. Assume that the swing behaves like the damped harmonic oscillator described in Eq. (14.12). (a) What is the value of γ? (b) Approximately what amplitude, relative to its original amplitude, will the swing have after 35 oscillations?

Solution (a) We assume that the swing oscillates at its natural frequency, so that the period T is

$$T = 2\pi\sqrt{\frac{L}{g}} = 2\pi\sqrt{\frac{2.50 \text{ m}}{9.81 \text{ m/s}^2}} = 3.172 \text{ s}.$$

Twenty oscillations will then take

$$20T = 63.44 \text{ s}.$$

Because the amplitude decreases exponentially to 0.5 of the original amplitude in time $t = 20T$, we can write

$$0.5 = e^{-\gamma t} = e^{-\gamma(63.44 \text{ s})}.$$

We may now determine γ by taking the natural logarithm of both sides of the equation. You can find the logarithm of 0.5 with a calculator:

$$\ln(0.5) = -0.6931.$$

The logarithm of the exponential is just the value of the exponent:

$$\ln\left(e^{-\gamma\,63.44\text{ s}}\right) = -\gamma\,(63.44 \text{ s}).$$

Thus,

$$0.6931 = \gamma\,(63.44 \text{ s}), \quad \text{and} \quad \gamma = 0.0109/\text{s}.$$

(b) Thirty-five oscillations will take

$$35T = 111.0 \text{ s},$$

so the amplitude, as a fraction f of the original amplitude, is

$$f = e^{-\gamma t} = e^{-(0.0109/\text{s})(111.0\text{ s})} = 0.297.$$

After 35 oscillations, the swing will have about one-third of its original amplitude.

*14.7 Forced Harmonic Motion and Resonance

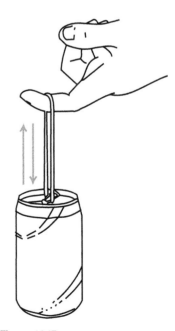

Figure 14.17
A soft drink can suspended from rubber bands can be used to demonstrate resonance.

Before continuing, try the following simple experiment. Make an oscillator by joining several rubber bands together and hanging an unopened soft drink can from the end (Fig. 14.17). You will find it easy to attach the can to the rubber band by looping the bottom rubber band under the pull-up tab. You may try some other combination of elastic elements and mass; the idea is to make an oscillator with a natural period of about one-half to one second so that you can easily observe what happens. Get a rough idea of the natural frequency of the system by looping one end of the rubber band around the tip of a finger, pulling the can down, and observing what happens when you release it.

Next, suspend the system from your finger and move your finger up and down slowly. You will find that the can moves up and down in phase with your finger, and with about the same amplitude. Increase the rate of your finger's motion and observe the change that occurs as the frequency of your finger comes closer to the natural frequency of the system. The amplitude of the can's motion increases greatly, and at the natural frequency of the system, a very small motion of your finger makes the can move up and down with a large amplitude. At

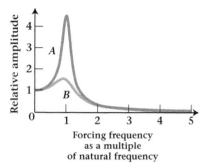

Figure 14.18

The response of a damped harmonic oscillator plotted as a function of the frequency of the driving force. Curve *B* corresponds to greater damping than does curve *A*.

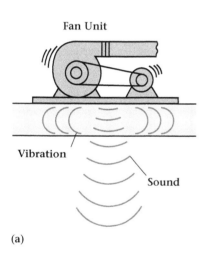

(a)

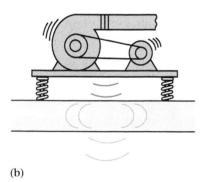

(b)

Figure 14.19

Example 14.9: (a) A fan bolted directly to the roof generates vibrations throughout the building. (b) Shock-mounting the fan on springs reduces the vibrations transmitted to the building, provided we choose the proper spring constants.

this point, energy is being fed into the system at the natural frequency of the system, a condition called **resonance.** The natural frequency is also known as the **resonant frequency.** As we will see in the next chapter, natural resonant systems usually have more than one resonant frequency.

As you continue to increase the frequency with which you move your finger up and down, you will find that the amplitude of the can's motion decreases. Eventually you will reach a frequency at which the can stays relatively motionless, even though you move your finger through quite a large distance.

What you have done is to observe the response of a lightly damped harmonic oscillator (the rubber bands and can) to an applied force as a function of the frequency of that force. Actually, rubber bands do not obey Hooke's law strictly, but the behavior of the system is close enough to a harmonic oscillator for us to study the general principles.

A graph of the amplitude of a forced damped harmonic oscillator as a function of the forcing frequency shows the behavior we have just described. In Fig. 14.18, two curves have been plotted, corresponding to different amounts of damping. As you would expect, large damping in the system causes the maximum amplitude at resonance to be lower than otherwise.

The idea of resonance is extremely important for mechanical and electrical systems because energy is most effectively transferred when it is supplied at the natural frequency of the system. When you push a swing to make it go higher, you push at its natural frequency. When you tune a radio or TV set, you are adjusting the natural, or resonant, frequency of the electrical circuit to match the frequency of the radio or TV station you want to receive. We will make additional use of the idea of resonance in Chapter 15 on waves.

Resonance effects can also have undesirable or even destructive effects. The rattle in a car's body or an annoying buzz in a stereo speaker is often due to resonance. Most people have heard that a powerful singer can shatter a glass by singing at the right frequency. Equally famous is the warning that a group of people should not march in step across a bridge, lest the frequency of the footsteps match some natural frequency of the bridge. These are all examples of resonance.

Frequently we need a system that does not transfer energy efficiently. An example is a mechanism for isolating sensitive apparatus from vibrations. A common solution to a problem of vibration is to fasten the source of vibration on an elastic mounting to cushion and absorb the shock. What may not be obvious is that the selection of the wrong elastic mounting can make the problem worse. Isolation is accomplished by decreasing the natural frequency of the system relative to the frequency of the vibration source. The reason this technique works can be seen from Fig. 14.18 and from recalling the experiment with the rubber band and the can. The least energy is transferred when the frequency of the driving force is much higher than the natural frequency of the system.

We have based our discussion of resonance, and the response of a system to forcing, entirely on the behavior of a mass attached to a spring that obeys Hooke's law. However, the same general principles and results apply to other oscillating systems, whether they be mechanical, electrical, or other.

▼

Example 14.9

The fan unit for a building's heating and air-conditioning system is rigidly mounted on the roof and runs continuously (Fig. 14.19a). The vibrations are transmitted throughout the structure of the building and generate unacceptable vibration levels. To reduce the vibration felt below, the system is to be attached to a spring-mounted slab. The fan shaft turns at 1800 rpm (revolutions per minute), and the combined mass of the unit and the mounting slab (Fig. 14.19b) is 576 kg. What is the proper stiffness constant for the springs used to support the slab? Assume four springs, one at each corner.

Strategy The oscillation system in this case consists of the motor, the fan, the mounting platform, and the springs. One rule of thumb sometimes used is that the driving, or disturbing, frequency should be at least 3 times the natural frequency of the system. For many cases, a factor of 5 is adequate, and for critical conditions, a factor of 12 or more is appropriate. We can achieve these factors by lowering the natural frequency of the system. If we choose a one-to-five ratio, which corresponds to a reduction in the force of the vibrations to the building of about 96%, the desired natural frequency of the system is

$$\frac{1}{5}(1800 \text{ rpm})\left(\frac{1}{60 \text{ s/min}}\right) = 6.0 \text{ Hz}.$$

Solution The proper springs can be selected by using

$$f = \frac{1}{T} = \frac{1}{2\pi}\sqrt{\frac{k}{m}}.$$

Solving for the spring constant k gives us

$$k = m(2\pi f)^2 = (576 \text{ kg})[2\pi(6.0/\text{s})]^2 = 8.19 \times 10^5 \text{ N/m}.$$

This would be the largest desirable spring constant if all of the mass were supported by one spring. Since there are four springs, one at each corner of the mounting slab, each one of these four springs will have a spring constant, or stiffness, of $\frac{1}{4}(8.19 \times 10^5 \text{ N/m}) = 2.05 \times 10^5 \text{ N/m}$.

▼

Summary

Useful Concepts

■ Many phenomena can be described by an equation such as Hooke's law,

$$F = -kx.$$

These phenomena are examples of simple harmonic motion and occur in electrical as well as mechanical systems.

■ For simple harmonic motion,

$$x = x_0 \cos 2\pi ft,$$

$$v = -v_0 \sin 2\pi ft = -\sqrt{\frac{k}{m}}\, x_0 \sin 2\pi ft,$$

$$a = -a_0 \cos 2\pi ft = -\frac{k}{m}\, x_0 \cos 2\pi ft.$$

■ The frequency is the reciprocal of the period,

$$f = \frac{1}{T}.$$

■ The potential energy of a stretched spring is

$$\text{PE} = \tfrac{1}{2}kx_0^2.$$

■ The period of a mass oscillating on a spring is

$$T = 2\pi\sqrt{\frac{m}{k}}.$$

■ The period of a simple pendulum is

$$T = 2\pi\sqrt{\frac{L}{g}}.$$

■ The displacement of a damped harmonic oscillator is the product of an exponentially decreasing term and an oscillating term:

$$y = y_0 e^{-\gamma t} \cos(2\pi ft).$$

■ Energy is transferred most effectively at the natural frequency of the system, a condition known as resonance.

Important Terms

You should be able to write the definition or meaning of each of the following:

periodic	phase angle
Hooke's law	natural period
restoring force	natural frequency
spring constant	simple pendulum
simple harmonic motion	damping
amplitude	resonance
simple harmonic oscillator	resonant frequency

▼ Conceptual Questions

14.1 Determine the effective spring constant of a bathroom scale by estimating the amount the scale compresses when you stand on it.

14.2 A glider on a horizontal air track is connected to the end of the track by a spring and placed on an elevator. What is the effect on the period of its oscillations when the elevator is (a) accelerated upward, (b) accelerated downward, (c) moving with a constant speed?

14.3 A hollow plastic sphere is held well below the surface of a swimming pool by a spring attached to the bottom. Do the vertical oscillations of the sphere show damped simple harmonic motion?

14.4 A lump of clay is dropped onto an upright spring. What determines the maximum compression of the spring? (*Hint:* Consider conservation of energy.)

14.5 Name as many examples as you can of harmonic motion found in nature.

14.6 Two metal blocks of different mass are suspended inside a large closed box by identical springs attached to the interior top of the box. When the box is at rest, the spring supporting the more massive block is longer than the other spring. Discuss what happens to the relative positions of the masses if the box is dropped from a great height.

14.7 A simple pendulum suspended from the ceiling of an elevator has a period T_0 when the elevator is not moving. What is the effect on the period when the elevator is (a) accelerated upward, (b) accelerated downward, (c) moving with a constant speed?

14.8 Consider the motion of a meterstick swinging from one end and that of a one-meter-long simple pendulum of the same mass. Are their periods the same? Give a physical reason for your answer.

14.9 You can consider an automobile suspension to be a forced damped harmonic oscillator, consisting of the springs and shock absorbers, which is forced by the wheels' up-and-down motion over bumps and ruts. What are some of the important design criteria? Should there be much or little damping?

14.10 If the outer case of an air conditioner rattles when the unit runs, what can you do that will probably make it stop?

14.11 Why is it that sometimes you hear rattles when you drive a car at one speed, but they go away when you drive faster or slower?

14.12 A cord and a spring with an equilibrium length equal to the length of the cord are hung from a frame inside a rapidly moving train. Equal masses are attached to the lower end of the cord and the spring. Which makes a greater angle with respect to the vertical when the train accelerates? Explain your answer.

▼ Problems

Hooke's law relates the force to the displacement for springs and systems that behave linearly. In some cases, we are interested in the applied or external force for which the force and displacement are in the same direction. In other cases, we are interested in the restoring force due to the spring. The restoring force is opposite in direction to the displacement. You should draw a diagram for each situation carefully indicating the direction of the forces and the displacements.

Section 14.1 Hooke's Law

14.1 A 15,000-N Pontiac Grand Prix is supported by four coil springs, each with a spring constant of 7.00×10^4 N/m. By how much is each spring compressed under the weight of the car if the weight is evenly distributed?

14.2 Determine whether the following two sets of data were taken from springs that obey Hooke's law. In each case, objects of increasing mass were hung from a suspended spring and the length of the spring measured. If Hooke's law is obeyed, determine the spring constant. If not, decide whether there is any part of the range over which Hooke's law is obeyed, and determine the spring constant for that part.

Mass (kg)	Length of Spring A (cm)	Length of Spring B (cm)
0.0	15.7	8.4
1.0	16.5	15.6
2.0	17.8	20.5
3.0	19.3	21.4
4.0	20.4	21.6
5.0	21.3	22.1
6.0	22.8	22.5
7.0	24.1	22.6
8.0	25.0	23.1
9.0	26.6	25.8
10.0	27.6	28.2

14.3 A coil spring has a spring constant of 54 N/m. If the full length of the spring is 35 cm when a 1.0-kg mass is hung from it, what is the equilibrium length of the spring when the 1.0-kg mass is removed?

14.4 A coil spring is extended by 2.50 cm when it supports a 1.00-N weight. If an identical spring is joined to the end of the first one, what is the extension of the combined spring when it supports the same 1.00-N weight? Assume the spring masses to be negligible.

14.5• A fisherman's spring scale is extended to a total length of 0.18 m when a 6.12-kg fish is suspended from it. If the spring constant is 1000 N/m, what is the total length of the spring when an 11.4-kg fish is suspended from it?

14.6• Two identical coil springs are mounted side by side so that they jointly support a weight hanger of 2.00 N. When an additional 4.00 N is added to the hanger, it is displaced downward by 5.00 cm. What is the force constant of the individual springs?

14.7• Two springs have the same spring constant. One of them is 0.400 m long, and the other 0.250 m long. If they are connected end-to-end between rigid supports 1.300 m apart, where will the connection point of the two springs lie relative to the supported end of the short spring?

14.8• A spring gun consists of a horizontal spring with $k = 50$ N/m that is compressed 17 cm when the gun is cocked. The gun fires a 150-g projectile. What is the initial acceleration of the projectile?

14.9•• A block hung from the ceiling on a vertical spring stretches the spring by one-fourth of its equilibrium length. The spring is taken down and the free end placed over a peg on a horizontal frictionless surface. The block is set in motion in a circular orbit about the peg with a linear speed of 5.00 m/s. The motion of the block causes the spring to extend by exactly the same amount it did when the spring was in the vertical position. Is the equilibrium length of the spring longer or shorter than your arm?

14.10•• A spring has an equilibrium length of 25.6 cm and a spring constant of 52.9 N/m. The spring is connected to the underside of the roof of a car and a 0.264 kg block suspended

from it. (a) How long is the spring when the car is at rest? (b) How long is the spring if the car is accelerating horizontally at 1.73 m/s²?

Section 14.2 The Simple Harmonic Oscillator

Hints for Solving Problems

Simple harmonic motion occurs when the acceleration is proportional to the negative of the displacement. In simple harmonic motion, maximum acceleration occurs at maximum displacement and zero velocity.

14.11 The position of a harmonic oscillator is described by $x = x_0 \cos 2\pi t/T$, where the displacement amplitude is $x_0 = 10$ cm and the period T is 0.25 s. Calculate the displacement at $t = 0.75$ s, at $t = 2.0$ s, and at $t = 2.3$ s.

14.12 A block moving with simple harmonic motion has a period of 2.0 s. The maximum displacement from equilibrium in any direction is 5.0 cm. (a) Write an equation to describe the displacement, given that at time $t = 0$ the displacement is zero and the velocity is positive. (b) Write an equation for the displacement, given that at time $t = 0$ the displacement is a maximum and the velocity is zero.

14.13 A harmonic oscillator with an amplitude of 30 cm has a displacement of 30 cm at $t = 0$. At $t = 0.20$ s, it has a displacement of 27 cm, without having passed through zero displacement. What is the period of the oscillator's motion?

14.14• A can of beans hung on a vertical spring is pulled down from its equilibrium position and released. It travels up and then back down to the position from which it was released in 0.75 s, traveling a total distance of 0.75 m. How far from its release position was the can 0.12 s after it was released?

14.15• A harmonic oscillator has a period of 0.314 s and an amplitude of 7.0 cm. At $t = 0$ it is at $x = 0$. (a) How far does it travel between $t = 0$ and $t = 0.063$ s? (b) How far does it travel between $t = 0.283$ s and $t = 0.345$ s?

14.16• Show that for a harmonic oscillator $v_0 = 2\pi x_0/T$, where x_0 is the amplitude of the displacement, v_0 is the amplitude of the velocity, and T is the period. (*Hint:* Use Fig. 14.6.)

14.17• A 0.50-kg air-track glider is attached to the end of the track by a horizontal coil spring of $k = 20.0$ N/m. The glider is displaced 15.0 cm from its equilibrium position and released, so that it oscillates back and forth on the track. (a) What is the maximum acceleration of the glider? (b) What is its acceleration at a time equal to one-eighth of the oscillator's period? (c) What is its position at a time equal to one-eighth of the oscillator's period?

14.18•• Show that for a harmonic oscillator the displacement x and velocity v are related by

$$x = x_0\sqrt{1 - \left(\frac{v}{v_0}\right)^2},$$

where x_0 is the maximum displacement and v_0 is the maximum velocity.

Section 14.3 Energy of a Harmonic Oscillator

Hints for Solving Problems

Assume that all the potential energy of a harmonic oscillator at maximum displacement is converted to kinetic energy at the equilibrium position.

14.19 The spring described in Example 14.1 is stretched to 5.0 cm beyond its equilibrium length. How much work is required to stretch the spring?

14.20 The potential energy stored in the compressed spring of a toy dart gun is 0.37 J. The spring constant is 29 N/m. By how much is the spring compressed?

14.21 Two joules are required to extend a spring by 0.25 m. What is the spring constant?

14.22 A 4.0-kg block oscillates with an amplitude of 0.080 m on a light spring of constant $k = 15$ N/m. (a) What is the maximum value of the block's velocity? (b) What is its maximum acceleration?

14.23• A 0.50-kg plush toy oscillates at the end of a long light spring of constant $k = 10.0$ N/m and negligible mass. The maximum speed of the toy as it oscillates is 0.30 m/s. (a) What is the amplitude of the oscillation? (b) How much energy is stored in the spring at its greatest extension?

14.24• A physics student wants to build a spring gun that when aimed horizontally will give a 20-g ball an initial acceleration of g by releasing a spring that has been compressed 15 cm. (a) What spring constant is necessary? (b) What is the velocity of the ball as it emerges from the gun?

14.25•• By substituting for v and x as functions of time in the expression for the total energy of a harmonic oscillator, show that the total energy is conserved; that is, show that the total energy is independent of time.

Section 14.4 Period of a Harmonic Oscillator

Hints for Solving Problems

The period of a simple harmonic oscillator made with a spring depends only on the mass and the spring constant or, for a simple pendulum, on the length and the acceleration of gravity.

14.26 A 0.400-kg brass block is attached to a spring of negligible mass. What is the value of the spring constant if the vibrational frequency is 0.550 Hz?

14.27 A 0.500-kg puppet oscillates at the end of a light spring of constant $k = 2.00$ N/m. (a) What is the frequency of the oscillations? (b) What is the period?

14.28 A 2.0-kg fish is attached to a spring of constant $k = 56$ N/m and of negligible mass. The spring is stretched 8.0 cm from equilibrium and released from rest. (a) What is the maximum speed of the fish as it oscillates? (b) What is the frequency of the oscillation?

14.29• A circus performer bobs up and down at the end of a long elastic rope at a rate of once every two seconds. By how much is the rope extended beyond its unloaded length when the performer hangs at rest?

14.30• The prongs of a 440-Hz tuning fork vibrate with simple harmonic motion. A scratch on the end of one of the prongs travels through a total distance of 1.00 mm as the prong moves from one extreme position to the other. (a) What is the maximum speed of the scratch? (b) What is the maximum acceleration of the scratch?

14.31• An oscillator with a 0.46-s period is made from a mass suspended from a spring. The mass is placed on a frictionless surface that makes a 45° angle with the horizontal, and the spring is attached at the top of the incline (Fig. 14.20). What is the new period of the oscillator?

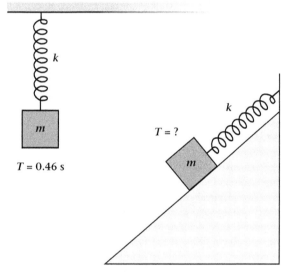

Figure 14.20
Problem 14.31.

14.32• One end of a light hacksaw blade is clamped in a vise with the long axis of the blade horizontal and with the sides vertical. A 0.845-kg mass is attached to the free end. When a steady sideways force of 20.5 N is applied to the mass, it moves aside 14.3 cm from its equilibrium position. When released, the blade moves back and forth with harmonic motion. Approximately how many complete oscillations will the blade make in 20 s when the force is removed?

14.33• A harmonic oscillator of frequency $f = 0.500$ Hz has an amplitude of 12.0 cm. (a) What is the maximum speed of its motion? (b) What is the maximum acceleration?

14.34• A 20.5 kg mass suspended on a spring is pulled down and released. The mass oscillates with a period of 0.750 s and an amplitude of 3.50 cm. What energy was initially stored in the spring before it was released?

14.35•• Plot on the same graph the potential energy, the kinetic energy, and the total energy of a harmonic oscillator as a function of time if $m = 0.10$ kg, $k = 20$ N/m, and $x_0 = 5.0$ cm. Plot for t between 0 and 0.6 s.

14.36•• A long 3.0-cm-diameter cylinder of ice is weighted at the bottom so that it floats upright in a container of water at 0°C. The mass of the cylinder with the weight is 300 g. When the cylinder is pushed down and released, it bobs up and down. Show that this motion is simple harmonic motion and find its frequency. (*Hint:* You will need to know the density of water at 0°C.)

14.37•• Two masses A and B freely slide in a cylinder (Fig. 14.21). The lower mass B is supported by a spring. When both A and B are in the cylinder, the period of the systems oscillation is 0.850 s. When the 2.00-kg mass A is removed, the period of the system is 0.350 s. What is the mass of B?

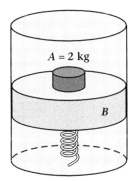

Figure 14.21
Problem 14.37.

Section 14.5 The Simple Pendulum

14.38 A 21-kg child swings on a playground swing 3.4 m long. (a) What is the period of her motion? (b) If her older brother, who weighs twice as much as she does, rides in the swing instead, what is the period of the motion? Assume the center of mass to be at the position of the seat in both cases.

14.39 A 30-kg child is playing on a swing of negligible mass. The child swings so high that at the peak of the motion her center of mass is 1.0 m above where it is at the bottom of the swing. How fast is the child moving when she passes through the minimum point of her swing?

14.40 A simple pendulum makes 83 complete swings in one minute. (a) What is its frequency? (b) What is its period of oscillation?

14.41 A child swings on a playground swing attached to chains 4.0 m long. (a) Calculate the period of the swing for small-amplitude oscillations. (b) What would be the new period if the seat height were raised 1.0 m? Assume the center of mass to be at the position of the seat.

14.42 Until 1987, a 22.25-m-long pendulum hung in the Smithsonian Institute, National Museum of American History. (a) Calculate the period of the pendulum for small-amplitude oscillations. (b) What would be the new period if the pendulum were reinstalled with a length one-third of its original length?

14.43 An 800-kg wrecking ball hangs from the end of a crane by a 30.0-m cable. If the crane operator quickly moves the end of the crane 3.00 m to the left, how many seconds pass before the wrecking ball passes below the end of the crane?

14.44 Students in an elementary physics laboratory measured the period of a simple pendulum to be 2.475 s. Careful measurement showed the length of the pendulum to be 151.8 cm. What was the acceleration of gravity in their laboratory?

14.45• Tarzan is across the river from Jane, who is in danger of being blown up by a time bomb set for 6.9 s. Tarzan can save Jane only by swinging across the river on a 21-m vine hung directly over the center of the river. Because Tarzan is clinging to another vine, he can swing over only with the force of gravity and is unable to push off. (a) Will he arrive in time to save Jane? If so, by what margin? (b) Where are Tarzan and Jane when the bomb goes off?

14.46• The lengths of pendulums with periods of two seconds are given for several locations. Find the distance through which an object will fall in a half second at these locations, neglecting air resistance: (a) St. Thomas, 99.11 cm; (b) New York, 99.32 cm; (c) London, 99.41 cm; (d) Spitzbergen, 99.61 cm.

14.47• A rule sometimes used by clock makers is that a pendulum oscillating with V oscillations per minute has a length L in inches given by $L = (187.6/V)^2$. Verify this expression.

14.48•• A pendulum makes 135 complete oscillations in 3.00 min. When carried on a train rounding a curve at 77.4 km/h, the same pendulum makes 136 complete oscillations in 3.00 min. What is the radius of curvature of the track?

*Section 14.6 Damped Harmonic Motion

14.49• A 94-cm simple pendulum is pulled aside a small distance and released. After 120 oscillations the amplitude is one-half of its starting value. The damping is proportional to the speed of the pendulum bob. (a) What is the value of the damping coefficient γ if the behavior is described by Eq. (14.12)? (b) What fraction of the original amplitude will remain after 15 min?

14.50•• Graph the motion of a damped harmonic oscillator described by Eq. (14.12) for which $\gamma = 0.30$/s and $2\pi f = 2.0$/s. Extend your graph out to $t = 12$ s. You may want to draw the exponential curves first. Next mark the maximum, minimum, and zeros of the cosine function and then sketch the displacement curve.

14.51•• A 1.26-m pendulum is pulled aside and released. Air resistance gives a damping coefficient of $\gamma = 0.02$/s. The support wire makes an angle of 3.30° with the vertical direction 1.50 s after the release. What was the angle from the vertical of the original displacement?

*Section 14.7 Forced Harmonic Motion and Resonance

14.52 Repeat the experiment with the rubber bands and drink can described in Section 14.7. This time determine the percent difference between your observed frequency of finger motion at the resonant frequency and the frequency of the system calculated from the spring constant and the mass of the can. Because of the assumptions, you should expect only approximate agreement. Determine the spring constant by measuring the extension of the rubber bands when the can is hung from them. (Assume that Hooke's law holds, neglect the mass of the metal can compared with the mass of the liquid, and, if necessary, assume the density of soft drinks to be the same as the density of water.)

14.53• What should be the length of the pendulum in Fig. 14.22 to give the 1.0-kg air-track glider the maximum amplitude if the spring constant is $k = 120$ N/m?

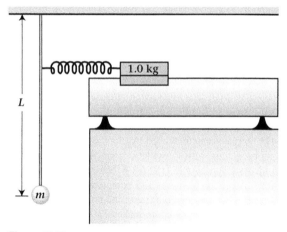

Figure 14.22
Problem 14.53.

14.54• A motor that turns at 12,000 rpm is suspended from above by a single spring to isolate the building from its vibration. If the natural frequency of the system is to be one-fourth of the vibration frequency, by how many centimeters should the spring extend beyond its unloaded length when the motor is hung on it?

14.55•• A 1550-kg Pontiac Grand Prix is supported by four coil springs, each with a spring constant of 7.00×10^4 N/m. (a) What is the natural oscillation frequency of this system? (b) The car bumps as it rolls over the tar strips when driven along a concrete highway. If the tar strips are 18.5 m apart, how fast is the car moving when the frequency of the bumps is resonant with the natural frequency?

Additional Problems

14.56 A 0.500-kg lead weight is attached to a spring of negligible mass. When the weight is set into motion, it oscillates with a period of 2.00 s. (a) What is the spring constant k? (b) What force is required to stretch the spring by 2.00 cm?

14.57 A clock pendulum has a period of 0.750 s. (a) How long is the pendulum? (b) How long must it be to have a period of 2.00 s?

14.58• Two 35-cm springs have different spring constants. If the springs are connected end to end and the outer ends are connected to supports that are 100 cm apart, the connection point is 45 cm from the nearest support. What is the ratio of the spring constants?

14.59• When a physics textbook is hung from a spring attached to the ceiling, the spring stretches 4.0 cm. The book is next hung from three springs exactly like the first one (Fig. 14.23). What is the total extension of the spring system?

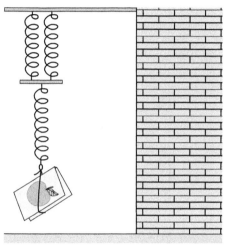

Figure 14.23
Problem 14.59.

14.60• A child's pail is filled with sand and hung from a vertical spring, extending the spring 14 cm. If the pail is pulled down an additional 28 cm and released from rest, what is the pail's initial upward acceleration?

14.61• When a box of cookies is hung on the end of a spring, the spring stretches by 5.90 cm. What is the oscillation frequency of the system if the box is pulled down and released?

14.62• A solid plastic block lies on a smooth floor. It is connected to the wall by a long horizontal coil spring with a spring constant of 86 N/m. If the block is pulled aside 37 cm and released, how much heat will have been generated before the block comes to rest?

14.63•• When a 3.00-kg cube of metal is hung from a spring, the spring stretches by 7.50 cm. The same block is placed on a frictionless horizontal surface and the spring connected to a support at the same level as the block. The block is pulled 3.00 cm away from its equilibrium position and released. What is the initial acceleration of the block?

14.64•• A person whirls a 0.250-kg stone in a 1.00-m-radius horizontal circle at the end of a string. The horizontal component of the force with which the person pulls on the string is 5.00 N. Write expressions for the projections of the displacement, velocity, and acceleration on a diameter of the circle.

14.65•• It is claimed that if a hole could be bored straight through the earth and if an object were dropped into the hole, the object would oscillate back and forth along this diameter with simple harmonic motion. Test this claim by assuming that the earth is of uniform density, getting an expression for the force on the object, and comparing the expression with Eq. (14.1). (*Hint:* A small object at a distance R from the center of a mass with spherical symmetry will experience a gravitational force toward the center that depends only on the mass inside an imaginary sphere of radius R. This is true whether the object is outside or inside the spherical mass.)

14.66•• A mass m is attached to a vertical spring and released. The mass oscillates but eventually comes to rest a distance h below its initial position when the spring was unstretched. Find expressions for the change in gravitational potential energy of the mass and for the energy stored in the spring as a function of m, h, and the acceleration of gravity. Explain why the two expressions are or are not the same.

14.67•• A simple pendulum is in an upward accelerating elevator. A student says that the 0.500-m-long pendulum has a period of 1.40 s. Another student in the same elevator finds that an object falls from rest through 1.00 m in 0.450 s. Given that both experimental results are subject to ± 2.00% accuracy, are the students' results in agreement?

14.68•• A clock pendulum that "ticks seconds" (has a period of two seconds) on earth is set up on the moon. What is the pendulum's period on the moon?

14.69•• A pendulum bob on a string of length L is arranged as shown in Fig. 14.24. The point marked P is a smooth peg and is at a distance $L/2$ below the support. Write an expression for the period for small oscillations of this system.

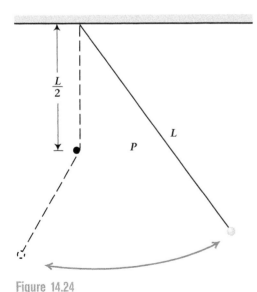

Figure 14.24
Problem 14.69.

14.70•• A mass is suspended from a fixed point by a light cord of length L. The mass is set in motion in a horizontal cir-

cle of radius R (Fig. 14.25). Such an arrangement is called a conical pendulum because the moving cord sweeps out the surface of an inverted cone. (a) Show that the frequency f of a conical pendulum is given by

$$f = \frac{\sqrt{g}}{2\pi(L^2 - R^2)^{1/4}}.$$

(b) Show that for L much greater than R the period of a simple pendulum is approximately the same as that of a conical pendulum of the same length.

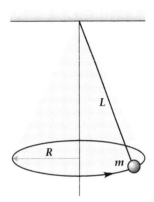

Figure 14.25
Problem 14.70.

14.71•• A U-shaped tube is partially filled with water. (a) Show that if the water is displaced from equilibrium, it executes simple harmonic motion. (b) Find an expression for the period of the oscillations. (Let the diameter of the tube be d and the total length of the water column be L.)

14.72•• Assume that the length of the water column in a very long upright U-shaped tube is 50 cm. If the damping coefficient γ is 0.30/s, how many oscillations must occur for the amplitude to decrease to one-fourth of its original value?

14.73•• A swing is hung from the limb of a tree. When a young child gets into the swing, it settles 2.0 cm. Because of the flexibility of the tree limb, the swing bobs up and down as well as swinging back and forth. When the swing is gently bobbed up and down with no swinging motion, the frequency is 10 times the frequency of the swing when it is gently swung so as not to excite bobbing motion. How long is the swing?

14.74•• The apparatus shown in Fig. 14.26 consists of a mass m attached to the end of a light rod (negligible mass) of length L and hinged at one end. A spring of spring constant k is joined to the rod a distance a from the hinged end. Show that the frequency of oscillation of this apparatus is

$$f = \frac{a}{2\pi L}\sqrt{\frac{k}{m}}$$

by first showing that it is equivalent to a mass hanging from a spring of constant $k(a/L)^2$.

14.75•• A simple pendulum consists of a bob of mass m supported by a thin metal wire with a linear thermal expansion coefficient α. At temperature T, the period for small amplitude oscillations of the pendulum is τ_0. Show that if the temperature increases by an amount ΔT, the period of the pendulum changes by $\Delta \tau = \frac{1}{2}\alpha\tau_0\,\Delta T$. You may use the approximation that $(1 + x)^{1/2} \approx 1 + \frac{1}{2}x$ for $x \ll 1$.

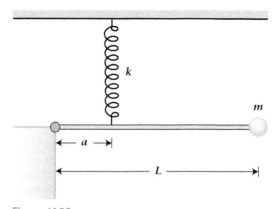

Figure 14.26
Problem 14.74.

Waves and Sound

15.1   Pulses on a Rope
15.2   Harmonic Waves
*15.3   Energy and Information Transfer by
          Waves
15.4   Sound Waves
*15.5   Measuring Sound Levels
15.6   The Doppler Effect

Physics in Practice: Room Acoustics

*15.7   Formation of a Shock Wave
15.8   Reflection of a Wave Pulse
15.9   Standing Waves on a String
15.10   Waves in a Vibrating Column of Air
*15.11   Beats

Physics in Practice: Hearing and the Ear

The study of periodic vibrations and waves is one of the oldest scientific studies. The Pythagoreans first established the connection between musical sounds and mathematics in the fourth century B.C. This study continued through the middle ages and was later developed by Huygens and Galileo. In the eighteenth century, an interest in musical instruments prompted the mathematical study of vibrating bodies and of the propagation of sound through air. By the nineteenth century, the study of sound had become an integral part of physics and was known as *acoustics.*

Studies of wave motion also advanced through research into the behavior of light, the discipline known as *optics.* Robert Hooke and Christiaan Huygens, contemporaries of Newton, believed light to be a form of wave motion, and Huygens developed a mathematical model for light waves. However, not until the early 1800s did Thomas Young firmly establish the wave nature of light. By the end of that century, Heinrich Hertz had established that what we now call radio waves were of the same nature as light waves. In the early twentieth century, wave concepts were used to develop the theory of quantum mechanics, which is sometimes called wave mechanics.

In our daily lives we see many examples of waves and oscillations: Radio and television waves reach around the world; musical sounds are created and modified by computers, as well as by traditional instruments; and ultrasound and x rays are commonly used in medical diagnosis and treatment.

There are similarities between vibratory motion and wave motion. We use mechanical concepts such as displacement, velocity, acceleration, and energy in describing them both. However, you must take care to distinguish between these two phenomena. As we develop the wave concept, we will point out both the similarities and the differences. ■

15.1 Pulses on a Rope

The simplest way to begin the study of waves is to think of the propagation of a pulse along a rope. If one end of a tautly stretched rope is suddenly snapped up and back down to its initial position, the action generates a wave pulse that travels along the rope to the other end (Fig. 15.1). As you can see from the figure, the displacement of the rope due to this wave pulse is at right angles to the direction in which the pulse travels. For this reason we call this type of motion a **transverse wave pulse.** If we watch any particular point of the rope very closely, we see that the motion of that point along the direction of the rope is very slight compared with its motion perpendicular to the rope. Each section of the rope makes a single oscillation up and down. But the oscillations are not independent, for each section of the rope is connected to the adjacent sections. Thus, the propagation of a transverse wave pulse along the rope is a collective motion of the whole rope, not simply the isolated behavior of any one section.

In addition to distinguishing between the motion of a pulse, or wave, and the motion of the medium (here, the rope), we must distinguish the kind of motions involved. For example, the velocity of a wave on a rope may be constant, while the transverse velocity of a point on the rope may be sinusoidal in time. In this case, the particles of the rope oscillate back and forth about an equilibrium position, while the wave propagates along the rope at its own speed. Waves on a rope, sound waves, and water waves all require a medium for their propagation. Electromagnetic waves, such as light and radio waves, are different because they do not require a medium for their propagation, as we will see in Chapter 20.

The wave pulse we have just described is called a **traveling wave.** The pulse occurs at one place at one time and at another place at a later time. The distance the pulse travels is proportional to the elapsed time. We have here a very general description of a wave: *A **wave** is a disturbance that transfers energy from one point to another without imparting net motion to the medium through which it propagates.* This description is quite general and, as you can see, does not require the wave to be repetitive.

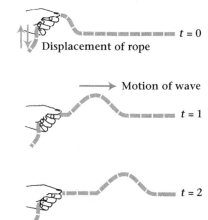

Figure 15.1

A wave pulse traveling along a rope. The displacement of the rope is vertical, whereas the motion of the wave pulse is horizontal.

Harmonic Waves

Let us now consider another special one-dimensional wave: a wave generated by the simple harmonic motion of one end of a long extended rope. In such a **harmonic wave,** the distance between successive maxima, or wave crests, is the **wavelength** λ (Fig. 15.2). As the end of the rope moves up and down with harmonic motion, it generates a sinusoidal wave. (Remember, a sinusoidal wave has the shape of a sine curve.) Note that while any given point on the *rope* moves up and down, the point does not undergo any displacement along the x axis. By contrast, any given point on the wave—a crest, say—moves one wavelength λ along the x axis in one period.

The displacement of a harmonic wave is a function of both position and time. At the instant of time $t = 0$ (Fig. 15.2), the displacement of the wave $y(x, t)$ is described by a sinusoidal function of position x,

$$y(x, t)|_{t=0} = y_0 \sin \frac{2\pi x}{\lambda},$$

where λ is the wavelength of the wave and y_0 is its amplitude. (That is, y_0 is the maximum vertical displacement of the rope from its equilibrium position.) However, if we look only at the position $x = 0$, the motion of the rope as a function of time is described by

$$y(x, t)|_{x=0} = -y_0 \sin \frac{2\pi t}{T},$$

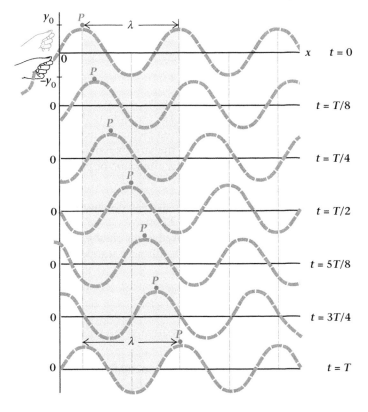

Figure 15.2
Harmonic waves traveling along a rope are generated by a sinusoidal motion of one end. A point on the crest of the wave, such as P, moves one wavelength λ in one period T.

where T is the period of the wave. (Compare this with Section 14.2.) The general mathematical form of a wave moving in the positive x direction, including both position and time, is given by

$$y(x, t) = y_0 \sin 2\pi\left(\frac{x}{\lambda} - \frac{t}{T}\right). \tag{15.1}$$

The function $y(x, t)$ describes the displacement of the rope at any position x and any time t. Equation (15.1) is the mathematical description of a *traveling harmonic wave* moving in the positive x direction. We could use a cosine function for this equation just as well, but we choose the sine function so that $y = 0$ when $x = 0$ and $t = 0$.

If we follow the motion of a single wave crest, we see that in one complete period it travels one full wavelength. The wave, therefore, is traveling with a speed v given by

$$v = \frac{\lambda}{T}.$$

Remembering that the frequency is the reciprocal of the period, we see that

$$v = \lambda f. \tag{15.2}$$

This relation between a wave's speed, frequency, and wavelength is very important. It is valid for all waves, mechanical or otherwise, and we shall frequently make use of it throughout this book.

Example 15.1

Figure 15.3 represents two snapshots of a wave on a rope. The snapshots were taken $\frac{1}{10}$ s apart. We know that the wave was traveling to the right and that it moved by less than one wavelength between pictures. Find its (a) wavelength, (b) wave speed, and (c) frequency. (d) Write an expression for the rope's displacement from its equilibrium position as a function of position and time. The maximum displacement is 3.0 cm.

Solution (a) Examining the figure, we see that the distance between two successive crests, or the wavelength, is $\lambda = 2.0$ m.
(b) During the $\frac{1}{10}$-s interval the wave moved to the right a distance of half a wavelength, or 1 m. The wave speed is the distance traveled divided by the time interval, or $v = 10$ m/s to the right.
(c) Since we now know both wavelength and speed, we can obtain the frequency from

$$f = \frac{v}{\lambda} = \frac{10 \text{ m/s}}{2.0 \text{ m}} = 5.0 \text{ s}^{-1} = 5.0 \text{ Hz}.$$

(d) We are given the maximum displacement or amplitude, $y_0 = 3.0$ cm, and just obtained a value for λ. Remembering that $T = 1/f = 0.20$ s, we can substi-

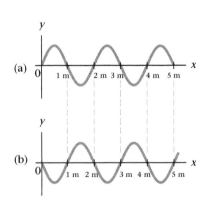

Figure 15.3
Example 15.1: A diagram of two snapshots of a wave on a rope. Picture (b) was taken $\frac{1}{10}$ s after picture (a). The scale is shown in meters. The amplitude of the wave is exaggerated to make it easier to see.

tute into Eq. (15.1) to get

$$y(x, t) = (3.0 \text{ cm}) \sin 2\pi\left(\frac{x}{2.0} - \frac{t}{0.20}\right) = (3.0 \text{ cm}) \sin (3.1x - 31t),$$

where x is given in meters and t in seconds.

▼

*15.3 ## Energy and Information Transfer by Waves

We experience the energy transferred by waves in many situations: We feel the force of an ocean wave, our skin is warmed by the light waves from the sun, we hear sound waves. Furthermore, most of the information that we receive comes to us by waves. Speech and music are transmitted by sound waves, radio and television by electromagnetic waves. The reflected light by which you read this page is a wave. How does the energy (and, hence, the information) transmitted by the wave depend on the properties of the wave? We answer this question by first considering how energy is transferred by a single pulse. Then we extend our results to get an expression for the energy of a harmonic wave.

At time $t = 0$, a small segment of the rope around point P in Fig. 15.4, with mass Δm and length Δl, is at rest and has no kinetic energy. The up-and-down hand motion provides the energy required to start the pulse along the rope. As the leading edge of the pulse reaches P, the segment Δl begins to move upward. As the wave crest passes the segment Δl, the segment moves to its highest position and then starts down again, possessing kinetic energy while it is in motion. When the entire pulse has passed P, the segment Δl returns to rest and again has no kinetic energy. The progress of the pulse along the rope corresponds to the flow of energy along the rope. Any other type of pulse, including a pulse traveling through the air, would transfer energy along the direction of propagation in a similar manner.

How much energy has been transferred past P during a time t? For a traveling harmonic wave on a rope, each point moves with simple harmonic motion in the transverse (y) direction. As we saw in Section 14.3, Eq. (14.7), in the absence of damping, the total energy of a harmonic oscillator is equal to its potential energy at maximum displacement y_0, that is, $\frac{1}{2}ky_0^2$. Also in Chapter 14, the relationship between mass, spring constant, and frequency was found to be $f = (1/2\pi)\sqrt{k/m}$. If we treat the segment of the rope as a harmonic oscillator with mass Δm moving at frequency f, we can rearrange the equation to find an effective spring constant $k = (2\pi f)^2 \Delta m$. The energy associated with the motion of this segment of the rope is then

$$\Delta E = \tfrac{1}{2}ky_0^2 = \tfrac{1}{2}(2\pi f)^2 \Delta m \, y_0^2$$

$$\Delta E = 2\pi^2 \Delta m \, f^2 y_0^2.$$

We now have an important result: The energy of a wave depends on the square of the amplitude of the wave. Thus, a wave with twice the amplitude of an otherwise equivalent wave (same frequency, same medium) will have four times as much energy.

To find the rate of energy flow, or power, we observe that Δm can be written as $\rho A \, \Delta l$, where ρ is the density, A the cross-sectional area, and Δl the length

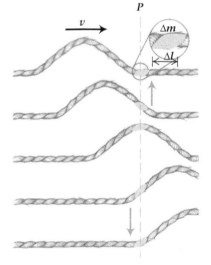

Figure 15.4
An element of mass Δm at point P is given kinetic energy as the wave pulse passes by with a speed v.

of the rope segment. In a time Δt, the wave with speed v passes a length $\Delta l = v \Delta t$, so that we can substitute $\Delta m = \rho A v \, \Delta t$ into the equation for ΔE. We obtain an expression for the energy transported in time Δt:

$$\Delta E = 2\pi^2 A \rho v f^2 y_0^2 \, \Delta t.$$

The rate at which energy propagates along the rope is the power P,

$$P = \frac{\Delta E}{\Delta t} = 2\pi^2 A \rho v f^2 y_0^2.$$

The more generally useful parameter is the **intensity** I, defined to be the power flowing through unit area. For the case at hand, the intensity in watts per square meter is

$$I = \frac{P}{A} = 2\pi^2 \rho v f^2 y_0^2. \tag{15.3}$$

Although we have derived this result for the specific case of waves on a rope, it does give the correct dependence of the intensity on the density of the medium, the wave velocity, the frequency, and the amplitude appropriate for any traveling harmonic wave.

Example 15.2

Waves of the same frequency and velocity travel along two identical ropes. The power transmitted down rope 1 is 0.30 mW. If the waves in rope 2 have an amplitude 1.6 times the amplitude of the waves in the first rope, how much power is transmitted along rope 2?

Solution We may write the ratio of the transmitted powers as

$$\frac{P_2}{P_1} = \frac{2\pi^2 A \rho v f^2 y_{02}^2}{2\pi^2 A \rho v f^2 y_{01}^2},$$

which becomes

$$\frac{P_2}{P_1} = \frac{y_{02}^2}{y_{01}^2}.$$

Thus

$$P_2 = P_1 \frac{y_{02}^2}{y_{01}^2} = 0.30 \text{ mW} \left(\frac{1.6^2}{1.0^2} \right) = 0.77 \text{ mW}.$$

15.4 Sound Waves

So far, we have been discussing **transverse waves,** such as a wave pulse along a rope, in which the particles of the rope move at right angles to the direction of propagation of the wave. However, waves also occur in which the particles of the wave medium move back and forth along the direction of propagation. Such waves are known as **longitudinal waves.** For example, if a stretched spring, such as a slinky, is alternately expanded and compressed, a compressional oscillation travels along the spring (Fig. 15.5). The sections of the spring where the coils

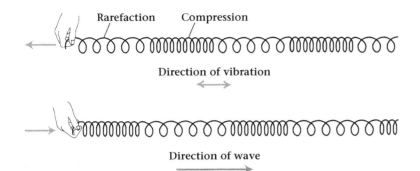

Rarefaction   Compression

Direction of vibration

Direction of wave

Figure 15.5
Example of a longitudinal wave in a spring. The direction of vibration is parallel to the direction of the wave.

are tightly packed are called *compressions,* and the sections where the coils are farther apart are called *rarefactions.* The terms compression and rarefaction are also used to describe relative density for other types of longitudinal waves.

Sound waves in air are longitudinal waves. The vibrations of a drumhead or loudspeaker exert varying pressure on the air. Increasing the pressure crowds the gas molecules together and pushes them against adjacent molecules. These molecules, in turn, strike their neighbors. The resulting pulse of compressed air moves away from the pressure source (Fig. 15.6). As the compression passes, the individual gas molecules move back to their original positions. Thus, while the wave travels in a longitudinal fashion, the molecules themselves only vibrate back and forth along the line of propagation.

Sound waves travel out in all directions from an isolated source and are therefore three-dimensional waves. The outward-moving compressions (or rarefactions) correspond to expanding spherical shells called **wavefronts** (Fig. 15.7). The radius of any shell increases at the speed of sound. If we are far away from the source, a small piece of the spherical wavefront will be approximately flat, or planar. We call these plane wavefronts or simply **plane waves.**

As the spherical wave expands, energy is conserved if the damping is negligible, as it is over short ranges in air. Therefore, the power passing through a spherical shell of one radius is the same as that passing through a shell of any

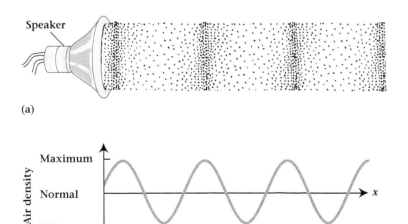

Speaker

(a)

(b)

Air density — Maximum / Normal / Minimum

x

Figure 15.6
(a) Representation of a sound wave in air. The wave is longitudinal. The more closely spaced dots indicate regions of higher density. (b) A graph of the density as a function of position.

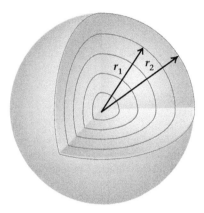

Figure 15.7
Waves expanding from a point source have spherical wavefronts.

other radius. The power passing through the shell of radius r is the product of the intensity I with the area of the shell, $4\pi r^2$. For two different radii r_1 and r_2, we can write

$$I_1 4\pi r_1^2 = I_2 4\pi r_2^2.$$

Upon rearranging, we get

$$\frac{I_2}{I_1} = \frac{r_1^2}{r_2^2}. \tag{15.4}$$

Thus, the intensity of a spherical wave decreases inversely with the square of its distance from the source.

Example 15.3

A loudspeaker on a tall pole standing in a field of tall grass generates a high-frequency sound at an intensity of 1.0×10^{-5} W/m² at the position of the ears of a person standing 8.0 m directly below it. If the person walks away from the pole so that she is 24 m from the loudspeaker, what is the sound intensity at the new position of her ears?

Solution The grass will almost completely absorb the high-frequency sound that reaches it, so the expanding sound wave reaching the listener's ears will be a section of a spherical wave with no additional effects from reflected waves. We can thus compare the intensities at the two positions:

$$\frac{I_2}{I_1} = \frac{r_1^2}{r_2^2},$$

$$I_2 = \frac{r_1^2}{r_2^2}I_1 = \frac{(8 \text{ m})^2}{(24 \text{ m})^2}(1.0 \times 10^{-5} \text{ W/m}^2)$$

$$I_2 = 0.11 \times 10^{-5} \text{ W/m}^2.$$

The speed with which sound waves propagate in air depends on atmospheric pressure, temperature, and humidity. At standard sea-level pressure and 0°C, the speed of sound in dry air is 331.5 m/s. The speed of sound at other temperatures is adequately represented by the expression

$$v(T) = (331.5 + 0.6T) \text{ m/s},$$

where the temperature T is in degrees Celsius. For the purpose of working problems in this text, it will be convenient to use the value of 340 m/s for the speed of sound. This value corresponds to the speed of sound in air at a temperature of approximately 15°C. (In other units, it is 1100 ft/s or 760 mi/h.)

Sound travels slowly enough to make us aware of its finite speed. The delay between a flash of lightning and the crash of thunder occurs because the speed of sound is much slower than that of light. For the same reason, a baseball outfielder can see the batter's swing before he hears the sound of the bat hitting the ball.

The vibration of a drumhead or a guitar body pushes against the air to produce pressure waves that propagate to our ears and are perceived as sound. The

Table 15.1	*Sound Speeds in Some Representative Materials at 15°C*
Material	**Speed (m/s)**
Air	340
Polyethylene	920
Helium	977
Water	1500
Marble	3810
Wood (oak) along the fiber	3850
Aluminum	5000
Iron	5120

response of human ears is limited to a range of frequencies from about 20 Hz to about 20,000 Hz. In general, as we grow older the upper limit of audible frequencies drops. It is not uncommon to find people with adequate hearing whose range of audible frequencies extends to only 10,000 or 15,000 Hz. Those frequencies between 20 Hz and 20,000 Hz are usually referred to as *audio,* or *sonic,* frequencies. Vibrational frequencies above 20,000 Hz are beyond our hearing and are referred to as *ultrasonic* frequencies. Similarly, extremely low frequencies are called *infrasonic* frequencies. Ultrasonic vibrations generate soundlike waves, but we do not hear them because of the limitations of our ears. It is well known that many animals, including dogs, can hear frequencies well above those audible to people.

The *pitch* of a sound or musical note is a subjective judgment of its highness or lowness. It is determined primarily by its frequency: a high pitch corresponds to a high frequency. However, the loudness of a sound at a given frequency can influence its apparent pitch.

Sound waves can propagate in solids and liquids, as well as in gases. The velocity of sound is much greater in denser solids and liquids than in air. The sound waves in liquids are longitudinal, just as in air. However, vibrations can propagate in solids as both longitudinal and transverse waves, and the corresponding wave speeds may be different. A list of representative sound speeds is given in Table 15.1.

There are many applications of ultrasonic waves. Because of their relatively short wavelengths, they can be focused into narrow beams and directed more easily than the longer waves of audible sound. (We will see this effect again in the discussion of wave optics in Chapter 24.) Figure 15.8 illustrates the use of ultrasonic waves to measure distances. A pulse of waves of frequency between 25 and 40 kHz is emitted from the ranging device, which automatically measures the time for the echo of the pulse to return. The distance to the wall or other object is computed from the travel time of the pulse and the speed of sound in air, taking into account the dependence of the speed on temperature and humidity. The computation is made by the microcircuits within the ranging device, and the result is displayed on a numerical panel. These instruments can measure with a precision of about 0.6 cm. Similar devices are used on some automatically focusing cameras to determine the proper position for the lens.

When the ultrasonic waves strike the wall in Fig. 15.8, they are partly reflected, partly transmitted, and partly absorbed. The reflections occur whenever

Figure 15.8
Ranging devices use ultrasonic waves to measure distances with a precision of 0.6 cm.

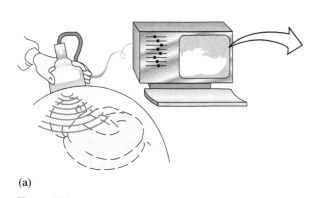

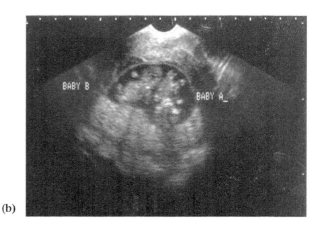

(a)   (b)

Figure 15.9
(a) Physicians can "see" a baby inside its mother's body by using the hand-held external probe of an ultrasonic imaging system. (b) An ultrasonic image of 10-week old human twins inside the mother's body.

the waves encounter a difference in density—here, the boundary between the air and wall. The amount of the reflection depends on the relative speeds of sound on each side of the boundary. (This behavior is a general property of waves, not just a property of ultrasonic waves.) The returning reflected signals from each boundary can be used to generate an image of the objects encountered by the waves. Within your body, incident ultrasonic waves are reflected from boundaries between tissues, bones, and fluids of different densities. Ultrasonic imaging is routinely used by physicians to "look" inside the human body (Fig. 15.9). The visual image is reconstructed from the information contained in the amplitude and phase of the reflected waves. Ultrasonic imaging is generally considered to be a safer technique than x-ray imaging.

Example 15.4

What is the wavelength of the sound waves when someone sings a "standard A" ($f = 440$ Hz)?

Solution Assume the room temperature to be about 15°C, so that the speed of sound is 340 m/s. We may use Eq. (15.2) to get

$$\lambda = \frac{v}{f} = \frac{340 \text{ m/s}}{440 \text{ s}^{-1}} = 0.77 \text{ m}.$$

*15.5   **Measuring Sound Levels**

The human ear is an extremely sensitive detector, capable of hearing sounds over an extremely large range of intensities. For example, a passing train generates sound intensities that may be 10^4 to 10^6 times greater than the sound intensity due to a buzzing mosquito, yet we can hear both sounds clearly. Such a range of pressure responsiveness is remarkable. Although our ears are sensitive to this enormous range of sound intensities, our subjective judgment of loudness does not directly correspond to the magnitude of the sound intensity. Experiments have shown that, to a good approximation, people perceive a sound to be about twice as loud as a reference sound when its intensity is ten times as large as that of the reference. A sound perceived to be four times as loud as a reference requires an increase in sound intensity by a factor of 100. This relationship is approximately logarithmic; that is, loudness is proportional to the logarithm of the sound intensity. Thus, it is natural to employ a scale of measurement that is also logarithmic.

The unit of sound intensity measurement is the **decibel,** dB. The decibel unit is one-tenth the size of the bel (a unit named in honor of the inventor of the telephone, Alexander Graham Bell). The **intensity level** L_I in decibels is defined to be ten times the logarithm of the ratio of two intensities I and I_0; that is,

$$L_I \text{ (in decibels)} = 10 \log_{10} \frac{I}{I_0}, \qquad (15.5)$$

where I_0 is the reference intensity. For example, if the intensity I exceeds the reference intensity I_0 by a factor of 4, the intensity level of I is 6 decibels (6 dB) above I_0: $L_I = 10 \log 4 = 10(0.6) = 6$ dB.

Since the measure of sound intensity level in decibels is really a comparison of two intensities, a given sound level cannot be stated in units of decibels unless the reference level is known. The standard reference level of sound intensity is 10^{-12} W/m^2, which is approximately the intensity that can just barely be heard by a person with good hearing. This intensity is called the threshold of hearing. The intensity level of a very quiet recording studio is about 20 dB, corresponding to a sound intensity 100 times greater than the quietest sound you can hear. Figure 15.10 shows a comparison of sound intensity levels due to various sources.

The ear does not respond equally well to all frequencies in the audio range. It is considerably more sensitive to frequencies between 2000 and 5000 Hz than to either higher or lower frequencies. For this reason, sound level meters are often designed to have a frequency response matching that of the human ear. A meter that does so is said to be A-weighted, and measurements are often given in A-weighted decibels, or dBA.

▼

Example 15.5

At a party, a stereo tape deck is playing at maximum volume. Suddenly a dancer trips over a wire, and one speaker stops playing. What is the reduction in sound intensity level, measured in dB?

Strategy Let's assume that the two speakers are balanced—that is, that an equal sound level is produced by each. When one fails, the resulting sound intensity is one-half of the initial intensity. This change can be expressed in dB by using Eq. (15.5).

Solution If we let the initial intensity be I_0 and the intensity with only one speaker be $I_0/2$, we find the

$$\text{intensity change in dB} = 10 \log \frac{I_0}{2I_0} = 10 \log \frac{1}{2} = -3 \text{ dB}.$$

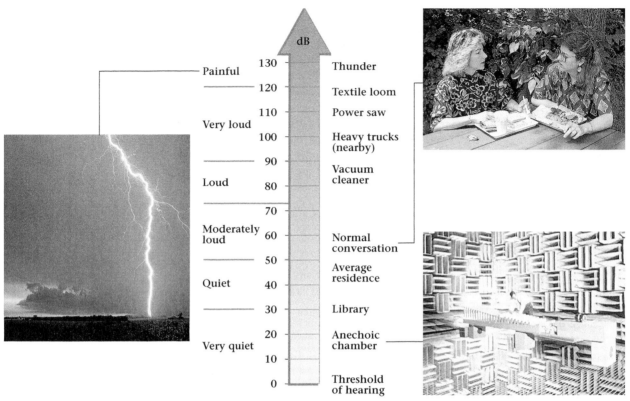

Figure 15.10
Approximate sound intensity levels for an assortment of familiar sound sources.

Discussion The reduction in sound level due to failure of one-half of the sound system is only 3 dB. Thus, a 3-dB reduction in sound level corresponds to reducing the intensity by a factor of one-half. Conversely, a 3-dB increase in sound level corresponds to twice as much sound intensity incident on the ear. In either case, it represents a small change in sound level in comparison with the range of hearing.

15.6 The Doppler Effect

Most of us are familiar with the rise and subsequent drop in pitch of an automobile horn as the car approaches and then passes. As the moving car approaches a stationary listener, the sound waves crowd together, causing an increase in the frequency of the sound heard. After the car has passed and is moving away from the listener, the waves spread out and the observed frequency is lower. This change in frequency associated with the relative motion between a sound source and a listener (observer) is called the **Doppler effect,** after Christian Doppler (1803–1853), the Austrian physicist who first explained the phenomenon.

We can understand the cause of the Doppler effect with the aid of Fig. 15.11, which shows a bob oscillating up and down on the surface of a container of water. Its motion causes circular water waves to spread out from the point of contact (Fig. 15.11a). When the bob is moved to the right, each wave crest moves

ROOM ACOUSTICS

Have you noticed that the same music group sounds better in one auditorium than in another, or that the same lecturer is easier to understand in one room than in another? What you hear depends not only on the source of the sound but also on the acoustical properties of the room.

About 1895, Professor Wallace Sabin of Harvard University discovered that one of the more important acoustical properties of a room is its reverberation time, which is the time for the sound pressure level to decrease by 60 dB. The reverberation time in a large stone-walled cathedral is several seconds, while a small, heavily carpeted and draped room has a much shorter reverberation time. Experience has shown that the optimum reverberation times depend on the size of the room and its intended use (Fig. B15.1).

The reverberation time in a given room is determined by the amount and type of sound-absorbing material present. The sound absorption a of a surface is the product of the actual surface area and the sound-absorption coefficient of the surface material (Table B15.1). The absorption unit is named the *metric sabin*. The total sound absorption in a room is the sum of the absorptions for the individual surfaces.

Sabin developed an empirical relationship between the reverberation time T_{60}, the volume V of the room, and the sound absorption a in the room. When distances are measured in meters, the reverberation time in seconds is

$$T_{60} = 0.16 \frac{V}{a}.$$

For example, a room 9 m wide × 12 m long × 4 m high has a volume of 432 m³. The total area of the walls is 168 m², and the areas of the ceiling and of the floor are 108 m² each. If the walls are plywood paneling, the floor is wood, and the

Figure B15.1 Optimum reverberation times at 500 Hz for rooms of different size and use.

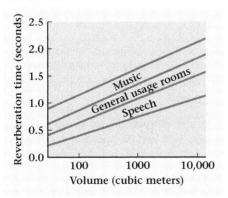

ceiling is gypsum board (dry wall), the total sound absorption at 500 Hz is 44.8 metric sabins. Therefore, the predicted reverberation time of the empty room is 1.5 s. This value is somewhat longer than is optimum for general use in a room of this size (Fig. B15.1). However, with seats and people in the room, the reverberation time is shortened. As an example, if the floor were three-quarters covered with students in tablet-arm chairs, approximately 30 metric sabins would be added. The new reverberation time would be less than a second, which is in the acceptable range. Such calculations are not expected to give the precise value of the actual reverberation time, but they do indicate the approximate value expected under specific conditions.

The overall acoustical quality of a room is influenced by the reverberation time at all frequencies, not just 500 Hz. Subjective descriptions of an auditorium's sound, such as *warm, live,* and *brilliant,* depend not only on the length but also on the frequency dependence of the reverberation time. For example, a *warm* sound is the result of a longer reverberation time in the lower, or bass, frequencies.

Modern auditorium design also includes computer simulation and scale models. The most successful designs result from the work of a skilled and experienced person using the best of technology, research, and artistry. Even then, the desired result is not always achieved for large halls. Electronic reinforcement, with amplification and delays, can help adjust an auditorium's acoustical properties, but it cannot turn a bad auditorium into a good one.

Table B15.1	*Typical Sound Absorption Coefficients*		
Material	**Absorption Coefficients at**		
	125 Hz	**500 Hz**	**2000 Hz**
Acoustical ceiling tile (3/4 in.)	0.76	0.83	0.99
Brick, unglazed	0.02	0.03	0.05
Carpet, heavy, on concrete	0.02	0.14	0.60
Concrete block, painted	0.10	0.06	0.09
Heavy drapes (to half area)	0.14	0.55	0.70
Concrete or terrazzo	0.01	0.02	0.02
Linoleum, or asphalt tile	0.02	0.03	0.03
Wood flooring	0.15	0.10	0.06
Gypsum board, 1/2 in.	0.29	0.05	0.07
Ordinary window glass	0.35	0.18	0.07
Plaster on lath	0.14	0.06	0.04
Plywood paneling, 3/8 in.	0.28	0.17	0.10
Person in an upholstered chair	0.39	0.80	0.92
Students in tablet-arm chairs	0.30	0.49	0.87

Source: From M. David Egan, *Architectural Acoustics* (New York: McGraw-Hill, 1988).

(a)

(b)

Figure 15.11
(a) A computer-generated image of circular waves spreading out from the point of contact of an oscillating bob in contact with the surface of water in a shallow tank. Notice that the waves spread out uniformly in all directions on the surface. (b) Image of the waves when the oscillating bob is moved to the right with constant speed $v_s = 0.4v_{wave}$. Notice how the waves ahead of the bob are crowded together, while those behind are spread apart.

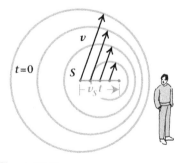

Figure 15.12
The Doppler effect: As a sound source moves toward an observer, the wavelength decreases, causing the observer to hear a higher frequency. During a time t, the wave advances a distance vt while the source advances a distance $v_s t$.

out as an expanding circle, but since the source is moving, it emits each successive wave at a different location. As a result, the waves moving in the same direction as the source are crowded together, while those moving in the opposite direction are spread farther apart (Fig. 15.11b). The wave speed is constant whether the source moves or not. Thus, where the wavelength is shortened, the frequency is increased, and where the wavelength is lengthened, the frequency is reduced.

Figure 15.12 also shows a source of sound waves moving to the right radiating spherical waves, shown here as circles. For this case of a source of frequency f moving toward an observer, we can readily determine the new frequency f' that the observer hears. During one period T of the source, the wave moves out a distance vT, where v represents the speed of sound. During this same time interval, the source, moving at a speed v_s, moves a distance $v_s T$. The difference between these two distances is the new wavelength λ':

$$\lambda' = (v - v_s)T.$$

The frequency is obtained from the wavelength in the usual way:

$$f' = \frac{v}{\lambda'} = \frac{v}{(v - v_s)T},$$

or, using the fact that $f = 1/T$,

$$f' = \frac{f}{(1 - v_s/v)} \qquad \text{(source approaching)}.$$

If the source is moving away from the observer, the wavelength reaching the observer is increased instead of shortened. Using the same argument as above, we find the new frequency by the same expression with a plus sign in front of the v_s/v term. The two cases can be written as one:

$$\boxed{f' = \frac{f}{(1 \mp v_s/v)},} \qquad \text{(moving source, stationary observer)} \qquad (15.6)$$

where the upper sign means that the source is approaching the observer (higher frequency) and the lower sign means that the source is moving away (lower frequency).

Example 15.6

A police car horn emits a 250-Hz tone when sitting still. What frequency does a stationary observer hear if the police car sounds its horn while approaching at a speed of 27.0 m/s (60 mi/h)? What frequency is heard if the horn is sounded as the car is leaving at 27.0 m/s?

Solution The apparent frequency for the approaching car is found from Eq. (15.6), where we use the negative sign and the speed of sound is taken as 340 m/s:

$$f' = \frac{250 \text{ Hz}}{1 - \dfrac{27 \text{ m/s}}{340 \text{ m/s}}} = 272 \text{ Hz}.$$

When the car passes, the frequency is lowered according to Eq. (15.6) with the positive sign, and f' becomes

$$f' = \frac{250 \text{ Hz}}{1 + \dfrac{27 \text{ m/s}}{340 \text{ m/s}}} = 232 \text{ Hz}.$$

For waves transmitted by a medium, such as sound waves in air, a slightly different Doppler formula results when the observer, rather than the source, is in motion. If a stationary observer hears a frequency f, an observer O moving with a speed v_o toward the source would hear a higher frequency f', because he would encounter wavefronts more rapidly as a result of his motion toward the source. In a time t, the stationary observer receives ft wave crests. In the same time t, the moving observer travels a distance $v_o t$, which corresponds to $v_o t/\lambda$ wavelengths. The total number of wave crests encountered is number of wave crests = $ft + v_o t/\lambda$. The resulting frequency is the number of waves divided by the time,

$$f' = f + \frac{v_o}{\lambda} = f + \frac{v_o f}{v} = f\left(1 + \frac{v_o}{v}\right) \qquad \text{(observer approaching)}.$$

If the observer were moving away from the source, fewer waves would reach him per second. The general result for a moving observer is

$$\boxed{f' = f\left(1 \pm \frac{v_o}{v}\right)} \qquad \text{(moving observer, fixed source)} \qquad (15.7)$$

where the plus sign corresponds to an observer approaching the sound source (higher frequency) and the minus sign corresponds to the observer moving away (lower frequency). Although this is similar to Eq. (15.6), the two equations are not quite the same. However, when v_s and v_o are much less than v, the two sets of formulas give essentially the same results.

Physicians detect blood flow and measure its speed by reflecting ultrasonic waves from blood moving toward the ultrasonic source (Fig. 15.13a). The reflected waves are Doppler-shifted to a higher frequency. When the reflected waves are combined with the incident waves, they produce a new wave at a frequency that is the difference between the reflected and incident frequencies. For a 2-MHz source and normal blood flow, the difference frequency is in the audio range.

The Doppler effect is not limited to sound waves alone but applies to other kinds of waves as well. It even applies to electromagnetic waves such as light and radar, although the formulas derived here for sound waves differ from the formulas that apply to light and radio waves. The correct equations to use for light are found in Chapter 25. In astronomy, the measured Doppler shifts in the light received from stars have been the principal sources of information on stellar motions. In more familiar situations, radar waves bounced off a moving target are Doppler-shifted as a result of the motion of the reflecting object. By measuring the shift in frequency of a radar wave beamed at a moving object, we can measure the speed of the object precisely. This technique has been widely adapted for measuring the speed of cars, planes, thunderstorms, and even baseballs (Fig. 15.13b).

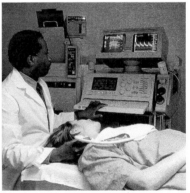

(a)

(b)

Figure 15.13
(a) Detecting blood flow in the carotid artery with ultrasonic waves. (b) Measuring the speed of a baseball with radar.

Example 15.7

If the police car in Example 15.6 were sounding its horn while stationary, what frequency would be heard by an observer who was approaching it at a speed of 27.0 m/s (60 mi/h)?

Solution Here we have the case of an observer moving toward a stationary source. Equation (15.7) with the plus sign is the appropriate expression:

$$f' = f\left(1 + \frac{v_o}{v}\right)$$

$$f' = 250 \text{ Hz}\left(1 + \frac{27 \text{ m/s}}{340 \text{ m/s}}\right) = 270 \text{ Hz}.$$

Notice that this is not the same answer as in Example 15.6.

*15.7 Formation of a Shock Wave

We have seen in the Doppler effect that the wavefronts produced by a moving source of sound are crowded together in the direction toward which the source is traveling. As the speed of the source increases, the crowding becomes more pronounced. What happens when the speed of the source becomes greater than the wave speed? In this case, the source moves faster than the waves and the arguments used to describe the Doppler effect no longer apply. Instead, the spherical waves expanding from the source at subsequent positions along the path of the source all combine, forming a single conical wavefront known as a **shock wave** (Fig. 15.14). Because the shock wave is composed of many wavefronts acting together, it has a large amplitude.

At time $t = 0$ the source emits a wave from point O. At a later time t, the wavefront has expanded to a radius $r = vt$ and the source has traveled a distance $v_s t$ to reach point S. Subsequent wavefronts also expand as indicated in Fig. 15.14, so that at time t they just reach the tangent line drawn from S to the wavefront centered at O. The resulting envelope of wavefronts forms a cone of half-angle θ given by

$$\sin \theta = \frac{v}{v_s}. \tag{15.8}$$

The ratio v_s/v, called the Mach number, is often used to give the speed in terms of the speed of sound. Thus, a speed 1.5 times the speed of sound is referred to as Mach 1.5.

When the shock wave is produced by an airplane moving at a speed greater than the speed of sound—that is, at supersonic speed—the shock wave is known as a sonic boom. Figure 15.15(b) shows the shock wave produced in air by a supersonic aircraft moving at Mach 1.1. Notice that in addition to the shock wave produced at the front end, lesser shock waves appear at the rear of the plane.

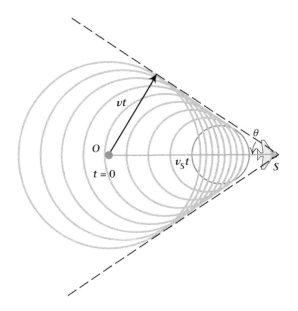

Figure 15.14
Shock waves are generated when the
source of sound moves faster than the
speed of sound waves in the medium.
The waves combine to produce a
conical wavefront.

High-speed aircraft often produce two or more shock waves, which are associated with the nose, the tail, and other projections on the aircraft.

15.8 Reflection of a Wave Pulse

One of the most interesting aspects of acoustics is the physics of music—how a violin or clarinet makes sound and why the sounds are as they are. To investigate these topics, we first need to know some other general properties of waves, including reflection and interference. We introduce these concepts by returning to our model of mechanical wave pulses traveling along a rope. These wave properties introduced here apply to all waves, and you will encounter them again when we discuss light waves.

When a wave traveling along a string reaches the end of the string, it is reflected. The exact way in which it is reflected depends on whether the end of the string is fixed or free to move. Let us examine the two cases separately.

When a wave pulse reaches the far end of a string that is fixed to a wall at that end, the wave does not suddenly stop, but is reflected. If no energy is dissipated at the far end of the string, the reflected wave has a magnitude equal to that of the incident wave; however, the direction of the displacement will be reversed (Fig. 15.16a). This reversal happens because as the pulse encounters the wall, the upward force of the pulse on the end of the string pulls upward on the wall. As a result, according to Newton's third law, the wall pulls downward on the string. This reaction force causes the string to snap downward, initiating a reflected pulse that moves off with an inverted (or negative) amplitude.

What happens, now, if the string is free to move at its far end? Again, a wave pulse traveling along the string is reflected when it reaches that end (Fig. 15.16b). But in this case we see that the reflected wave has the same direction of displacement as the incident wave. As the pulse reaches the end of the string, the string moves up in response to the pulse. As the end of the string begins to

(a)

(b)

Figure 15.15
A shock wave generated by (a) a bullet
and (b) an aircraft traveling at
supersonic speeds.

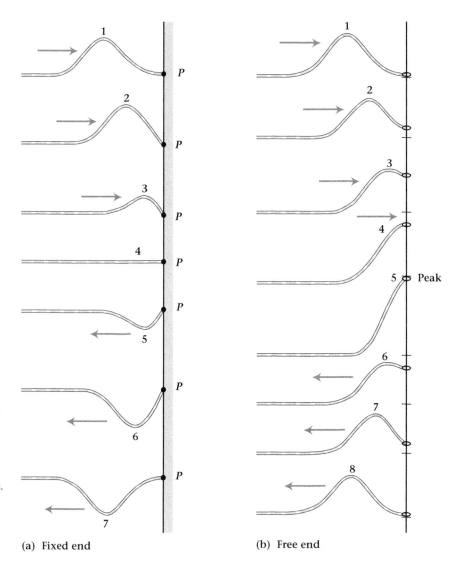

Figure 15.16
(a) Reflection of a wave pulse from a fixed end point. The direction of displacement of the reflected wave is inverted. (b) Reflection of a wave pulse from an end that is free to move. The direction of displacement of the reflected wave is unchanged. (Numbers indicate the sequence of motion.)

(a) Fixed end   (b) Free end

return to its initial position, it starts a pulse back along the string, just as if the end motion were due to some outside force. The result is a pulse exactly like the incident wave pulse, except that its direction of travel is reversed.

15.9 Standing Waves on a String

If two wave pulses are started along a rope from opposite ends, the waves will meet, pass through each other, and continue their motion as though nothing had happened. The resultant wave observed during the time the two individual waves overlap is the algebraic sum of the individual amplitudes (Fig. 15.17). The same behavior is displayed by sound waves: When two or three people are talking in the same room, you can distinguish the individual voices even if they speak simultaneously. The sound of each person's voice is not disturbed by the others.

The loudness of the combined sound does vary, however, depending on how many voices are heard simultaneously. This effect is an example of superposition. The **principle of superposition** says that at any instant, the resultant combination wave is the algebraic sum of all the component waves. The principle of superposition applies to many types of wave motion and so has enormous impact—it allows us to analyze combinations of waves.

Let us consider the vibrational behavior of a taut, but flexible, string held fixed at each end. A guitar string is a good example. If the string is pulled aside at some point and then released, it begins to vibrate. We can obtain a description of its motion by analyzing it in terms of oppositely directed wave pulses originating at the point where the initial displacement occurred. These waves travel back and forth along the string, undergoing reflection each time they reach the ends of the string. The resulting motion of the string is then the superposition of the amplitudes of all these pulses.

Imagine that the guitar string oscillates with harmonic motion. For a given string, the speed of waves along the string depends on the tension in the string. If the tension is constant, the speed of the waves is also constant. Now, suppose a wave propagates along the string and back and reaches the origination point at just the right time so that the displacement of the reflected wave is in the same direction as the displacement of the next wave. Then the two displacements add together, and the resulting wave has a larger amplitude. The two waves are said to be *in phase,* and the resulting build-up of amplitude is called **constructive interference.** At many other frequencies (and wavelengths), the displacements of the waves are in opposing directions. These waves are said to be *out of phase,* and their amplitudes tend to cancel. This effect is called **destructive interference.** Thus, waves of these frequencies are suppressed.

If the string is driven periodically, it responds by vibrating at the frequency of the driving force. However, the amplitude of the vibration will be much greater if the string is driven at a resonance frequency. On the other hand, if the string is struck sharply and thereafter allowed to vibrate on its own, only the resonant frequencies will persist.

The lowest resonant frequency of vibration of the string (or other object) is called its **fundamental frequency.** Resonant frequencies that are integer multiples of the fundamental frequency are called **harmonic frequencies.** For our string, the fundamental frequency is the first harmonic; the frequency that is double this value is the second harmonic, and so on. All resonant frequencies higher than the fundamental, whether they are integer multiples of the fundamental or not, are called **overtones.** For example, the overtones of an idealized drum head are not harmonic but stand in the frequency ratio of $1.0:1.6:2.1:2.3$.

Each resonant frequency corresponds to an oscillation of the entire string. For the present case, the ends of the string are fixed. The vibrational motion with lowest frequency (first harmonic) is shown in Fig. 15.18(a); this vibration corresponds to a sinusoidal motion of the entire string moving up and down between the supports. At any instant the displacement of the string is described by a sine curve; but this curve does not travel along the string, as we have seen for traveling waves. Instead, the whole string moves up and down. We have a **standing wave.** Such a wave can be represented as the product of two sine functions: one that describes the shape of the waveform and another that gives the time dependence. In Problem 15.82 you are asked to use the principle of superposition to find a mathematical expression for this standing wave.

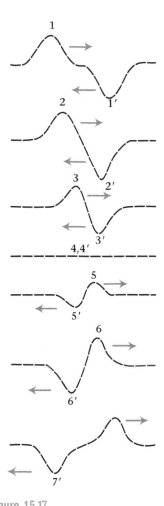

Figure 15.17

Two wave pulses moving in opposite directions pass through each other. The resultant wave is the algebraic sum of the individual waves. (Numbers indicate the sequence of motion for each wave pulse.)

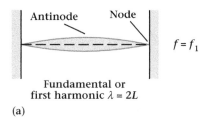

(a)

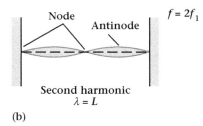

(b)

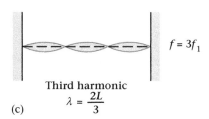

(c)

Figure 15.18
Standing waves on a string. The points labeled as nodes do not move. The points that vibrate with maximum amplitude are called antinodes.

Since each end of the string does not move, the end points must be special. They are **nodes**—points of zero vibrational amplitude—and the distance between adjacent nodes is always one-half of the wavelength. Halfway between each pair of nodes is an **antinode,** a point on the string that vibrates with the greatest amplitude. Thus, the fundamental vibration of a string with fixed end points has a node at each end and a single antinode in between. The length of the string is half a wavelength. The fundamental frequency of the string depends on the speed of waves along the string and on the length of the string. The lowest frequency of vibration of the string is

$$f = \frac{v}{\lambda} = \frac{v}{2L},$$

where L is the length of the string and v is the speed of the wave along the string. Other resonant frequencies also occur. Since the two end points are nodes, the length of the string must be an integral number of half wavelengths. Thus, the distance between the ends can be $\lambda/2$, $2(\lambda/2)$, $3(\lambda/2)$, etc. That is, for a string of length L, the resonant wavelengths must be consistent with

$$L = n\frac{\lambda}{2} \qquad \text{where } n = 1, 2, 3, \ldots.$$

For fixed L, there is a wavelength λ_n associated with each integer n,

$$\lambda_n = \frac{2L}{n}.$$

The frequency is obtained from Eq. (15.2),

$$f_n = \frac{v}{\lambda_n} = n\frac{v}{2L}. \tag{15.9}$$

For flexible strings, the transverse wave speed is given in meters per second by

$$v = \sqrt{\frac{T}{\mu}}, \tag{15.10}$$

where T is the tension in the string in newtons and μ is the linear mass density in kilograms per meter. Standing waves on a stretched flexible string have resonant frequencies given by

$$f_n = \frac{n}{2L}\sqrt{\frac{T}{\mu}}, \qquad n = 1, 2, 3, \ldots. \tag{15.11}$$

Increasing the tension in the string raises the speed of waves along it and thus raises the natural vibrational frequencies. When you hear a stringed instrument being tuned, the musician is adjusting the tension in the strings. In addition, by pressing the string down at different points on the fingerboard, it is possible to shorten the vibrational length of the string—and thus increase the fundamental frequency—by varying amounts. That is how a musician is able to play many different notes with one string (Fig. 15.19).

Figure 15.19
A guitar player changes the length of the vibrating string by pressing the string against the neck of the instrument with her fingers.

Example 15.8

(a) What is the wave speed of a guitar string whose fundamental frequency is 330 Hz if the length of string free to vibrate is 0.651 m? (b) What is the tension if the string's linear mass density is 0.441 g/m?

Strategy (a) The wave speed may be determined from Eq. (15.2), which relates wave speed, frequency, and wavelength. The wavelength of the fundamental frequency is twice the free length of the string.
(b) The tension in the string may be obtained from the wave speed and the linear density of the string through the relationship of Eq. (15.10).

Solution (a) The wave speed is found from the product of the wavelength and the frequency.

$$v = f\lambda = f(2L) = (330 \text{ Hz})(2)(0.651 \text{ m}) = 430 \text{ m/s}.$$

(b) The wave speed is related to the tension by

$$v = \sqrt{\frac{T}{\mu}}.$$

Squaring both sides and rearranging gives

$$T = \mu v^2 = (0.441 \text{ g/m})(10^{-3} \text{ kg/g})(430 \text{ m/s})^2$$
$$T = 81.5 \text{ N}.$$

Recall from our earlier discussion that the harmonic frequencies of a vibrating string are integer multiples of the fundamental frequency. A frequency of twice the fundamental frequency is called the second harmonic or first overtone; one of three times the fundamental is the third harmonic or second overtone; and so on. Not all harmonics are present in all vibrating systems.

A plucked string vibrates in a complicated way, with many of its harmonics contributing to its motion. In fact, it is this combination of harmonics that gives a vibrating string its distinctive sound. What's more, the particular combination of harmonics present in motion of the string depends on where it is plucked. A string plucked in the center has only odd-numbered harmonics (Fig. 15.20). The

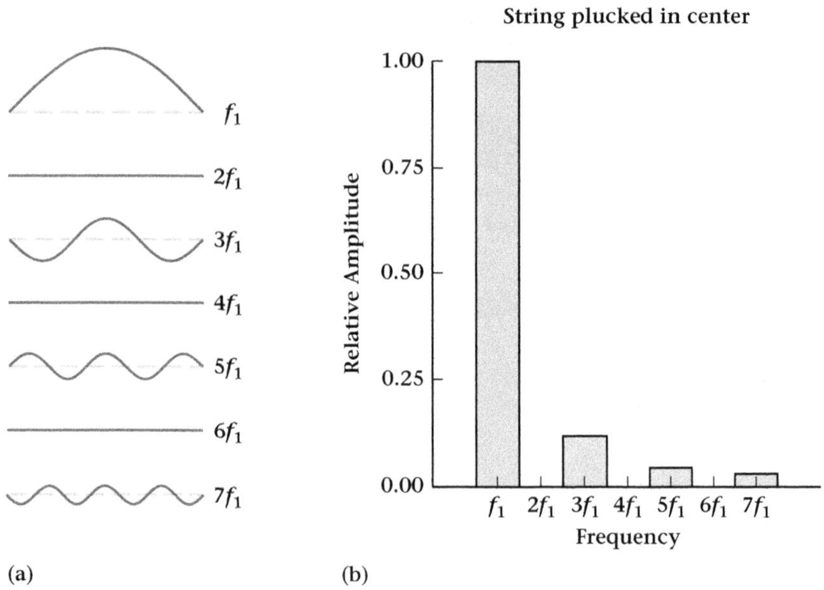

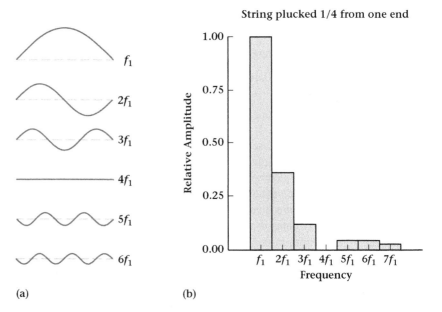

Figure 15.20
(a) A string plucked in the center has only odd-numbered harmonics. The sum of these harmonics with appropriate amplitudes and phases gives the proper shape of the string. (b) The bar chart shows the correct relative amplitude of each harmonic. The amplitudes in the wave diagram have been exaggerated for clarity.

same string plucked at a point 1/4 of its length from one end has an entirely different set of harmonics (Fig. 15.21). The resulting sounds are different.

The distinctive sounds of different musical instruments depend on the harmonic content of the sound waveforms produced by the instruments and on how the waves are excited. For example, is the string excited by being plucked, struck, or bowed? Similarly, the mixture of harmonics makes a human voice distinctive. You recognize someone's voice not just because of its pitch and the way that person enunciates, but also because of that person's particular combination of overtones.

Figure 15.21
(a) A string plucked 1/4 of its length from one end lacks all harmonics that are integer multiples of $4f_1$. The sum of the allowed harmonics with appropriate amplitudes and phases gives the proper shape of the string. (b) The bar chart shows the correct relative amplitude of each harmonic. The amplitudes in the wave diagram have been exaggerated for clarity.

The sound from many musical instruments, such as pianos, guitars, and violins, originates in a set of strings, each vibrating with a specific fundamental frequency. In music, the term *frequency* is not usually employed, but other terms are used to describe essentially the same thing. When the frequency of two tones is in the ratio of 1:2, they are said to be one *octave* apart. Between these two tones, each octave contains intermediate tones, arranged in a sequence that is repeated in every octave. Specifically, in Western music the octave is divided into twelve semitones, of which seven are selected to form a major or minor scale. A scale is just a regular series of tones arranged in order of frequency. A scale using the full sequence of twelve semitones is called a chromatic scale.

To Western ears, pleasing combinations of tones are those with frequencies that stand in whole-number ratios, such as 1:2, 4:5, and even 4:5:6. Without going into detail, we will say that difficulties arise when this idea is used to fill an octave with twelve tones. Therefore, several scales have been developed that almost satisfy the requirements. The scale to which most musical instruments are tuned today is called the *equal-tempered scale.* In this scale each of the twelve tones in an octave has a frequency $\sqrt[12]{2}$ times the frequency of the previous one. As you can see in Table 15.2, the frequency ratios are not exactly whole numbers, although they are fairly close.

Although we refer to an acoustic guitar or a violin as a "stringed instrument," the sound does not come directly from the string. The string has too little surface area and insufficient amplitude to set much air in motion. Instead, the sound you hear from a guitar or violin comes from the body of the instrument, which is made to vibrate by the oscillating string. The frequency that is heard depends on the length of the particular string plucked or bowed. As we noted earlier, this length is determined by the performer, who chooses where to press the string to the fingerboard.

The quality of the tone you hear, say, from a violin, results primarily from the way the body of the violin is made. The vibrating string forces the body to vibrate and give off sound. The construction of the instrument determines the

Table 15.2	*Frequencies of the Notes in an Octave Beginning with Middle C*		
Name	Equal-tempered Frequency	Ratio to C_4	Nearest Whole-number Ratio to C_4
C_4	261.63	1.0000	1.0000
$C_4\#$	277.18	1.0594	
D_4	293.66	1.1224	1.1250 (9/8)
$D_4\#$	311.13	1.1892	
E_4	329.63	1.2599	1.2656 (81/64)
F_4	349.23	1.3348	1.3333 (4/3)
$F_4\#$	369.99	1.4142	
G_4	392.00	1.4983	1.5000 (3/2)
$G_4\#$	415.30	1.5874	
A_4	440.00	1.6818	1.6875 (27/16)
$A_4\#$	466.16	1.7818	
B_4	493.88	1.8877	1.8984 (243/128)
C_5	523.25	2.0000	2.0000

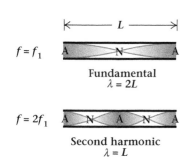

$f = f_1$

Fundamental
$\lambda = 2L$

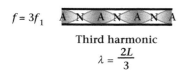

$f = 2f_1$

Second harmonic
$\lambda = L$

$f = 3f_1$

Third harmonic
$\lambda = \dfrac{2L}{3}$

Figure 15.22
Standing waves in an open pipe. The ends of the pipe are antinodes. The fundamental resonant wavelength is twice the length of the pipe.

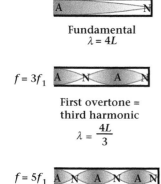

Fundamental
$\lambda = 4L$

$f = 3f_1$

First overtone =
third harmonic
$\lambda = \dfrac{4L}{3}$

$f = 5f_1$

Second overtone =
fifth harmonic
$\lambda = \dfrac{4L}{5}$

Figure 15.23
Standing waves in a pipe closed at one end. The fundamental resonant wavelength is four times the length of the pipe.

relative strength of the overtones for each tone that the body radiates. The maker must choose exactly which pieces of wood to use, their thickness at every point, the way in which the parts are joined, the finishing process, and many other details of the construction. Although it is now fairly well known what acoustical properties a violin must have to give it a good tone over its entire range, to actually build a good instrument requires knowledge, skill, and practice.

15.10 Waves in a Vibrating Column of Air

Hollow pipes have long been used for making musical sounds. Flutes, organ pipes, and children's whistles produce sounds in similar ways. To understand how they work, let us examine the behavior of air in a hollow pipe that is open at both ends. If you blow air across one end, the disturbance due to the moving air at that end propagates along the pipe to the far end. When it reaches the far end, part of the wave is reflected, much as a wave is reflected along a string whose end point is free to move. Since there is motion of the air at that end, the end point is an antinode with respect to the flow of air (Fig. 15.22). All harmonic frequencies are possible, just as for a string, because the pipe open at both ends has the same symmetry as the string fixed at both ends. And, as with the string, the fundamental wavelength is twice the length of the pipe.

If one end of the pipe is closed off, the air is not free to move any further in that direction and the closed end becomes a node. The resonant behavior of the pipe is completely changed. Since one end is a node and the other is an antinode, the lowest frequency (longest wavelength) vibration has no other nodes or antinodes between the ends. Thus, the fundamental wavelength is four times the length of the pipe (Fig. 15.23). The fundamental frequency is therefore a factor of 2 lower than for a pipe of the same length but open on both ends.

Above the fundamental frequency, the next resonant vibrational mode in our closed pipe has both an antinode and a node between the ends. Since this mode represents the next higher frequency, it is called the first overtone. But it is not the first harmonic. Its wavelength is one-third of the fundamental wavelength and its frequency is three times the fundamental, so it is the third harmonic. Similarly, the next higher frequency, the second overtone, is the fifth harmonic. Thus, for a pipe closed at one end, not all harmonics are possible; only odd-numbered harmonics can be excited.

What harmonics are excited also depends on the initiating disturbance. For example, if you blow gently across the top of a pop bottle, it resonates softly at its fundamental frequency. But if you blow much harder, you hear the higher pitch of an overtone because the faster airstream creates higher frequencies in the exciting disturbance. This same effect can also be achieved by increasing the air pressure to an organ pipe.

Example 15.9

The second overtone of standing waves in a pipe closed at one end is 512 Hz. How long is the pipe?

Strategy The fundamental resonant wavelength of a pipe closed at one end is four times the length of the pipe. For such a pipe, only odd harmonics, such as the first, third, fifth, seventh, ..., occur. The second overtone in such a series is the fifth harmonic, which has a wavelength

$$\lambda = \frac{4L}{5},$$

as shown in Fig. 15.23, where L is the length of the pipe.

Solution The frequency of the second overtone is

$$f = \frac{v}{\lambda} = \frac{5v}{4L}.$$

We can rearrange this equation to solve for L. Upon inserting the numerical values, we get

$$L = \frac{5v}{4f} = \frac{5(340 \text{ m/s})}{4(512 \text{ s}^{-1})} = 0.83 \text{ m}.$$

*15.11 Beats

When two sound sources that have almost the same frequency are sounded together, an interesting effect occurs. You hear a sound with a frequency that is the average of the two. However, the loudness of this sound repeatedly grows and then decays, rather than being constant. Such repeated variations in amplitude are called **beats,** and the occurrence of beats is a general characteristic of waves.

If the frequency of one of the wave sources is changed, there is a corresponding change in the rate at which the amplitude varies. This rate is called the beat frequency. As the frequencies come closer together, the beat frequency becomes slower. Thus, a musician can tune a guitar to another sound source by listening for the beats while increasing or decreasing the tension in each string. Eventually the beats become so slow that they effectively vanish, and the two sources are then in tune.

Beats are easily explained by considering two sinusoidal waves y_1 and y_2 of the same amplitude y_0, but of different frequencies f_1 and f_2. The superposition principle says the combined amplitude y is the algebraic sum of the individual amplitudes:

$$y = y_1 + y_2$$
$$y = y_0 \sin 2\pi f_1 t + y_0 \sin 2\pi f_2 t$$
$$y = y_0(\sin 2\pi f_1 t + \sin 2\pi f_2 t).$$

Using the trigonometric identity for the sum of the sines of two angles, we have*

$$y = \left(2y_0 \cos 2\pi \left(\frac{f_1 - f_2}{2}\right) t\right) \sin 2\pi \left(\frac{f_1 + f_2}{2}\right) t. \qquad (15.12)$$

---

*The following relationship follows from the definition of the trigonometric functions:

$$\sin A + \sin B = 2 \cos \frac{A - B}{2} \cdot \sin \frac{A + B}{2}.$$

Physics in Practice

HEARING AND THE EAR

How good are human ears as detectors of sound? We can hear sounds ranging from the faint buzz of a mosquito's wings to the roar of a jet engine. In each case, air is set in vibration. Eventually the vibrations of the air reach your ear and act on your eardrum, letting you hear the sound. The human ear is an exceptional detector because it works over such a wide range of intensities and frequencies.

Your ears are not equally sensitive to all frequencies. In Fig. B15.2 we plot the intensity of the softest sound heard at different frequencies. The lowest region of the curve corresponds to the range of frequencies where the ear is most sensitive, which is in the range of 3–4 kHz. This is the frequency range of the upper notes on a piano.

We can see just how sensitive the ear is by using the relationship between vibrational amplitude and intensity given in Eq. (15.3). To find the amplitude of a sound that can just be heard by a person with good hearing, we use the value for the minimum detectable intensity, 10^{-12} W/m², and a frequency of 4000 Hz corresponding to the most sensitive frequency region. On using these values, along with representative values for the other parameters, we find a vibrational amplitude of about 3×10^{-12} m. This truly is a small displacement; it is approximately 1/100 of the diameter of the oxygen molecules

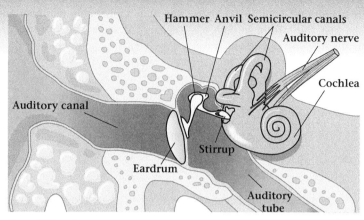

Figure B15.3 Schematic diagram of the human ear.

that make up the air. Your eardrum is unquestionably very sensitive to respond to such small fluctuations.

On the other hand, a sound loud enough to cause pain, say 120 dB or louder, has an amplitude of about 3×10^{-6} m. Though this value is quite a bit larger than the amplitude of the softest sound, it is still quite small. If a sheet of paper were of this thickness, a stack of 400 sheets would be about as thick as a dime.

Figure B15.3 shows a schematic diagram of the human ear. The auditory canal of the outer ear acts in an interesting way as an amplifier for certain frequencies. Consider the canal to be a pipe closed at one end by the eardrum. In Section 15.10, we discuss the resonant frequencies of such pipes. The average length of the auditory canal is about 2.5 cm, with a resonant frequency of 3400 Hz. Fig B15.2 shows an increase in sensitivity in the region of this resonance. It is interesting to note that this is also the frequency range of a baby's cry. This is, however, somewhat higher than the range of adult human speech, which lies primarily in the 500–2000 Hz region. Passive hearing aids that do not require batteries have been designed that effectively shift the resonance region downward toward the range of adult speech.

Beginning in the midteens, a gradual decrease in the sensitivity of hearing begins—both in frequency range and threshold of hearing. A young child may be able to hear sounds with frequencies as high as 40 kHz. By the teens, this upper limit has dropped to about 20 kHz, and from then on a relatively steady decrease of about 160 Hz per year is observed. For people 50 years old, an upper limit of 10–15 kHz is typical.

Temporary loss of hearing often follows exposure to a single, short, loud noise. For the most part, the ear recovers from such short duration overloads. More damaging are extended and repeated loud noises. People who work in loud environments are known to suffer permanent and irreversible hearing loss. For this reason they often wear special headgear or earplugs to reduce the sound's intensity level at their ears. Musicians who play loud music for long periods also frequently wear hearing protectors.

Figure B15.2 Frequency response of the human ear.

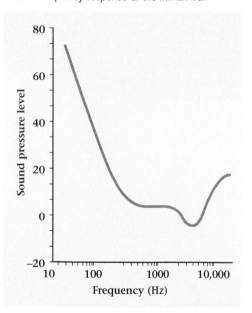

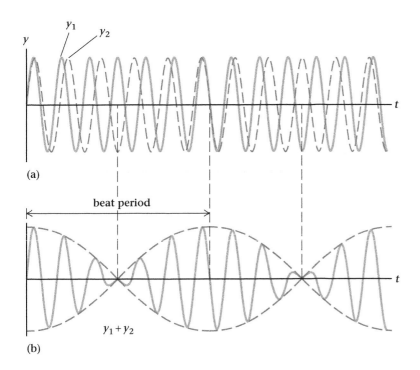

Figure 15.24
(a) Two waves of slightly different frequencies add to produce a wave (b) that oscillates with the average of their frequencies. The resulting amplitude also oscillates, with a beat frequency equal to the difference between the source frequencies.

This equation represents the amplitude of a sound wave with a frequency that is the average of the two source frequencies (the sine term) and with a slowly varying amplitude (the cosine term) (Fig. 15.24). Our sensation of loudness depends on the intensity, which is proportional to the square of the amplitude. The rate at which the loudness maxima occur is the beat frequency. Its magnitude is the difference in the two source frequencies, $|f_1 - f_2|$. Beats can easily be heard up to frequencies of about 10 Hz. Beyond that, they are hard to distinguish.

Summary

Useful Concepts

■ The general expression for a one-dimensional traveling wave is

$$y(x, t) = y_0 \sin 2\pi \left(\frac{x}{\lambda} - \frac{t}{T} \right).$$

■ The relationship between the speed, wavelength, and frequency of a wave is

$$v = \lambda f.$$

■ For a spherically expanding wave, the intensity decreases with the square of the distance from the source.

■ The intensity level L_I of a sound is measured in decibels relative to a reference sound intensity I_0:

$$L_I \text{ (in dB)} = 10 \log_{10} \frac{I}{I_0}.$$

■ The observed frequency change due to motion of the source or observer is called the Doppler shift. The frequency heard is given by

$$f' = \frac{f}{(1 \mp v_s/v)} \qquad \text{moving source,}$$

$$f' = f(1 \pm v_o/v) \qquad \text{moving observer.}$$

The upper sign in these equations corresponds to approaching motion and the lower sign corresponds to leaving.

■ If the speed of the source exceeds the speed of the wave, a shock wave is formed. The shock wavefront makes an angle θ with the direction of motion of the source, given by

$$\sin \theta = \frac{v}{v_s}.$$

■ The transverse wave speed v in a flexible string or wire is given by

$$v = \sqrt{\frac{T}{\mu}},$$

where T is the tension in the string and μ is the mass per unit length of the string.

■ The frequency of standing waves in a string is

$$f_n = \frac{n}{2L}\sqrt{\frac{T}{\mu}}, \qquad n = 1, 2, 3, \ldots.$$

■ When two sounds of almost the same frequency are heard at the same time, the sensation is of a single tone whose amplitude is rising and falling. These variations in amplitude are called beats. The rate at which they occur, called the beat frequency, is

$$|f_1 - f_2|.$$

Important Terms

You should be able to write the definition or meaning of each of the following:

transverse wave pulse	Doppler effect
traveling wave	shock wave
wave	principle of superposition
harmonic wave	constructive interference
wavelength	destructive interference
intensity	fundamental frequency
transverse waves	harmonic frequencies
longitudinal waves	overtones
wavefronts	standing wave
plane waves	nodes
decibel	antinode
intensity level	beats

Conceptual Questions

15.1 List as many transverse and longitudinal waves as you can.

15.2 You can estimate the distance to a lightning flash by counting the seconds that elapse between the time you see the flash and when you hear the accompanying thunder. (a) The approximate distance in miles is obtained by dividing the time in seconds by 5. Explain why this is so. (b) Estimate the distance to a lightning flash that you see 10 s before you hear the thunder.

15.3 The speed of sound in helium is much faster than in air at the same temperature and pressure. Use this fact to explain the observation that if you fill your lungs with helium and try to talk, your voice will be higher pitched than normal.

15.4 A stereo amplifier is said to have a channel separation of 40 dB. Explain what this means.

15.5 If an organ pipe is placed in a large chamber in which the air pressure is reduced to slightly below atmospheric pressure, will the frequency of the sounded note change?

15.6 If the whine of a bullet were 1000 Hz as it passed through the air, what would you hear if the bullet were traveling away from you with the speed of sound?

15.7 Describe what you will hear in the following situation: You swing a constant-frequency source attached to a string around your head in a 1-m-diameter horizontal circle. You are standing near a brick wall that reflects the sound.

15.8 Discuss why the lower-pitched strings in most musical instruments are wrapped with a thin coil of wire.

15.9 If you moisten your finger and rub it around the rim of a thin-stemmed glass, you often produce a sound. How is this tone produced? On what does it depend? Why must you wet your finger? What changes will take place if the glass is half filled with water?

15.10 How could you get a stretched string to vibrate in only its second harmonic mode?

15.11 What does it mean to say that musical scales are logarithmic?

Problems

Section 15.2 Harmonic Waves

Hints for Solving Problems

For harmonic waves, assume that $y = 0$ at $x = 0$ when $t = 0$ (corresponding to a sine wave). Remember the fundamental relationship $v = \lambda f$.

15.1 Write the general expression for a traveling harmonic wave of amplitude y_0 moving in the negative x direction with wavelength λ and period T.

15.2 A harmonic wave moving in the positive x direction has an amplitude of 3.0 cm, a speed of 40 cm/s, and a wavelength of 40 cm. Calculate the displacement due to the wave at (a) $x = 0.0$ cm, $t = 2.0$ s and (b) $x = 10$ cm, $t = 20$ s.

15.3 Harmonic waves are sent along a rope at a speed of 10 m/s. What is the frequency of the wave if successive wave crests are 2.5 m apart?

15.4 Radio waves travel with the speed of light, approximately 3.00×10^8 m/s in both vacuum and air. What are the wavelengths of the radio signals from (a) an FM station broadcasting at 97.5 MHz, (b) a standard broadcast AM station operating at 560 kHz, and (c) a shortwave station operating at 11,900 kHz?

15.5 The human eye is sensitive to light of wavelengths from about 400 to 700 nm. What range of frequencies does this range correspond to? Take the speed of light to be 3.00×10^8 m/s.

15.6 A shortwave receiver has "90-m band" written on one end of the dial and "11-m band" on the other. What range of frequencies does this radio receive? Take the speed of radio waves to be 3.00×10^8 m/s.

15.7• At $x = 15.0$ cm and $t = 2.00$ s, the displacement of a traveling wave is 8.66 cm. The amplitude of the wave is 10.0 cm, and its wavelength is 8.00 cm. What is its period? Assume the smallest positive phase angle.

15.8• A cart moves with a constant speed of 0.30 m/s in the x direction. A 2.3-kg lead brick is hung from a support on the cart with a spring of spring constant $k = 20$ N/m. The brick is pulled down 6.0 cm below the equilibrium point and released at $t = 0$. Write an expression for the y coordinate of a red dot painted on the center of the brick as a function of x and t. Assume that $x = 0$ when $t = 0$ and call the equilibrium position $y = 0$.

15.9• A strip of paper is pulled along at 20 cm/s at a right angle to the plane of a 0.49-m-long pendulum. The pendulum has a small, continuously running ink-jet device attached to the bob, which is arranged so that it marks the position of the pendulum on the paper (Fig. 15.25). The bob is held 8.0 cm to one side and released at $t = 0$. Write the equation for the wave drawn on the paper.

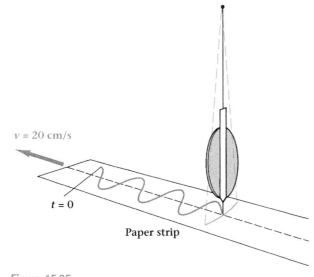

$v = 20$ cm/s

$t = 0$

Paper strip

Figure 15.25
Problem 15.9.

15.10• Rewrite the general expression for a traveling harmonic wave moving in the positive x direction in terms of the angular frequency ω and the wave number $k = 2\pi/\lambda$.

*Section 15.3 Energy and Information Transfer by Waves

15.11 A child sends traveling waves along a rope that passes through the narrow slits in a picket fence. The waves are transmitting 0.30 W. Another child puts some boards on the fence to restrict the amplitude of the waves that can pass, so they become only one-third of the original amplitude. Assuming that the speed of the waves is constant, what must the first child do to maintain the same level of power transmission?

15.12 A 6.0-m-long string has a mass of 8.5 g. Transverse waves propagate along the string with a speed of 189 m/s. One end of the string is forced to oscillate at 120 Hz with an amplitude of 0.53 cm. What power is transmitted along the string? You may want to use the expression for the power given in Problem 15.13.

15.13• Show that the expression for the power transmitted by a harmonic wave on a rope can also be written as

$$P = \tfrac{1}{2}\, \mu v\, \omega^2\, y_0^2,$$

where μ is the mass per unit length of the rope and $\omega = 2\pi f$.

Section 15.4 Sound Waves

Hints for Solving Problems

Assume the speed of sound in air to be 340 m/s, corresponding to a temperature of about 15°C, and ignore variations due to temperature unless specifically stated otherwise in the problem. The speed of sound in other materials is found in Table 15.1.

15.14 What are the shortest and longest wavelengths produced in air by a stereo system that has a useful range of 50 to 17,000 Hz?

15.15 What is the wavelength of a 2.00-kHz sound wave (a) in air, (b) in helium, and (c) in water?

15.16 (a) Calculate the frequencies of the pressure waves in air having the following wavelengths: 3.4 mm, 3.4 cm, 34 cm, 340 cm, and 34 m. (b) Which of these frequencies can be heard by human ears?

15.17 What is the wavelength of the waves produced in air by an ultrasonic distance-measuring device if the frequency is 40 kHz?

15.18 Calculate the speed of sound in dry air at a temperature of 28°C.

15.19 When sounded, two identical car horns produce sound intensities at your ear in the ratio of 6:1. If the nearer car is 8.0 m away from you, how far away is the other car? (*Hint:* Assume spherical wavefronts.)

15.20 You are 10 m from a loudspeaker, where you hear a sound intensity I_0. How far must you be from the speaker to reduce the sound intensity that you hear to $I_0/3$? (*Hint:* Assume spherical waves.)

15.21● Show that for spherical harmonic traveling waves the amplitudes y_i at distances r_i from the source are related through

$$\frac{y_1}{y_2} = \frac{r_2}{r_1},$$

where the subscripts 1 and 2 refer to different locations.

15.22● Reference is sometimes made to a singer's "hitting high C." What is the wavelength of this sound at 12°C? (The frequency of high C, more precisely called C_6, is 1047 Hz.)

15.23● A loudspeaker sounds a 600-Hz tone. What is the difference in the wavelength of the sound waves produced in air at −3°C and at 38°C?

15.24●● The ultrasonic distance-measuring device shown in Fig. 15.8 emits waves at a specific frequency. The time between sending and receiving the pulse is measured to within $\pm T$, where T is the wave period. Show that the measured distance is accurate to within $\pm \lambda/2$, where λ is the wavelength.

*Section 15.5 Measuring Sound Levels

15.25 The sound in a classroom is 63,000 times as intense as the minimum threshold of hearing. What is the intensity level of this sound in decibels?

15.26 What is the ratio of the sound intensity near a textile loom to that in a library?

15.27 An audio amplifier has a power gain of 120,000. Express this gain in units of decibels.

15.28 In a good FM radio receiver, the radio signal detected may be as much as 65 dB greater than the noise signal. What is the ratio of signal intensity to noise intensity?

15.29 The upper limit of the intensity level of sound waves is about 194 dB. This intensity corresponds to 100% modulation of the air; that is, the amplitude of the pressure oscillations corresponds to that of atmospheric pressure. What intensity (in watts per square meter) would be required to generate this level of sound?

15.30 When you are listening to music at 78 dB, what is the intensity of the sound at your ears? Express your answer in watts per square meter.

15.31● By how many decibels do you reduce the sound intensity level due to a source of sound if you quadruple your distance from it? Assume that the waves expand spherically.

15.32●● Five identical looms operating in a textile mill produce a sound intensity level of 85 dB. If two additional looms are put into operation in the same room, what is the new sound intensity level?

15.33●● The sound intensity level in a factory is 93 dB when seven identical metal stamping machines are all in operation. If four of the machines are shut down for maintenance, what is the sound intensity level due to the remaining machines?

Section 15.6 The Doppler Effect

Hints for Solving Problems

Remember to use the correct sign of v_s or v_o when calculating Doppler shifts.

15.34 A train approaching a station at a speed of 34 m/s sounds a 2000-Hz whistle. (a) What is the apparent frequency heard by an observer standing at the station? (b) What is the change in frequency heard as the train passes by?

15.35 A train going 40 m/s approaches a crossing bell whose frequency is 820 Hz. (a) What frequency is heard by passengers on the approaching train? (b) What frequency is heard by passengers after the train passes the bell?

15.36● You are standing by the railroad track when a train sounding a 750-Hz whistle passes you at 80 km/h. What is the difference in the frequencies you hear as the train approaches and departs?

15.37● A 440-Hz source has been sounding in air for a long time. (a) What frequency will you hear if you move away from it at 0.90 times the speed of sound? (b) What frequency will you hear if you move away from it at the speed of sound?

15.38● A car traveling 30 m/s overtakes another car going only 25 m/s. When the faster car is still behind the slower one, it sounds a horn of frequency 1500 Hz. What is the frequency heard by the driver of the slower car?

15.39● If you move at 18 m/s toward a 2300-Hz source that is moving toward you with a ground speed of 30 m/s, what frequency do you hear?

15.40●● If you detect a frequency shift of 30 Hz in the 6000-Hz bell of a bicycle as it approaches and then leaves you, how fast is the bicycle going? [*Hint:* You may find it helpful to use the approximation that for $x \ll 1$, $1/(1 \pm x) \approx 1 \mp x$.]

15.41●● A trailer truck traveling east at 28 m/s sounds a 1000-Hz horn. (a) What frequency is heard by an approaching driver headed west at 38 m/s? (b) What frequency is heard if the driver is headed east away from the truck at 38 m/s ?

15.42●● (a) Derive an expression for the frequency as a function of time that you would hear if you dropped a source of frequency f_0 from a tall tower. (b) Derive an expression for the frequency heard by an observer on the ground.

*Section 15.7 Formation of a Shock Wave

Hints for Solving Problems

The speed of sound in several materials is found in Table 15.1.

15.43 What is the speed of the air flow around a model airplane in a wind tunnel if the half-angle of the shock wave is 42°? Give your answer as a Mach number.

15.44 A rocket model in a wind tunnel generates a shock wave with a half-angle of 65° when the gas is flowing at 400 m/s. What is the speed of sound in the gas?

15.45 What is the half-angle for the shock wave generated by the Concorde aircraft when it is flying at Mach 2.1?

15.46 A projectile moving at a speed of 418 m/s through an atmosphere of pure nitrogen creates a shock wave with a half-angle of 53°. What is the speed of sound in nitrogen?

15.47• A bullet traveling in helium at 15°C creates a shock wave with a half-angle of 45.0°. What is the half-angle of the shock wave if the bullet travels with the same velocity through air at the same temperature?

15.48• You hear the sonic boom of a high-speed jet plane exactly 3.0 s after it passes directly overhead in level flight. At the time you hear the boom, you see the plane at an angle of 20° above the horizon. (a) How fast is the plane traveling? (b) What is the altitude of the plane? Assume that the speed of sound at the altitude of the plane is 325 m/s.

Section 15.9 Standing Waves on a String

Hints for Solving Problems

Be sure to determine whether a vibrating string or column of air has nodes or antinodes at its ends. Remember the distinction between overtones and harmonics.

15.49 What is the wave speed in a guitar string stretched between supports 0.65 m apart if the fundamental frequency of the string is 392 Hz?

15.50 A nylon string is stretched between supports 1.20 m apart. Given that the speed of transverse waves in the string is 800 m/s, find the frequency of the fundamental vibration and the first two overtones.

15.51 An experiment shows that a pulse propagates with a speed of 260 m/s along a nylon cord subject to a tension of 68.0 N. What is the mass per unit length of the cord?

15.52 Two adjacent strings on an unusual stringed instrument have the same mass per unit length and are subjected to the same tension. One of the strings is 1.44 times as long the other. What is the ratio of the fundamental frequency of the longer string to the second harmonic of the other one?

15.53 A wire stretched between supports 50 cm apart has a fundamental frequency of 400 Hz. Can it be resonantly excited by an object vibrating at a frequency of (a) 2000 Hz and (b) 3000 Hz?

15.54• (a) How far does a transverse pulse travel in 1.23 ms on a string of density 5.47×10^{-3} kg/m under tension of 47.8 N? (b) How far will the pulse travel in the same time if the tension is doubled?

15.55• A steel wire is stretched taut between supports one meter apart. (a) What is the fundamental wavelength of vibration of the wire? (b) What is the fundamental frequency if the

speed of sound in the wire is 2050 m/s? (c) What is the wavelength of the fundamental frequency in air?

15.56• The vibrations from an 800-Hz tuning fork set up standing waves in a string clamped at both ends. The wave speed in the string is known to be 400 m/s for the tension used. The standing wave is observed to have four antinodes and an amplitude of 2.0 mm. How long is the string?

15.57• A 5.00-kg mass is suspended from the ceiling by a 20.0-g wire 1.60 m long. What is the fundamental frequency of the wire?

15.58• What is the ratio of frequencies of a higher note to a lower note that is 16 semitones below it on the equal-tempered scale?

15.59• A string stretched between two supports sets up standing waves with two nodes between the ends when driven at a frequency of 230 Hz. (a) What order harmonic is such a wave? (b) What is the frequency of the fundamental? (c) At what frequency will the wave have three nodes?

15.60•• A uniform string of linear density 10 g/m is tied to the ceiling of an elevator. A 5.0-kg mass is hung from the other end of the string at a point 1.00 m from the ceiling. If the elevator accelerates upward at 0.10 g, what is the fundamental frequency of the string?

Section 15.10 Waves in a Vibrating Column of Air

15.61 Calculate the fundamental frequency and the first three overtones of a hollow pipe 36 cm long and open at both ends.

15.62 (a) What is the fundamental frequency of a hollow tube 50 cm long and open at both ends? (b) What would be the frequency if the tube were closed at one end?

15.63• Calculate the fundamental and first three overtones of a hollow pipe 25 cm long and closed at one end.

15.64• Low-frequency standing waves can sometimes be generated in tall cylindrical structures, such as unused smokestacks. (a) What would be the frequency of the fundamental acoustical vibration in a 50-m-tall smokestack if it were closed at the bottom? (b) What would be the frequency of the first three overtones?

15.65• Singing in the shower is a habit with some people, even those who do not normally sing elsewhere. To get some insight into the reason for this, calculate the first four harmonics associated with each of the linear dimensions of a 1.65 m × 2.30 m × 2.43 m room and put them in ascending order. Assume that the speed of sound is $v = 340$ m/s.

*Section 15.11 Beats

15.66 Two tuning forks are sounded simultaneously, and a beat frequency of 2.0 Hz is heard. If the frequency of the higher-pitched fork is 262 Hz, what is the frequency of the other one?

15.67 How many beats are heard when two organ pipes, each open at both ends, are sounded together if one pipe is 60 cm long and the other is 61 cm long?

15.68• Two identical guitar strings are stretched with the same tension between supports that are not the same distance apart. The fundamental frequency of the higher-pitched string is 400 Hz, and the speed of transverse waves in both wires is 150 m/s. How much longer is the lower-pitched string if the beat frequency is 3.0 Hz?

15.69• Piano tuners use overtones and beats as an aid in tuning a piano. If a tuner hears a beat frequency of 1.0 Hz between the second harmonic of a string whose fundamental frequency is 440 Hz and the third harmonic of another note, what is the other note? Assume that the tuner has already determined that the second harmonic of 440 Hz is the higher of the two frequencies.

15.70•• Two strings are each 1.00 m long with a mass of 0.10 g. Both are subjected to the same tension and are located in an elevator. One string is stretched between fixed supports. One end of the other string is fixed to the ceiling of the elevator while the other end supports a 6.00-kg mass. When the elevator is at rest, both strings vibrate with the same fundamental frequency. When the elevator accelerates upward, the notes are different and a beat frequency of 2 Hz is heard. What is the acceleration of the elevator?

Additional Problems

15.71 If one sound is 25 dB greater than another sound, what is the ratio of their intensities?

15.72 A wire of mass 0.030 kg is stretched between fixed supports a distance 1.50 m apart. (a) If the tension in the wire is 850 N, what is the speed of a wave along the wire? (b) How does the wave speed compare with the speed of sound in air?

15.73• Rewrite the expression for the speed of sound as a function of temperature so that the speed is in feet per second and the temperature in degrees Fahrenheit.

15.74• A car moving with a speed of 20 m/s sounds a horn of frequency 1000 Hz. (a) What is the frequency heard by a stationary observer positioned ahead of the car? (b) What frequency does the observer hear if the wind is blowing at a speed of 5 m/s from the car toward the observer?

15.75• An automobile passes by on the street blowing its horn. A music student standing on the sidewalk observes that the pitch of the horn drops a musical third; that is, the frequency heard after it passes is only 27/32 of the frequency heard when it was approaching. (a) Calculate the speed of the car in meters per second. (b) Also give your answer in units of kilometers per hour.

15.76• The six strings of a classical guitar are all 65.5 cm long and are tuned to frequencies of 82, 110, 147, 196, 247, and 330 Hz. The mass per unit length of the set of strings is, starting with the one of lowest frequency, 5.05×10^{-3}, 3.71×10^{-3}, 2.21×10^{-3}, 1.01×10^{-3}, 0.58×10^{-3}, and 0.44×10^{-3} kg/m. (a) What is the tension in each string? (b) What is the total string force?

15.77•• A student whirls an electronic buzzer around her head. The buzzer, which makes an 800-Hz tone when at rest, is swung on a string in a 0.75-m-radius horizontal circle at three revolutions per second. Derive an expression for the frequency as a function of time of the sound heard by a distant observer.

15.78•• The text following Eq. (15.7) claims that when v_s and v_o are much less than v, the Doppler formulas for moving source and for moving observer give essentially the same results. (a) Show that the claim is true, and (b) determine the limiting value of $v_o = v_s$ for which the two formulas agree to within 1.0%. (c) Make a graph of the % difference as a function of v_s/v.

15.79•• A traveling wave has a wavelength of 0.25 m and a period of 0.10 s. (a) If you stand in one place, how many crests pass you per second? (b) If you travel in the same direction as the wave at a speed of 1.0 m/s, how many crests pass you in one minute? (c) If you travel in the same direction as the wave at a speed of 3.0 m/s, how many crests do you intercept in one minute? (d) If you go in the opposite direction from the direction of the wave motion at 0.50 m/s and start from a crest at $t = 0$, how far away from you will that same crest be at $t = 32$ s?

15.80•• Show that the change in wavelength $\Delta\lambda$ of the sound from a source due to a change in the temperature of the air ΔT is approximately

$$\Delta\lambda \approx (1.8 \times 10^{-3})\lambda\,\Delta T,$$

where $\Delta\lambda$ and λ are in meters and ΔT is in degrees Celsius.

15.81•• In Chapter 12 we stated that the speed of sound in a gas is proportional to v_{rms} of the gas molecules and therefore is proportional to the square root of the temperature in kelvins. In this chapter we asserted that the speed of sound is well represented by a constant plus a term that is proportional to the temperature in degrees Celsius. Compare these two statements by plotting both predictions on the same graph from 0°C to 100°C and determining the maximum percentage difference between the two predictions in the specified temperature range. (*Hint:* The expression from Chapter 12 may be written in the form $v = 331.5\sqrt{T/273.15}$, where T is in kelvins.)

15.82•• Show that the expression for a standing wave,

$$y = 2y_0 \cos\left(2\pi\,\frac{x}{\lambda}\right) \cdot \sin\left(2\pi\,\frac{t}{T}\right),$$

may be derived by adding together two traveling waves that are of the same amplitude y_0 and same frequency but that travel in opposite directions.

15.83•• A copper and a steel pipe are of the same diameter and length at 8°C. The fundamental frequency of the air resonance of both is 180 Hz at this temperature when open at both ends. How many beats per second will be heard at 27°C?

Appendices

Appendix A: Formulas from Algebra, Geometry, and Trigonometry

BINOMIAL THEOREM

For any positive integer n, the quantity $(a + b)^n$ may be represented by a series of $n + 1$ terms:

$$(a + b)^n = a^n + na^{n-1}b + \frac{n(n-1)}{2!}\,a^{n-2}b^2 + \frac{n(n-1)(n-2)}{3!}\,a^{n-3}b^3 + \cdots + nab^{n-1} + b^n.$$

BINOMIAL SERIES

For any n and $|x| < 1$, the quantity $(1 + x)^n$ may be represented by the infinite series:

$$(1 + x)^n = 1 + nx + \frac{n(n-1)}{2!}\,x^2 + \frac{n(n-1)(n-2)}{3!}x^3 + \cdots,$$

where $m! = m(m-1)(m-2)(m-3) \cdots (1)$.

When $|x| \ll 1$, each successive term is so much smaller than the preceding term that the higher order terms may be neglected and the series may be approximated by the first two terms only. For example, when $|x| \ll 1$:

$$(1 + x)^2 \approx 1 + 2x$$

$$\frac{1}{1 + x} = (1 + x)^{-1} \approx 1 - x$$

$$\sqrt{(1 + x)} = (1 + x)^{\frac{1}{2}} \approx 1 + \frac{1}{2}x$$

$$\frac{1}{\sqrt{(1 + x)}} = (1 + x)^{-\frac{1}{2}} \approx 1 - \frac{1}{2}x$$

AREA AND VOLUME

Area of a rectangle of sides a and b:

$$A = ab$$

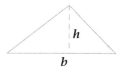

Area of a triangle with base b and height h:

$$A = \frac{1}{2}bh$$

Area of a circle of radius r:

$$A = \pi r^2$$

Area of a sector of a circle when θ is the angle between the radii (in radians):

$$A = \frac{1}{2}r^2\theta$$

Area of an ellipse with semiaxes a and b:

$$A = \pi a b$$

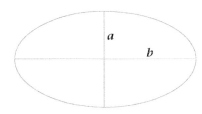

Area of the curved surface of a spherical segment of height h, radius of sphere r:

$$A = 2\pi r h$$

Area of the surface of a sphere of radius r:

$$A = 4\pi r^2$$

Volume of a sphere of radius r:

$$V = \frac{4}{3}\pi r^3$$

Volume of a cylinder of radius r and height h:

$$V = \pi r^2 h$$

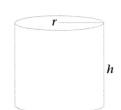

CONIC SECTIONS

Ellipse

Definition: A plane cutting a cone at an angle to the symmetry axis makes an elliptical cross section.

Description: At any point on an ellipse, the sum of distances to two fixed points (foci) is the same. The semimajor axis is labeled a and the semiminor axis is labeled b.

$$\frac{x^2}{a^2} + \frac{y^2}{b^2} = 1$$

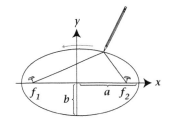

Parabola

Definition: A plane cutting a cone parallel to a side makes a parabolic cross section.

Description: At any point on a parabola, the distance to a fixed point (focus) equals the distance to a fixed line (the directrix).

$$y = -\frac{1}{2d}x^2$$

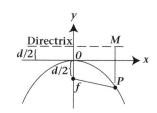

Hyperbola

Definition: A plane cutting a cone parallel to its axis makes a hyperbolic cross section.

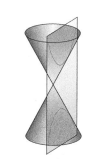

Description: At any point on a hyperbola, the difference between the distances to two fixed points (foci) is the same.

$$\frac{x^2}{a^2} - \frac{y^2}{b^2} = 1$$

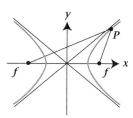

TRIGONOMETRIC RELATIONSHIPS

$\sin^2 x + \cos^2 x = 1$

$\sin (x \pm y) = \sin x \cos y \pm \cos x \sin y$

$\cos (x \pm y) = \cos x \cos y \mp \sin x \sin y$

$\tan (x \pm y) = \dfrac{\tan x \pm \tan y}{1 \mp \tan x \tan y}$

$\sin 2x = 2 \sin x \cos x$

$\cos 2x = \cos^2 x - \sin^2 x$

The law of cosines: In any triangle with angles A, B, and C and opposite sides a, b, and c, respectively,

$$a^2 = b^2 + c^2 - 2bc \cos A$$

Appendix B: The International System of Units

DEFINITIONS OF THE SI BASE UNITS

1. **unit of length (meter)**   The 17th General Conference on Weights and Measures (CGPM, 1983) abolished the former definition of the meter and adopted a new definition, which reads: *The meter is the length of the path traveled by light in vacuum during a time interval of 1/299 792 458 of a second.* The old prototype of the meter, which was legalized by the 1st CGPM in 1889, is still kept at the International Bureau of Weights and Measures (BIPM).

2. **unit of mass (kilogram)**   The 1st CGPM (1889) legalized the international prototype of the kilogram. The 3d CGPM (1901) declared: *The kilogram is the unit of mass; it is equal to the mass of the international prototype of the kilogram.* This prototype made of platinum-iridium is kept at the BIPM under conditions specified by the 1st CGPM in 1889.

3. **unit of time (second)**   The second was defined originally as 1/86 400 of the mean solar day. Because a more precise definition was needed, the 13th CGPM (1967) replaced the astronomical definition of the second by the following: *The second is the duration of 9 192 631 770 periods of the radiation corresponding to the transition between the two hyperfine levels of the ground state of the cesium-133 atom.*

4. **unit of electric current (ampere)**   The 9th CGPM (1948) adopted the ampere for the unit of electric current, with the following definition: *The ampere is that constant current which, if maintained in two straight parallel conductors of infinite length, of negligible circular cross section, and placed 1 meter apart in vacuum, would produce between these conductors a force equal to 2×10^{-7} newton per meter of length.*

5. **unit of thermodynamic temperature (kelvin)**   The 13th CGPM (1967) adopted the name kelvin (symbol K), and defined the unit as follows: *The kelvin, unit of thermodynamic temperature, is the fraction 1/273.16 of the thermodynamic temperature of the triple point of water.* In addition to the thermodynamic temperature (symbol T), expressed in kelvins, use is also made of Celsius temperature (symbol t) defined by the equation $t = T - T_0$, where $T_0 = 273.15$ K by definition.

6. **unit of amount of substance (mole)**   The following is the definition of the mole, adopted by the 14th CGPM (1971): *The mole is the amount of substance of a system that contains as many elementary entities as there are atoms in 0.012 kilogram of carbon 12. When the mole is used, the elementary entities must be specified and may be atoms, molecules, ions, electrons, other particles, or specified groups of such particles.*

7. **unit of luminous intensity (candela)**   The unit based on flame or incandescent filament standards before 1948 was replaced initially by a unit based on a Planckian radiator (a blackbody) at the temperature of freezing platinum. Because of the difficulties, and new experimental techniques, the 16th CGPM (1979) adopted the following definition: *The candela is the luminous intensity, in a given direction, of a source that emits monochromatic radiation of frequency 540×10^{12} hertz and that has a radiant intensity in that direction of (1/683) watt per steradian.*

Appendix C: Alphabetical List of Elements

Name	Symbol	Atomic number	Name	Symbol	Atomic number	Name	Symbol	Atomic number
Actinium	Ac	89	Hassium	Hs	108	Radium	Ra	88
Aluminum	Al	13	Helium	He	2	Radon	Rn	86
Americium	Am	95	Holmium	Ho	67	Rhenium	Re	75
Antimony	Sb	51	Hydrogen	H	1	Rhodium	Rh	45
Argon	Ar	18	Indium	In	49	Rubidium	Rb	37
Arsenic	As	33	Iodine	I	53	Ruthenium	Ru	44
Astatine	At	85	Iridium	Ir	77	Rutherfordium	Rf	104
Barium	Ba	56	Iron	Fe	26	Samarium	Sm	62
Berkelium	Bk	97	Krypton	Kr	36	Scandium	Sc	21
Beryllium	Be	4	Lanthanum	La	57	Seaborgium	Sg	106
Bismuth	Bi	83	Lawrencium	Lr	103	Selenium	Se	34
Bohrium	Bh	107	Lead	Pb	82	Silicon	Si	14
Boron	B	5	Lithium	Li	3	Silver	Ag	47
Bromine	Br	35	Lutetium	Lu	71	Sodium	Na	11
Cadmium	Cd	48	Magnesium	Mg	12	Strontium	Sr	38
Calcium	Ca	20	Manganese	Mn	25	Sulfur	S	16
Californium	Cf	98	Meitnerium	Mt	109	Tantalum	Ta	73
Carbon	C	6	Mendelevium	Md	101	Technetium	Tc	43
Cerium	Ce	58	Mercury	Hg	80	Tellurium	Te	52
Cesium	Cs	55	Molybdenum	Mo	42	Terbium	Tb	65
Chlorine	Cl	17	Neodymium	Nd	60	Thallium	Tl	81
Chromium	Cr	24	Neon	Ne	10	Thorium	Th	90
Cobalt	Co	27	Neptuniun	Np	93	Thulium	Tm	69
Copper	Cu	29	Nickel	Ni	28	Tin	Sn	50
Curium	Cm	96	Niobium	Nb	41	Titanium	Ti	22
Dubnium	Db	105	Nitrogen	N	7	Tungsten	W	74
Dysprosium	Dy	66	Nobelium	No	102	(Ununbium)	Uub	112
Einsteinium	Es	99	Osmium	Os	76	(Ununnilium)	Uun	110
Erbium	Er	68	Oxygen	O	8	(Unununium)	Uuu	111
Europium	Eu	63	Palladium	Pd	46	Uranium	U	92
Fermium	Fm	100	Phosphorus	P	15	Vanadium	V	23
Fluorine	F	9	Platinum	Pt	78	Xenon	Xe	54
Francium	Fr	87	Plutonium	Pu	94	Ytterbium	Yb	70
Gadolinium	Gd	64	Polonium	Po	84	Yttrium	Y	39
Gallium	Ga	31	Potassium	K	19	Zinc	Zn	30
Germanium	Ge	32	Praseodymium	Pr	59	Zirconium	Zr	40
Gold	Au	79	Promethium	Pm	61			
Hafnium	Hf	72	Protactinium	Pa	91			

Answers to Odd-Numbered Problems

1.1 (a) Uniform spherical ball on a level floor. (b) Uniform spherical ball on a tilted floor. (c) For (a) ball has a flat spot or is nonuniform and for (b) ball is asymmetric and begins to roll toward the heavier side.
1.3 Die is weighted toward the 2 spot.
1.5 Cube may be hollow if floating in water. Alternately, cube is solid but floats in a liquid that is denser than the cube.
1.7 2.5 cm^3
1.9 30 cm
1.11 1.6×10^8
1.13 m/s^2
1.15 180 cm
1.17 64.7 km
1.19 80.8 miles/h
1.21 \$22.66/m^2
1.23 \$0.282/L
1.25 768 cm^2
1.27 6.6
1.29 0.549°
1.31 1.58×10^6 revolutions
1.33 (a) 5.50×10^3 kg/m^3, (b) 2.30×10^{17} kg/m^3, (c) 184 m
1.35 5.94×10^3 cm^3
1.37 (100 ± 2) cm^2
1.39 3.27×10^3
1.41 28 people/km^2
1.43 1.02×10^{-4} m or 0.102 mm
1.45 0.040 mm
1.47 $A = xy \pm xy\left(\dfrac{\Delta x}{x} + \dfrac{\Delta y}{y}\right)$
1.49 0.06 mm
1.51 3.3×10^3 bricks
1.53 6×10^{10} gallons
1.55 1.64×10^4 mm^3
1.57 8.7 L/100 km
1.59 761 mi/h
1.61 (a) 1 min = 60,000 ms, (b) 1 century = 3.16 Gs
1.63 (a) $h = \frac{4}{3}R$
1.65 $\pi/6$
1.67 $V = \pi r^2 h \pm 2\pi r h \Delta r \pm \pi r^2 \Delta h$

2.1 4.7 km south of the base
2.3 19 cm from the left edge
2.5 (a) C, (b) A, (c) C, (d) 0 m, (e) A, (f) 2 m

2.7 $x_1 = 9.09$ km, $x_2 = -5.30$ km, $x_3 = -2.52$ km
2.9 64.1 km/h
2.11 1.0 h
2.13 3.77×10^8 m
2.15 (a) 8 km/h, (b) 264 km/h
2.17 (a) 12 km/h north, (b) 140 km/h
2.19 90 m
2.21 -48 m/s
2.23 56 km/h
2.25 at $x = 5$ the slope ≈ 0.70, at $x = 10$ the slope ≈ 1.4
2.29 A_1 is the distance graph and A_2 is the velocity graph. B_1 is the velocity graph and B_2 is the distance graph. C_1 is the velocity graph and C_2 is the distance graph. D_1 is the distance graph and D_2 is the velocity graph.
2.31 750 m
2.33 7 s; The slope is greatest at 7 s.
2.35 30 m
2.37 15 m/s
2.39 5.4 m/s^2
2.41 At 10 s, a = 1.25 m/s^2, at 30 s, a = 0.28 m/s^2
2.43 (a) A and F, B and E, C and G, (b) A and I, B and K, C and H.
2.45 (a) 3.0 m/s^2, (b) 38 m
2.47 (a) zero, (b) 400 m
2.49 31.7 m/s
2.51 At 20 mi/h, 42 ft; at 40 mi/h, 124 ft; at 50 mi/h, 180 ft
2.53 (a) 19.4 m/s, (b) 27.9 m/s
2.55 $a = \dfrac{v^2}{\sqrt{2}L}$
2.57 3.34 s
2.59 0.929 m/s^2
2.61 20 m/s
2.63 1.6 rev/s
2.65 45.6 m
2.67 68 km/h
2.69 (a) 1900 km/h, (b) 11 km/h, (c) 170
2.71 -6.6 m/s
2.73 (a) 144° W of N, (b) 72° E of N
2.75 1.2 s
2.77 13 m
2.79 At $t = 1$, $v = -0.4$ cm/s; at $t = 3$, $v = -1.5$ cm/s
2.81 39 m

3.1 (a) $C = 5$ blocks, (b) $\theta = 53°$ N of E
3.3 (a) 40 km, (b) 117° from E

3.5 6.2 units at 136°
3.7 (a) A at 0°, (b) 0, (c) 1.73A at 90°, (d) 2A at 180°
3.9 50 m, 100 m, $\theta = 63°$
3.11 $x = 10$, $y = 12$
3.13 $A = 7.8$, $\theta = -52°$
3.15 891 m at 11.7° above the horizontal
3.17 magnitude = 20.4, x component = -9.57
3.19 $D = 10$, $\theta = 97°$
3.21 (a) 13 at $-8.7°$, (b) 17 at 114°
3.23 (a) yes, (b) 13.7 km
3.25 Relative speed of attendant is 2 km/h. Relative speed of the passenger is 6 km/h.
3.27 (a) 30 min, (b) 6.5 km
3.29 (a) 160 km/h, (b) -160 km/h, (c) -10 km/h and -170 km/h
3.31 273 km/h at 4.6° with respect to E
3.33 400 km, 2.9° W of S
3.35 (a) 0.495 s, (b) directly beneath where it was dropped, (c) 34.4 m
3.37 3.9 m
3.39 1.0 km
3.41 2.9 m/s
3.45 3.1 m/s
3.47 (a) 8.86 m, (b) 71.7°
3.49 (a) 18.8 m, (b) 7.68°
3.51 (a) 56 cm, (b) 26.6°, (c) 56°
3.53 (a) 1.4 s, (b) 11 m
3.55 (a) 6.12 m, (b) 5.94 m
3.57 14 at 69°
3.59 635 m
3.61 (a) 15.6 m, (b) 14.7 m
3.63 (a) 29.4 m/s, (b) 44.1 m
3.65 22.0 m
3.67 $\frac{1}{4}R \tan \theta$
3.69 $y_{max} = \frac{1}{4}R_{max}$

4.1 334 N
4.3 0.908F
4.5 22.8 m/s^2
4.7 2.40 × 10^5 N
4.9 8.2 m
4.13 10.1 kg
4.15 2.27 kg
4.17 480 N
4.19 0.1%
4.21 (a) 1420 N, (b) 235 N, (c) 145 kg
4.23 (a) 1.4 kg, (b) 18 N
4.25 16 N
4.27 (a) 5.8 × 10^2 N, (b) 6.8 × 10^2 N, (c) 5.8 × 10^2 N, (d) 4.1 × 10^2 N, (e) 6.7 × 10^2 N
4.29 (a) The reaction force is the force of the table on the book and is equal to the weight of the book. (b) The reaction force is the force of the book on the earth and is equal to the weight of the book. (c) The reaction force is the force of the table on the book and is less than the weight of the book. The

reaction force to the gravity force is the force of the book on the earth and is equal to the weight of the book.
4.31 650 N before and after braking, 780 N during braking
4.33 (a) 167 N, (b) 150 N, (c) 115 N
4.35 8.5 cm
4.37 (a) 2.0 m/s^2, (b) 1.0 N
4.39 accelerating upward
4.41 0.485
4.43 (a) -4.00 m/s^2, (b) 0.408
4.45 1.4 m/s^2
4.47 0.185
4.49 (a) 3.7 m/s^2, (b) 31 N
4.51 (a) 0.64 m/s^2, (b) $T_1 = 24$ N, $T_2 = 37$ N
4.53 30°
4.55 284 N
4.57 35 lb ≈ 154 N
4.59 49°
4.61 1.3 kg
4.63 $T_1 = 16.3$ N, $T_2 = 18.4$ N
4.65 (a) 30°, (b) 0.67 m/s^2
4.67 0.58
4.69 0.51
4.71 3.3 m/s^2
4.73 (a) 100 N, (b) 1100 N, (c) 1600 N
4.75 (a) 4.5 s, (b) 61%
4.77 (a) 4.9 m/s^2, (b) 320 N
4.79 0.786 m/s^2 to the left
4.81 (a) 1.30 m/s^2, (b) $T_1 = 41.3$ N, $T_2 = 40.2$ N
4.83 (a) no, (b) 2.0 m, (c) both monkey and mirror fall
4.85 0.81 kg

5.1 1.3 mm
5.3 (a) $\pi/2$ rad, (b) 9.4 in.
5.5 6.0 × 10^{-3} m/s^2 toward the sun
5.9 (a) 4.0 Hz, (b) 25 rad/s
5.11 (a) 6.28 rad/s, (b) 12.6 m/s, (c) 79.0 m/s^2
5.13 41 km/h
5.15 2.2 × 10^3 N
5.17 49 m/s
5.19 13.9°
5.21 73.9 N
5.23 (a) 5.12 N, (b) 33.3°
5.25 (a) 2.69 m/s, (b) 3.27 N
5.27 (a) 2.11g, (b) 3.11
5.29 2.1 rad/s
5.31 9.54 AU
5.33 4.23 × 10^7 m
5.35 0.91%
5.37 0.165
5.39 0.900
5.41 1.7%
5.43 17 kg
5.45 In an inertial frame the accelerations are $a_{moon} = 2.70 × 10^{-3}$ m/s^2, $a_{earth} = 3.32 × 10^{-5}$ m/s^2.
5.47 1.90 × 10^{27} kg
5.49 6.72 × 10^{-11} N · m^2/kg^2
5.51 (a) $F_{near} = 5.90 × 10^{-3}$ N, $F_{far} = 5.90 × 10^{-3}$ N, (b) $F_{near} = 3.44 × 10^{-5}$ N, $F_{far} = 3.22 × 10^{-5}$ N,

(c) Force of the sun is about the same, but force of the moon changes by 7% from near to far.

5.53 (a) 4.23×10^7 m. (b) No, only equatorial orbits are allowed.

5.55 267 N

5.57 (a) $v = R\sqrt{\dfrac{4}{3} G\rho\pi}$, (b) $R = 8.1 \times 10^3$ m

5.59 9.80 m/s² directed radially toward center of earth.

5.61 1.2×10^{-10} m/s² toward the midpoint of the line joining the two masses

5.63 2.2 AU

5.65 3.08 km

5.67 0.60 Hz

5.69 (a) 6.02×10^{24} kg, (b) 5.54×10^3 kg/m³

5.71 (a) $0.94g$, (b) $2.9g$

5.73 0.58 Hz

5.75 37 rev/min

5.77 (a) $4.4 \times 10^{-3}g$, (b) $1.1 \times 10^{-3}g$, (c) $4.4 \times 10^{-4}g$

6.1 1.4×10^3 J

6.3 (a) 64 N, (b) 1.3×10^3 J

6.5 6.7 m/s

6.7 (a) 35 N, (b) 35 N

6.9 2.63 J

6.11 4.0 J

6.13 3.53 N at 26.6° from the x axis

6.15 3×10^8 gallons

6.17 (a) 1.6×10^{15} W, (b) 2.0×10^{10} m², (c) 0.20%

6.19 38 m/s

6.21 4

6.23 (a) 3.7×10^4 J, (b) 7.4×10^4 J

6.27 196 J

6.29 4.7×10^4 N/m

6.31 3.0×10^3 N/m

6.33 (a) 2.3×10^2 J, (b) 7.5×10^2 J

6.35 11.3 m/s

6.37 3.7 m/s

6.39 6.70 m/s

6.41 (a) 11.7 m/s, (b) 1.6 m/s²

6.43 1.7 m/s

6.45 223 m

6.47 (a) 4.43 m/s, (c) 29.4 N

6.49 $3R$

6.51 (a) 2.9×10^4 J, (b) 44 m/s

6.53 6.02 m/s

6.55 (a) $-mgL \sin 34°$, (b) $mgL \sin 34°$, (c) No change in KE because speed is constant. From conservation of energy we find that $-\Delta\text{PE} = W_{\text{friction}}$ in agreement with the results computed in parts (a) and (b).

6.57 200

6.59 no

6.61 \$0.25

6.63 3.1 GW

6.65 42 kW

6.67 8.0°

6.69 0.688 J

6.71 (a) 91%, (b) 170

6.73 1.25 kg

6.75 0.0033 J

6.77 0.0740 m

6.79 3.5 m/s

6.81 60°

7.1 4.79×10^4 kg · m/s

7.3 The Mazda's momentum is greater.

7.5 (a) 4.9×10^6, (b) 1.2×10^8

7.7 (a) 20.0 km/s, (b) 10.9 m/s

7.9 0.238 kg · m/s

7.11 (a) 0.490 kg · m/s directed horizontally, (b) 1.32 kg · m/s at 68.3° below the horizontal

7.13 (a) 17.4 m/s, (b) 17.4 m/s

7.15 4.17 N

7.17 (a) 60 N, (b) 60 N in the opposite direction

7.21 Work $= \bar{F} d = mgh = \text{PE}_{\text{initial}}$.

7.23 (a) -0.607 kg · m/s, (b) -1.21 kg · m/s, -304 N, -607 N

7.25 0.12 kN

7.27 0.095 s

7.29 -2.47 m/s

7.31 0.43 m/s

7.33 -22.5 cm/s, 13.1 cm/s

7.35 1.13 km/s

7.37 (a) 2120 m/s, (b) 1980 m/s

7.39 6.8×10^2 N/m

7.41 $\dfrac{\sqrt{2gh}}{3}$

7.43 2.78 m/s at 70° from the initial direction of travel of the 1300-kg car

7.45 7 m/s at an angle of 1.56° from the direction of the train

7.47 14 km/h at 28° from the x axis

7.49 $v_1 = 2.22$ m/s and $v_2 = 1.26$ m/s

7.51 390 m/s

7.53 9.2 mi/h

7.55 (a) 2.7 m/s², (b) 4.1 m/s²

7.57 1.8 m/s

7.59 0.37 m/s

7.61 4.2 N · s

7.63 (a) 1.61 m, (b) 3.16 m

7.65 0.94

7.67 $m_2/m_1 = 1.1$

7.69 (a) 7.35 m/s, (b) 3.51 m

7.71 Throwing sequentially is best.

7.73 (a) 1.45 m/s, (b) 0.735 J, (c) $\text{KE}_{\text{final}} = \frac{1}{2}\text{KE}_{\text{initial}}$.

7.75 230 N

8.1 no

8.3 2.8 m/s

8.5 yes

8.7 1.01 m

8.9 $v_1 = -v_0$, $v_2 = +v_0$

8.11 $v_1 = -2.0$ m/s, $v_2 = +2.0$ m/s

8.13 (a) 23 m/s, (b) yes

8.15 no

8.17 (a) 5.35×10^4 J, (b) Because of momentum conservation, some of the energy is needed to keep the cars in motion.

8.19 $H = \dfrac{8}{9} \dfrac{v_0^2}{g} - \dfrac{7}{9} h$

8.25 0.75

8.27 Incident deuteron moves at 45° to initial direction, struck deuteron moves at −45° to initial direction.

8.29 0.79 v_0

8.31 -7.63×10^{28} J

8.33 6.26×10^7 J

8.35 0.02 R_E

8.37 7.91×10^3 m/s

8.39 $v_0 = \sqrt{\dfrac{3GM_E}{2R_E}}$

8.41 -1.4×10^6 J

8.43 1.1 R_E

8.45 5.04 km/s

8.47 1.05

8.49 (a) 8.86×10^{-3} m, (b) 2.05×10^{30} kg/m³

8.55 390 N, 13 m

8.57 7.2×10^6 J

8.59 Choose the positive direction as the direction of motion of mass m_1. Then, $v_1' = 1.15$ m/s and $v_2' = -0.495$ m/s.

8.61 (b) $r = 0.90 R_M$

8.63 $2\sqrt{\dfrac{2h + v^2/g}{g}}$

8.65 3/8

8.67 60°

8.69 −135° from the y axis

8.71 0.100 g

9.1 ω(second hand) = 0.105 rad/s, ω(minute hand) = 1.75×10^{-3} rad/s, ω(hour hand) = 1.45×10^{-4} rad/s

9.3 (a) 20 m/s, (b) 2.1×10^5 rad/s²

9.5 (a) 524 rad/s − 1885 rad/s, (b) 19.7 m/s − 70.7 m/s, (c) 6.7×10^2 rad/s²

9.7 (a) 139 rad/s, (b) 359 m

9.9 2.6 m

9.11 (a) 83.8 rad/s, 356 rad/s, (b) 227 rad/s², (c) 42.0 rev

9.13 32 N

9.15 41.5°

9.17 500 N

9.19 (a) 330 N, (b) 270 N

9.21 2.1 kg

9.23 (a) 1.01 kN, (b) 794 N

9.25 $F_{\text{hands}} = 460$ N, $F_{\text{feet}} = 276$ N

9.27 930 N

9.29 3.5 m

9.31 4.4×10^4 N

9.33 $W = \dfrac{4F^2L_0}{\pi Y D^2}$

9.35 9.4 rad/s

9.37 (a) $\dfrac{\tau}{I}t$, (b) $\dfrac{\tau R}{I}t$

9.39 0.58 rad

9.41 (a) 0.047 kg · m², (b) 0.68 m

9.43 6.48 m/s

9.45 7.08×10^{33} kg · m²/s

9.47 29.0 rev/min

9.49 1.9×10^{-2} J

9.51 35 J

9.53 22 rad/s

9.55 Hoop: 5.0 m/s, disk: 5.7 m/s

9.57 $v_{\text{rolling}} = \dfrac{1}{\sqrt{2}} v_{\text{sliding}}$

9.61 (a) 2.34 m/s, (b) 1/3

9.65 $a = \dfrac{g}{1 + \dfrac{I}{mR^2}}$

9.67 9.8 N · m

9.69 2.4 kg

9.71 100 N

9.73 (a) 200 N, (b) 700 N

9.77 2.5 cm

9.79 (a) KE $= \frac{1}{2}|\text{PE}|$, (b) $-\frac{1}{2}G\dfrac{Mm}{r}$

9.81 (b) $\sqrt{\frac{4}{3} gh}$

9.83 3.5 m/s

10.1 (a) 0.752×10^3 kg/m³, (b) oak

10.3 2.17 MPa

10.5 10.0 km

10.7 0.0150 m²

10.9 (a) 410 kPa, 2.7 MPa, (b) 82 kPa

10.11 11.1 kPa

10.13 1.26×10^5 N

10.15 147 kPa

10.17 18.5 cm

10.19 0.70 g/cm³

10.21 1650 kg

10.23 48.5 m³

10.25 76%

10.27 0.0918 N

10.29 (a) 1.6 kg, (b) 1.8 kg

10.31 (b) Net force on m_1 is $F_{1\text{net}} = F_{b1} - m_1g - T$, net force on m_2 is $F_{2\text{net}} = T + m_2g - F_{b2}$, where T is the tension in the string, (c) $a = \frac{1}{2}\rho g\left(\dfrac{1}{\rho_1} - \dfrac{1}{\rho_2}\right)$

10.33 73×10^{-3} N/m

10.35 0.29 m

10.37 9

10.39 −3.1 kPa

10.45 3.8 kPa

10.47 19%

10.49 1:4:9

10.51 (a) 65 Pa · s, (b) 7.2 Pa · s

10.53 0.66 m/s

10.55 1.14×10^5 N, 6.40×10^4 N, fuel consumption proportional to v^2

10.57 19 Hz

10.63 0.150 mm

10.65 0.11 m³/h
10.67 3.2×10^5 Pa
10.69 6.7×10^{-3} m², 1.25×10^4 Pa
10.71 2.95×10^6 N
10.73 0.91 m/s
10.75 13 cm
10.77 (a) 0.50×10^{-3} m³, (b) 18.7×10^3 kg/m³,
(c) 13.6×10^3 kg/m³, (d) mercury
10.79 0.11
10.81 85°C

11.1 (a) 136°F, (b) −129°F
11.3 −269°C = −452°F
11.5 77.35 K = −320.4°F
11.7 +2.67°, +0.44°, −1.22°, −2.33°
11.9 (a) $T(°N) = \frac{5}{14}[T(°F) - 70]$, (b) $T(°N) = \frac{9}{14}T(°C) - 13.6$
11.11 $2.9 \times 10^5/°C$
11.13 2.1 cm
11.15 1.6 L
11.17 86°C
11.21 1.6 L
11.23 1.2 cal
11.25 0.15 kcal
11.27 6.83×10^3 cal
11.29 0.36°C/s
11.31 0.019°C
11.33 101 g
11.35 89°C
11.37 1.2°C
11.39 45.5°C
11.41 4.28×10^5 J
11.43 2.92×10^5 cal
11.45 100°C
11.47 5.4 cm³/min
11.49 0.5 g of ice, 1.0 g of water
11.51 0°C
11.53 8.8 kW
11.55 459 W/m², 5.67×10^4 W/m², 4.59×10^6 W/m²,
5.95×10^6 W/m²
11.57 yes
11.59 5760 K
11.61 18.3 h
11.63 5980 K
11.65 9.0 mm
11.67 6.04 W
11.69 2.99×10^6 J
11.71 (a) 8.6×10^5 J, (b) 5.7×10^4 W, (c) 2.7×10^2 °C
11.73 10 cm
11.75 48.3 g
11.79 0.50 cal/g°C
11.81 All the water remains.

12.1 13.0 m
12.3 107 cm
12.5 5.2×10^{19} N
12.7 1.26×10^5 Pa

12.11 10.3 m
12.13 0.943 L
12.15 (a) 546 K, (b) 746 K, (c) 2546 K
12.17 40°C
12.19 22.5 L
12.21 (a) 1.00, (b) in the same place (exactly in the center)
12.23 4.1×10^7 Pa
12.25 1.7×10^{-3} m³
12.27 4.75, 5.55
12.29 2.18×10^{-6} m
12.31 1.04×10^{-20} J
12.33 1.5 kg/m³
12.35 1.05
12.37 (a) 1.24×10^{-24} kg, (b) No
12.39 3030 J
12.41 1.1 kJ
12.43 $0.50 \, P_0$
12.45 (a) 5.54 km, (b) 11.1 km
12.47 $f(v_\mathrm{m})\Delta v = \dfrac{4}{e}\sqrt{m/2\pi kT}\,\Delta v$
12.49 1.46
12.51 (a) 0.63 mol, (b) 18 g
12.53 1.6 cm
12.55 (a) 2.44×10^{25}, (b) 1.52×10^5 J, (c) 1.34×10^3 m/s
12.57 (a) 1.41×10^5 K, (b) 1.60×10^5 K. (c) Ratio of nitrogen to oxygen is slightly smaller at upper regions.
12.59 $d = \dfrac{P_0 x}{\rho g(L - x)} + x$

A12.1 −0.061
A12.5 49 particles/min
A12.7 19.38

13.1 22.0 kJ
13.3 29.2 kJ
13.5 impossible
13.7 6.7 kJ
13.9 260 J
13.13 (a) 60 J, (b) heat is given out, (c) −65 J
13.15 (a) 0.502, (b) 0.424
13.17 (a) 26 J, (b) 9 J
13.19 0.020
13.21 $P_0 V_0$
13.23 111 K
13.25 $\frac{1}{2}P_1(V_1 - V_0)$
13.27 actual efficiency = 0.175, theoretical efficiency = 0.308
13.29 0.80
13.31 (a) 0.98, (b) 0.19
13.33 14
13.35 (a) 21, (b) 8.9
13.37 −32°C
13.39 (a) 143 J, (b) 200 J
13.41 68 W
13.43 3.03 kJ/K
13.45 8.8 MW/K
13.47 643 J/K
13.49 (a) 550 J/K, (b) −510 J/K, (c) 40 J/K
13.51 0.22

13.53 15 mJ/K
13.55 42 J
13.57 (a) 97 W, (b) 0.33 W/K
13.59 56% more
13.63 (b) 875 J, (c) 500 J, (d) 375 J
13.65 0.64%

14.1 5.36 cm
14.3 17 cm
14.5 23 cm
14.7 0.575 m
14.9 longer than your arm
14.11 10 cm, 10 cm, 3.1 cm
14.13 2.8 s
14.15 (a) 6.7 cm, (b) 8.1 cm
14.17 (a) 6.0 m/s^2, (b) -4.2 m/s^2, (c) 10.6 cm
14.19 1.2×10^{-2} J
14.21 64 N/m
14.23 (a) 0.067 m, (b) 2.2×10^{-2} J
14.27 (a) 0.318 Hz, (b) 3.14 s
14.29 0.99 m
14.31 0.46 s
14.33 (a) 37.7 cm/s, (b) 118 cm/s^2
14.37 0.408 kg
14.39 4.4 m/s
14.41 (a) 4.0 s, (b) 3.5 s
14.43 2.75 s
14.45 (a) Tarzan saves Jane 2.3 s before the bomb explodes. (b) They are over the middle of the river when the bomb explodes.
14.49 (a) 3.0×10^{-3}/s, (b) 0.069
14.51 $-6.76°$
14.53 8.2 cm
14.55 (a) 2.14 Hz, (b) 39.6 m/s
14.57 (a) 0.140 m, (b) 0.994 m
14.59 6.0 cm
14.61 2.05 Hz
14.63 3.92 m/s^2
14.67 yes
14.69 $5.36\sqrt{L/g}$
14.71 $T = 2\pi\sqrt{L/g}$
14.73 2.0 m

15.1 $y(x,t) = y_0 \sin 2\pi\left(\dfrac{x}{\lambda} + \dfrac{t}{T}\right)$

15.3 4.0 Hz
15.5 4.3×10^{14} Hz $- 7.5 \times 10^{14}$ Hz
15.7 1.17 s
15.9 $y(x) = 8.0$ cm $\cos 2\pi\left(\dfrac{x}{0.28\text{ m}}\right)$

15.11 The child must triple the frequency.
15.15 (a) 0.170 m, (b) 0.489 m, (c) 0.750 m
15.17 8.5 mm
15.19 20 m
15.23 0.041 m
15.25 48 dB
15.27 50.8 dB
15.29 2.51×10^7 W/m^2
15.31 -12 dB

15.33 89.3 dB
15.35 (a) 916 Hz, (b) 724 Hz
15.37 (a) 44 Hz, (b) You will not hear it.
15.39 2656 Hz
15.41 (a) 1210 Hz, (b) 968 Hz
15.43 Mach 1.49
15.45 28°
15.47 14.2°
15.49 510 m/s
15.51 1.01 g/m
15.53 (a) yes, (b) no
15.55 (a) 2.0 m, (b) 1025 Hz, (c) 0.33 m
15.57 19.6 Hz
15.59 (a) third harmonic, (b) 77 Hz, (c) 307 Hz
15.61 470 Hz, 940 Hz, 1420 Hz, 1890 Hz
15.63 340 Hz, 1020 Hz, 1700 Hz, 2380 Hz
15.65 70, 74, 103, 140, 148, 206, 210, 222, 280, 296, 309, and 412 Hz
15.67 4.6 Hz
15.69 293 Hz
15.71 316
15.73 $v = [1052.2 + 1.1T(°\text{F})]$ ft/s
15.75 (a) 29 m/s, (b) 104 km/h
15.77 $f' = (800$ Hz$)(1 + 0.04 \cos 6\pi t)$
15.79 (a) 10, (b) 360, (c) 120, (d) 96 m
15.81 1% at 100°C
15.83 0.018

16.1 90 N
16.3 1.8 km
16.5 4.2 nC
16.7 0.29
16.9 (a) 1.24×10^{36}, (b) No
16.11 (a) -320 N, attractive, (b) $+40$ N, repulsive
16.13 1.50 μC, 4.50 μC
16.15 2.3 nC/h
16.17 -0.84 N (toward the origin)
16.19 $\left(\sqrt{2} + \dfrac{1}{2}\right)k\dfrac{q^2}{L^2}$ diagonally outward

16.21 Force on each end charge is 7.7 N outward. Force on center charge is zero.
16.23 2.34×10^{-14} N
16.25 8.00×10^5 N/C
16.27 zero
16.31 3.13×10^4 N/C
16.33 7.50×10^{-3} N at 36.9°
16.35 3.29 μC
16.39 1.7×10^5 N/C in the $-x$ direction
16.41 (a) 0, (b) 1.3×10^5 N/C
16.43 (a) -3.95×10^5 N $\cdot$ m^2/C, (b) inward
16.45 0.206 N $\cdot$ m^2/C

16.49 (a) $F = -\dfrac{\rho q r}{3\epsilon_0}$, (b) $r = r_0 \cos \omega t$, with $\omega = \sqrt{\dfrac{\rho q}{3\epsilon_0 m}}$

16.51 8.5×10^{-27} N $\cdot$ m
16.53 3.89 mm
16.55 -1.1×10^{-25} J
16.57 (a) zero, (b) No, because the field is not constant over the surface.

16.59 2.50×10^4 N/C

16.61 (a) negative y direction, (b) $\dfrac{p}{4\pi\epsilon_0 x^3}$

16.63 0.119 m

16.65 2.3 N diagonally inward

16.67 1.49×10^3 C

16.69 zero, $\dfrac{Q(r^3 - a^3)}{4\pi\epsilon_0 r^2 (b^3 - a^3)}$, $\dfrac{Q}{4\pi\epsilon_0 r^2}$

16.73 (a) $-y$ direction, (b) $\dfrac{p^2}{2\pi\epsilon_0 r^3}$

17.1 6.14×10^{-18} J

17.3 0.11 pC

17.5 2×10^{-3} C

17.7 (a) 36 V, (b) 3.6×10^{-8} J

17.9 7.58×10^6 m/s

17.11 -1.18 V

17.13 (a) 1.2 MV/m, (b) 64 kV/m, (c) 1.8×10^5 V

17.15 (a) 9.2×10^6 V, (b) 9.4×10^6 V

17.17 (a) 15.3 J, (b) 15.3 J

17.19 (a) 2.40×10^5 m/s, (b) 1.03×10^7 m/s

17.21 (a) 2.50×10^5 eV, (b) 4.00×10^{-14} J, (c) 6.92×10^6 m/s

17.23 $Q/2$

17.25 (a) first sphere, (b) second sphere

17.27 60 V

17.29 375 μC

17.31 120 V

17.33 1.33 μF

17.35 0.83 nF

17.37 0.869 μC

17.39 1.84×10^{-20} J

17.41 0.192 N

17.43 (a) 3.2×10^{-17} J, (b) 200 eV, (c) 8.4×10^6 m/s

17.45 15 kV

17.47 208 V

17.49 2.8×10^{-3} m^2

17.51 5.6

17.53 $CV = \kappa \epsilon_0 AE$, where E is the dielectric strength

17.55 0.50 nF

17.57 (a) 0.050 μC, (b) 1.25×10^{-7} J

17.59 (a) 2.1×10^{-4} J, (b) 1.3×10^{-3} J

17.61 45 V

17.63 5000 eV $= 8.01 \times 10^{-16}$ J

17.65 4.6×10^6 V

17.67 (a) $\sigma/\epsilon_0 E$, (b) 3.8

17.69 $\Delta W = \frac{1}{2} C_0 V_0^2 (\kappa - 1)$

17.71 (a) 0, (b) 11 J

17.73 0.70 nF

18.1 (a) 0.50 C, (b) 30 C

18.3 13.9 A

18.5 4.16 nA

18.7 53.2 mA

18.9 5.0 Ω

18.11 0.54 Ω

18.13 no

18.15 0.00 A, 0.10 A, 0.20 A, 0.30 A, 0.40 A, 0.50 A, 0.60 A

18.17 9.8×10^{-8} $\Omega \cdot$ m, iron

18.19 6.4 Ω

18.21 0.969

18.23 (a) 1.25 A, (b) 96.0 Ω

18.25 6.67 A

18.27 \$1.44

18.29 \$1.80

18.31 (a) 420 Ω, (b) higher, (c) resistance increases with temperature

18.33 (a) 0.090 A in left resistor, zero in right resistor, (b) 0.090 A in each resistor

18.35 16 Ω

18.37 400 Ω

18.39 (a) 58 mA, (b) 0.87 V

18.41 (a) 45.2 V, (b) 34.0 V

18.43 3.662 Ω

18.45 8.5 μF

18.47 5.9 μF

18.49 (a) 160 pF, (b) 106 pF

18.51 6.5 μF

18.53 seven combinations: 5, 7.5, 10, 15, 22.5, 30, 45 μF

18.55 (a) 12 V, (b) 180 μC, 300 μC, (c) 1.1×10^{-3} J, 1.8×10^{-3} J

18.57 0.94 Ω

18.59 (a) 5.9 Ω, (b) 8.0 V

18.61 (a) yes, (b) no

18.63 (a) no, (b) The lamp can be operated with either the toaster or the iron.

18.65 11 m

18.67 1.6¢

18.69 23 kg

18.71 5.9 Ω

18.73 (a) 60.0 mA, (b) 0 A in series with switch, 60.0 mA for others

18.75 (a) 9.0 V, (b) 2.4 W

18.77 53 mA

18.79 (a) $R_1 = 22$ Ω, $R_2 = 80$ Ω, $R_3 = 100$ Ω, (b) $I_1 = 0.36$ A, $I_2 = 0.20$ A, $I_3 = 0.16$ A, (c) $P_1 = 2.9$ W, $P_2 = 3.2$ W, $P_3 = 2.56$ W, (d) 66 Ω, (e) 0.36 A, (f) 8.6 W

19.7 80 A $\cdot$ m^2

19.9 2.9×10^{-9} T

19.11 1.11×10^{-4} Wb

19.13 2 μB

19.15 20 A

19.17 0.0228 N

19.19 0.0457 T

19.21 $F = VBA/\rho$

19.23 1.41×10^{13} m/s^2

19.25 The motion is helical with a radius of 0.879 cm.

19.27 8.5×10^{-21} kg $\cdot$ m/s

19.29 (a) 4.79×10^5 m/s, (b) 1.92×10^{-16} J

19.31 11.4 MHz

19.33 34 GHz

19.37 14 cm

19.39 (a) 0.016 N/m, (b) repel

19.41 1.25 A

19.43 8.0 A

19.45 2.6 mT

19.47 0.14 A $\cdot$ m^2

19.49 1.2×10^{-4} N · m
19.51 50 V
19.53 2.5×10^{-2} Ω in parallel with the galvanometer
19.55 $\theta = NIAB/\kappa$
19.57 7.72 mT
19.61 (a) $B = \mu_0 NI/2\pi r$, (b) B varies with position within the torus, (c) zero
19.63 0.27 T
19.65 8.31 turns/m
19.67 The maximum moment occurs for $N = 1$.
19.69 1.58×10^5 m/s

20.1 0.11 V
20.5 0.56 mV
20.7 0.18 T
20.9 (a) from c to d, (b) from d to c, (c) from d to c, (d) from c to d
20.11 (a) 4.8 mV, (b) 19 mV, (c) 9.6 mV, (d) 19 mV
20.13 0.17 mV
20.15 (a) Blv, (b) Blv, (c) Blv/R, (d) B^2l^2v/R
20.17 0.53 mV
20.19 0.16 mV
20.21 2.3×10^{-5} V
20.23 190 V
20.25 300 V
20.27 10
20.29 3.6
20.31 10.0
20.33 (a) 2.5 A, (b) 0.50 A, (c) 60 W
20.35 37.5 mA
20.37 -0.26 mV, The induced polarity opposes the current.
20.39 0.54 A/s
20.41 208
20.45 5.8×10^{-5} J
20.47 (a) 0.11 J, (b) 0.24 W
20.49 8.6 J/m^3
20.51 0.15 m
20.53 4.740×10^6 m/s
20.55 (a) $E_0 = 0.87$ kV/m, $B_0 = 2.9 \times 10^{-6}$ T, (b) The amplitude of the magnetic field is 5.8% of the earth's field.
20.57 400 V
20.59 (a) 15 mV, (b) 9.4×10^{-5} W
20.61 (a) 520 kW, (b) 440 kV, (c) \$360,000
20.63 8.8 A
20.65 40 V
20.69 850 mH
20.71 0.32 H
20.73 $L_1 = 0.056$ H, $L_2 = 0.11$ H

21.3 (a) 30 ms, (b) 0.63
21.5 1.1 ms
21.7 (a) 10 s, (b) 80 mΩ
21.11 12 μs
21.13 39 μF
21.15 (a) $5\tau_C$, (b) 0.24 s
21.17 50.0 Hz
21.19 170 V
21.23 19.4 V

21.25 (a) 160 Ω, (b) 56 mA
21.27 (a) 69 Ω, (b) 72 mA
21.29 6.10 Ω
21.31 33 μF
21.33 (a) 42 mA, (b) 60 mA
21.35 0.15 A
21.37 (a) 0.27 A, (b) 42°, (c) 24 W
21.39 (a) $-2.8°$, (b) $-90°$, (c) 0°
21.41 1.13 μF or 1.07 μF
21.43 32 kHz
21.45 (a) 690 Hz, (b) 1500 Ω
21.47 (0.24 A) cos(10,000t)
21.49 (a) 0.14 A, (b) 75 Hz
21.51 (a) 521 Ω, (b) 274 Hz, (c) 470 Ω
21.53 0.693τ
21.55 (a) $V_m/2$, (b) $V_m/\sqrt{2}$
21.57 (a) V/R, (b) V/R

22.1 (a) 32°, (b) 28°
22.3 parallel to the symmetry axis
22.5 2.249×10^8 m/s, 2.29×10^8 m/s, 1.240×10^8 m/s
22.7 72°
22.9 no
22.11 31 cm
21.13 (a) 12.8°, (b) 1.1 mm
22.15 (b) $d = \dfrac{t \sin(\theta_1 - \theta_2)}{\cos\theta_2}$
22.17 42.2°
22.19 97.2°
22.21 (a) 2.18 cm, (b) 0.599
22.23 $86.8° \le \alpha \le 99.6°$
22.25 (a) 17 cm, (b) $+0.33$
22.29 0.86 m
22.31 (a) at the 30 cm mark, (b) 15 cm
22.33 14.4 cm
22.35 44.4 cm, $-4.1\times$
22.37 0.46 m
22.39 0.56 cm
22.41 (a) 13.7 cm, (b) 175 cm
22.43 9 cm to the left of the diverging lens
22.45 $+3$
22.47 (a) 60 cm, the image is real and inverted, (b) -15 cm, the image is virtual and erect.
22.49 (a) -6.67 cm, (b) -5.45 cm, (c) -3.75 cm
22.51 -0.32 m
22.55 ethyl alcohol
22.57 3
22.63 $0.39R$ from the back surface of the sphere
22.65 0.34 m
22.67 $c = ND\omega/\pi$
22.69 8 cm to the left of the diverging lens
22.71 (a) approximately 0.40 m, (b) 0.43 m

23.1 29 diopters
23.3 0.33 m
23.5 -1.00 diopter
23.7 0.40 m
23.9 -3.4 diopters

23.11 $+12$ diopters
23.13 $20.6°$
23.15 1.4 mm
23.17 $2.5\times$, $1.6\times$, and $4.1\times$
23.19 (a) 4.2 cm, (b) $3\times$
23.21 $f/4.3$
23.23 9.0 cm
23.25 $f/3.4$
23.27 2.2 cm
23.29 (a) no, (b) 1/115 s
23.31 $85°$, $44°$, $10°$
23.33 $f/5.6$ for background alone and $f/11$ for second exposure
23.35 (a) 33.3 cm, (b) 54.4 cm
23.37 1.6 mm
23.39 2.9 mm
23.41 2.03 mm from the objective lens
23.43 $-14\times$
23.45 $-10\times$
23.47 0.27 rad
23.49 (a) $-8.12\times$, (b) 40.6 cm
23.51 15.1 cm
23.53 (a) $+10$ cm, (b) $+2.5$ cm
23.55 200 cm
23.57 7.0 diopters
23.59 7.8 cm

23.61 (a) 15 cm, (b) $-\dfrac{2}{3}\times$

23.63 $f/1.6$
23.67 9.3 m
23.69 (a) 0.54 m, (b) 1.85 diopters, (c) 0.54 m
23.71 (c) 1.33

24.3 (a) 1.82×10^8 m/s, (b) 384 nm
24.5 (a) 180 nm, (b) 319 nm
24.7 Waves converge at $R/2$ in front of the mirror, where R = radius of curvature of the mirror.
24.9 $25°$
24.11 589 nm
24.13 (a) 7.4×10^{-3} rad, (b) 4.65 cm
24.15 1.75×10^{-4}
24.17 No wavelength of visible light is possible.
24.19 1.51 mm
24.21 90 nm
24.23 (a) 143 nm, (b) 71 nm
24.25 714 nm (for red), 556 nm (green), 455 nm (blue)
24.27 12 mm
24.29 630 nm
24.31 12 cm
24.33 3
24.35 seven beams exist, corresponding to four orders
24.37 86.7 μm
24.39 3.36×10^{-4} rad
24.41 31 km
24.43 1.3 km
24.45 0.34 mm
24.47 320 m
24.51 0.88 I_{m}
24.53 $56.7°$

24.55 (a) 1.66, (b) flint glass
24.57 (a) $0.50I_0$, (b) $0.50I_0$, (c) $0.25I_0$
24.59 (a) 20%, (b) 15%
24.61 680 nm
24.63 590 nm
24.65 480 nm
24.67 (a) no overlap, (b) overlap
24.69 for $m = +1$, $\theta = -10.6°$, for $m = -1$, $\theta = -54.7°$
24.71 (a) along a north-south line, (b) none
24.73 830 lines/mm

25.1 (a) -2 km/h, (b) 14 km/h
25.3 0
25.5 $-0.34c$
25.7 $0.89c$
25.9 (a) c, (b) c
25.13 4
25.15 6:00:01.28
25.17 66.8 ms
25.19 1.21 y
25.21 0.93 c
25.23 1.8×10^{-7} s
25.25 150 m
25.27 $0.60c$
25.29 1.4 m
25.31 70 min
25.33 (a) -7.7×10^{-11} m, (b) 3800 km/h
25.35 1.64×10^{-13} J
25.37 14 years
25.39 4.50×10^{-20} kg · m/s
25.41 5.55×10^7 m/s
25.43 $0.87c$
25.45 $0.87c$
25.47 $0.996c$
25.49 (a) $0.51\ m_0c^2$, (b) $1.5\ m_0c^2$
25.51 78 MHz
25.53 (a) 98 MHz, (b) 151 MHz
25.55 (a) moving away, (b) $0.11c$
25.57 $3.8 \times 10^{-13}\ f_0$
25.59 1.2×10^{-3} Hz, positive
25.61 18 ns
25.63 $0.50c$ away
25.65 -245 ns
25.67 (a) -3.76 ms, (b) younger

26.3 (a) No, results are probably untrue. (b) Yes, the results are probably true.
26.5 0.751 g
26.7 singly charged
26.9 2.1 L
26.17 5.86×10^{22}/cm^3
26.19 1.76×10^{-10} m
26.21 1.69×10^{-10} m
26.23 $31.0°$, $64.7°$, and $107°$
26.25 9.54×10^{-5} m
26.27 760 V
26.31 2.9 m
26.33 1.25×10^7 m/s

26.35 0.50

26.37 15 d

26.39 1.22×10^4 Bq

26.41 (b) $t_{1/2}$ = 3.5 h, 0.20/h, (c) 2600 disintegrations/min

26.43 (a) 2.6×10^{12} Bq, (b) 71 Ci

26.45 3.2×10^{-14} m

26.47 4.11×10^{-10} m

26.49 1040/min

26.51 For incident particle, recoil the velocity is $-0.82v_0$ and its energy is $0.67KE_0$. For the struck particle the velocity is $0.18v_0$ and the energy is $0.33KE_0$.

27.1 656.21 nm, 486.08 nm, 434.00 nm, and 410.13 nm

27.3 396.97 nm in the ultraviolet

27.5 7630 K

27.7 569 nm

27.9 2.08×10^{-19} J

27.11 413 nm

27.13 (a) 906 nm, (b) 2.20×10^{-19} J

27.15 (a) $p = \dfrac{hf}{c}$, (b) 1.76×10^{24}/s, (c) 737 kW, (d) not practical

27.17 689 nm

27.19 3.48×10^{-11} m

27.21 2.104 eV

27.23 0.11 eV

27.25 (a) 1.38×10^{-11} m, (b) 2.18×10^{19} Hz

27.27 (a) 2.14 eV, (b) no

27.29 (a) 853 nm, (b) 1.45 eV

27.31 4.76×10^{-10} m

27.33 364.6 nm

27.35 (a) 12.8 eV, (b) 96.9 nm

27.37 1460 nm

27.39 91.16 nm

27.41 1.097×10^7/m

27.43 (a) 10.2 eV, (b) 122 nm

27.45 (a) 1.09×10^6 m/s, (b) $v/c = 3.65 \times 10^{-3}$

27.47 (a) 40.5 keV, (b) 80.8 keV

27.49 (a) 1.67×10^{-10} m, (b) 1.94×10^{-10} m

27.51 25.9 kV

27.53 copper

27.55 zinc

27.57 122 nm, 91.1 nm

27.59 3.10×10^3

27.61 (a) 1.51 eV, (b) 0, (c) 3.65×10^{14} Hz

27.63 1.05×10^5 K

28.1 1.14×10^{19} Hz

28.5 16.9 keV

28.7 2.0×10^7 m/s

28.9 12.4°

28.11 1.2×10^{-34} m

28.13 proton

28.15 4.09×10^{-11} m

28.17 16.8 eV

28.19 1.8×10^{-12} m

28.21 8.68°

28.23 0.20 nm

28.25 3.45×10^{-11}

28.27 4.58 ns

28.29 (a) 1.1×10^{-24} kg · m/s, (b) 3.8 eV

28.33 1.0×10^{-11} m

28.37 $E_1 = 6.0 \times 10^{-20}$ J, $E_2 = 2.4 \times 10^{-19}$ J, $E_3 = 5.4 \times 10^{-19}$ J

28.39 1.7×10^{-27} kg

28.41 no

28.43 8100

28.45 1.0×10^{-6}

28.47 2 subshells

28.49 7

28.51 5.79×10^{-5} eV

28.53 3.7×10^{-24} J

28.55 (a) 9.27×10^{-5} eV, (b) 1.34 cm

28.57 Two 1s states, two 2s states, six 2p states, and one 3s state. In this notation, the number is the value of n and the letter labels the value of l.

28.59 For the N shell, n = 4. The possible values of l are 0, 1, 2, and 3. Each of these subshells has $2(2l + 1)$ states or $2 + 6 + 10 + 14$ = 32 total states.

28.61 (a) 16.4 keV, (b) 0.8 keV

28.63 8.62°

28.67 $h^2/8\pi^2 m(\Delta x)^2$

28.71 Lowest energies for (n_x, n_y) of (1,1), (1,2) = (2,1), (2,2), (1,3) = (3,1), (3,2) = (2,3), (1,4) = (4,1).

$$E_{1,1} = \frac{2\,h^2}{8mL^2},\ E_{1,2} = \frac{5\,h^2}{8mL^2},\ E_{2,2} = \frac{8\,h^2}{8mL^2},\ E_{1,3} = \frac{10\,h^2}{8mL^2},$$

$$E_{2,3} = \frac{13\,h^2}{8mL^2},\ E_{1,4} = \frac{17\,h^2}{8mL^2}.$$

29.1 16 min

29.3 7.3×10^5 Bq

29.5 6.5

29.9 20

29.11 53 protons and 73 neutrons, 26 protons and 30 neutrons, 82 protons and 125 neutrons

29.13 35.5

29.15 24.3

29.17 1.0×10^{-42} m^3

29.19 $^{209}_{83}$Bi

29.23 510 MeV, 1740 MeV

29.25 27.410 MeV

29.27 (a) 8×10^{-37}, (b) no

29.29 $^{230}_{90}$Th

29.31 electron

29.33 reaction cannot take place

29.35 (a) $^{66}_{30}$Zn, (b) $^{38}_{18}$Ar

29.37 (a) yes, 5.98 MeV, (b) no, Q = -3.95 MeV

29.39 (a) actinium series, (b) thorium series

29.41 (a) uranium series, (b) actinium series

29.43 0.019 MeV

29.47 (a) yes, 4.87 MeV, (b) 4.78 MeV

29.49 0.27 m

29.51 (a) 5.0 Gy, (b) 0.50 Gy

29.53 1.8 mSv

29.55 1.4×10^{14}

29.57 $^{14}_{7}\text{N}$
29.59 0.672 MeV
29.61 $^{116}_{46}\text{Pd}$
29.63 3.27 MeV
29.65 1.944 MeV
29.67 4.27 MeV
29.69 6.05 MeV, 1.71×10^7 m/s
29.71 0.16 μg

30.1 9.48×10^5
30.3 423 MHz
30.5 1.786 eV
30.7 (a) 1.960 eV, (b) 1.078 eV
30.9 0.809 eV, infrared
30.11 4.0
30.13 0.82
30.15 0.80
30.17 (a) 0.80, (b) 0.72, (c) 6.1
30.19 47.1°
30.21 Three beams at 0° and ± 23.9°
30.23 0.11°
30.25 (a) 1.77 eV, (b) 3.10 eV
30.27 3000 K
30.29 (a) 690 nm, (b) 967 nm
30.31 5.7
30.33 (a) orange, (b) purple
30.35 (a) no light emerges, (b) red, (c) red, (d) blue
30.37 violet, violet, blue, and red
30.39 Measuring from the central maximum, maxima of the violet light occur at distances of 0.82 mm, 1.64 mm, 2.46 mm, 3.28 mm, 4.10 mm. Maxima of the orange light occur at 1.23 mm, 2.46 mm, and 3.69 mm. The first five color fringes are: violet; orange; violet; orange + violet (= magenta); and violet.
30.41 V = 0.78, I_{max}/I_{min} = 8.1
30.43 3.3×10^{-5} mm

31.1 0.411 nm
31.3 0.324 nm
31.5 $\sqrt{3}a_0/4$
31.7 5.5×10^4 K
31.9 2.54×10^{28} electrons/m^3
31.11 (a) 11.94 eV, (b) 103.6 nm, (c) 7.00 eV
31.13 (a) 3.65 eV, (b) ultraviolet, (c) no

31.15 8.37×10^{-15} s
31.17 6.72×10^{-3} m²/V · s
31.19 (a) 4.4×10^{-3} m²/V · s, (b) 2.5×10^{-14} s
31.21 (a) 3.1×10^{-4} m/s, (b) 2.7 h
31.23 233 nm, ultraviolet
31.25 1090 nm
31.27 $1.3 \times 10^{-6}/\Omega \cdot$ m
31.29 $8.4 \times 10^{28}/$m³
31.31 (b) $-y$ direction
31.33 $0.70/\Omega \cdot$ m
31.35 0.58 V
31.37 + 0.52 A
31.39 (a) 2.8 V, (b) 4.5 V
31.41 (a) 13 mA, (b) 14 mA, (c) 92 mW
31.43 890 nm
31.45 (a) 400 m², (b) 570 m²
31.47 (a) 2.06 eV, (b) 2.39×10^4 K
31.49 (a) 3.4×10^{-3} Ω, (b) 4.35×10^{-3} m²/V · s, (c) 4.35×10^{-2} m/s
31.51 (a) No current passes through the lower diode. (b) No current passes through the upper diode. (c) yes

32.3 1.022 MeV
32.5 1.17×10^{19} J, 585 years
32.7 Photons emerge in opposite directions, each with an energy of 0.511 MeV.
32.9 160 m_e
32.13 105.2 MeV
32.15 (a) 0.055 m, (b) 7.68 m
32.17 6.9×10^6
32.19 7×10^{-20} kg · m · s^{-1}
32.21 1.7 m
32.23 (a) 6.2×10^{-20} m, (b) 5.2×10^{-5} R_0
32.25 (a) $3.8 \times 10^{14}/$m³, (b) 190 km
32.27 (a) cannot take place: reaction does not conserve baryon number, (b) allowed, (c) cannot take place: reaction does not conserve charge.
32.29 $\bar{u}\,\bar{u}\,\bar{d}$
32.31 (a) can occur, (b) cannot occur, (c) can occur, (d) can occur
32.33 −536 MeV; The reaction requires energy.
32.35 (a) 2.5×10^{31} molecules, 7.5×10^5 kg, 750 m³
32.37 (a) 38 MeV, (b) 96 MeV/c

Photo Credits

Chapter 1—Opener: © Stone/Matt Lambert; 1.1: © Tom Pantages; 1.2a,b: © Jones & Childers; 1.5: © NASA; 1.9: © Jones & Childers; 1.10a: © Stone/NASA; 1.10b: © Visuals Unlimited/Stanley Flegler; 1.10c: © Tom Stack & Associates/Bill & Sally Fletcher; 1.10d: © PhotoEdit/Michael Newman; 1.10e: © Visuals Unlimited/Science VU; Box 1.1: © Lucent Technologies.

Chapter 2—Opener: © Stone/Jess Stock; 2.21: © Tom Stack & Associates/Spencer Swanger; 2.25: © Boeing; 2.27 top: © Ben Rose; 2.27 bottom: © Ben Rose; 2.29: © Six Flags Over Georgia; Box 2.1: © Bettmann/Corbis; Box 2.2: © Fundamental Photographs/Richard Megna.

Chapter 3—Opener: © Stone/Stuart Westmorland; 3.23: © Fundamental Photographs/Richard Megna; 3.25: © Jones & Childers; 3.35: © Stone.

Chapter 4—Opener: © AllSport USA/Andrew D. Bernstein; 4.2: © Jones & Childers; 4.5a: © Jones & Childers; 4.7a: © Jones & Childers; 4.8a: © Sports Illustrated/Andy Hayt; 4.8b: © Image Bank-Boston/Marc Romanelli; 4.8c: © Jones & Childers; 4.9: © Lockheed Martin Aeronautical; 4.13a: © Jones & Childers; 4.16: © NASA; 4.23: © Uzi Landman and W.D. Luedtke, School of Physics, Georgia Institute of Technology, Atlanta, GA; 4.24: © Stone/Ambrose Greenway; 4.33: © Stone/David Ball; Box 4.1: © Bettmann/Corbis; Box 4.2: © NASA; Box 4.3: © AllSport USA/Craig Jones; Box 4.4: © Courtesy of Goodyear Tire & Rubber Company.

Chapter 5—Opener: © JPL/NASA; 5.4: © Photri/McCauley; 5.5: © Image Bank-Boston/Steve Dunwell; 5.9: © Six Flags Over Georgia; 5.13: © International Equipment Company; 5.17: © NASA; 5.22: © Jones & Childers; 5.25: © Six Flags Over Georgia; 5.26: © NASA; Box 5.1: © Bettmann/Corbis; Box 5.2: © Courtesy of Intelsat.

Chapter 6—Opener: © Image Bank/Terje Rakke; 6.7: © Visuals Unlimited/M. & D. Long; 6.8: © FPG International/Jeff Divine; 6.9: © Tom Stack & Associates/Greg Vaughn; 6.14: © Sports Chrome; 6.20: © Image Bank/Andre Gallant; Pg. 200: © Jeff Greenberg/Visuals Unlimited; Box 6.3: © Stone/Bruce Ayres.

Chapter 7—Opener: © Stone/World Perspectives; 7.1: © AllSport USA/Mike Powell; 7.6: © Stone/Charles Thatcher; 7.15: © NASA.

Chapter 8—Opener: © Image Bank/Gary S. Chapman; 8.2: © Fundamental Photographs/Richard Megna; 8.10: © Photo Researchers, Inc./Bernice Abbott; 8.13, 8.15: © PhotoDisc; 8.19: © Space Telescope Science Institute; 8.20: © Janice Olson & Associates/© Arbor Scientific; Box 8.1: © Jones & Childers; Box 8.2: © Visuals Unlimited/Richard C. Walters; Box 8.3: © Visuals Unlimited/L. Connor; Box 8.4: © Visuals Unlimited/Science VU; Box 8.5: © Tom Stack & Associates/Charlie Palek.

Chapter 9—Opener: © Jones & Childers; U9.1: © Image Bank; © AllSport USA/Vandystadt; 9.25a: © Sports Illustrated/Heinz Kluetmeier; 9.26a: © Sports Chrome/Rob Tringali Jr.; 9.26b: © Sports Chrome/Rob Tringali Jr.; 9.33: © NHPA/Angence Nature; 9.35: © Ringling Bros.; Box 9.1: © FPG International/Richard H. Smith; Box 9.2b, Box 9.3a, Box 9.4a,b: © Jones & Childers.

Chapter 10—Opener: © Stephen Frisch Photography; 10.6a: © Cenco; Ex. 10.3: © Rick Smoak/Rick Smoak Photography; 10.11: © Courtesy of Goodyear Tire & Rubber Company; Pg. 318: © R.D. Edge; 10.14: © The Harold E. Edgerton Foundation, 1997, Courtesy of Palm Press, Inc.; 10.15: © Jones & Childers; 10.17: © Image Bank-Boston/Joe Devenney; 10.24: © University of Minnesota/This image was generated from simulations carried out by the Team for Advanced Flow Simulation and Modeling at the Army HPC Research Center, Minneapolis, Minnesota; 10.25: © Image Bank-Boston/Peter Miller; 10.26: © Illinois Institute of Technology/Photography by Thomas Corke & Hassan Narib/Fluid Dynamic Research Center; 10.27c: © F.N.M. Brown; 10.31: © AllSport USA/Todd Bodine; Box 10.3: © E.R. Weibel, Department of Anatomy, University of Berne; Box 10.7: © Lockheed Martin Aeronautical.

Chapter 11—Opener: © Tom Stack & Associates/TSADO/NASA; 11.1: © Jones & Childers; 11.3: © Jones & Childers; 11.8a: © Triborough Bridge and Tunnel Authority; 11.8b: © William E. Ferguson Ph.D.; 11.9c: © Jones & Childers; 11.12a: © Stone/Thomas Del Brase; 11.12b, 11.15: © Jones & Childers; Pg. 361: © B. Mahoney/The Image Works Inc.; Box 11.1: © Jones & Childers.

Chapter 12—Opener: © Visuals Unlimited/Gerald & Buff Corsi; 12.3: © The Granger Collection; 12.4a-c: © Jones & Childers; 12.11: © Bettmann/UPI/Corbis; Box 12.1: © Skyship Cruise Ltd.; Box 12.2: © Tom Stack & Associates/Spencer Swanger.

Chapter 13—Opener: © Stone/Donovan Reese; 13.5: © University of South Carolina/Thomas Cooper Library; 13.7a: © SIU/Visuals Unlimited; 13.8a: © Photri; 13.8b: © Photri/B. Tippenreyter; 13.8c: U.S. Department of Defense; 13.15a,b: © Jones & Childers; 13.16a: © FPG International/Eugene Gebhardt; 13.16b: © George Steinmetz; 13.16c: © Jones & Childers; 13.17: Courtesy of Tennessee Valley Authority.

Chapter 14—Opener: © Unicorn Stock Photos/Pamela Whiting; 14.13: © Digital Instruments, Inc.

Chapter 15—Opener: © Stone/John Turner; 15.9: © Jones & Childers; 15.10b: © FPG International/Visual Horizons; 15.10c: © Barry Blanchard; 15.10d: © AT&T Archives; 15.11a,b: © Prof. Bill Melton, UNC Charlotte; 15.13a: © Photo Researchers, Inc.; 15.13b: © AllSport USA/Kirk Schlea; © 15.15a: © The Harold E. Edgerton Foundation, 1997, Courtesy of Palm Press, Inc.; 15.15b: © NASA Langley Research Center/Dr. Leonard Weinstein; 15.19: © Jones & Childers.

Chapter 16—Opener: © Tom Stack & Associates/Wm. L. Wantland; 16.1: © Tom Pantages; 16.2: © FPG International/Michael Stoklos; 16.13c, 16.16b, 16.17b: © Tom Pantages; 16.23: © Museum of Science, Boston.

Chapter 17—Opener: © Museum of Science, Boston; 17.6: © Tom Pantages; 17.7: © National Electrostatics Corporation; 17.8: © Photo Researchers, Inc./George Bernard; 17.12a,b: © Jones & Childers; 17.14b: © Tom Pantages; 17.21: © Jones & Childers; Box 17.2: © The Granger Collection/Currier & Ives.

Chapter 18—Opener: © Stone/Paul Dance; 18.1: © Stock Montage; 18.2: © Jones & Childers; 18.3: © Jones & Childers; 18.10: © Tom Pantages; 18.13a, 18.15a,b: © Jones & Childers; Box 18.2: © Westlight/Chuck O'Rear; Box 18.4: © Bruce Ayres/Tony Stone Images.

Chapter 19—Opener: © Visuals Unlimited/C.P. George; 19.1: © Tom Stack & Associates/Jon Feingersh; 19.3c: © Jones & Childers; 19.4a: © Jones & Childers; 19.4b,c: © Jones & Childers; 19.6a: © Danmarks Tekniske Museum; 19.8b: © Jones & Childers; 19.33: © Argonne National Laboratory; 19.32a,b: © G. E. Medical Systems; Box 19.1: © Photo Researchers, Inc./CNRI/Science Photo Library; Box 19.2: © G. E. Medical Systems.

Chapter 20—Opener: © Visuals Unlimited/Milton H. Tierney, Jr.; 20.1: © The Granger Collection/Thomas Phillips; 20.15: © Jones & Childers; 20.16a,b: DENSO Research Laboratories; 20.18a,b: © Jones & Childers; 20.20: © Cavendish Laboratory, University of Cambridge Department of Physics; 20.21a: © Jones & Childers; Box 20.2: © Varian.

Chapter 21—Opener: © Stone/Jon Riley; Pg. 665: © David J. Sams/Stock, Boston.

Chapter 22—Opener: © Stone/Pete Saloutos; 22.1: © IBM Corporation/Almaden Research; 22.3: © Jones & Childers; 22.6, 22.8a, 22.10b: © Jones & Childers; 22.12b: © Stone/Franz Edson; 22.13a: © Jones & Childers; 22.13b: © Photo Researchers, Inc./Deep Light Productions; 22.14b,c,e, 22.36a,b: © Jones & Childers.

Chapter 23—Opener: © PhotoDisc; 23.6a,b,c: © Jones & Childers; 23.8a: © Nikon; 23.13: © Canon U.S.A.; 23.15: © Jones & Childers; 23.16: © Jones & Childers; Box 23.1: © MMT Observatory; Box 23.2: © European Southern Observatory.

Chapter 24—Opener: © Visuals Unlimited/John D. Cunningham; 24.1: © Jones & Childers; 24.5: © Bill Melton, UNC Charlotte; 24.6: © Bill Melton, UNC Charlotte; 24.7a: © Bill Melton, UNC Charlotte; 24.9a,b, 24.10: © Bill Melton, UNC Charlotte; 24.11b: © Jones & Childers; 24.12: © University of South Carolina/Thomas Cooper Library; 24.15: © Jones & Childers; 24.18a,b: © Bill Melton, UNC Charlotte; 24.19: © Fundamental Photographs; 24.20: © Jones & Childers; 24.24a, 24.25: © Jones & Childers; 24.28, 24.29: © Space Telescope Science Institute; 24.30: © NASA; 24.31: © Electron Microscopy Center, The University of South Carolina;

24.42, 24.45: © Jones & Childers; 24.47: © University of Notre Dame/Paul Chagnon.

Chapter 25—Opener: © Stock Montage; 25.14: © Palomar Observatory/California Institute of Technology; 25.21a: © Space Telescope Science Institute; 25.21b: © Space Telescope Science Institute; Box 25.1: © Photo Researchers, Inc./Science Photo Library; Box 25.2: © Anglo-Australian Observatory/David Malin; Box 25.4C, Box 25.4L, Box 25.4R: © Dr. Ping Kang Hsiung;

Chapter 26—Opener: © Tom Stack & Associates/Brian Parker; Pg. 824: © Bettmann/Corbis; Pg. 824: © American Institute of Physics; Pg. 824: © American Institute of Physics; Pg. 825: © American Institute of Physics; Pg. 825: © American Institute of Physics; Pg. 825: © American Institute of Physics; Pg. 835: © Will & Deni McIntyre/Photo Researchers; 26.1a,b: © Jones & Childers; 26.1c,d: © University of South Carolina/Thomas Cooper Library; Pg. 843: © Tim Dominick/The State Newspaper; 26.6: © Jones & Childers; 26.8b, 26.9: © Reynolds Historical Library; © Jones & Childers; 26.10: © University of South Carolina/X-Ray Laboratory; 26.14a: © National Gallery of Art; 26.14b: © National Gallery of Art; 26.17a,b: © Tom Pantages; Box 26.2a: © Erwin W. Mueller; Box 26.2b: © Erwin W. Mueller; Box 26.3: © Park Scientific Instruments.

Chapter 27—Opener: © Sony; Pg. 854: © Bettmann/Corbis; Pg. 854: © American Institute of Physics; Pg. 854: © Stock Montage; Pg. 855: © Stock Montage; Pg. 855: © Stock Montage; Pg. 855: © American Institute of Physics; 27.1: © Jones & Childers; 27.2a: © Fundamental Photographs/Wabash Instrument Corporation; 27.2b,c,d,e: © Fundamental Photographs/Wabash Instrument Corporation; 27.4a: © Jones & Childers; 27.4b: © Jones & Childers; Box 27.2: © Anglo-Australian Observatory/Royal Observatory Edinburgh.

Chapter 28—Opener: © Stone/John McDermott; © Bettmann/Corbis; 28.1: © Edmund Scientific Company; 28.4: © Omicron Associates; 28.5a,b,c: © University of South Carolina, Electron Microscopy Center; Box 28.3: © University of South Carolina, Electron Microscopy Center.

Chapter 29—Opener: © Photo Researchers, Inc./Stevie Grand/Science Photo Library; Pg. 927: © Dr. Robert Friedland/Science Photo Library/Photo Researchers, Inc.; Pg. 931: © Tom White/Palmetto Baptist Medical Center; Pg. 932 and Pg. 934: © Jones & Childers; U29.4: © Jones & Childers; 29.14; © University of Tennessee/Edward L. Hart; 29.15: © CERN; 29.18: © Smithsonian Institution/MIT/Science Services; 29.24: © Oak Ridge National Laboratory; Box 29.1: © American Institute of Physics.

Chapter 30—Opener: © American Bank Note; 30.7: © Siemens Components, Inc., Isalin, NJ; 30.11a,b,c, 30.16, 30.18, 30.20a, 30.25a,b: © Jones & Childers; 30.26: © ERIM; 30.27: © Electro Optical Industries; Box 30.2: © Jones & Childers.

Chapter 31—Opener: © Stone/Rene Sheret; 31.3: © Oak Ridge National Lab; 31.4: © Jones & Childers; 31.5b: © Digital Instruments Inc., Santa Barbara, CA; 31.8, 31.20: © Jones & Childers; 31.28: © AT&T Archives; 31.33, 31.34, 31.35: © Jones & Childers.

Chapter 32—Opener: © Stone/John Warden; 32.1a, 32.3a: © Lawrence Berkeley Laboratory, University of California; Pg. 1005: © Jones & Childers; 32.4a,b: © DESY, Hamburg, Germany; 32.5: © Aerometric; 32.6b: © DESY, Hamburg, Germany; 32.8a: © PhotoDisc; 32.8b: © Fermilab; 32.8c: © NASA; 32.10: © National Geographic Society Image Collection/Joe Stancampiano; 32.11, 32.12: © NASA; Box 32.1: © NASA Goddard Flight Center; Box 32.2: © NASA.

Index

Note: Page numbers followed by *def.* refer to definitions; page numbers followed by *tab* refer to tables.

A

Aberrations, lens, 711–714
Abscissa, 33*def.*
Absolute zero, 348*def.*
Absorbed dose, 931
Absorption spectra, 854
ac (alternating current), 636
Acceleration, 40–44
   air resistance and, 49
   angular, 265*def.*, 266
   average, 40–42, 40*def.*, 78
   centripetal, 148*def.*, 150–151, 266
   constant, 44–48, 44*def.*, 47*tab.*,
     106–107, 107*tab.*
   force and, 106–107
   free fall and, 48–52, 49*tab.*
   graphical interpretation of, 42–43
   of gravity, 49–50, 110
   instantaneous, 42–44, 42*def.*,
     78–79
   of mass on spring, 437
   in simple harmonic motion, 440
   tangential, 265
   units of, 108*tab.*
Accelerator, 1011–1013
   charged-particle, 607–609
   linear, 649
Accommodation, by eye, 722–724
Acoustics, 463
   room, 475
Actinium series, 924
Action potential, 669
Action-reaction forces, 112–116
Active medium, 951
Activity, 842
Addition
   parallelogram method of, 66, 67
   triangle method of, 66
   vector, 65–68, 69–71
Adhesion, molecular, 320–321
Adiabatic process, 406, 409
   of Carnot cycle, 413, 414
Aerodynamic drag, 332

Air
   light reflection from, 757
   pressure of, 374–376
Air column, waves in, 486–487
Air conditioner, 418–420
Air pump, 375–376
Air track, 103, 106, 216
Airfoil, 330
Airplane
   flight of, 330
   motion within, 104
Airship, 317, 378
ALEPH detector, for radioactivity, 930
Allowed band, for electrons, 985
Alpha radiation, 184–185, 840–841,
     841*tab.*, 913, 925–926
   quality factor for, 932*tab.*
   scattering of, 845–846
Alternating current, 636
   transformer for, 640–642
Alternating current circuit
   capacitive time constant of, 665
   effective values of, 667–668, 670
   impedance and, 675
   inductive time constant of, 663
   RC, 664–667
   reactance and, 670–673
   resonant, 676–678
   RL, 662–664
   RLC, 673–676
Alternators, 635–639
Altitude sickness, 392
Alveoli, 323
Amber, 496
Ammeter, 615
Amorphous solids, 975, 976
Ampere (A), 559*def.*, 610–611
Amplitude, in simple harmonic
     motion, 439*def.*
Ampère-Maxwell law, 648
Ampère's law, 616–618, 646*tab.*
Analysis, 5*def.*
Aneroid barometer, 315

Angle
   Bragg, 834
   Brewster, 774–775
   critical, 691–692*def.*
   radian measure of, 146*def.*
Angle of incidence, 685–687,
     691–692
Angle of reflection, 685–687, 747
Angle of refraction, 689–690, 747–748
Angular acceleration, 265*def.*
   vs. centripetal acceleration, 266
   and torque, 282
Angular frequency, 151*def.*
Angular magnification, 727*def.*, 733
Angular momentum, 184–185,
     286–287, 287*def.*
   conservation of, 287–291
   quantization of, 868
Angular velocity, 151*def.*, 264–267,
     265*def.*
Antinode, 482
Antiparticles, 1004–1006
Antireflection coating, 758
Appearance of moving objects, 800
Arch bridge, 280
Archimedes' principle, 315, 317–320
Area under a curve, 39
ARGUS detector, 1013
Aristotle, 50, 109, 823
Arterioles, blood flow through,
     328–329
Aspheric lens, 713, 738
Astigmatism, 724
Astronomical telescope, 734
Astronomical unit (AU), 160*def.*
Atmosphere (atm), 309*tab.*, 375*def.*
Atmospheric pressure, 309, 315,
     374–376
Atom(s), 823–825. *See also* Atomic
     nucleus; Electrons
   Bohr's theory of, 867–872
   decay of, 841–842. *See also*
     Radiation

Atom(s)—*Cont.*
  energy states of, 862–870, 950, 977, 979–981
  ground state of, 869–870
  metastable state of, 952
  microscopic viewing of, 839
  observation of, 839
  plum-pudding model of, 844
  size of, 830–831
  spectroscopic study of, 853–858
  structure of, 844–847
  wave function of, 900
  wave theory of, 898–900
Atomic clock, 8, 812–813
Atomic force microscope, 446–447
Atomic mass, 919–920, 920*tab.*
Atomic mass number, 916
Atomic nucleus, 845–847
  binding energy of, 919–921
  composition of, 916
  daughter, 921, 923
  discovery of, 844–847
  energy of, 919–921
  fission of, 938–941
  forces of, 918–921
  hard sphere model, 917
  isotope, 916, 917
  liquid drop model, 939
  mass of, 919–920, 920*tab.*
  neutron of, 913–915, 915*tab.*, 1010*tab.*
  parent, 921, 923
  proton of, 913, 915*tab.*, 1010*tab.*, 1018–1019
  proton-electron model of, 914
  proton-neutron model of, 916
  Q value of, 923, 936, 939
  radius of, 846–847, 917–918
  stability of, 841–844, 921–924.
    See also Radiation
  strong force of, 102, 918–919, 1005, 1008–1009, 1015*tab.*
  weak force of, 103, 1015*tab.*, 1018–1019
Atomic number, 916
Atomic theory
  of Bohr, 867–870
  of Dalton, 825
Atomic weight, 916
Atwood, George, 116
Atwood's machine, 116–118, 116*def.*, 295
Audio frequency, 471
Aurora australis, 1007
Aurora borealis, 1007
Automobile(s)
  air flow around, 331, 332
  average net force for, 185

  battery-operated, 428
  collision of, 218–219, 222–223
  forces on, 154–155, 156–157
Automobile tires
  friction of, 127
  gauge pressure of, 309, 383–384
Average acceleration, 40–42, 40*def.*, 78
Average angular acceleration, 265*def.*
Average speed, 29*def.*
Average velocity, 30–31*def.*, 78
Avogadro, Amadeo, 825
Avogadro's number, 381, 826, 827–830

B

Back emf, 638–639
Background radiation, 932, 933*tab.*
Balance
  center of mass and, 274
  torsional, 167, 499
Ballistic pendulum, 220–221
Balloons, 378, 388
  gas laws and, 378, 380
Balmer, Johann, 854
Balmer lines, 857
Balmer series, 855, 857–858, 871–872
Balmer's formula, 855
Band theory, of solids, 984–987
Banked curve, 156–157
Bar magnet, 595–596
Barium, emission spectrum of, 854
Barometer, 315
Barometric formula, 390–394
Barrier penetration, of particles, 897–898
  and alpha decay, 925
Baryons, 1009, 1010*tab.*, 1014
  quark composition of, 1016, 1016*tab.*
Basal metabolic rate, 202
Base units, 7–11, 7*def.*, 7*tab.*
  conversions of, 11–12
  prefixes for, 9–11
  symbols for, 8–9
Baseball
  air flow about, 334, 335
  forces on, 211, 212–213
  projectile motion of, 85–86, 333
Battery, 558–559, 560
  internal resistance of, 581–583
  terminal potential difference of, 582
Beats, 487, 489
Becquerel (Bq), 841, 931
Becquerel, Henri, 824, 840
Beta minus particle, 926

Beta plus particle (positron), 926
Beta radiation, 840–841, 841*tab.*, 913, 926–928
  quality factor for, 932*tab.*
Bicycle pedal, torque on, 271–272
Bifocal lenses, 724
Big Bang theory, 4–5, 1019–1022
Billiard balls, collision of, 224, 236, 237, 242–245
Bimetallic strip, 352
Binding energy, of nucleus, 919–921
Binoculars, 735
Binomial theorem, A–1
Biological effects of radiation, 931–935
Biot-Savart law, 609
Black hole, 256–257
Blackbody, 2–3
Blackbody radiation, 2–4, 365, 858–861
Blimp, 317
Blood flow, 328–329
  Doppler measurement of, 477
Blood flow meter, 635
Blood pressure, 316
Body fat, by hydrostatic weighing, 317–318
Body heat, radiative loss of, 366
Bohr frequency condition, 867
Bohr magneton, 901
Bohr, Niels, 855, 867–868, 881
Bohr radii, 868
Boiling, 360
Boltzmann constant, 388*def.*
Boltzmann, Ludwig, 425
Born, Max, 894
Boundary layer, in fluid flow, 334
Boxcars, collision of, 240–241
Boyle, Robert, 49, 376
Boyle's law, 376–377
Bragg angle, 834
Bragg, William Henry, 825, 833, 872
Bragg, William Lawrence, 825, 833–834
Bragg's law, 833–834
Brahe, Tycho, 97, 157, 683
Breaking stress, 281
Brewster angle, 774–775
Brewster's law, 774–775
Bridges, 280–281, 351
British thermal unit (Btu), 354, 356*tab.*
Brownian motion, 828–830
Bubble chamber, 930
Bullet, speed of, 220–221
Buoyancy, 315, 317–320
Buoyant force, 317–319, 317*def.*, 329
Burn, steam, 361
Butterfly, 246

C

Calorie, 202, 202*tab.*, 355, 356*tab.*
Calorimetry, 356–360
Camera, 712, 713, 728–732
Capacitance, 539*def.*
  dielectrics and, 545–548
  of parallel capacitors, 578–579
  of series capacitors, 579–580
Capacitive reactance, 672
Capacitive time constant, 665
Capacitors, 539–540, 539*def.*
  in combination, 578–581
  dielectrics of, 545–548
  energy density of, 549
  energy storage in, 548–550
  in parallel, 578–579, 580
  parallel-plate, 540–542
  in series, 579–580, 581
Capillary action, 321–322
Carbon composition resistor, 563
Carbon-14, half-life of, 843–844
Carbon-zinc dry cells, 582
Carnot cycle, 413–417
  efficiency, 414–415
  reverse, 417–420
Carnot engine, 412–417
Carnot, Sadi, 412
Cartesian coordinate system, 27
Cathode rays, 832, 835–838
Cavendish, Henry, 167
Cell, electric, 558
Celsius temperature scale, 347*def.*, 348, 349
Centaurus A galaxy, 798
Center of gravity, 162, 273
Center of mass, 273–274, 273*def.*, 801
  balance and, 274
  human, 274
Centrifuge, 155–156
Centripetal acceleration, 148*def.*, 150–151, 266
Cesium chloride, crystal structure of, 977
Cesium-beam clock, 8
Chadwick, James, 914
Chain reaction, 939, 940
Changing mass, 225–226
Charge carriers, density of, 988–990
Charge, electric
  conservation of, 497–498
  elementary, 500
  fractional, 500, 1015
  positive and negative, 497
  quantization of, 500, 826
Charged-particle accelerator, 607–609
Charles and Gay-Lussac's law, 379–381, 380*def.*

Charles, J. A. C., 378
Charm (quantum number), 1016
Chemical atomic mass, 916
Cherenkov radiation, 941
Chromatic abberation, 712
Circuit, 559*def.*
  alternating-current, 662–668, 670
  energy in, 565, 567–571
  ground potential of, 572
  household, 583–585
  Kirchhoff's rules of, 572–578
  open, 571, 572
  power in, 565, 567–571
  RC, 664–667
  resonant, 676–678
  RL, 662–664
  RLC, 673–676
  rms, 668
  short, 571–572
  symbols for, 567
Circuit breaker, 584, 585
Circular current loop, magnetic field of, 611, 614
Circular motion, 146–152
  angular frequency of, 151*def.*
  angular velocity of, 151*def.*
  force for, 152–157
  frequency of, 149*def.*
  period of, 149*def.*
  simple harmonic motion and, 438–440
  uniform, 146–152, 147*def.*
Circumference
  of circle, 13, 146
  of earth, 147
Classical mechanics, 97
Clausius, Rudolph, 421, 422
Clocks, 8, 9*def.*
  in motion, 794–795, 812–813
  at rest, 795
COBE, 5, 1020
Coefficient, drag, 332, 332*tab.*
Coefficient of friction, 124, 124*tab.*
Coefficient of performance
  of heat pump, 418–419, 418*def.*
  of refrigerator, 418*def.*, 419
Coefficient of thermal expansion
  linear, 350–352, 350*def.*, 353*tab.*
  volume, 352–354, 352*def.*, 353*tab.*
Coherent fiber bundle, 693, 694
Coherent light, 955–957
Cohesion, molecular, 320–321
Cold weld, 126
Collimating lens, 771
Collision(s)
  elastic, 216, 235–236, 264*def.*
    between equal masses, 237, 244–245

    in one dimension, 236–242
    in two dimensions, 242–245
    between unequal masses, 238–239, 240–241
  inelastic, 216, 217, 236*def.*
  perfectly inelastic, 216–224, 216*def.*
  conservation of momentum in, 216–221, 223
    in one dimension, 216–221
    in two dimensions, 221–224
Color filters, 965
Color television, 966
Color temperature, 962*def.*, 964*tab.*
Color vision, 866
Colors, by addition, 965
Coma, 711
Commutator, 636
Compact disc optical system, 997
Compact disc stamping die, 447
Complementary, 966
  light and, 962, 964–965
  primary, 965, 966
  in scapfilm, 756
  by subtraction, 966, 967
  of visible spectrum, 962*tab.*
Components of vectors, 68–69
Compound microscope, 732–734
Compression, of longitudinal waves, 469
Compressive strain, 279*def.*
Compton, Arthur, 880, 882–883
Compton effect, 882–884
Compton wavelength, 884
Concave lens, 696
Concave mirrors, 707–710
Condensed matter, 974–977
Condenser, 539
Conduction, thermal, 363
Conductivity, electrical, 981–984, 982*def.*
Conductor(s), 497*def.*
  electric field inside, 512
  electric resistance of, 561–562
  electron flow through, 559–560, 981–984
  equipotential surface of, 537
  resistivity of, 563–565, 565*tab.*
Cones, retinal, 866
Conic sections, A–2
Conservation law(s), 192
  of angular momentum, 287–291
  of electric charge, 497–498
  of linear momentum, 214–216, 223, 801, 802–805
  of mechanical energy, 189–197, 293–295
  symmetry and, 246–247
Conservative force, 189–190

Constant acceleration, 44–48, 44*def.*, 47*tab.*, 106–107, 107*tab.*
Contact force, 102
Continuity, equation of, 322, 324
Continuous wave laser, 953–954
Convection, in heat transfer, 363
Converging lenses, 694–696, 704
Conversion factor, 11
Convex lens, 701
Convex mirrors, 710–711
Cooling, by evaporation, 361
Coordinate system, 27
    versus reference frame, 28
Copenhagen interpretation, 881
Copernicus, Nicolas, 97
Copper sulfate, magnetic susceptibility of, 620
Correspondence principle, of Niels Bohr, 881–882
Cosine, of angle, 94*def.*
Cosmic radiation, 5, 6, 933*tab.*, 1007
Cosmology, 1019–1022
Coulomb (C), 500
Coulomb, Charles, 499
Coulomb's law, 499–503
Couple, 272*def.*
Critical angle, 691–692*def.*
Critical damping, 452
Crookes, Sir William, 832
Crookes' tube, 832
Crystal(s), 823–824, 832–835, 974–976. *See also* Metals; Semiconductors
    band model of, 984–987
    covalent, 976, 977
    diffraction, 832–834
    electric conductivity and, 981–984
    free-electron model of, 977, 979–981
    grains of, 975
    ionic, 975–976
    liquid, 975, 978
    metallic, 976–977, 979–981
    single, 975
    tunneling microscopy of, 974–975
    unit cell of, 974
Crystalline solid, 974
Curie (Ci), 931
Curie law, 619
Curie temperature (TC), 621
Curie-Weiss law, 621
Current. *See also* Electric current
Current density, 981–982, 981*def.*
Cyclotron, 607–609

D

Dalton, John, 825
Damping, of harmonic oscillator, 449, 451–453

Dark matter, 1022
D'Arsonval, Jacques Arséne, 615–616
Davisson, C. J., 881, 887
dc (direct current), 636
De Broglie, Louis, 880, 885
De Broglie waves, 885–887
De Motu, 99
Decay, radioactive, 841–844, 921–928
Decibel, 473*def.*
Defibrillator, 586, 665
Definite proportions, law of, 824
Degree (temperature interval), 347
Delta (D), 28*def.*
Delta (D) *x,* 28
Deltoid muscle, 277–278
Democritus, 823
Density, 310*def.*, 310*tab.*
    current, 981–982
    of earth, 164–165, 167
    probability, 894
    unit of, 310
Depletion zone, of semiconductors, 991
Detectors in elementary particle physics, 930, 1011–1013
Deuteron, magnetic forces on, 606–607
Dewer flask, 367
Diamagnetism, 619
Diamond, crystal structure of, 977
Dielectric, 545–548
    strength of, 545*tab.*, 547*def.*
Dielectric constant, 545*def.*, 545*tab.*
Diffraction, 759–761, 759*def.*
    electron, 887, 894–895
    multiple-slit, 762–764
    single-slit, 759–761
    x-ray, 832–835
Diffraction grating, 763
Dimension, 7, 7*def.*
Diode, 992–993
    laser, 997
    light-emitting, 996–997
Diode laser pointer, 882
Diopter, 724*def.*
Dipole
    electric, 516–518, 516*def.*
        moment of, 517*def.*
    magnetic, 595–596*def.*
        moment of, 598*def.*
Dirac, Paul A. M., 1004
Direct current, 559. *See also* Electric current
Direct current generator, 636–637
Dispersion, of light, 712–713, 768–770
Displacement, 28*def.*, 31
    graphical interpretation of, 33, 34, 39–40
    of harmonic wave, 465–466
    representation of, 64

Dissipative forces, 198
Diverging lenses, 694, 695, 703
Doping, of semiconductor, 990–991
Doppler effect, 474, 476–478
    relativistic, 807–808, 810–811
Dose equivalent, of radiation exposure, 932, 933*tab.*
Dose, radiation, 931*def.*
    maximum permissible, 932*tab.*
Dosimeter, 932–933
Drag
    form, 331–332
    viscous, 329, 331
Drag coefficient, 332, 332*tab.*
Drift velocity, of electrons, 559
Du Fay, Charles-François, 497
Dynamic equilibrium, 128*def.*, 273
Dynamics, 25*def.*

E

Ear, 488
    sound perception by, 470–471, 472–473
Earth
    circumference of, 147
    density of, 164–165, 167
    escape speed and, 252–257
    magnetic poles of, 596–597
    tides of, 296
Eddington, Sir Arthur S., 425
Effective dose equivalent, of radiation, 932, 933*tab.*
Effective value, of alternating current, 667–668, 670
Efficiency, thermal, 414*def.*
Einstein, Albert, 788, 855, 863
    special relativity of, 786–787
Einstein photoelectric equation, 863–864
Elastic collision, 216, 235–236*def.*
    between equal masses, 237, 244–245
    in one dimension, 236–242
    in two dimensions, 242–245
    between unequal masses, 238–239, 240–241
Elastic limit, 279, 281
Elastic modulus, 279, 279*tab.*
Elastic potential energy, 188–189
Elastic region, 279
Elasticity, 278–279, 281
Electric charge, 496–499
    capacitor storage of, 539–542, 548–550
    of cathode rays, 836–838
    of common objects, 497, 501*tab.*
    conservation of, 497–498
    Coulomb's law of, 499–503

of electron, 838
elementary, 500
quantization of, 500, 826–827
unit for, 500
Electric circuit. *See* Circuit
Electric conductor. *See* Conductor
Electric current, 558–559*def.*,
    558–560, 981–984
alternating, 636, 640–642. *See also*
    Alternating current circuit
density of, 981–982
direct, 559
direction of, 559
hazards of, 586
induced, 629–631
magnetic field of, 598–600,
    609–612, 630–631
magnetic forces on, 602–603
resistance and, 561–563, 982–983
saturation, 993
SI unit for, 559
sign of, 559
Electric current loop, 611–614
Electric dipole, 516–518, 519
Electric field, 505–508, 505*def.*
electric potential and, 532
equipotential surfaces and, 536–537
Gauss's law and, 513–516
of parallel-plate capacitor, 540–542
superposition of, 508–510
uniform, 532
Electric flux, 510–512, 510*def.*
Electric forces, superposition of,
    503–505
Electric generators, 635–639
Electric insulator, 497*def.*
Electric motor, 638–639
Electric potential, 526, 527–532,
    528*def.*
energy and, 536–537
Electric potential difference, 529*def.*,
    tab.
across conductor, 560, 981–982
Electric resistance, 561–563
Electric shock, 586
Electrical conductivity, 981–984,
    982*def.*
Electrocardiogram, 435
Electrocardiography, 669
Electrodynamic flow meter, 635
Electroencephalogram, 669
Electrolysis, 826–827
Electromagnetic energy
in capacitor, 548–550
of electric dipole, 518
in electric field, 548–549
in magnetic field, 644–645
Electromagnetic force, 102, 1015*tab.*,
    1018–1019

Electromagnetic induction, 630
Electromagnetic spectrum, 685
Electromagnetic waves, 648, 650–653
energy density of, 652
irradiance of, 652–653
speed of, 651
Electromagnetism, 495
Electromotive force (emf), 560*def.*
of alternator, 636, 637
back, 638–639
of dc generator, 636, 637
Faraday's law of, 629–631
induced, 629–630, 642–
    644
Lenz's law of, 630–632
motional, 633–635
Electron(s), 915, 1010*tab.*
acceleration of, 507
charge of, 836–838
Compton wavelength of, 884
de Broglie wavelength of, 885–886
diffraction of, 887, 894–895
discovery of, 835–838
drift velocity of, 559, 982
electric potential energy of, 530
energy states of, 862–870, 950,
    977, 979–981
energy-level diagram of, 871
Fermi energy of, 979–980
ground state of, 869
Hall effect and, 988–990
mass of, 838
of metallic crystal, 977, 979–981
mobility of, 983*def.*
momentum of, 883
photoelectric emission of, 861–866,
    863*tab.*
probability density for, 894–895
quantum numbers for, 905–907
Schrödinger's equation for, 889
of semiconductors, 987–991
spin of, 904–905
wavelength of, 884, 885–886, 889
Electron capture, 926, 927
Electron microscope, 768, 888
Electron volt (eV), 535–536, 535*def.*,
    864
Electroscope, 498–499
Electrostatic force(s)
Coulomb's law of,
    499–503
Gauss's law of, 510–512
Electrostatic generator, Van de Graaff,
    533–535
Electrostatics, 496*def.*
Electroweak force, 1018
Elementary charge, 500
Elementary particles, 1013–1015,
    1015*tab.*

e/m, 837
Embossed hologram, 963
emf. *See* Electromotive force
Emission spectrum, 854
Emissivity, 365–366
Endoscopes, 693–694
Energy, 176, 181–182, 181*def.*, 799,
    801
alternative sources of, 427–428
of atom, 862–870, 950, 977,
    979–981
of atomic nucleus, 919–921
capacitor storage of, 548–550
conservation of, 189–197, 293–295
of electric circuit, 565, 567–571
electric potential and, 536–537
of electromagnetic wave, 652–653
entropy and, 425
in exercise, 202
Fermi, 979–980
of fission, 938–941
in food, 202
of fusion, 943–944
of harmonic oscillator, 442–444
internal, 389–390, 405*def.*
kinetic, 182–185. *See also* Kinetic
    energy
of magnetic field, 644–645
mass change and, 799, 801–802
nuclear, 919–921, 938–941,
    943–944
potential, 185–189. *See also*
    Potential energy
quantization of, 4, 896–897
radiation of, 363–367
rotational, 291–293, 292*def.*
thermal pollution and, 426–428
total, 191*def.*
transformation of, 182
units of, 182, 182*tab.*, 355, 356*tab.*
wave transfer of, 467–468
work and, 181–182
zero-point, 897
Energy density, of electric field, 549
Energy gap, 986*tab.*
Energy levels
atomic, 897, 899
diagrams, 193
nuclear, 928
Engine, 410–417
Carnot, 412–417
Diesel, 412, 416
gasoline, 416
heat, 407, 408, 410–417
Otto, 412, 416
reversible, 415
steam, 410–411
thermal efficiency of, 414*def.*,
    415*tab.*

Entropy
    second law of thermodynamics and, 422–426
    statistics of, 425–426
    of universe, 426
Equal-tempered scale, 485
Equation(s)
    Bernoulli's, 324–326
    for constant acceleration in one dimension, 44–45, 47*tab.*
    of continuity, 322, 324
    kinematic, 267*tab.*
    Poiseuille's, 327
    quadratic, 62
    Schrödinger's, 889
    simultaneous, 143–144
    of state, 381
    thin-lens, 701–707
    for unit conversion, 11
    vector, 78–79
Equilibrium
    of conductor, 512
    dynamic, 128*def.*, 273
    first condition for, 272
    rotational, 273
    second condition for, 273
    static, 128–132, 128*def.*, 272–278
    thermal, 345, 346, 366, 404–405
    translational, 128*def.*, 272
Equipotential line, 536
Equipotential surface, 536–537, 536*def.*
Equivalent dose, 932
Equivalence principle, 809–813, 812*tab.*
Eratosthenes, 147
Escape speed, 252–257, 253*def.*
Estimate, 15–18
    order-of-magnitude, 15–18
Evaporation, cooling by, 361
Exclusion principle, 904
Exercise
    calories for, 202*tab.*
    energy use in, 202
    power output, 200–201
Expanding universe, 808, 1019
Exponential function, 400–402, 400*tab.*, 401*tab.*
Exposure
    photographic, 730
    radiation, 931, 932–933, 932*tab.*, 933*tab.*
Eye, human, 722–725
    accommodation by, 722–724
    cross section of, 722
    laser surgery on, 957
    light refraction by, 722
    photosensitivity of, 866
    resolution of, 767
Eyepiece, 726, 732, 734

F

Fahrenheit, Gabriel, 349
Fahrenheit temperature scale, 347*def.*, 348, 349
False-color infrared photography, 968, 969
Far point, 723
Farad (F), 539*def.*
Faraday (F), 826*def.*
Faraday cage, 512
Faraday, Michael, 628, 629, 826
Faraday's law, 629–633, 646*tab.*, 648
Farsightedness, 723, 724
Femur, compression of, 281
Fermi energy, 979–980
Fermi theory of beta decay, 927
Fermions, 979
Ferrimagnetism, 621
Ferromagnetism, 596–597, 619, 620–621
Feynman, Richard, 124
Fiber optics, 693–694
Fibrillation, 586
Field
    electric, 505–508. *See also* Electric field
    gravitational, 166, 168
    magnetic, 596–597. *See also* Magnetic field
Field lines, 168, 506
    electric, 506
    and equipotential, 536–537
    gravitational, 168
    magnetic, 597, 599
Film, holographic, 961
Filter
    color, 965–968
    electrical, 995
    uv blocking, 772
First Bohr radius of hydrogen atom, 869
First law of thermodynamics, 405–410
Fission, nuclear, 938–941
Fizeau, Armand Hippolyte Louis, 686
Flight, 330
Flow
    laminar, 322, 324–326, 329, 331
    streamline, 322
    turbulent, 322, 331–332, 333–335
Fluid(s), 307–335, 308*def.*
    Archimedes' principle of, 315, 317–320
    Bernoulli's equation for, 324–326
    boundary layer of, 334
    flow of, 322, 324–326
    form drag and, 331–332
    hydrostatic pressure of, 308–312
    laminar flow of, 322, 324–326, 329, 331
    Pascal's principle of, 312–315
    Poiseuille's law of, 327–329
    speed of, 326
    Stokes's law and, 329, 331–333
    streamline flow of, 322, 324–326
    surface tension of, 320–322
    terminal speed and, 329, 331–333
    turbulent flow of, 322, 331–332, 333–335
    viscosity of, 327–329, 328*tab.*
    viscous drag and, 329, 331
    volume of, 308
Fluorescent lamp, 964–965, 964*def.*
Flux
    electric, 510–511*def.*
    magnetic, 599*def.*
f-number, 730–731, 730*tab.*
Focal length
    of spherical mirror, 708
    of thin lens, 695
Focal point, 695
Foot-pound, 178*def.*
Forbidden zones, for electrons, 985
Force(s), 98*def.*, 100–103, 102*tab.*, 1015*tab.*
    action-reaction, 112–116
    on Atwood's machine, 116–118
    buoyant, 317–319, 317*def.*, 329
    centripetal, 152–153*def.*, 154–157
    conservative, 189–190, 189*def.*
    constant, 106–107, 107*tab.*
    contact, 102
    dissipative, 198
    electric, superposition of, 503–505
    electromagnetic, 102, 1015*tab.*, 1018–1019
    frictional, 123–128, 190, 197–199
    fundamental, 102, 102*tab.*
    gravitational, 102, 160, 162–164, 1015*tab.*, 1018–1019
    impulsive, 211–212
    inverse-square, 97
    lines of, 168
    magnetic, 602–607
    net, 100*def.*
    nonconservative, 190, 197–199
    normal (perpendicular), 111*def.*
    restoring, 435–436
    strong (nuclear), 102, 918–919, 1005, 1008–1009, 1015*tab.*, 1018–1019

torque and, 269–272
unified theory of, 1018–1019
units of, 108*tab.*
varying, 179–181
weak, 103, 1015*tab.*, 1018–1019
weight and, 109–112
work and, 177–181
Forced harmonic motion, 453–455
Form drag, 331–332
Fovea, 866
Fractional, 279
Franklin, Benjamin, 538
Fraunhofer, Joseph, 854–855, 856
Fraunhofer lines, 854–856, 871–872
Free electron model of metals,
    977–981
Free space, permittivity of, 500
Free-body diagram, 116, 117–118
Freely falling bodies, 48–53, 49*tab.*
Frequency, 149*def.*
    angular, 151
    beat, 487, 489
    cyclotron, 607–609, 1011
    Doppler effect and, 474, 476–478
    fundamental, 481*def.*, 482
    harmonic, 481*def.*
    of harmonic oscillator, 445, 454
    infrasonic, 471
    pitch and, 471
    resonant, 454, 481–482, 677
    of sound, 470–471
    spatial, 961
    ultrasonic, 471–472
Fresnel lens, 738, 739
Friction, 123–128, 123*def.*, 190,
    197–199
    of automobile tires, 127
    coefficient of, 124, 124*tab.*
    in electricity production, 496, 497
    in energy transformation, 197–199
    harmonic motion and, 449, 451–453
    kinetic, 124–125
    reduction of, 128
    static, 124–125
Fringe visibility, 956
Frisch, Otto, 938
Fuel rods, 941
Full-wave rectifier circuit, 994–995
Fundamental constants, back end
    pages
Fundamental forces, 102*tab.*
Fundamental frequency, 481*def.*
Fundamental particles, 1003–1019
Fundamental units, 7–11, 7*def.*, 7*tab.*
Fuse, 584
Fusion
    heat of, 360*def.*, 361*tab.*
    nuclear, 943–944

G
Gait, 450
Gal, 167*def.*
Galilean relativity, 785–786
Galilean telescope, 734
Galilean velocity addition formula,
    787
Galileo, 48–53, 81
Galvani, Luigi, 557–558
Galvanometer, 614–615
Gamma knife, 843
Gamma radiation, 840–841, 841*tab.*,
    913, 928
    quality factor for, 932*tab.*
Gas(es)
    Boyle's law of, 376–377
    Charles and Gay-Lussac's law of,
        379–381
    ideal, 385*def.*
    ideal gas law of, 381–384
    internal energy of, 389–390
    kinetic energy of, 388–390
    kinetic theory of, 384–388
    molecular mass of, 381, 382*tab.*
    molecular speeds of, 390–394
Gas constant *R,* 381
Gasoline engines, 416
Gauge pressure, 309, 383–384
Gaussian surface, 511–515, 544
Gauss's law, 511–512, 646*tab.*, 648
    for magnetism, 599
    quantitative approach to,
        513–516
Gay-Lussac, J. L., 378, 825
Gay-Lussac's law, 379–381, 380*def.*
Geiger, Hans, 845
Geiger tube, 928–929
General theory of relativity, 813–816.
    See also Relativity
Generator, 635–639, 636*def.*
Genetic effects of radiation, 1007
Geodesic, 814
Geosynchronous orbits, 173
Germanium crystal, 986
Germer, Lester H., 887
Glass, 975, 976
Gliders
    collision of, 216, 217, 239,
        241–242
    motion of, 103, 106–107, 107*tab.*,
        118–119
Golf ball, air flow about, 335
Goudsmit, Samuel, 904
Gradient-index lens, 739
Grains, of crystal, 975
Gram (g), 108*tab.*
Gram atomic mass, 826*def.*
Grand unification theory, 1018–1019

Gravitation, universal, 160, 162–164
Gravitational field strength, 166,
    166*def.*, 168
Gravitational force, 102, 160,
    162–164, 1015*tab.*, 1018–1019
    accelerated motion and, 809–813
Gravitational lenses, 815
Gravitational potential energy,
    186–188, 190–191, 245,
    248–250
Gravitational potential, motion in,
    250–252
Gravitational red shift, 808–809
Gravity
    acceleration of, 49–50, 110
    center of, 162, 273
    field of, 166, 168
    light deflection by, 814–816
    meter, 167
    tides and, 296
Gray (Gy), 931
GRIN, 739
Ground, 529
Ground potential, of electric circuit,
    572
Ground state, 869
Guericke, Otto von, 375
Guitar, 483, 485
Guitar string, 481, 483

H
Hadrons, 1010*tab.*, 1013*def.*, 1014
Hafele-Keating experiment, 812
Hahn, Otto, 938
Hale Telescope, 737
Half-life, radioactive, 842–844,
    842*def.*, 842*tab.*, 913
    biological, 948
Half-wave rectifier circuit, 994–995
Hall effect, 988–990
Hall probes, 989, 990
Halley, Edmund, 99
Hammer throw, 266–267
Harmonic frequency, 481*def.*
Harmonic oscillator, 440–441
    damped, 449, 451–453
    energy of, 442–444
    forced motion of, 453–455
    natural frequency of, 445, 454
    natural period of, 445
    period of, 444–447
Harmonic waves, 465–467
    traveling, 466
Hauksbee's electrostatic machine, 496
Haüy, René Just, 823–824
Hearing, 488
Heart, 669
    power of, 201, 203

Heat. *See also* Temperature
  calorimetry of, 356–360
  as energy transfer, 344, 354, 403
  and first law of thermodynamics, 405
  of fusion, 360*def.*, 361*tab.*
  measurement of, 356–360, 357*tab.*
  mechanical equivalent of, 354–355
  transfer of, 363–367, 365*tab.*
  of transformation, 360–361, 360*def.*, 361*tab.*
  units of, 355, 356*tab.*
  of vaporization, 360*def.*, 361, 361*tab.*
Heat capacity, 357*def.*, 357*tab.*
Heat death, of universe, 426
Heat engine, 407, 408, 410–417
  Carnot, 412–417
  efficiency of, 414*def.*, 415*tab.*
Heat pump, 418–420
Heat reservoir, 412–413
Heat sink, 413
Heisenberg, Werner, 881, 890
Heisenberg's uncertainty principle, 990–993
Helium-neon laser, 953–955
Henry (H), 643*def.*
Henry, Joseph, 628
HERA accelerator, 1011, 1012
Hertz (Hz), 149*def.*
Hertz, Heinrich, 648, 861
Higgs particle, 1018
Hindenburg, 378
Holes, in semiconductor, 987–988
Hologram, 958
  production of, 959–961
  white-light, 963
Holography, 957–962
  film for, 961
Home power distribution, 583–586
Honeycomb, 246–247
Hooke, Robert, 99, 435
Hooke's law, 179–181, 435–438
Horsehead Nebula, 856
Horsepower (hp), 199*def.*
Horseshoe magnet, 597, 615
Hot-air balloon, 317, 378, 380–381
Household circuit, 583–585
Hovercraft, 128
Hubble Space Telescope, 737, 766–767
Human energy, 202
Huygens, Christian, 210, 448, 648, 746, 824
Huygens' principle, 746–747
Hydraulic lift, 314–315
Hydrodynamics, 30
Hydrogen
  absorption spectrum of, 871–872

Bohr's theory of, 867–868
  emission spectrum of, 854, 857
  ground state of, 869–870
  wave theory of, 898–900
Hydrostatic pressure, 308–312
Hydrostatic weighing, 317–318
Hyperbaric chamber, 313
Hyperbola, A–3
Hyperons, 1009
Hyperopia, 723

I

Ice cream churn, 360–363
Ice skater, 289–290
Iceberg, submerged volume of, 319–320
Iceland spar, 823
Ideal gas, 385*def.* *See also* Gases
Ideal gas law, 381–384
Image
  real, 697
  virtual, 697
Image conduit, 693, 694
Image distance, 697
Impedance, 675*def.*
Impulse, 211–214, 212*def.*
Impulsive forces, 211–212
Impure semiconductors, 990–991
Incandescence, 2–3
Incandescent lamp, 962, 964*def.*
Incidence of, angle of, 685–687, 691–692
Incoherent fiber bundles, 693, 694
Index of refraction, 689–691, 689*def.*, 690*tab.*, 712
Indicator diagram, 410–411
Inductance, 642–644
Induction
  charging by, 498
  Faraday's law of, 629–633
Inductive reactance, 673
Inductive time constant, 663
Inductor, 643
Inelastic collisions, 216, 217, 236*def.*
Inertia, 50, 103–105, 103*def.*
  moment of, 279, 282–286, 282*def.*, 284*tab.*
Inertial frame of reference, 104–105. *See also* Relativity
Information, wave transfer of, 467–468
Infrared pyrometer, 349
Infrared spectrum, 685
Infrasonic frequencies, 471
Infusion, 312
Instantaneous acceleration, 42–44, 42*def.*, 78–79
Instantaneous angular acceleration, 265*def.*

Instantaneous velocity, 36–40, 37*def.*, 78
Insulator, 497*def.*
Integrated circuit, 534–535
Intensity level (dB), of sound, 473*def.*, 474
Intensity, of wave, 468*def.*, 469–470
Interference
  constructive, 481, 750, 755
  destructive, 481, 750–751, 755
  pattern, 752, 762, 895
  in thin films, 755–759
Interferometer, 786
Internal combustion engine, 416
Internal energy, 405*def.*
  of gases, 389–390
International System of Units, 7, 7*tab.*
Inverse-square force, 97
  electrostatics and, 499–503
  gravitation and, 97, 160–164
Inverting telescope, 734–735
Ion microscope, 839
Iris, 722, 730
Irradiance, 652–653
Isobaric process, 407, 409
Isochoric process, 406–407, 409
Isothermal process, 406, 409
  of Carnot cycle, 413, 414
Isotope, 916*def.*, 917

J

Jet engine, 135, 412
Joule (J), 178*def.*, 182*tab.*, 355, 356*tab.*
Joule, James Prescott, 178, 355
Joule's apparatus, 355, 356
Joule's law, 569–570
Junction, *pn*, 991–993
Junction rule, 572

K

Kamerlingh Ohnes, H., 566
Kaon, 1009, 1010*tab.*
Keck telescope, 737
Kelvin temperature scale, 348, 349, 379
Kepler, Johannes, 97, 161
Kepler's laws, 97, 157–160
  first, 158
  second, 158, 159, 290–291
  third, 158, 159, 163–164
Kiln, 2–3, 859
Kilocalorie, 202, 202*tab.*, 355, 356*tab.*
Kilogram (kg), 8, 107*def.*, 108*tab.*
Kilowatt-hour (KWh), 182*tab.*, 571*def.*
Kinematics, 25*def.* *See also* Motion; Vector(s)
Kinetic energy, 182–183*def.*, 182–185
  in collisions, 216–221

of gases, 388–390
of photoelectrons, 862–864
and Q value, 925, 936
relativistic, 805–806
rotational, 291–293, 292*def.*
translational, 183*def.*
Kinetic theory of gases, 384–388
Kirchhoff's current rule, 572
Kirchhoff's rules, 572–576
    application of, 576–578
Kirchhoff's voltage rule, 572
    application of, 576–578

L
Lake, freezing of, 354
Laminar flow, 322, 324–326, 329, 331
Laplace, P. S., 256
Laser(s), 951–953
    continuous wave, 953–954
    diode, 997
    helium-neon, 953–955
    for holography, 959–962
    light of, 955–957
    light properties of, 955–957
    ruby, 951–953
Laser speckle, 955–957
LASIK, 957
Latent heat of transformation, 360*def.*
Lateral magnification, 699
Lave, Max von, 833
Law of conservation of mechanical
        energy, 191
Law of inertia, 50
Law of universal gravitation, 160,
        162–164
Laws of planetary motion, 97,
        158–159, 159*tab.*
Laws of thermodynamics, 405–422
LCD, 978
Lead shielding, for radiation, 934
LED, 996
Leg, model of, 450
Length, 8
    contraction of, 799, 800
    proper, 797
Lenses
    aberrations of, 711–714
    achromatic, 713
    aspheric, 713–714
    bifocal, 724
    of camera, 728–731
    chromatic aberration of, 712–713
    collimating, 771
    coma of, 711, 712
    combination of, 704–707, 712
    of compound microscope, 732–734
    converging, 694–696, 704
    diverging, 694, 695, 703
    of eye, 722–725

focal length of, 695
focal point of, 695, 696
Fresnel, 738, 739
gradient-index, 739
gravitational, 815
image distance from, 697–698
image location and, 696–700
light passage through, 695–696, 697
of magnifying glass, 725–728
object distance from, 697
ray tracing for, 696–700
resolution of, 764–768
of slide projector, 731–732
spherical aberration of, 711, 712
strength of, 724
of telescope, 734–736, 737
thin, 694–696, 695*def.*, 701–707
thin-lens equation for, 701–707
transmission spectra of, 771, 772
trifocal, 724
varifocal, 736, 738
zoom, 738
Lensmakers' equation, 719
Lenz, Heinrich, 628
Lenz's law, 630–631
Leptons, 1009, 1010*tab.*, 1013*def.*,
        1014–1015
Lever arm, 270, 270*def.*
Leyden jar, 538
Lift pump, 374
Light
    additive primary colors of,
        965–966, 967
    angle of incidence of, 685–687,
        691–692
    angle of reflection of, 685–687, 747
    angle of refraction of, 689–690,
        747–748
    coherence of, 955–957
    color and, 962, 964–969
    color temperature of, 962, 964*def.*
    critical angle of, 691–692*def.*
    diffuse reflection of, 687
    dispersion of, 712–713, 768–770
    Doppler effect and, 807–809,
        810–811
    double-slit diffraction of, 762,
        895–896
    fringe visibility of, 955–956
    gravitational deflection of, 814–816
    laser, 955–957
    models of, 685–686
    photoelectric effect of, 861–866
    ray of, 684
    Rayleigh scattering of, 775–776
    red shift of, 808, 809
    reflection of, 685, 687–689, 691–693
    refraction of, 689–691, 712–713,
        722

retinal sensitivity to, 866
scattering of, 775–777
single-slit diffraction of, 894–895
spatial coherence of, 956–957
spectrum of, 651–652, 685,
        763–764, 962, 962*tab.*
specular reflection of, 687
speed of, 651–652, 686, 786
stimulated emission of, 950–951
subtractive primary colors of, 966,
        967
temporal coherence of, 956
thin film reflection of, 755–759
threshold frequency of, 863
total internal reflection of, 691–693
wave theory of. *See* Light waves
wavelength of, 684–685, 746–747,
        751, 753
Light guides, 693, 694
Light pipes, 693–694
Light waves
    coherence of, 751–752
    constructive interference of, 750, 751,
        756
    destructive interference of, 750–752
    dispersion of, 768–770
    Doppler effect and, 807–809,
        810–811
    double-slit diffraction of, 749–755,
        762, 895–896
    interference of, 749–755
    length of, 684–685, 746, 751, 753
    multiple-slit diffraction of,
        763–764
    polarization of, 772–775
    reflection of, 747–749
    refraction of, 747–749
    single-slit diffraction of, 759–761,
        894–895
    thin-film interference of, 755–759
Light-emitting diode, 996
Lightning, 495–496, 538
Lightning rod, 538
Line, slope of, 34–35, 35*def.*
Linear accelerators, 649
Linear expansion, thermal, 350*def.*,
        351–354, 353*tab.*
Linear magnification, 699, 732–733
Linear momentum, 105*def.*, 211*def.*,
        801
    conservation of, 214–216, 223, 801,
        802–805
    mass and, 225–226
    in one-dimensional collisions,
        216–221
    rate of change of, 105–106
    relativistic, 802–805
    in two-dimensional collisions,
        221–224

Lines of force, 168, 506
Liquid, 345
    density of, 354
    thermal expansion of, 354
Liquid crystal, 975
Liquid crystal display, 978
Lodestone, 594, 620
Logarithms, 402
Longitudinal waves, 468–472
Loop rule, 572
    application of, 576–578
Lorentz contraction, 799
Luminescence, optically stimulated, 933
Lungs
    function of, 411
    surface tension of, 323
Lyman series, 871

M

Mach number, 478
Magdeburg hemispheres, 375–376
Magnet, 595–597
Magnetic dipole, 595–596*def.*, 613
Magnetic dipole moment, 598*def.*, 618
Magnetic domains, of ferromagnetic solid, 619, 620–621
Magnetic field, 596–597
    Ampère's law of, 616–618
    Biot-Savart law of, 609
    of circular current loop, 611, 614
    of electric current, 598–600
    with electric current, 609–612
    electric current effects of, 602–603
    of electric current loop, 611–614
    energy of, 644–645
    magnetic flux through, 630, 642–643
    of rectangular current loop, 612–613
    right-hand rule of, 598–599
    of solenoid, 617
    units of, 602–603
Magnetic flux, 599*def.*, 600, 630
    Faraday's law of, 629–630
    unit of, 630
Magnetic force
    on current-carrying wire, 602–603
    on deuteron, 606–607
    on moving charged particles, 603–607
    right-hand rule of, 602
Magnetic materials, 618–621
Magnetic mirrors, 944
Magnetic moment, of current loop, 613–614
Magnetic permeability of free space, 611

Magnetic quantum number, 899, 901–902, 906*tab.*
Magnetic resonance imaging, 601
Magnetic susceptibility, 618–620, 618*def.*
Magnetism
    with electric current, 597–600
    Gauss's law for, 599, 646, 648
    types of, 618–621, 619*tab.*
Magnetization, 618*def.*
Magneton, Bohr, 901*def.*
Magnification
    angular, 727*def.*, 733
    lateral, 699, 733
    linear, 699, 733
    of magnifying glass, 726–728
    of microscope, 733
    of telescope, 734–736
Magnifying glass, 725–728
Maltese Cross tube, 832
Malus's law, 773
Manometer, 315
Marsden, E., 845
Mass, 8, 107*def.*, 799, 801
    center of, 273–274, 273*def.*, 801
    changes in, 225–226, 799, 801–802
    rest, 805
    units of, 107, 108*tab.*
    and weight, 109–112
Mass-energy relation, 801–802
Matter
    condensed, 974–977
    phases of, 345, 360–363
    quark model of, 1015–1018, 1016*tab.*
Maxwell, James Clerk, 391, 629, 647–648
Maxwell-Boltzmann distribution function, of gas speeds, 392–394
Maxwell's electromagnetic equations, 647–648
Mayer, Julius, 355
Measurement, 12–14
    exactness of, 12–14
    modeling and, 2–7
    scientific notation for, 9–10
    SI units for, 7, 7*tab.*, 10*tab.*
    significant figures in, 12–14
    units of, 7–11, 7*tab.*, 10*tab.*
Mechanical energy, 181–182
    conservation of, 189–197, 293–295
    total, 191
Mechanics. *See also* Motion
    Newtonian, 96
    quantum, 4, 880–882. *See also* Quantum mechanics
    statistical, 426
Meitner, Lise, 942

Mendeleev, Dimitri, 827
Mercury, emission spectrum of, 854
Mesons, 1009, 1010*tab.*
    quark composition of, 1016*tab.*
Metallic crystals, 976–977
Metals. *See also* Semiconductors
    band model of, 985–986
    electric charge transport through, 988–990
    electric conductivity of, 981–983
    electric resistivity of, 563–565, 565*tab.*, 982–983
    free-electron model of, 977, 979–981
    photoelectric effect on, 861–866, 863*tab.*, 981
    photoelectric work function of, 863, 863*tab.*
    specific heat of, 357*tab.*, 359–360
    thermal expansion of, 351–352, 353*tab.*
Meter (m), 8
Meyer, Lothar, 827
Michelson-Morley experiment, 786
Microelectromechanical devices, 639
Microscope, 704
    atomic force, 446–447
    compound, 732–734
    electron, 888
    resolving power of, 768
    tunneling, 974, 975
Microwave ovens, 519
Microwave radiation, 5, 8, 519, 649–650, 685
Milikan, Robert A., 838
Mirrors
    concave, 707–710
    convex, 710–711
    in laser system, 951, 952–953
    light reflection from, 685, 687–691
    parabolic, 711
    plane, 687–688
    spherical, 707–711
Mobility, 983*def.*
Model, 1*def.*, 2–7, 97, 147, 384, 416, 650, 684, 844, 867–868, 917, 924, 1015
Moderator, 941
Mole, of gas, 381
Molecular mass, of gases, 381, 382*tab.*
Molecular speeds, of gases, 390–394
Moment
    dipole (electric), 517*def.*
    dipole (magnetic), 598*def.*
Moment arm, 270, 270*def.*
Moment of inertia, 282–286, 282*def.*, 284*tab.*

Momentum
  angular, 184–185, 286–287, 287*def.*
    conservation of, 287–291
    quantization of, 868
  linear, 105*def.*, 211*def.*, 801
    conservation of, 214–216, 223,
      801, 802–805
    mass and, 225–226
    in one-dimensional collisions,
      216–221
    rate of change of, 105–106
    relativistic, 802–805
    in two-dimensional collisions,
      221–224
Monochromatic light, 755, 757
Monopole, magnetic, 595, 1019
Moon
  centripetal acceleration of, 150–151
  rocket projection to, 253–255
  tides and, 296
Moseley, Henry, 855, 872–875
Moseley's law, 873–874
Motion. *See also* Force(s); Vector(s)
  acceleration and, 40–44
  average speed and, 29
  average velocity and, 30–31, 44
  Brownian, 828–829
  circular, 146–152. *See also* Circular
    motion
  components of, 81–82
  constant acceleration and, 44–48,
    44*def.*, 47*tab.*
  coordinate system and, 27
  friction and, 123–128
  Galileo's experiments on, 48–53,
    49*tab.*
  in gravitational potential, 250–252
  gravity and, 48–53, 49*tab.*
  harmonic, 438–442
  instantaneous velocity and, 36–40
  linear, 103–104
  Newton's first law of, 103–105
  Newton's second law of, 105–109,
    214–216
  Newton's third law of, 112–116
  periodic. *See* Periodic motion
  planetary, 97, 145, 157–160,
    159*tab.*
  projectile, 81–87, 152
  reference frame and, 26–28
  relative velocity and, 72–77
  rotational, 267–269, 267*tab.*
  simple harmonics, 434, 438–442
  translational, 128–132
  velocity and, 30–31, 33–40
Motional emf, 633–635
Motor, 638–639
Mountain sickness, 392
Movie projector, 732

Moving objects, appearance of, 800
MRI, 601
Multiple Mirror Telescope, 737
Muon, 1008, 1010*tab.*
  momentum of, 804–805
  time dilation experiment with,
    795–796
Muscle, 177, 202, 669
Music, 479–486, 485*tab.*
Musical scales, 485
Myopia, 723

N

Natural frequency, of harmonic
  oscillator, 445
Natural period, of harmonic oscillator,
  445
Natural radioactive decay series, 924
Near point, 723
Nearsightedness, 723
Negative charge, 497
Net force, 100, 100*def.*
Neutrino, 927, 1010*tab.*
  mass of, 1019
Neutron, 915*tab.*, 1010*tab.*
  discovery of, 913–915
  thermal, 941
Newton (N), 107, 108*tab.*
Newton, Isaac, 97, 99, 210, 376, 736
Newtonian mechanics, 96
Newtonian telescope, 736
Newton's law(s), 132, 133
  applications of, 116–123
  first, 103–105
  problem-solving strategies for, 119
  second, 105–109, 214–216
  third, 112–116
  of universal gravitation, 160,
    162–164
Node, 482*def.*
Noether's principle, 246–247
Nonconservative force, 197–199
Noninertial frame of reference, 104
Normal (perpendicular) force, 111*def.*
North pole, 596–597
n-type semiconductor, 991
Nuclear binding energy, 918–920
Nuclear fission, 938–941
Nuclear force, 102, 918–921, 1005,
  1008–1009
Nuclear fusion, 943–944
Nuclear power plant, 939–941
Nuclear reaction, 935–938
  fission, 938–941
  fusion, 943–944
  threshold energy of, 936–938
Nuclear size, 918
Nucleons. *See* Neutron; Proton
Nucleus. *See* Atomic nucleus

O

Object distance, 697
Objective lens, 732
Observer
  in quantum mechanics, 882
  in relativity, 786, 791
Octave, 485
Ocular, 732
Oersted, Hans Christian, 597–598
Ohm, 561*def.*
Ohm's law, 561, 562
Oil film, light reflection from,
  757–758
Open electric circuit, 571, 572
Opera glasses, 735
Optical activity, 777
Optical axis, 695
Optical fibers, 693–694
Optical lenses, 694–696
Optical pumping, of laser medium,
  952
Optical resonator, 951
Optoelectronic device, 996
Orbital quantum number, 899, 900*tab.*,
  901–902, 906*tab.*
Order-of-magnitude estimates, 15–18
Ordinate, 33
Orion Nebula, 767
Oscillations, simple harmonic,
  438–442
OSL dosimeter, 933
Osmotic pressure, 829
Otto cycle, 416
Otto, Nicholas, 416
Overdamped motion, 452
Overtones, 481*def.*
Oxygen, hyperbaric, 313

P

Parabola, A-3, of projectile motion,
  82–83
Parabolic reflector, 711
Parallel connection
  of capacitors, 578–581
  of resistors, 572–578
Parallelogram method, of addition, 66,
  67
Parallel-plate capacitor, 540–542
  electric field of, 540–542
Paramagnetism, 619–620
Paraxial approximation, 696, 698
Particles
  versus antiparticles, 1004–1006
  classification of, 1010*tab.*,
    1013–1018, 1016*tab.*
  detection of, 1011–1013
  elementary, 1006–1015, 1010*tab.*
Pascal (Pa), 309*tab.*

Pascal's principle, 312–315
Paschen series, 871
Pauli exclusion principle, 904–905
Pauli, Wolfgang, 880, 904
Pendulum, 447–449
    ballistic, 220–221
    leg modeled as, 450
    period of, 448–449
    simple, 447–449
Penzias, Arno, 5, 6
Perihelion, advance of, 815
Period, 149*def.*
    of circular motion, 149
    of harmonic oscillator, 440,
        444–447
    of planets, 159*tab.*
    of simple pendulum, 448–449
    of wave, 465–466
Periodic motion, 434–455, 434*def.*
    damped, 449, 451–453
    of gait, 450
    Hooke's law of, 435–438
    of pendulum, 447–449
    simple harmonic, 438–442
    types of, 435
Periodic table, 827–828, 872, 905,
        back end pages
Permeability of free space, 611
Permittivity of free space, 500, 542
Perpetual motion machine, 409–410
Perrin, Jean, 825, 828–830
PET scan, 927
Phase angle, 441
Phase change on reflection, 755
Phases, of matter, 345, 360–363,
        361*tab.*
Phasor, 674
Photodiode, 996
Photoelectric effect, 861–866, 861*def.*,
        981
    Einstein's explanation of, 863–864
    and work function, 863*def., tab.*
Photography, 712, 713, 728–732
    color, 966, 967, 968
    infrared, 968, 969
Photomultiplier tube, 928–930
Photons, 863, 915*def.*, 1010*tab. See also*
        Light
    and Compton effect, 882–884
    energy of, 860
    in laser system, 950–953
    momentum of, 883–884, 885
    in photoelectric effect, 863–864
    spontaneous emission of, 950
    stimulated emission of, 950–951
    vision and, 866
Photoreceptors, in the eye, 866
Photorefractive keratectomy, 957

Physics, 1*def.*
    modern, 4
    problem-solving guidelines for,
        19–21
    quantum, 4. *See also* Quantum
        mechanics
    study methods for, 18–19
Pi (π), 13
Pincipia, 99
Pions, 1005, 1008–1009, 1010*tab.*
Pipe, vibrations in, 486–487
Pitch, of sound, 471
Planck, Max, 854, 860
Planck's constant, 860
Plane mirror, 688
Plane of incidence, 687
Plane waves, 469, 470
Planets
    motion of, 97, 145, 157–160,
        159*tab.*
    orbits of, 97, 290–291, 815–816
Plasma, 943
pn junction, 991–994
pn junction diode, 992–994
Poiseuille's law, 327–329
Polarization, of light, 772–775
    by scattering, 775–777
Polaroids, 773
Pollution, thermal, 426–428
Polycrystalline solid, 975
Position-time curve, 33–36
    slope of, 34–35, 35*def.*
Positron, 915, 926, 1004
Positron emission tomography, 927
Postulates of special relativity,
        786–787
Potential, electric, 527–532
Potential energy, 185–189
    dipole orientation and, 518
    elastic, 188–189
    electric, 527
    gravitational, 186–188, 190–191,
        245, 248–250
    reference level and, 186
    zero reference for, 248
Potential energy diagrams, 193–197
Potential well, 896
Powell, C. F., 1008
Power, 199–201, 199*def.*, 200*tab.*,
        201*def.*
    of electric circuit, 565, 567–571
Powers of ten, 10
Prefixes, for SI units, 9–11, 10*tab.*
Presbyopia, 723
Pressure, 308–309*def.*
    atmospheric, 309, 315, 374–376
    blood, 316
    gas, 376–377

    gauge, 309
    hydrostatic, 308–312
    measurement of, 309, 315, 316
    scuba diving and, 313–314
    units of, 309, 309*tab.*
Primary colors, 965
Principal quantum number, 868,
        899–900, 900*tab.*, 906*tab.*
Principia, 97–98
Principle of complementarity, 887
Principle of equivalence, 809–813
Principle of superposition, 481, 503
Prism, 712–713, 768–770
Prism spectroscope, 770–771
PRK, 957
Probability
    in quantum theory, 881
    and thermodynamics, 425–426
Probability density, 894
Problem-solving strategies, 19–21
    for adding vectors, 70
    for calorimetry problems, 358
    for comparing quantities, 150, 415
    for conservation of linear
        momentum, 217, 223
    for electric charge, 500
    for free-body diagrams, 117
    for gravitational potential energy,
        187
    for induced current, 632
    for induced emf, 632
    for magnetic forces, 605
    for Newton's laws, 119
    for one-dimensional elastic
        collisions, 239
    for projectile motion, 81
    for ray tracing, 699
    for relative velocity, 74
    for statics problems, 274
Projectile motion, 81–87, 152
Projector, 731
Proper length, 797*def.*, 799
Proper mass, 805*def.*
Proper time, 795*def.*
Proportional symbol, 49
Proton, 913*def.*, 915*tab.*, 1010*tab.*
    instability of, 1018–1019
    magnetic forces on, 606
Proust, J. L., 824
p-type semiconductor, 991
Pulley, forces on, 116–118, 120–123
Pulmonary surfactant, 323
Pulse, wave, 464
Pumping, of laser medium, 951
Pure semiconductors, 987–988
PV diagram, 409, 410–411
Pyrometer, 349
Pythagorean theorem, 20

Q

Q value, 923*def.*, 936
  in fission, 939
Quality factor, for radiation, 932,
  932*def.*
Quantization
  of angular momentum, 868
  of change, 826–827
  of energy, 863–864
  of space, 901–904
Quantum, 860
Quantum mechanics, 4
  barrier penetration and, 897–898
  versus classical mechanics, 880–882
  Compton effect and, 882–884
  de Broglie waves and, 885–887
  energy quantization in, 896–897
  Pauli exclusion principle and,
    904–905
  Schrödinger's equation and, 889,
    893–896
  space quantization in, 901–904
  statistical nature of, 894–896
  in three dimensions, 898–900,
    900*tab.*
  uncertainty principle and, 890–893
Quantum numbers, 868, 899–900,
  900*tab.*, 906*tab.*
Quarks, 1015–1018, 1016*tab.*

R

R (universal gas constant), 381
R value of insulation, 364–365*def.*,
  365*tab.*
Rad, 931
Radian, 146*def.*, 265
Radiant heater, 568
Radiation, 925–926
  alpha, 184–185, 840–841, 841*tab.*,
    845–846, 913, 925–926
  annual effective dose exposure to,
    932, 933
  background, 932, 933*tab.*
  beta, 840–841, 841*tab.*, 913,
    926–928
  biological effects of, 931–932,
    932*tab.*
  blackbody, 2–4, 365, 858–860
  cancer and, 931
  Cherenkov, 941
  cosmic, 1007
  cosmic background, 5, 6, 1020
  detection of, 928–930
  effective dose equivalent of, 932,
    933*tab.*
  exposure to, 931, 932–933, 932*tab.*,
    933*tab.*

gamma, 840–841, 841*tab.*, 913,
  928
  genetic effects of, 931
  in heat transfer, 363, 365
  induced transmutation and,
    935–938
  maximum permissible doses of,
    932, 932*tab.*
  measurement of, 931–935
  in medicine, 843, 922, 931, 934
  microwave, 5, 519, 685
  natural, 924
  quality factor for, 932, 932*tab.*
  shielding against, 934
  somatic effects of, 931
Radiation sickness, 931
Radiation therapy, 843, 931
  linear accelerators for, 649
Radioactive decay, 841–844, 921–924.
  See also Radiation
Radioactivity, 840–841, 840*def.*, 913.
  See also Radiation
Radius, Schwarzschild, 256
Radon, 934
Rainbow, 769–770
Rainbow hologram, 963
Range of a projectile, 87
Rankine, W. J. M., 176
Rarefaction, longitudinal wave, 469
Ray
  cosmic, 1007
  of light, 684*def.*
Ray tracing, 696–700
  problem-solving strategy for, 699
  for spherical mirror, 709–710
Rayleigh criterion, 764–768
Rayleigh scattering, 775–777
RC circuit, 664–667
Reactance, 670–673
Rectifier, 992
Rectifier circuit, 993–996
Rectifier equation, 993
Red shift
  gravitational, 812
  of light, 808, 809, 812
Reference frame, 26–27, 26*def.*
  versus coordinate system, 28
  inertial, 104–105. *See also*
    Relativity
  noninertial, 104
Reflection
  angle of, 685–687, 747
  diffuse, 687
  Huygens' principle of, 747–749
  of light, 685, 687–689, 691–693
  specular, 687
  total internal, 691–693
  of wave pulse, 479–480, 755

Reflection hologram, 963
Refracting astronomical telescope,
  734–735
Refraction, 689*def.*
  angle of, 689–690, 747–748
  Huygens' principle of, 747–749
  index of, 689–691, 689*def.*, 690*tab.*,
    712
  law of, 689
  of light, 689–691, 747–749
Refrigerators, 417–420
Relative velocity
  in one dimension, 72–73
  in two dimensions, 73–77
Relativity
  atomic clock test of, 812–813
  of Doppler effect, 807–808
  equivalence principle and, 809–813,
    812*tab.*
  Galilean, 785–786
  general, 813–816
  of kinetic energy, 805–806
  length contraction and, 797, 799,
    800
  of momentum, 802–805
  principle of, 785–786
  simultaneity and, 791–793
  special, 786–787
  time dilation and, 794–797,
    812–813, 812*tab.*
  twin paradox of, 798
  velocity addition and, 787, 789–790
Rem, 932
Reservoir, heat, 413
Resistance, 561–563, 561*def.*,
  982–983
Resistivity, 563–565, 982–983
Resistors, 563
  in parallel, 574–575
  in series, 572–574, 576
Resolution
  of human eye, 767
  in optics, 764–768
  of vectors, 68–71
Resolving power, 764–768
Resonance, 453–454*def.*, 453–455,
  677
Resonant circuit, 676–678
Resonant frequency, 454, 677
  of RLC circuit, 676–678
  of vibrating air column, 486
  of vibrating string, 482
Rest mass, 805*def.*
Restoring force, 435–436
Resultant, of vector addition, 65*def.*
Retina, photosensitivity of, 866
Reverberation time, 475, 475*tab.*
Reversible process, 409

Reynolds number, 333–334
Right-hand rule for direction
    of angular momentum, 287
    of current loop dipole, 613
    of magnetic field about a current,
        598–599
    of magnetic force on a wire,
        602–603
    of magnetic force on moving
        charge, 604
    of magnetic moment, 613
    of torque, 271
Rigid body, 264–266, 264*def.*
    angular acceleration of, 265–266
    angular velocity of, 264–265
RL circuit, 662–664
RLC circuit, 673–676
Rocket, 225–226, 250–256
    propulsion of, 225–226, 250–252,
        253–255
    velocity of, 220
Rods, 866
Roemer, Ole, 349, 686
Roentgen (R), 931
Roentgen, Wilhelm Konrad, 824,
        832, 833
Roller coaster, 193–194, 195–197
Rolling bodies, 293
Room, acoustical quality of, 475
Root-mean-square current, 668
    of current, 668
    of speed, 387
    of voltage, 668
Rope
    pulses on, 464
    waves on, 464, 465–468
Rotational energy, 291–293, 292*def.*
Rotational equilibrium, 273
Rotational motion, 267–269, 267*tab.*
    torque and, 269–272
Rounding off, 13–14
Royal Society, 99, 210, 376, 538
Ruby laser, 951–953
Rumford, Count (Benjamin
        Thompson), 355
Running, mechanical principles of,
        450
Russell's traction, 100–101
Rutherford, Ernest, 825, 840, 845–846
Rydberg constant, 857
Rydberg equation, 870
Rydberg formula, 857

S
Sabin, 475*def.*
Sabin, Wallace, 475
Satellite, period of, 165–166
Saturation current, 993

Savart, Felix, 609
Scalar, 64*def.*
    vector multiplication by, 67
Scale, musical, 485
Scanning electron microscope, 888
Scanning tunneling microscope, 839
Scattering
    of alpha radiation, 845–846
    Bragg, 833–834
    Compton, 882–884
    Rayleigh, 775–776
    Tyndall, 776
Schrödinger, Erwin, 881, 889
Schrödinger's equation, 889
Schwarzschild radius, 256
Scientific notation, 9–10
Scintillation counter, 929–930
Scuba diver, 313–314
Second (s), 8*def.*
Second condition for equilibrium, 273
Second law of thermodynamics,
        421–422
    entropy and, 422–426
Sedimentation, Stokes's law and, 331
Self-inductance, 642–644
Semiconductor radioactivity detector,
        930
Semiconductors, 986*def., tab.*
    depletion zone of, 991
    doping of, 990–991
    electric charge transport through,
        988–990
    energy gap of, 986*tab.*
    Hall effect and, 988–990
    impure, 990–991
    n-type, 991
    pn junction of, 991–994
    p-type, 991
    pure, 987–988
Series connection
    of capacitors, 578–581
    of resistors, 572–578
Series limit, 857
Shielding, against radiation, 934
Shock, electric, 586
Shock wave, 478–479
Short electric circuit, 571–572
Shutter speed, 729–730
SI units, 7, 7*tab.*, A–4
Sievert (Sv), 932
Sigma, 1010*tab.*
Significant figures, 12–14
Silicon crystal, 986
Silicon *pn*-junction diode, 562
Simple harmonic motion, 438–442
Simple harmonic oscillator, 438–442
Simple pendulum, 447–449
Simultaneity, relativity and, 791–793

Sine, of angle, 94*def.*
Single lens reflex camera, 712
Single-slit diffraction, 759–761
Sink, heat, 413
Sky, color of, 775
Skydiver, 333
Skylight, polarization of, 777
Sled, forces on, 129–130
Slide-projector, 731–732
Slope of line, 34–35, 35*def.*
Small angle approximation, 448, 719
Snell's law, 689, 747–748
Snowflake, 246
Soap bubbles, 323
Soap film, light reflection from, 756–
        757
Sodium chloride, crystal structure of,
        976, 977
Sodium, emission spectrum of, 854
Solar cells, 996
Solar spectrum, 854, 856, 962
Solenoid, 617–618, 617*def.*, 645
Solids
    amorphous, 975, 976
    band theory of, 984–987
    crystalline, 974. *See also* Crystal(s);
        Metals
    polycrystalline, 975
Sonic boom, 478
Sonic frequencies, 470–471
Sound, 468–472
    acoustic environment of, 475,
        475*tab.*
    Doppler effect and, 474, 476–478
    frequencies of, 470–471
    intensity level of, 472–474, 473*def.*
    speed of, 470–471, 471*tab.*
Sound-absorption coefficients, 475*def,*
        tab.
South pole, 596–597
Space
    quantization of, 901–904
    three-dimensional, 26–27
Spatial coherence, 956–957
Spatial frequency, 961
Special theory of relativity, 786–787.
        See also Relativity
Specific gravity, 310–311*def.*
Specific heat, 357*def.*, 357*tab.*
Specific heat capacity, 357
Speckle pattern, of laser light, 955
Spectrograph, 771
Spectrometer, 770, 771
Spectrometry, x-ray, 873
Spectrophotometer, 771
Spectroscope, 770–771
Spectroscopy, 853–855, 853*def.*
    Rydberg formula for, 857

Spectrum, 770–771
    absorption, 854–855, 871–872
    blackbody, 3–4, 858–861, 858tab.
    electromagnetic, 685
    emission, 854
    light, 651–652, 685, 763–764, 962,
        962tab.
    solar, 854, 856, 962
    visible, 685, 962tab.
    x-ray, 873
Specular reflection, 687
Speed, 37def.
    average, 29def., 37
    of bullet, 220–221
    of camera lens, 731
    constant, 29
    escape, 252–257, 253def.
    within fluid, 329, 331–333
    of fluids, 326
    of light, 651–652, 686, 763–764,
        786
    molecular, 390–394
    rms, 387
    of sound, 470–471, 471tab.
    terminal, 329, 331–333
Spherical aberration, 711
Spherical mirrors, 707–711
Spherical wave, 469
Sphygmomanometry, 316
Spontaneous emission, 950
Spring
    compression of, 469
    force on, 102, 179–181
    Hooke's law and, 179–181
    kinetic energy of, 442–444
    longitudinal waves in, 468–469
    longitudinal waves of, 468–469
    mass suspension from, 435–442
    potential energy of, 188–189,
        194–195, 442
    rarefractions of, 469
    restoring force on, 435–436
    as scale, 436–437
    total energy of, 443
Spring constant, 437
Stable isotopes, 916, 921–924
Standard Model, 1021
Standard temperature and pressure,
    387, 397
Standing waves, 480–486
Star, escape speed of, 256
State variables, 381, 409
Static equilibrium, 128–132, 128def.,
    272–278
Static friction, 127
Statistical mechanics, 425–426
Steam burns, 361
Steam engine, 410–411

Stefan-Boltzmann law, 365–366
Stern and Gerlach experiment, 903
Stimulated emission, 950–951
Stokes's law, 329, 331–333
Stopping potential, 862
Storage ring, 1012
Strain
    compressive, 279def.
    tensile, 279def.
Strangeness (quantum number), 1016
Strassman, Fritz, 938
Streamline, 322, 324
Stress, tensile, 278def.
String
    standing waves on, 480–486
    vibration of, 480–486
Strong (nuclear) force, 102, 918–919,
    1005, 1008–1009, 1015tab.
Stud finder, 547
Styrofoam cooler, 364–365
Sunglasses, 775
Sunlight, spectral distribution, 962
Superconducting magnet, 566, 601, 618
Superconductivity, 566
Superconductor, 566, 619
Supernova, 1007
Superposition, principle of, 481, 503
Surface tension, 320–322, 320def.,
    321tab.
    of lungs, 323
    unit of, 320
Surfactant, 321
    pulmonary, 323
Susceptibility, 618–619
Suspension bridge, 280–281, 351
Symbols
    for electric circuit, 567
    for measurement, 7tab., 8–9
    for vector, 64
Symmetry, 246–247
Synchronized clocks, 791
System, thermodynamic, 405
Systolic pressure, 316

T

Tangent, of angle, 94def., 101
Tangential acceleration, 265
Telescope, 734–736
    achromatic, 713
    astronomical, 734
    development of, 737
    Galilean, 734
    Hale, 737
    Hubble, 16, 256, 737, 766, 815
    Keck, 737
    Newtonian, 736
    resolving power of, 766–767

Television, color, 965–966
Temperature, 345def. See also Heat
    Celsius scale for, 347, 348
    changes in, 358–359
    Curie, 621
    Fahrenheit scale for, 347, 348, 349
    gas volume and, 379–381
    versus heat, 354–355
    Kelvin scale for, 348, 379
    kinetic-theory definition of, 388–389
    materials expansion with, 350–354,
        353tab.
    molecular kinetics and, 388–389
    phases of matter and, 345, 360–363
Temporal coherence, 956
Tensile strain, 279def.
Tensile stress, 278def.
Tension, 116–119, 116def., 130–132
    surface (g), 320–322, 321tab.
Terminal potential difference, of
        battery, 582
Terminal speed, 329–333
Tesla (T), 598, 602–603def., 630
Tevatron, 1012
Thermal conductivity, 363–364,
        365tab.
Thermal conductor, 363–364
Thermal efficiency, 414def., 415tab.
Thermal energy, 344–345, 355, 403,
        412, 427
Thermal equilibrium, 345, 346, 366,
        404–405
Thermal expansion, 350–354
    linear coefficient of, 350–352,
        350def., 353tab.
    volume coefficient of, 352–354,
        352def., 353tab.
Thermal insulator, 363–364
Thermal neutrons, 941
Thermal pollution, 426–428
    energy and, 426–428
Thermal resistance, 364–365, 365tab.
Thermodynamic system, 405
    adiabatic processes of, 406, 409
    isobaric processes of, 407, 409
    isochoric processes of, 406–407, 409
    isothermal processes of, 406, 409
    reversible processes of, 409
    state variables of, 409
Thermodynamics, 403def.
    first law of, 405–410
    second law of, 421–422, 422–426
    zeroth law of, 404–405
Thermometer, 345, 349
    bimetallic strip, 352
    ear, 349
    infrared, 349
    liquid-in-glass, 346–347

Thermometry, 346–348, 350
Thermostat, 352
Thick lens, 695
Thin film, light reflection from, 755–759
Thin lenses, 694–696, 695*def.*
  in combination, 712, 719
  Gaussian equation for, 701–702
  Newton equation for, 719
Thompson, Benjamin (Count Rumford), 355
Thompson, G. P., 887
Thompson, J. J., 824, 836–838
Thorium series, 924
Threshold energy, in nuclear reaction, 936
Threshold light frequency, in photoelectric effect, 862–863
Thrust, of rocket motor, 226*def.*
Thévenin's theorem, 582–583
Thyroid gland, radionuclide examination, 922–923
Tides, 296
Time, 8, 794–797
  proper, 795
  and space, 786–787
Time constant
  capacitive, 665
  inductive, 663
Time dilation, relativity and, 794–797, 812–813, 812*tab.*
Tire-pressure gauge, 309
Tires, automobile, 127
Tokamak, 944
Tones, musical, 485, 485*tab.*
Toroid, 626, 658, 944
Torque, 269–272, 269*def.*
  and angular acceleration, 282
  on compass needle, 598, 600
  on current loop, 612–614
  direction of, 271
  on electric dipole, 516–518
  moment of inertia and, 282–286
  units of, 271
Torricellian tube, 374, 375
Torricellian vacuum, 374
Torsional balance, 167, 499
Total internal reflection, 691–692*def.*
Tourmaline, 773
Townes, Charles, 950
Track-visualization devices, for radioactivity detection, 930
Traction, Russell's, 100–101
Transformation, heat of, 360–361, 360*def.*, 361*tab.*
Transformer, 640–642
Translational equilibrium, 128*def.*, 272
Translational kinetic energy, 183

Transmission lines, for electric power, 641
Transmutation, nuclear, 935–938
Transverse wave pulse, 464
Transverse waves, 464–468
Traveling harmonic wave, 466
Traveling wave, 464
Triangle method, of vector addition, 66
Trifocal lenses, 724
Trigonometry, 94–95
Truss bridge, 280
Tube, fluid flow through, 324–326
Tuning fork, 435
Tunneling microscope, 974, 975
Tunneling, of particles, 897–898
  in alpha decay, 925
Turbulent flow, 322, 331–332, 333–335
Twin paradox, 798
Tyndall scattering, 776

U

Uhlenbeck, George, 904
Ultrasonic frequencies, 471
Ultrasonic imaging, 472
Ultrasonic ranging, 471
Ultrasonic waves, 471–472
Ultraviolet radiation, 685
  blocking filter, 771, 772
Uncertainty in measurement, 12–14
Uncertainty principle, 890–893
Unified theory, 1018–1019
Uniform circular motion, 146–152
Unit cell, 823–824*def.*, 974
Unit conversion, 11–12
Units, of measurement, 7–11, 7*tab.*, 10*tab.*
  conversion of, 11–12
  prefixes for, 9–11, 10*tab.*
  SI, 7, 7*tab.*, 10*tab.*, A–4
  symbols for, 7*tab.*, 8–9
Universal gas constant R, 381*def.*
Universal gravitation constant G, 162, 164–166, 164*def.*
Universal gravitation, law of, 160, 162–164
Universe, heat death of, 426

V

Vacuum flask, 367
Vacuum, Torricellian, 374
Valence band, for electrons, 987
Van de Graaff accelerator, 1011
Van de Graaff electrostatic generator, 533–535, 936

Van Musschenbroek, Pieter, 538
Vaporization, heat of, 360, 360*def.*, 361, 361*tab.*
Varifocal lens, 736, 738
Vector(s), 64*def.*
  addition of, 65–68, 69–71
  components of, 68–71
  equations for, 78–79
  magnitude of, 65*def.*
  negative of, 66, 68
  representation of, 64
  resolution of, 68–71
  scalar multiplication by, 67
  subtraction of, 66–67, 68
  symbol for, 64
  in three dimensions, 71
  translation of, 66
Vector sum, 65*def.*
Velocity, 34–35*def.*
  angular, 151*def.*, 264–267, 265*def.*
  average, 30–31*def.*, 44, 78
  constant, 103
  drift, 559
  graphical interpretation of, 33–36, 39–40
  instantaneous, 36–40, 37*def.*, 78
  kinematic equations for, 47
  nonuniform, 40
  recoil, 219
  relative, 72–77
  vector definitions of, 78–80
Velocity addition, 787, 789–790
Velocity-time curve
  for acceleration, 42–43
  area under, 39–40
Venturi meter, 326
Verrazano-Narrows bridge, 351
Vibrating air column, 486–487
Vibrating string, 480–486
Villard, Paul, 840
Viscosity, 327–329, 328*tab.*
  of blood, 328–329
Viscous drag, 329, 331
Visible spectrum, 685
Vision, 722–725, 866
Volt, 528*def.*, 529*tab.*
Volta, Count Alessandro, 558
Voltage
  Hall, 988–990
  rms, 668, 670
  transformer for, 640–642
Voltaic pile, 558
Voltmeter, 615–616
Volume thermal expansion, 352–354
Volumes, law of, 825
Von Guericke, Otto, 375–376
Von Laue, Max, 833

W

Walking, mechanical principles of, 450
Water. *See also* Fluid(s)
  density of, 354
  lift pump for, 374
  light refraction by, 770
  molecules of, 518–519
Watt, James, 199, 404
Watt-second, 571
Wave(s), 464*def. See also* Frequency
  in air column, 486–487
  antinode of, 482
  beats of, 487, 489
  circular, 746
  constructive interference of, 481, 750
  de Broglie, 885–887
  destructive interference of, 481,
    750–751
  diffraction of, 759–761
  Doppler effect and, 474, 476–478
  electromagnetic, 648, 650–653
  energy transfer by, 467–468
  fundamental frequency of, 481
  harmonic, 465–467, 466*def.*
  Huygens,' 746–749
  information transfer by, 467–468
  intensity of, 468*def.,* 469–470
  interference of, 479, 749–755
  light. *See* Light waves
  longitudinal, 468–472, 469*tab.*
  nodes of, 482
  plane, 469, 470
  power transmitted by, 467–468
  radio, 650, 685
  reflection of, 479–480, 747
  refraction of, 748
  on rope, 464, 465–468
  shock, 478–479
  sound, 468–472
     speed of, 470–471, 471*tab.*

  spherical, 470
  standing, 480–486
  on string, 480–486
  superposition of, 481
  transverse, 464 – 468
  traveling, 464*def.*
  ultrasonic, 471–472
Wave equation, Schrödinger, 889
Wave function, 889*def.*
  interpretation of, 893–896
  in three dimensions, 898–900
Wave model of light, 684–685
Wave packet, 890, 985
Wave pulse, 464
  reflection of, 479–480
  transverse, 464
Wave surface, 747
Wavefront, 469, 470, 747
Wavelength, 465*def.*
  Compton, 884*def.*
  de Broglie, 885–886*def.*
  of light, 684–685
Wave-particle duality, 884, 895
Weak nuclear force, 103, 1015*tab.,*
  1018–1019
Weber (Wb), 630*def.*
Weight, 109–110*def.,* 109–112
  in elevator, 114–116
Weightlessness, 115–116
Weston, Edward, 615
Wheatstone's bridge, 590
Wide Field Planetary Camera,
  766–767
Wien displacement law, 859
Wilson, Robert W., 5, 6
Work, 177–179, 177*def.*
  in Carnot cycle, 411, 414
  energy and, 181–182
  and first law of thermodynamics,
    405–407

  negative, 178, 197–198
  positive, 178
  in stretching spring, 180
  time rate of, 199–201
  varying force and, 179–181
Work function, 863*def., tab.*
Work-energy theorem, 183
Wren, Christopher, 99
Wright brothers, 60, 330

X

X rays, 833–836
  Bragg's scattering of, 833–834
  Compton scattering of, 882–884
  dental, 934
  diffraction of, 832–835
  medical, 934
  production of, 835
  quality factor for, 932*tab.*
  spectrum of, 873
X-ray diffraction, 832–835
X-ray spectrometry, 873
X-ray tube, 835

Y

Young, Thomas, 176
Young's double slit experiment,
  749–755, 895, 955
Young's modulus, 279, 279*tab.*
Yukawa, Hideki, 1006, 1008
Yukawa potential, 1006, 1008

Z

Zeeman effect, 901–904
Zeppelin, 378
Zero, absolute, 348, 379
Zero-point energy, 897
Zeroth law of thermodynamics, 405
Zoom lens, 736, 738

Physical Constants

NAME	SYMBOL	VALUE
Speed of light	c	$2.997\ 924\ 58 \times 10^8$ m $\cdot$ s^{-1} (exact)
Planck constant	h	$6.626\ 075\ 5 \times 10^{-34}$ J $\cdot$ s
		$4.135\ 669\ 2 \times 10^{-15}$ eV $\cdot$ s
Gravitational constant	G	$6.672\ 59 \times 10^{-11}$ m^3 $\cdot$ kg^{-1} $\cdot$ s^{-2}
Boltzmann constant	k	$1.380\ 658 \times 10^{-23}$ J $\cdot$ K^{-1}
		$8.617\ 385 \times 10^{-5}$ eV $\cdot$ K^{-1}
Molar gas constant	R	$8.314\ 510$ J $\cdot$ mol^{-1} $\cdot$ K^{-1}
Charge of electron	e	$1.602\ 177\ 33 \times 10^{-19}$ C
Permeability of vacuum	μ_0	$4\pi \times 10^{-7}$ N $\cdot$ A^{-2} (exact)
Permittivity of vacuum	ϵ_0	$8.854\ 187\ 817 \times 10^{-12}$ F $\cdot$ m^{-1}
Coulomb constant	$1/4\pi\epsilon_0$	$8.987\ 552 \times 10^9$ N $\cdot$ m^2 $\cdot$ C^{-2}
Faraday constant	F	$96\ 485.309$ C $\cdot$ mol^{-1}
Mass of electron	m_e	$9.109\ 389\ 7 \times 10^{-31}$ kg
		$0.510\ 999\ 06$ MeV
Mass of proton	m_p	$1.672\ 623\ 1 \times 10^{-27}$ kg
		$938.272\ 31$ MeV
Mass of neutron	m_n	$1.674\ 928\ 6 \times 10^{-27}$ kg
		$939.565\ 63$ MeV
Avogadro's number	N_A	$6.022\ 136\ 7 \times 10^{23}$ mol^{-1}
Stefan-Boltzmann constant	σ	$5.670\ 51 \times 10^{-8}$ W $\cdot$ m^{-2} $\cdot$ K^{-4}
Unified atomic mass unit	u	$1.660\ 540\ 2 \times 10^{-27}$ kg
		$931.494\ 32$ MeV
Rydberg constant	R_∞	$10\ 973\ 731.534$ m^{-1}
Bohr magneton	μ_B	$9.274\ 015\ 4 \times 10^{-24}$ J $\cdot$ T^{-1}
Bohr radius	a_0	$0.529\ 177\ 249 \times 10^{-10}$ m
Standard atmosphere	atm	$101\ 325$ Pa
Wien displacement law constant	b	$2.897\ 756 \times 10^{-3}$ m $\cdot$ K

Physical Properties

NAME	SYMBOL	VALUE
Acceleration of gravity	g	$9.806\ 65$ m $\cdot$ s^{-2}
Mass of sun	M_S	1.99×10^{30} kg
Radius of sun		6.96×10^8 m
Mass of earth	M_E	5.98×10^{24} kg
Radius of earth (average)		6.38×10^6 m
Radius of earth's orbit		1.50×10^{11} m = 1 AU
Mass of moon	M_M	7.35×10^{22} kg
Radius of moon		1.74×10^6 m
Radius of moon's orbit		3.84×10^8 m
	$\pi =$	$3.141\ 593$
	$e =$	$2.718\ 282$

Periodic Table of the Elements

Legend (key):
- 1 — Atomic number
- H — Symbol
- 1.00794 — Atomic weight

Numbers in brackets [ ] are for longest lived isotopes of elements without stable isotopes.

Periods	1	2	3	4	5	6	7	8	9	10	11	12	13	14	15	16	17	18
1	1 H 1.00794																	2 He 4.00260
2	3 Li 6.941	4 Be 9.01218											5 B 10.811	6 C 12.011	7 N 14.00674	8 O 15.9994	9 F 18.99840	10 Ne 20.1797
3	11 Na 22.98977	12 Mg 24.3050											13 Al 26.98154	14 Si 28.0855	15 P 30.97276	16 S 32.066	17 Cl 35.4527	18 Ar 39.948
4	19 K 39.0983	20 Ca 40.078	21 Sc 44.95591	22 Ti 47.867	23 V 50.9415	24 Cr 51.9961	25 Mn 54.93805	26 Fe 55.845	27 Co 58.93320	28 Ni 58.6934	29 Cu 63.546	30 Zn 65.39	31 Ga 69.723	32 Ge 72.61	33 As 74.92159	34 Se 78.96	35 Br 79.904	36 Kr 83.80
5	37 Rb 85.4678	38 Sr 87.62	39 Y 88.90585	40 Zr 91.224	41 Nb 92.90638	42 Mo 95.94	43 Tc [98]	44 Ru 101.07	45 Rh 102.90550	46 Pd 106.42	47 Ag 107.8682	48 Cd 112.411	49 In 114.8	50 Sn 118.710	51 Sb 121.75	52 Te 127.60	53 I 126.90447	54 Xe 131.29
6	55 Cs 132.90543	56 Ba 137.327	57–71 Rare Earths	72 Hf 178.49	73 Ta 180.9479	74 W 183.84	75 Re 186.207	76 Os 190.23	77 Ir 192.217	78 Pt 195.08	79 Au 196.96654	80 Hg 200.59	81 Tl 204.3833	82 Pb 207.2	83 Bi 208.98037	84 Po [209]	85 At [210]	86 Rn [222]
7	87 Fr [223]	88 Ra [226]	89–103 Actinides	104 Rf [261]	105 Db [262]	106 Sg [263]	107 Bh [262]	108 Ha [265]	109 Mt [266]	110 Uun [269]	111 Uuu [272]	112 Uub [277]						

57 La 138.9055	58 Ce 138.9055	59 Pr 140.90765	60 Nd 144.24	61 Pm [145]	62 Sm 150.36	63 Eu 151.965	64 Gd 157.25	65 Tb 158.92534	66 Dy 162.50	67 Ho 164.93032	68 Er 167.26	69 Tm 168.93421	70 Yb 173.04	71 Lu 174.967
89 Ac 227.0278	90 Th 232.0381	91 Pa 231.035	92 U 238.0289	93 Np [237]	94 Pu [244]	95 Am [243]	96 Cm [247]	97 Bk [247]	98 Cf [251]	99 Es [252]	100 Fm [257]	101 Md [258]	102 No [259]	103 Lr [262]

Based on 1993 IUPAC values.